Papers on

EVOLUTION

Flowering heads of Tragopogon. *See page 337.*

Papers on
EVOLUTION

Selected by

PAUL R. EHRLICH
Stanford University

RICHARD W. HOLM
Stanford University

PETER H. RAVEN
Stanford University

Little, Brown and Company   BOSTON

CONTENTS

Introduction ix

SECTION I

Changes in Populations

Introduction 3

The genetic factor in population ecology, by L. C. BIRCH 5

Experimental studies on natural selection in the butterfly, *Maniola jurtina,* by W. H. DOWDESWELL 25

Larval color pattern in *Papilio demodocus,* by C. A. CLARKE, C. G. C. DICKSON, and P. M. SHEPPARD 39

House sparrows: Rapid evolution of races in North America, by R. F. JOHNSTON and R. K. SELANDER 47

Selection response and genetics of parathion resistance in the Pacific spider mite, *Tetranychus pacificus,* by L. A. ANDRES and T. PROUT 55

Regional differentiation in plant species, by J. CLAUSEN, D. D. KECK, and W. M. HIESEY 60

Taxonomic and evolutionary implications of lawn races in *Prunella vulgaris* (Labiatae), by A. P. NELSON 80

SECTION II

The Origin of Species

Introduction 97

Stage of speciation of two allopatric populations of chorus frogs (*Pseudacris*), by W. F. BLAIR and M. J. LITTLEJOHN 99

Allochronic speciation in field crickets, and a new species, *Acheta veletis,* by R. D. ALEXANDER and R. S. BIGELOW 105

Character displacement, by W. L. BROWN, JR., and E. O. WILSON 118

The evolutionary implications of the cytological polymorphism and phylogeny of the *virilis* group of *Drosophila,* by W. S. STONE, W. C. GUEST, and F. D. WILSON 134

The origin of *Clarkia lingulata,* by H. LEWIS and M. R. ROBERTS   146

Evolution in the genus *Cucurbita,* by T. W. WHITAKER and W. P. BEMIS   159

SECTION III

Reticulate Evolution

Introduction   169

Hybridization of the habitat, by E. ANDERSON   173

Ancestor of corn, by P. C. MANGELSDORF   182

Hybridization and introgression in *Cowania* and *Purshia,* by H. C. STUTZ and L. K. THOMAS   197

Hybridization in the buntings (*Passerina*) of the Great Plains, by C. G. SIBLEY and L. L. SHORT, JR.   210

Natural hybridization and amphiploidy in the genus *Tragopogon,* by M. OWNBEY   230

SECTION IV

Major Features of Evolution

Introduction   245

The endemic fish fauna of Lake Lanao, and the evolution of higher taxonomic categories, by G. S. MYERS   247

Homage to Santa Rosalia; or, why are there so many kinds of animals? by G. E. HUTCHINSON   262

Experimental studies of mimicry in some North American butterflies. Part I. The monarch, *Danaus plexippus,* and viceroy, *Limenitis archippus archippus,* by J. V. Z. BROWER   276

Chromosome variability and geographic distribution in insects, by B. JOHN and K. R. LEWIS   292

Evolution of the horned dinosaurs, by E. H. COLBERT   314

History of the fauna of Latin America, by G. G. SIMPSON   333

The bearing of the living *Metasequoia* on problems of Tertiary paleobotany, by R. W. CHANEY   362

Evolution of the psilophyte paleoflora, by D. I. AXELROD   375

Evolution of the nests of bees, by C. D. MICHENER   387

The significance of floral constancy among bees of the genus *Diadasia* (Hymenoptera, Anthophoridae), by E. G. Linsley and J. W. MacSwain   400

A fossil ant colony: New evidence of social antiquity, by E. O. Wilson and R. W. Taylor   405

Some problems and guiding principles of angiosperm phylogeny, by R. F. Thorne   415

A method for deducing branching sequences in phylogeny, by J. H. Camin and R. R. Sokal   434

Construction of phylogenetic trees, by W. M. Fitch and E. Margoliash   450

SECTION V

The Evolution of Man

Introduction   465

Man and natural selection, by T. Dobzhansky   467

The crucial evidence for human evolution, by W. E. Le Gros Clark   482

Early man in East Africa, by P. V. Tobias   496

The analysis of primate evolution with particular reference to the origin of man, by S. L. Washburn   523

Ecology and the protohominids, by G. A. Bartholomew, Jr., and J. B. Birdsell   541

How many people can the world support? by J. H. Fremlin   559

Pagination of the papers in this collection is indicated by the boldface number centered at the bottom of the page. Other page numbers appearing on certain papers refer to original publication.

INTRODUCTION

This volume is a selection of papers dealing with what most biologists think of when they hear the word "evolution": microevolution, speciation, and phylogeny. Evolutionary theory remains, in a period of revolutionary advances in the biological sciences, the central unifying theme of the entire discipline. It explains such diverse phenomena as the semi-conservative replication of DNA, the appearance of staphylococci resistant to antibiotics, and the large size of the human brain. It makes sense of the variety of beetles, seeds, sense organs, blood cells, and cytochromes. It puts us in our place in nature, explains why we have not been satisfied with our lot, and lets us predict some of the consequences of our massive attempts to bend nature to our will.

One might thus reasonably claim that all biological research deals with evolution. And, indeed, the variety of papers which might have been assembled as *Papers on Evolution* seemed to us almost unlimited. We have, therefore, had to make rather arbitrary decisions in our selection. We have omitted papers which might be thought of as falling within the area of population genetics, since a fine sample from this discipline may be found in Spiess's *Papers on Animal Population Genetics* (1962). We also have not included the work of Lewontin and Hubby (1966), and others, dealing with the level of heterozygosity in natural populations, for it seemed out of context in the absence of related papers on such subjects as genetic load and variability in natural populations, some of which are found in the Spiess book. We wish, however, to emphasize our strong belief that population genetics is central to all evolutionary thinking. A basic knowledge of this field is a prerequisite to understanding in depth the papers collected here. We have reprinted only one paper in the area of what has been called molecular evolution. Recent advances in molecular biology doubtless are of paramount importance to evolutionists. As yet, however, the influence of these advances on the mainstream of evolutionary thought has not been extensive.

We have attempted to include both recent papers and ones which have not been reprinted in other collections. Because of space limitations we have selected mostly short articles. In general, we have proceeded from the view that the main purpose of such a collection is to give the student a feeling for the original literature in the field. The collection should serve as supplementary reading in undergraduate courses in evolution and is designed to accompany texts of the general level of the one by Ehrlich and Holm (1963).

We have divided our selection into five sections of unequal length: changes in populations, the origin of species, reticulate evolution, major features of evolution, and evolution of man. Obviously the assignment of particular papers to these sections is somewhat arbitrary. In the brief introductions to the sections we have tried to place the papers in context and to provide references which, along with those cited in the papers themselves, will give the student entry into much of the literature of evolutionary biology. What follows in this introduction is a very brief precis on the current state of evolutionary thought, intended to provide a general framework for the entire collection.

In the broadest sense, evolution may be defined as "change in organisms in the course of time." Since the Darwinian revolution, when a plausible explanation for such changes was presented, biologists have attacked the problem of what mechanisms are involved in evolutionary change and how organisms interact with each other and their environments across the stretches of geological time.

When and how life originated is still a matter for speculation. There are, of course, alternative theories which differ in many important respects, but because of space limitations, we have not included a selection of papers on this subject. It is clear, however, that basic among the processes involved in the origin of life were the formation of organic compounds, the segregation and partition of these into cells and organelles, the coupling of systems for the utilization of energy with synthetic systems, and the establishment and integration of the processes involved in replication of cells. Self-replication found in present-day organisms involves protein synthesis controlled by nucleic acids. Perfect replication of molecules for an indefinite period of time is impossible. Therefore it was inevitable that proto-organisms and organisms would vary with respect to the constellation of molecules found in their cells. Natural selection is therefore also inevitable in the course of replication, leading to change through time and the differentiation of lines of descent.

In modern organisms, a line of descent does not consist of a sequence of individuals, but of a series of cyclically occurring phases. One cycle is a developmental sequence which we customarily think of as comprising all of the stages from the beginning of one diplophase (the zygote) to the beginning of the next. Changes in the genetic information lead to changes in the developmental sequence. It is the accumulation of these genetically initiated changes that constitutes evolution. And it is important to remember that evolution involves the entire life cycle. All stages of a life cycle are essential to survival and reproduction and thus equally important from the standpoint of selection.

Reproduction of individuals leads to the formation of aggregations called populations. These, or subsets of these, may form interbreeding populations, which are variously described taxonomically. Communities are aggregations of diverse populations which become structured with respect to the cycling of matter and the flow of energy. Communities owe their existence to the mutuality of the tolerance ranges of the constituent organisms at a particular time and place. Limits for the physiological functioning of individuals are set by their genotypes, determined at the time of zygote formation. The array of genotypes found in the newly formed zygotes is the resultant of many different genetic and environmental factors and complex interactions among them. Critical to insight into the genetic functioning of populations is an understanding of properties described by the Hardy-Weinberg law. This law is essence states that, in the absence of evolutionary forces, in an idealized population the frequencies of alleles and genotypes in the population will not change. That is, the population will remain in a neutral genetic equilibrium. This idealized equilibrium state represents a baseline against which changes caused by evolutionary forces and other factors may be measured. Mutation, differential migration, genetic drift, and selection cause deviations from this equilibrium, and the ways in which these forces may do so have been formulated mathematically. Their effects depend upon the interactions among them as well as upon the structure of the population and the feedback of population structure on the forces themselves. Theoretical descriptions of possible responses of populations to various combinations of forces have been developed. By considering populations in terms of shifting and interacting arrays of gene frequencies, the evolutionist has the means of analyzing his observations with some degree of rigor and precision.

In this series of collected papers are a number of examples of specific analyses of situations in nature or in the laboratory. It becomes apparent from a study of these examples that although it is relatively easy to demonstrate evolutionary changes, it is much more difficult to apportion the responsibility for the changes among the various evolutionary forces. This problem can be traced in large part to the multiplicity of complex interactions which are possible within and between genetic and developmental systems. Extensive studies still are needed on a wide sample of organisms before generalities on the relative contribution of the various factors can be made with confidence.

The genetic system of a population determines how many new gene combinations are produced in a period of time. Many plants and animals exhibit special cytogenetic mechanisms controlling the amount and nature of genetic recombination. They include chromosomal inversions and translocations, which produce relatively small groups of linked genes; polyploidy with its varying effects upon recombination; and apomixis, in which recombination may be largely or completely eliminated. In the long run, apomixis in particular and some of these other mechanisms are thought to be disadvantageous. Since they are common in both plant and animal populations, they obviously confer at least a short-range selective advantage.

All available evidence indicates that differentiation in isolation is the primary source of the diversity of living things. No two diploid populations between which gene flow is reduced or absent can be identical genetically. In addition, they are exposed to different combinations of evolutionary forces and thus are certain to become further differentiated genetically. Should differentiation exceed a certain point, the populations will not reunite if contact between them is once again established. Determining the nature of this genetic point of no return is very difficult in most organisms. Developing generalizations concerning it from the variety of cases studied has led to great controversy among evolutionists and taxonomists. Populations so distinct in physiology and ecology that their future merger seems unlikely may still occasionally exchange genetic information. And this reciprocally obtained genetic variation may stimulate further evolution.

In view of the time available for the evolution of organisms as we know them today, mutation, recombination, selection, and drift are sufficient to account for the diversity of life. Observed discontinuities in variation patterns are the result largely of extinction. From the perspective of viewing the fossil record, the major patterns of phylogenetic change have been classified as: splitting of phylogenetic lines, phyletic evolution (change through time without splitting), and quantum evolution (rapid evolutionary change as a new adaptive zone is penetrated). In some groups it has been possible to estimate past rates of evolution, and these rates seem to have differed widely in the course of time and between major groups. We have chosen several papers in which major evolutionary patterns in plants and animals are discussed.

Man himself, of course, is the product of both biological and cultural evolution. There is no reason to believe that his biological evolution differs in kind from that of other diploid, outcrossing organisms. Cultural evolution, change in the large body of nongenetic information shared by human beings, is closely tied to biological evolution in a complex feedback system. *Homo sapiens* is the only organism to study its evolutionary past and to consider its evolutionary future. Only recently has he become aware of the possible evolutionary consequences of his actions. It remains to be seen what the consequences of his knowledge will be.

BIBLIOGRAPHY

EHRLICH, P. R., and R. W. HOLM. 1963. *The Process of Evolution.* McGraw-Hill Book Co., New York.

LEWONTIN, R. C., and J. L. HUBBY. 1966. A molecular approach to the study of genetic heterozygosity in natural populations. II. Amount of variation and degree of heterozygosity in natural populations of *Drosophila pseudoobscura.* Genetics **54:** 595–609.

SPIESS, E. B. 1962. *Papers on Animal Population Genetics.* Little, Brown and Company, Boston.

SECTION I

Changes in Populations

BIRCH, L. C. 1960. The genetic factor in population ecology. Am. Nat. **94**: 5–24.

DOWDESWELL, W. H. 1961. Experimental studies on natural selection in the butterfly, *Maniola jurtina*. Heredity **16**: 39–52.

CLARKE, C. A., C. G. C. DICKSON, and P. M. SHEPPARD. 1963. Larval color pattern in *Papilio demodocus*. Evolution **17**: 130–137.

JOHNSTON, RICHARD F., and ROBERT K. SELANDER. 1964. House sparrows: Rapid evolution of races in North America. Science **144**: 548–550.

ANDRES, LLOYD A., and TIMOTHY PROUT. 1960. Selection response and genetics of parathion resistance in the Pacific spider mite, *Tetranychus pacificus*. Jour. Econ. Entom. **53**: 626–630.

CLAUSEN, JENS, DAVID D. KECK, and WILLIAM M. HIESEY. 1941. Regional differentiation in plant species. Am. Nat. **75**: 231–250.

NELSON, ANDREW P. 1965. Taxonomic and evolutionary implications of lawn races in *Prunella vulgaris* (Labiatae). Brittonia **17**: 160–174.

1

How populations adjust to the vagaries of the environment is the essential theme of the seven papers on changes in populations—what is often called "microevolution." The first paper, by Birch,* asks the critical question of what selection selects for—and comes up with one possible answer, higher r, the rate of increase. This paper, as well as others in this section, emphasizes the unity in population biology and the futility of ignoring ecological thought in evolutionary problems, and vice versa.

In selecting the papers for this section we have decided against reprinting certain zoological papers which have become widely known as textbook examples. Thus, for instance, works on microevolution in populations of *Biston* (Kettlewell, 1958), *Cepaea* (Cain and Sheppard, 1954; LaMotte, 1951), and *Natrix* (Camin and Ehrlich, 1958) have not been included. Selection in natural populations has not been neglected, however. Dowdeswell's work* represents a fine series of papers by Dowdeswell, Ford, McWhirter, and others on natural populations of the satyrine butterfly, *Maniola jurtina*. These papers describe one of the most extensive studies of evolution in natural populations, research that is particularly interesting in that it has demonstrated sharp geographic boundaries between different phenotypes in the absence of isolation. Students may be interested in a contrasting situation in another butterfly, *Euphydryas editha* (Ehrlich, 1965; Ehrlich and Mason, 1966). Here isolated populations show very little phenotypic differentiation. The selective importance of larval color pattern in a lepidopteran *Papilio demodocus* is the subject of the paper by Clarke, Dickson, and Sheppard.* This work is analogous to that mentioned above in *Biston*, *Cepaea*, and *Natrix* in that the characters studied seem to have obvious selective advantage (as opposed to the *Maniola* and *Euphydryas* studies, where the measured variables seem to be only associated with the characteristics actually responsible for reproductive differentials).

Direct studies on selection operating in natural populations of animals are relatively scarce. There are, however, a great many in which the action of natural selection can be inferred. Especially interesting among those are investigations of changes in imported species since they give us a basis for judging how rapidly selection may shape populations. Johnston and Selander's analysis* of house sparrow populations is an example of such a study. Their conclusions have recently been supported by Packard (1967). The amount of information which can be inferred about changes in populations by careful phenetic analysis of samples taken at one point in time is shown by Soulé (1966).

One of the most commonly observed examples of evolutionary change in nature has been the development of pesticide-resistant strains among various insects and mites. The paper by Andres and Prout* shows how the genetic

* Paper included in this section.

3

basis of resistance may be established, and throws light on the important question of the diversity or resistance mechanisms.

Changes in populations of plants have usually been approached from a rather different point of view than those in animal populations. Many plants have a high degree of phenotypic plasticity, and it becomes important, therefore, to distinguish genetic changes in populations from phenotypic responses of individuals. Leaders in such studies have been Clausen, Keck, and Hiesey,* and their paper is a survey of their work on regional differentiation. A recent study by Nelson* of the relationship between phenotypic and genotypic responses in the genus *Prunella* under strong selective forces is also included. Because of their close connection with the substrate and the ease of transplanting and growing cloved individuals, plants are particularly suited to this type of research. Other interesting studies are those of Kemp (1937) on meadow plants and of Bradshaw (summary, 1962) on plants exposed to lead mine tailings.

BIBLIOGRAPHY

BRADSHAW, A. D. 1962. The taxonomic problems of local geographical variation in plant species. System. Assoc. Publ. **4**: 7–16.

CAIN, A. J., and P. M. SHEPPARD. 1954. Natural selection in *Cepaea*. Genetics **39**: 89–116.

CAMIN, J. H., and P. R. EHRLICH. 1958. Natural selection in water snakes (*Natrix sipedon*) on islands in Lake Erie. Evolution **12**: 504–511.

EHRLICH, P. R. 1965. The population biology of the butterfly, *Euphydryas editha*. II. The structure of the Jasper Ridge Colony. Evolution **19**: 327–336.

EHRLICH, P. R., and L. G. MASON. 1966. The population biology of the butterfly, *Euphydryas editha*. III. Selection and the phenetics of the Jasper Ridge Colony. Evolution **20**: 165–173.

KEMP, W. B. 1937. Natural selection within plant species as exemplified in a permanent pasture. Jour. Hered. **28**: 329–333.

KETTLEWELL, H. B. D. 1958. A survey of the frequencies of *Biston betularia* (L.) (Lep.) and its melanic forms in Great Britain. Heredity **12**: 51–72.

LaMOTTE, M. 1951. Recherches sur la structure génétique des populations naturelle de *Cepaea nemoralis* L. Bull. Biol. Suppl. **35**: 1–239.

PACKARD, G. C. 1967. House sparrows: Evolution of populations from the Great Plains and Colorado Rockies. Syst. Zool. **16**: 73–89.

SOULÉ, M. E. 1966. Trends in the insular radiation of a lizard. Amer. Nat. **100**: 47–64.

THE GENETIC FACTOR IN POPULATION ECOLOGY

L. C. BIRCH

Department of Zoology, University of Sydney, Sydney, Australia

INTRODUCTION

The ecological problem of populations has to do with the numbers of animals and what determines these numbers. The genetical problem of populations has to do with the kind or kinds of animals and what determines kind. These two disciplines meet when the questions are asked, how does the kind of animal (i.e., genotype) influence the numbers and how does the number of animals influence the kind, i.e., the genetical composition of the population? These questions are as much ecological as they are genetical.

GENETIC AND PHENOTYPIC PLASTICITY

Chapman (1928) made a fundamental contribution to animal ecology when he introduced the important idea that the ecological characteristics of a species can be measured and regarded as constants in the sense in which chemical substances can be defined precisely in terms of certain constant characteristics. Such were birth-rate, death-rate, rate of development and so on. He considered these as characteristics of the species in the same way in which a taxonomist might regard certain morphological features as characterizing the species. Chapman had the idea that one day the ecologist would have at his disposal a table of ecological constants for the different species he worked with. Since Chapman's day some ecologists have attempted to measure quantitatively these qualities of ecological importance. The initial problem was to define them precisely. We need only recall Chapman's concept of "biotic potential" and the changes this concept has undergone, to appreciate the time and thought that was necessary to transform this into something that was both measurable and meaningful. The concept of dispersal is another example. At one time dispersal was the subject of anecdotes and little more. Today it can be studied precisely with the tools of statistics and chemistry.

It was perhaps fortunate that the attention of ecologists was directed by Chapman toward the end of defining more precisely ecological characteristics of animals, before they became confused by the fact that such qualities are not really constants at all. They are probably not constant even for a particular genotype, particularly if the genotype has phenotypic plasticity,

Reprinted by permission of the author and publisher from
THE AMERICAN NATURALIST, 94, 5–24 (1960).

by which is meant the ability of the genotype to survive and multiply in a wide range of environments. However, populations consist of an array of genotypes and we now know, at least for quite a number of species, that this array changes both in space and in time. Instead of thinking of ecological characteristics of species as constants, we have been forced by genetics to think of them as fluctuating between certain values or even drifting in time to different mean values. Likewise we have to think of a transect in the spatial distribution of the species as revealing a spectrum of values corresponding to a spatial genetic spectrum. From a long term evolutionary point of view this characteristic of genetic plasticity has made evolution or transformation of species possible. From a short term ecological point of view it enables a species to live in a wide range of environments. And in a changing environment it enables the species to cope with change by changing itself. A change in environment may mean a new "ecological opportunity" for a species which has genetic plasticity. Genetic plasticity and phenotypic plasticity are two ways in which species are adapted to survive and multiply in a wide range of environments or, which amounts to the same thing, are adapted to cope with a change in environment. Since change is a more characteristic feature than stability in environments, these two sorts of plasticity are of fundamental significance for the ecologist to recognize and study.

The basis of genotypic plasticity is diversity of genotypes on which selection can operate. As a mechanism of adaptation to changing environment it can only be effective when the length of generation is shorter than the time within which the environment changes. For example, it is of no use to an elephant as an adaptive mechanism to seasonal change in the environment. But it is for Drosophila which can complete several generations in a season. On the other hand, it could presumably be of value to the elephant in adapting the species to long term changes in its environment such as must have occurred in the evolution of elephants.

Adaptation through genotypic plasticity is only possible when there is considerable genetic variability available at all times. The source of such variability is twofold: mutation and, in sexual organisms, recombination of genes. Recurrent mutation is the main source of genetic variability in bacteria, algae and protozoa. But mutation rates are, for the most part, so low that the effectiveness of mutation on its own has been questioned for all but such organisms as these which multiply at a prodigious rate. A high rate of increase combined with intense selection can lead to rapid change despite relatively low mutation rates. With sexual organisms mutation rate is reinforced with the element of stored variability which means that there is a reserve of variability over and above that which mutation alone can provide. This important aspect of adaptation in sexual organisms has been discussed in detail by Dobzhansky (1951) and Waddington (1957) and others, to whom reference should be made for details. Suffice it to indicate here the main genetic mechanisms involved in stored or concealed variability.

(a) Genes which have no phenotypic expression will be stored in the gene pool since it is the phenotype which is selected. Two mechanisms are involved, dominance and canalizing selection. Recessive genes concealed by dominant alleles will only become expressed phenotypically when homozygous. A tremendous store of recessive genes is concealed in heterozygotes. This was first shown by Tschetwerikoff in 1927 (see Dobzhansky, 1951) in natural populations of *Drosophila melanogaster* and has been amply confirmed for numerous other species by Dobzhansky (1951) and others since. Canalizing selection tends toward a stability of the phenotype through selection of genes which make the organism insensitive to abnormal environments (Waddington, 1957). Genes for a canalized character will inevitably be stored.

(b) Polygenic inheritance favors stored variability (Mather, 1941, 1943). This variability becomes released in linked polygene complexes when crossing over occurs and such released variability can be adaptive when environment changes.

(c) Heterosis or superiority of heterozygote over the homozygotes. This is the essential condition for balanced polymorphism in Mendelian populations. If a mutant produces a heterotic heterozygote, natural selection will retain this mutant in the population even if the homozygote is lethal. This mechanism has been extensively studied by Dobzhansky (1951) and his colleagues in Drosophila populations which exhibit polymorphism in chromosomal inversions. Heterosis is the mechanism by means of which a diversity of chromosomal inversions is maintained in the population. This diversity adapts the species to a wider variety of environments than would otherwise be possible (Dobzhansky et al., 1950). The existence of heterosis of single pairs of genes is more difficult to establish. The superiority of the heterozygote carrier of sickle-cell anaemia in malarial environments may be such an example (Allison, 1955). Other examples may occur in man (Dobzhansky, 1958) and Drosophila (Wallace, 1958).

A striking example of the release of stored variability with change in environment is Waddington's (1957) experiment in which he finds that in some flies of *Drosophila melanogaster* a cross-vein in the wing is missing when they are reared at a high temperature. The abnormality does not occur at normal temperatures. By selecting for cross-veinless flies at high temperature, Waddington found that the character was genetically determined. In his selected stock the character appeared irrespective of whether they were raised at low or high temperatures. The capacity to respond to high temperature in this way is resident in the normal unselected flies. The character cannot however be selected until environment favors its phenotypic expression. From this experiment Waddington argues for the genetic assimilation of adaptive characters induced by environment. One need only suppose that cross-veinlessness was adaptive at high temperatures to see his point. The capacity for response to environment is inherited. All the environment does is to cause the genes already present, but concealed, to be expressed. Once expressed the new phenotypes can be selected. This mechanism would be far more effective in adapting a species to changed environment than reliance on random recurrent mutation alone.

Genetic plasticity and diversity of genotype is of no advantage in an environment which is constant in its properties except as an insurance against possible change in the future. Lewontin (1958) has pointed out that in a constant environment if a homozygote arose which was superior or equal in fitness to the heterozygote then fixation of that allele would result. This he claims to have demonstrated in a population cage of *Drosophila pseudoobscura* which initially contained two chromosomal inversions but after 1000 days the population was nearly homozygous for one inversion. The homozygous population is the "narrow specialist"; the heterozygous population may be less fit in any one environment but this is the price it pays for being able to live in a variety of environments by virtue of the diversity of its genotypes.

A balance between flexibility and stability of the genetic composition of a population is attained by a variety of genetic mechanisms. Chromosomal inversions are one way of tying up blocks of genes which have been proved to be of adaptive value in selection. Inversions suppress crossing over with consequent reduction in variability. This would be advantageous in some environments. But where the environment is constantly providing new challenges, such as on the periphery of the distribution of a species, greater genetic flexibility may be necessary for survival. This is borne out by the finding of a decreased number of inversions at the periphery of the distribution as compared with the center in certain populations of Drosophila (see later). Another mechanism for maintenance of a balance between stability and flexibility of the genotypic composition of the population is the alternation of sexual and asexual generations. In the asexual generation genotypes are kept stable. The change from asexual to sexual phase is related to change in environment. The sexual generation occurs when the environment becomes unfavorable and so provides the species at this stage with an increase in genetic variability (see Lewontin, 1957, for examples of this).

Huxley (1942) and more recently Lewontin (1957) have argued that there has been a general trend in evolution in which genotypic plasticity is gradually supplanted or replaced by phenotypic plasticity. Man's ability to alter his environment instead of being altered by it is an example of phenotypic plasticity, for this enables man to live in a wide variety of environments. Phenotypic plasticity does not necessarily involve the ability to alter the environment but more importantly the ability of a genotype to survive and reproduce in a wide variety of environments. Examples of this may be found more readily in the higher animals than in the lower. However it is not as yet possible to say to what extent one does supercede the other in passing from lower to higher organisms. Genotypic plasticity is, no doubt, the main method of adaptation in bacteria, protozoa and algae. It is a feature of many insects which have a high rate of increase (see Dobzhansky, 1951; Andrewartha and Birch, 1954; De Bach, 1958). Bullock (1955) has shown that plasticity of one sort or another is common amongst a variety of marine invertebrates but he makes no distinction between genetic and phenotypic plasticity in his review. Battaglia (1958) provided an example of genetic plasticity in a marine copepod and suggested a number of others. Nevertheless phenotypic adaptation to temperature alone in lower organisms has been demonstrated in bacteria, planaria, crayfish, crab, clam, limpet, various annelids and a great variety of insects (Fry, 1958). In the vertebrates genetic plasticity is well illustrated by races with different tolerances to temperature in the frog *Rana pipiens* (Moore, 1949) and in fish in the two-spined stickleback (Heuts, 1956). The stickleback also has races with different tolerances to salinity. The existence of genotypic plasticity in fishes is also evident from the success of fish culturists in selecting for higher fecundity and faster growth rates. On the other hand the great amount of work on acclimatization of fishes has been singularly unsuccessful in revealing much genetic plasticity. This may simply mean that genetic diversity is more difficult to detect in fish than in other animals. Some reasons why this may be so have been given by Fry (1957). Hart's (1952) study of freshwater fishes in the North American continent from widely different environments showed very little conclusive evidence for genetic diversity; on the other hand, his work and that of Fry (1957, 1958) shows that phenotypic plasticity in relation to temperature is common in freshwater fishes. Homoiothermy confers a high degree of phenotypic plasticity in birds and mammals making genetic plasticity less necessary in some circumstances. But of course genetic plasticity is still a feature of homoiotherms and without it evolution could not occur.

There is a succession of levels at which adaptation could be studied; the genes involved, the chemical intermediaries between the genes and the immediate phenotypic effects they produce, such as increased resistance to cold or increased ability to disperse, and the ultimate effect of these phenotypic changes on birth-rate and death-rate. The purpose of this paper is to relate genetics with birth-rate and death-rate, for it is birth-rate and death-rate which ultimately determine the number of animals. The immediate phenotypic expression of the genes is also the province of genetics and ecology but this will not be considered further here.

THE INFLUENCE OF GENETIC COMPOSITION ON THE RATE OF INCREASE "r"

Species differ in their capacity to increase in numbers during favorable periods when increase is possible. One species can be compared to another in this respect by comparing their innate capacities for increase or intrinsic rates of natural increase, r_m (Andrewartha and Birch, 1954, chapter 3). Such comparisons show quite clearly that species differ genetically in their capacities to increase in numbers. When we come to question how capacity for increase is selected in evolution it is necessary to discuss the rate of increase in terms of the actual rate of increase, r, characteristic of the natural environment in which the species lives. The statistic r_m is an abstraction from nature in so far as it is a measure of a rate of increase when certain components of environment are excluded.

Natural selection will tend to maximize r for the environment in which the species lives, for any mutation or gene combination which increases the chance of genotypes possessing them contributing more individuals to the next generation (that is, of increasing r) will be selected over genotypes contributing fewer of their kind to successive generations. This is the usual meaning of fitness of a genotype. The tendency of natural selection to maximize r does not necessarily mean that natural selection will tend to make the numbers of the species a maximum. The maximization of r would tend to this end except in so far as mechanisms have evolved which put a limit to the numbers in unit space, irrespective of rates of increase. The extent to which such mechanisms may exist is discussed below.

The rate of increase is the difference between the two components of increase: birth-rate and death-rate. The maximization of r through selection does not necessarily imply that natural selection will tend to increase birth-rate or to decrease death-rate, but that it will tend to maximize the difference between them. An animal has a certain amount of energy to dissipate in its life. Some of this energy will go into functions associated with reproduction, some of it will go into activities such as dispersal and escape from predators and some of it will go into the functions associated with just being alive. The partitioning of energy between these various functions will be such as to maximize the chance for survival and multiplication. Selection for clutch size in birds and litter size in mammals are rather special examples as we shall see later. An increase in the size of the clutch or litter to numbers so great that offspring cannot get enough food for survival from the parents is unadaptive. There is good evidence that selection will tend to produce a clutch size corresponding to the number of young that can be successfully reared. This may vary from one part of a bird's range to another (Lack, 1956; Moreau, 1944). Similarly a balance has to be struck between the number of eggs laid by an animal such as a fish and the size of the egg. Survival of fry hatched from large eggs may be greater than survival of fry hatched from small eggs. Selection may favor a small number of large eggs rather than a greater number of small eggs (Svardson, 1949; Rodd, 1946). Tsetse flies have a birth-rate which is probably the lowest of any insect. The offspring are laid as mature larvae about to pupate and only one larva is produced at a time. Their energy is concentrated into a few offspring born in a mature stage of development rather than in a large number of eggs. Survival of the immature stages is made maximum by virtue of the advanced stage at which the young are born.

Evidence that natural selection has not pushed birth rates to the attainable maximum is provided by those domestic and laboratory animals in which artificial selection has been effective in increasing the birth rate or egg-laying rate. But this gain is purchased at the expense of other traits that would be important in survival in nature (see Cole, 1957; Smith, 1954).

In contrast to the tsetse fly, adult Mayflies (Ephemeroptera) produce a large number of eggs and then die after a brief adult life without feeding at all. There is presumably in these insects a selective advantage in concentrating the energy of life into early egg-production in the adult and survival of the long-lived immature stages, rather than in survival of the adult with egg production covering a longer period. An insect which can mature eggs without feeding, such as the Mayfly, has an evolutionary advantage when adult food is scarce over an adult which has to feed to mature its eggs. The adults of blowflies normally require protein in their adult diet for maturation of eggs. But Nicholson (1957) has produced a strain of the blowfly *Lucilia cuprina* which can mature some eggs without protein in its diet (from protein taken in the larval diet) by raising them in very crowded cultures where protein is in short supply. Insects which do not feed at all as adults have evidently taken this step some stages further.

These are a few of the variety of ways in which the life history of a species is patterned by selection and presumably in each case to maximize the difference between birth-rate and death-rate. Early production of litters, larger litters, closer spacing of litters and biassing of the sex-ratio in favor of females and higher survival of pre-reproductive and reproductive stages would each (other things remaining the same) increase r. Cole (1954, 1957) has pointed out that which particular ones which would be most effective depends upon the pattern of life history of the species. For example, species that reach maturity early can gain more from increasing litter size than from living longer and producing more litters. In species that mature more slowly it may be more advantageous to live longer and produce more litters than to increase litter size. Life history changes that involve a biassing of the sex-ratio are peculiar in the payment exacted from an evolutionary point of view. An increase in the proportion of females in the population may decrease the chance of females finding a mate. An answer to this may be found in asexual reproduction. But this would usually involve loss in genetic plasticity. A combination of the two may be best both from an ecological point of view (Cole, 1957) and from an evolutionary point of view (Wright, 1931). Whatever change occurs in the pattern of the life history a balance has to be found between the most appropriate reproductive and survival pattern.

Direct evidence of selection for rate of increase is provided by Bateman's (unpublished thesis, 1958) study of populations of the trypetid fruit fly *Dacus tryoni* collected from different geographic areas in Australia. He measured the innate capacity for increase r_m of population from four places along a 2,000 mile stretch of coastal country in Eastern Australia. In this example there is reason to suppose that the statistic r_m reflects the real capacity of the species to increase in numbers in the places where they live. There were significant differences in the capacities for increase of the four populations. These differences have probably developed through selection in the last fifty years, for evidence suggests that the fly has spread from its tropical home into temperate latitudes during this period. The differences which he found were correlated with differences in temperature in the four places from which the populations came. For example, the most northern population (from Cairns in the tropics) had the lowest value of r_m at 20°C. and the highest at 30°C. The population from Sydney 1500 miles south had the highest value of r_m at 20°C. and the lowest at 30°C. Increase in the innate capacity for increase at 20°C. was doubtless one factor which enabled the species to become established in Sydney. The main evolutionary changes which occurred in the life history pattern to bring this about were increase in the number of progeny and in the life expectancy of the adult. For example, if we compare the populations from Cairns and Sydney we find that at 20°C. the number of progeny produced is greater for the Sydney population at all ages of the parent female and that they start laying eggs several weeks earlier. In the tenth week the Sydney strain lays nearly 30 times as many eggs as the Cairns strain. By the 20th week it lays about twice as many eggs. This may be an illustration of the principle that a rise in the innate capacity for increase can be most readily obtained by increasing the rate of egg production early in a female's life. The survivorship of adults of the Sydney strain is also greater at all ages than that of the Cairns strain at this temperature. The Sydney climate has evidently imposed a selection at 20°C. whereas in Cairns selection at such a temperature could hardly occur.

It would be a fascinating field of study to investigate the genetics of such evolutionary changes in life history patterns. A possible lead in this direction has been given by Carson's (1958) striking experiment with *Drosophila melanogaster*. He established experimental populations of flies over several generations in which the numbers fluctuated around a fairly constant level. He then introduced a "foreign" gene into these populations. There was a rapid three-fold increase in size of the population which was maintained for fifteen generations, after which the experiment was terminated. The increase in total numbers of the populations involves an increase in birth-rate or a decrease in death-rate or both. One gene was responsible for the change. His evidence was in favor of the hypothesis that these changes were the result of new heterotic combinations of genes produced after the foreign gene was introduced.

The evolution of heterosis following recombination and consequent change in fitness of genotypes has also been demonstrated in laboratory cultures of *Drosophila pseudoobscura* by Dobzhansky (1957). Seasonal changes in the frequency of chromosomal inversions in natural populations of this species in California (Wright and Dobzhansky, 1946) suggest that the rate of increase r of populations of *D. pseudoobscura* is a function of the different kinds of inversions in the third chromosome. Some combinations permit increase in the spring, others permit increase in the summer. In some unpublished experiments of my own I have found that when the trypetid fruit fly *Dacus tryoni tryoni* was bred together with the color variant known as *D. tryoni neohumeralis* in the one population cage, and provided that its initial frequency was only 20 per cent, its rate of increase in the population declined until none were left after 35 weeks at 25°C. But when the initial frequency of *tryoni* was 80 per cent the rapid decline in numbers was halted after 20 weeks and this coincided with an increase in frequency of hybrids. From then on for the 100 weeks in which the experiment has continued *tryoni* has persisted in the population together with *neohumeralis* and their hybrids. The initial high frequency of *tryoni* gave this variant sufficient time to introduce its genes into the populations through the hybrids that were formed, so permitting a balanced population of the two types and their hybrids to evolve. Both *tryoni* and *neohumeralis* have changed genetically in this experiment, for the degree of sexual isolation that exists between the original populations had largely disappeared after 100 weeks. A genetic change in *tryoni* in this experiment has altered its rate of increase permitting it to persist in the mixed population whereas in the initial experiment its rate of increase decreased in the course of the experiment.

Family selection. The tendency of natural selection to maximize the rate of increase r poses a dilemma. It is easy to imagine that a low rate of increase could be advantageous under some circumstances in which large numbers would result in serious depletion of resources of food and space, with consequent starvation and death. The chance of annihilation from this cause would be reduced if the birth-rate were lowered and this resulted in greater chance of offspring surviving. However, selection for lower birth-rate can only occur when parents and progeny remain as a family during the rearing stages or in circumstances which are strictly analagous to a family situation. Selection for clutch size in birds is a classic example of selection operating on the individuals of a family unit. It is the families of optimum size that are selected. In social insects sterility for the bulk of the colony has evolved. This has happened because the colony is a family. Here it is the parents whose family organization is best for survival who are selected. Darwin recognized that sterile castes of social insects could only evolve as a result of selection operating on a family kept together as a unit. If the progeny of one colony mixed freely with the progeny from another then sterility could hardly evolve. This is sometimes called, with a lot of other unrelated things, selection in which the population is the unit of selection. This however is a misleading phrase for what is always selected are individuals. In selection for clutch size the individuals selected are those whose parents laid neither too many nor too few eggs. The regulation of the fecundity of the queen bee and the regulation of the number of reproductive individuals in the colony of the termite *Kalatermes flavicollis* are further examples of evolution of lowered birth-rate (Emerson, 1958).

Can selection favor the individual with a low birth-rate (other things being equal) in cases other than the closely knit family? The following hypothetical example is perhaps one sort of situation in which selection might operate in this direction. Let us suppose that a species of mosquito lays its eggs in pools of water with insufficient food for more than a few larvae. If each pool received eggs from one female only then the female which laid the smaller number of eggs would tend to be selected. We shall suppose that those which laid large numbers of eggs produced no living progeny because of overcrowding in the pool. If different females laid their eggs together in the same pool then selection will not favor the mosquito which lays the smaller number of eggs. This would be analagous to mixing the clutches of several birds. However we could imagine an intermediate situation in which, despite the fact that mosquitoes laid their eggs in the same pools, some pools by chance might have eggs laid in them by mosquitoes of low fecundity. In so far as this occurred selection might favor the genotype of low fecundity especially if the smaller number of eggs is also correlated with larger eggs. In this model the pool is analagous to a family. I find some difficulty in supposing that this could be at all common in nature. The possibility should not however be overlooked. In these examples in which selection operates on individuals in a family, or something analogous to a family, selection still favors those genotypes with higher r, though in these cases the higher r is achieved by lowered birth-rate.

The general statement that selection will tend to maximize r is quite consistent with the fact that genotypes of low adaptive value may not be selected out of a population. In balanced polymorphism the homozygotes have lower adaptive values than the heterozygote. Similarly a genotype may have qualities of advantage to the species but of no advantage to itself. The theoretical concept of the "altruistic gene" (Haldane, 1932; Wright, 1949) is an example of this. Such a gene would increase in the population so long as the presence of such genotypes increased the chance of the population as a whole to survive and multiply. Too many of them might of course be disadvantageous. But even in this case selection still tends to maximize r for the population.

Territoriality. The tendency of selection is to bring r to a maximum. Yet there are numerous disadvantages in overcrowding and a high rate of increase would tend to produce overcrowding. The disadvantages of high numbers would be overcome if there were mechanisms to stop increase when density reached a certain critical maximum. Some forms of territoriality may serve this end. This does not involve selection for a low rate of increase but selection for cessation of increase when numbers are high. Such mechanisms would have the advantages which a high rate of increase confers without the disadvantage of high total numbers. Intraspecific strife in territorial muskrats may serve such an end. By fighting when their numbers reach a certain density in relation to cover muskrats prevent further increase in numbers (Errington, 1943). Muskrats only tolerate a certain number of their kind in any one marsh but when numbers are low they can increase at a fast rate and without serious intraspecific strife. Territoriality may in some cases serve to conserve resources, though there is no general agreement among ecologists that this is so. However, it does seem to result in lower numbers per unit area than would be the case without it. Territoriality is common in birds and mammals (Gibb, 1956; Hinde, 1956). But apart from ants (Brian, 1955) it seems to be rarely recorded in invertebrates with a few possible exceptions such as dragon flies (Moore, 1952; Jacobs, 1955) and crabs (Crane, 1941).

The slaughter of drones in Apidae and Meliponidae has a similar effect of getting rid of excess individuals in the colony (Emerson, 1958). These are examples of special mechanisms which will tend to keep population density at a low level, possibly even at an optimum level. They are in a different category from the more common effects of increased density in reducing birth-rate and increasing death-rate such as is observed in crowded experimental cultures of beetles and blowflies. A characteristic of these cultures is the enormous number of insects per unit space despite the effect of high density in reducing r.

We may then have to think of natural selection as having two tendencies, on the one hand to increase the rate of increase (with its attendant advantages) and on the other toward the evolution of mechanisms which stop increase when a critical density is reached.

THE INFLUENCE OF THE NUMBER OF ANIMALS ON GENETICAL COMPOSITION

In laboratory populations of insects the birth-rate falls and the death-rate rises with increase in density. This has been demonstrated also in some natural populations of certain birds and mammals which exhibit territorial behavior (Andrewartha and Birch, 1954, chapter 9). It has often been assumed that selection will be greatest in crowded populations because mortality rate is greater. There are however selective differences between some genotypes which exist whether the individuals live in a crowd or not. Genotypes homozygous for lethal or semilethal genes are examples of this. Furthermore the selective differences between genotypes may be a function of density and instead of disappearing at low densities the selective values may even be reversed. In uncrowded populations of *Drosophila pseudoobscura* the inversion Chiracahua was favored over Standard. When larvae only or larvae and adults were crowded at a high density the Standard arrangement of the genes was favored over Chiracahua. When larvae and adults were crowded there was selective mortality of larvae but not of adults. When neither were crowded and there was no opportunity for selective mortality there were selective differences evidently in the rate of egg-laying (Birch, 1955). Similarly I have found a reversal of selective values in two color variants of the Queensland fruit fly *Dacus tryoni tryoni* and *D. tryoni neohumeralis* depending upon whether the adults and larvae were crowded or not. In a population cage at 25°C. the type *neohumeralis* was favored and increased in frequency when adults and larvae were crowded. In relatively uncrowded cages the type *tryoni* was favored over *neohumeralis* and increased in frequency.

Nicholson (1957) kept cultures of the blowfly *Lucilia cuprina* under crowded conditions supplying the population with a fixed amount of larval and adult food at regular intervals. In all ten of his cultures the character of the oscillations in numbers changed about the 400th day. Nicholson showed that this was due to a genetic change in the population. Acute shortage of protein in the experiments had resulted in the selection of flies which could produce and lay eggs in complete absence of protein. Such flies would have a selective advantage in these experiments as there was a severe shortage of protein. Normal adults require protein for production of eggs. Presumably the flies which do not need it in adult food can mature eggs on the protein in their bodies which was derived from larval food. The shortage of protein was in this case caused by high density of flies in relation to the amount provided daily. Nicholson's experiments were not designed to tell if this peculiar quality of flies would be selected when flies were uncrowded but on a diet lacking protein.

Laboratory experiments with *Drosophila melanogaster* have demonstrated that selective differences in survival of larvae are a function of both the density of larvae and the genotype of larvae with which they are crowded. Lewontin (1955) found that a particular genotype was favored in the presence of certain genotypes but at a disadvantage in the presence of others. Parsons (1958) has since demonstrated the same thing.

The complexity of selection of a particular genotype in relation both to density and kind of genotypes with which it lives has been unravelled in a series of complex experiments with *Drosophila pseudoobscura* by Dobzhansky (1957), Levene, Dobzhansky and Pavlovsky (1954), Levene, Pavlovsky and Dobzhansky (1958). They have shown that the selective values of flies carrying a particular chromosomal inversion is a function of both the kind and number of other chromosomal inversions in the population. In population cages containing flies with different chromosomal inversions the selective values of the inversions change as the frequency of the different inversions change. The selective values of a particular inversion will depend not only on its own frequency but on the frequency and kind of the other inversions present in the population.

Oscillations. These considerations of laboratory experiments suggest that change in genetic composition in relation to density may provide a clue to the vexed problem of the causes of oscillations in numbers in certain animal populations. Oscillations are characteristic of confined populations of the beetles Tribolium and Calandra studied in the laboratory and also of some natural populations. Park has consistently found that when populations of *Tribolium confusum* are maintained in vials for long times with regular renewal of food the numbers undergo a long term oscillation. The time between successive peaks was about 500 days when cultures were kept at 29°C. Birch found that two species of Calandra grain weevils gave similar long term oscillations with about 280 days between successive peaks at 25°C. (see Andrewartha and Birch, 1954, chapter 9). These oscillations appear to be quite different in nature from the short term oscillations obtained by Nicholson with Lucilia which appear to be explained quite satisfactorily by the massive deaths of larvae or adults when food was completely exhausted. This never happened in Park's or Birch's experiments. It is conceivable that such oscillations as they found could be due to selection favoring certain genotypes at high density and others at low density. As yet experiments have not been done to test this.

This hypothesis has been suggested as an explanation of outbreaks and declines of certain insect pests in Europe (Franz, 1950) and as a possible explanation of the unsolved problem of four year cycles in the vole *Microtus agrestis* in Wales (Chitty, 1957). Chitty has evidence of the existence of a hemolytic disease which is common when voles are dense and numbers are declining and rare when voles are increasing in numbers. There is some evidence that the disease may be genetic. Chitty postulates a gene or genes for the disease which confer some advantage on the voles living under crowded conditions at least upon heterozygotes and which is at a disadvantage when voles are not crowded.

When we come to examine the evidence from natural populations for the influence of density on selection and therefore on genetical composition little is to be found. This may simply mean that it has not been looked for. Williamson (1958) reviewed such evidence as is available and concluded from a number of suggestive cases that the only substantial one was Gershenson's (1945) work in Russia on change in proportion of black forms of the hamster *Cricetus cricetus* with change in number.

Drift. Fluctuations in numbers also suggests the possibility of genetic drift in isolated populations of small absolute size. Kerr and Wright (1954 a, b, c) demonstrated the operation of random drift as well as selection in populations of very small size (four pairs). Dobzhansky and Pavlovsky (1957) have shown experimentally that the results of selection were different in populations of *Drosophila pseudoobscura* containing different chromosomal inversions, depending upon whether the initial population consisted of 20 or 4000 flies. Variability in chromosome frequency was very much greater between populations initiated with the smaller number of flies. Their explanation is that natural selection started with populations which were more like one another in the experiments initiated with many flies but with populations which were less like one another in the populations initiated with only 20 flies.

Extinction. A final aspect of small numbers is the problem of extinction. Because ecologists study species that are extant on the face of the earth today and not the much greater number of species that are extinct they are inclined to regard the existence of extinct species as a peculiar problem. They tend to pose the question thus—what prevents species from becoming extinct? In view of the fact that extinction seems to be the inevitable fate of all species it might be more realistic to put the question thus—what it is that enables species to remain extant for as long as they do in the face of changing environment? Ecologists have attempted to answer this type of question largely in the terms of ecology. It is claimed for example by some of the adherents of the so-called "density-dependent" school of thought that in the absence of "density-dependent" factors populations would quickly become extinct. An alternative point of view has been that the chance of extinction during a low phase in fluctuation in numbers is reduced by the patchiness of the environment or the discontinuity of the population in space. The genetic factor which may be all important in this discussion is the capacity of species to change genetically during unfavorable periods when its numbers are drastically reduced. Combinations of genes which will enhance the chance for survival and multiplication will tend to be selected. During such exigencies genetic plasticity is a safety factor reducing the chance of extinction. It is not of course a guarantee of the continuance of the species any more than either of the ecological arguments can guarantee survival of the species (Birch, 1957). In an environment subject to change, populations of the polymorphic species will become extinct less often than the monomorphic one.

The peculiar characteristics of diapause, hibernation and migration are adaptations which have presumably been evolved in relation to such adverse influences as extreme dryness and cold. Similarly peculiarities of behavior such as aggregation and the instincts which serve to bring the sexes together in sparse populations are evidently adaptations evolved to overcome the hazards of low numbers.

THE INFLUENCE OF OTHER SPECIES ON GENETICAL COMPOSITION

The genetical composition of a population may change in space and time as a result of the selective action of almost any component of environment (Andrewartha and Birch, 1954, chapter 15). Most of the examples in preceding sections were concerned with genetic change in relation to the numbers of the animal present and to weather. The numbers of another species present in an animal's environment may also be a selective agency. This has now been well established for a number of predators but as yet little direct evidence has been found of selection due to non-predators in an animal's environment.

The outstanding examples of the selective action of predators are Cain and Sheppard's work on predation by birds on the land snail *Cepaea nemoralis*, summarized by Sheppard (1958); the work of Ford and Kettlewell on industrial melanism in moths summarized by Kettlewell (1956, 1958, 1959); and Brower's (1958a, b, c) studies on selective predation on mimetic and non-mimetic butterflies. In each of these examples the authors have succeeded in demonstrating that predators tend to select the conspicuously colored prey so conferring an advantage on the cryptically colored individuals. Over 70 species of moths have evolved black populations in industrial areas in the last 100 years. Kettlewell (1959) has found a number of genetic mechanisms responsible for the dark forms. In some species a single dominant gene changes the animal from white to black in one step. In some populations of *Gonodontis bidentata* polygenes are responsible for darkness. In some populations of *Lymantria monacha* three dominant genes are responsible for producing the black forms. Kettlewell also quotes one case of blackness being due to a recessive gene and another where the gene was incompletely dominant.

Concerning the possible selective role of non-predators in the environment of an animal Brown and Wilson (1956) cite a number of examples of several species with overlapping ranges. They refer to various species of ants, frogs and birds in which the related species show more divergence in various characters in the region of overlap than elsewhere. Most of the variations they refer to are morphological but some are physiological. They suggest that the differences have been evolved in the region of overlap as a means of preventing gene flow between two related species. These may be examples of change in genetic composition as a result of the presence of another sort of animal, the change having taken place before the two forms were completely sexually isolated. However there is not any evidence on which to make a judgment as to whether this is simply a case of evolution of isolating mechanisms in the region of overlap or whether genetic change was promoted by selection in response to direct interference of one form by the other or in relation to shortage of common resource. Brown and Wilson assume the latter. It may have been either or both.

PERIPHERAL POPULATIONS

Populations on the periphery of the distribution present some special ecological and genetical problems. Usually the environment is more severe at the periphery. The ecological problem is how the species manages to survive there and secondly how it sometimes spreads from there to previously uncolonized regions. The occupancy of some peripheral areas is temporary or is reinforced by invasions from within the distribution. Thus the moth *Heliothis armigera* is found in places where it can not overwinter, such as in the state of Minnesota, as a result of migrations of adults from the south. At the periphery the species is usually rarer than elsewhere, a fact which Andrewartha and Birch (1954) interpret as being due to the shortness of the favorable period when numbers can increase before an unfavorable period and a negative rate of increase supervene. This is merely an intensification of factors which operate in a less extreme way elsewhere in the distribution. But the severity of the environment must impose extremely severe selection and this would seem to be corroborated by the findings of Townsend (1952) for *Drosophila willistoni* and Carson (1955) for *Drosophila robusta* that homozygosis, so far as chromosomal inversions are concerned, increases from the center of the distribution to the margins. In the marginal areas where environment is hostile few chromosomal inversions are successful. But those that are successful enable the species to survive there. Another aspect of this hypothesis is that a species with many chromosomal inversions can occupy a greater variety of environments than one with few. This concept is supported by the wide distribution of *Drosophila willistoni* and *D. paulistorum* which have 44 and 34 chromosomal inversions respectively and the very restricted distribution of its sibling species *D. tropicalis* and *D. equinoxialis* which have each only four chromosomal inversions (da Cunha et al., 1950; Dobzhansky et al., 1950). Chromosomal inversions con-

fer adaptability on the species in an environment which varies either in time
or in space. Polymorphism in the center of the distribution is maintained at
the expense of a certain degree of genetic plasticity which crossing over
confers and which is presumably of greatest advantage at the margins of the
distribution. There the species is on the frontier of its distribution and is
subject to the constant threat of extinction. It is there that variability has
to be welded into new combinations to meet a constantly changing and hostile environment. Speculation as to the importance of peripheral populations
in evolution on a grand scale has been made by Mayr (1954) and Brown
(1957) but these considerations go beyond the scope of this paper.

SUMMARY

The genetic plasticity of populations implies that the numbers of animals,
which is what the population ecologist studies, may be a reflection of
change in genetic composition either in space or in time. Alternatively the
number of animals may itself be a cause of genetic change. These genetic
aspects of ecology will be more important when genetic plasticity is more
characteristic than phenotypic plasticity. In relation to changing environment genetic plasticity can only be adaptive when the length of the generation is less than the time the environment takes to change. Both types of
plasticity exist throughout the animal and plant kingdoms. In some groups
of animals in which phenotypic plasticity is common, as in fishes, it is extremely difficult to establish the extent to which genetic plasticity exists.
Adaptation through genetic plasticity depends upon a continuous source of
genetic variability. The source is mutation and in addition, in sexual organisms, recombination of genes. Sex also introduces the possibility of stored
variability which is another source of variability available to the species.
The sources of stored variability are, dominance, canalizing selection, linked
polygenes in which crossing over occurs and heterosis. A balance between
flexibility and stability of genetic composition is attained by a variety of
genetic mechanisms of which chromosomal inversions and alternation of
sexual and asexual generations are two.

From an ecological point of view the significance of change in genetical
composition of a population is its effect on the rate of increase r, that is on
birth-rate and death-rate. The tendency of natural selection is to maximize
r. This does not mean that natural selection will tend to increase birth-rate
to the absolute maximum possible and to reduce death-rate to the absolute
minimum possible. But it will tend to maximize the difference between them.
Life histories have been patterned by natural selection to this end. The
rate of increase r can be increased by a variety of alterations to the life
history pattern. The ones which will be useful will depend upon the environment the animal lives in. An increase in r may be achieved through
natural selection by a decrease in the birth-rate. This can occur in one sort
of situation only and that is when progeny and parents remain together as a
family, at least during the rearing stage. This sort of selection has resulted
in characteristic clutch sizes in birds and sterile castes in the social in-

sects. Selection for low birth-rate could, in theory, occur in non-family organisms under special circumstances in which the offspring of the one or a few parents tended to be reared in isolation from those of other parents. Although selection cannot favor a low rate of increase, it may favor the development of mechanisms which cause a cessation of increase when a certain critical density is reached. Some forms of territoriality may serve this end.

Concerning the influence of numbers of animals on their genetic composition, there is experimental evidence that some genotypes are favored in a crowd and others are favored when sparse. Further the survival value of a genotype is a function not only of the number of other genotypes around it but also of their kind. These findings in experimental populations may be important in resolving the causes of oscillations in numbers in some experimental and possibly in some natural populations; and secondly they suggest a role for genetic plasticity in reducing the chance of extinction.

ACKNOWLEDGMENTS

Earlier drafts of this paper were read and criticized by Dr. M. A. Bateman, Joint Unit of Animal Ecology, University of Sydney; Professor L. C. Cole, Cornell University; Professors Th. Dobzhansky, Columbia University, A. E. Emerson and Thomas Park, University of Chicago; and Dr. J. M. Rendel, C.S.I.R.O. Section of Genetics, University of Sydney, to all of whom I acknowledge a debt of gratitude. As a result of their help and criticism much of the paper was rewritten but this does not mean that any one of them will necessarily agree with all the concepts put forward nor can they be held responsible for what is in the paper.

LITERATURE CITED

Allison, A. C., 1955, Aspects of polymorphism in man. Cold Spring Harbor Symp. Quant. Biol. 20: 239-255.

Andrewartha, H. G., and L. C. Birch, 1954, The distribution and abundance of animals. University of Chicago Press, Chicago, Ill.

Bateman, M. A., 1958, Ecological adaptations in geographic races of the Queensland fruit-fly Dacus (Strumeta) tryoni. Frogg. Unpublished thesis, University of Sydney, Sydney, Australia.

Battaglia, Bruno, 1958, Balanced polymorphism in Tisbe reticulata, a marine copepod. Evolution 12: 358-364.

Birch, L. C., 1955, Selection in Drosophila pseudoobscura in relation to crowding. Evolution 9: 389-399.

1957, The role of weather in determining the distribution and abundance of animals. Cold Spring Harbor Symp. Quant. Biol. 22: 203-218.

Brian, M. V., 1955, Food collection by a Scotch ant community. J. Animal Ecol. 24: 336-351.

Brower, J. Z., 1958a, Experimental studies of mimicry in some North American butterflies. Part 1. The Monarch Danaus plexippus, and Viceroy Limenitis archippus archippus. Evolution 12: 32-47.

1958b, Experimental studies of mimicry in some North American butterflies. Part 2. *Battus philenor* and *Papilo troilus, P. polyxenes* and *P. glaucus.* Evolution 12: 123-136.

1958c, Experimental studies of mimicry in some North American butterflies. Part 3. *Danaus gilippus berenice* and *Limenitis archippus floridensis.* Evolution 12: 273-285.

Brown, W. L., 1957, Centrifugal speciation. Quart. Rev. Biol. 32: 247-277.

Brown, W. L., and E. O. Wilson, 1956, Character displacement. Syst. Zool. 5: 49-64.

Bullock, T., 1955, Compensation for temperature in the metabolism and activity of poikilotherms. Biol. Revs. 30: 311-342.

Carson, H. L., 1955, The genetic characteristics of marginal populations of Drosophila. Cold Spring Harbor Symp. Quant. Biol. 20: 276-287.

1958, Increase in experimental populations resulting from heterosis. Proc. Nat. Acad. Sci. 44: 1136-1141.

Chapman, R. N., 1928, The quantitative analysis of environmental factors. Ecology 9: 111-122.

Chitty, D., 1957, Self regulation of numbers through changes in viability. Cold Spring Harbor Symp. Quant. Biol. 22: 277-280.

Cole, L. C., 1954, The population consequences of life history phenomena. Quart. Rev. Biol. 29: 103-137.

1957, Sketches of general and comparative demography. Cold Spring Harbor Symp. Quant. Biol. 22: 1-15.

Crane, J., 1941, Crabs of the genus Uca from the west coast of Central America. Zoologica 26: 297-310.

Cunha, A. B. da, H. Burla and Th. Dobzhansky, 1950, Adaptive chromosomal polymorphism in *Drosophila willistoni.* Evolution 4: 212-235.

De Bach, P., 1958, Selective breeding to improve adaptations of parasitic insects. Proc. 10th Int. Cong. Ent. 4: 759-768.

Dobzhansky, Th., 1951, Genetics and the origin of species. Columbia University Press, New York, N. Y.

1957, Mendelian populations as genetic systems. Cold Spring Harbor Symp. Quant. Biol. 22: 385-393.

1958, Evolution at work. Science 127: 1091-1098.

Dobzhansky, Th., H. Burla and A. B. da Cunha, 1950, A comparative study of chromosomal polymorphism in sibling species of the *willistoni* group of Drosophila. Amer. Nat. 84: 229-246.

Dobzhansky, Th., and O. Pavlovsky, 1957, An experimental study of interaction between genetic drift and natural selection. Evolution 11: 311-319.

Emerson, A. E., 1958, The evolution of behavior among social insects. *In* Evolution and behavior, eds., A. Rowe and G. G. Simpson. pp. 311-335.

Errington, P. L., 1943, Analysis of mink predation upon muskrats in north central United States. Res. Bull. Iowa Agr. Exp. Sta. 320: 797-924.

Franz, J. von, 1950, Über die genetischen Grundlagen des Zusammenbruchs einer Massenvermehrung aus inneren Ursachen. Zeit f. angen. Entomologie 31: 228-260.

Fry, F. E. J., 1957, The lethal temperature as a tool in taxonomy. Colloq. Int. de Biol. Mar. Stn. Biol de Roscoff Ann. Biol. 33: 205-219.

1958, Temperature compensation. Ann. Rev. Physiol. 20: 207-224.

Gershenson, S., 1945, Evolutionary studies on the distribution and dynamics of melanism in the hamster (*Cricetus cricetus* L.). Genetics 30: 207-251.

Gibb, J., 1956, Territory in the genus Parus. Ibis 98: 420-429.

Haldane, J. B. S., 1932, The causes of evolution. Harper & Brothers, New York and London.

Hart, J. S., 1952, Geographic variations of some physiological and morphological characters in certain freshwater fish. Publ. Ont. Fish Res. Lab. 72: 1-79.

Heuts, M. J., 1956, Temperature adaptation in *Gasterosteus aculeatus* L. Publ. Stazione Zool. Napoli 28: 44-62.

Hinde, R. A., 1956, The biological significance of territories of birds. Ibis 98: 340-369.

Huxley, J., 1942, Evolution: the modern synthesis. Allen & Unwin, London.

Jacobs, M. E., 1955, Studies on territorialism and sexual selection in dragonflies. Ecology 36: 566-587.

Kerr, W. E., and S. Wright, 1954 a, Experimental studies of the distribution of gene frequencies in very small populations of *Drosophila melanogaster*. I. Forked. Evolution 8: 172-177.

1954 b, Experimental studies of the distribution of gene frequencies in very small populations of *Drosophila melanogaster*. II. Bar. Evolution 8: 225-240.

1954 c, Experimental studies of the distribution of gene frequencies in very small populations of *Drosophila melanogaster*. III. Aristapedia and spineless. Evolution 8: 293-302.

Kettlewell, H. B. D., 1956, A resume of investigations on the evolution of melanism in the Lepidoptera. Proc. Roy. Soc. London B 145: 297-303.

1958, A survey of the frequencies of *Biston betularia* and its melanic forms in Great Britain. Heredity 12: 51-72.

1959, New aspects of the genetic control of industrial melanism in the Lepidoptera. Nature 183: 918-921.

Lack, D., 1956, The evolution of reproductive rates. *In* Evolution as a process, eds., J. Huxley, A. C. Hardy and E. B. Ford. pp. 143-156.

Levene, H., O. Pavlovsky and Th. Dobzhansky, 1958, Differences in the adaptive values of certain genotypes in *Drosophila pseudoobscura* on the composition of the gene pool. Evolution 12: 18-23.

1954, Interactions of the adaptive values in polymorphic experimental populations of *Drosophila pseudoobscura*. Evolution 8: 335-349.

Lewontin, R. C., 1955, The effects of population density and composition on viability in *Drosophila melanogaster*. Evolution 9: 27-41.

1957, The adaptations of populations to varying environments. Cold Spring Harbor Symp. Quant. Biol. 22: 395-408.

1958, Studies on heterozygosity and homeostasis. II. Loss of heterosis in a constant environment. Evolution 12: 497-503.

Mather, K., 1941, Variation and selection of polygenic characters. J. Genetics 41: 159-193.

1943, Polygenic inheritance and natural selection. Biol. Rev. 18: 32-62.

Mayr, E., 1954, Change of genetic environment and evolution. *In* Evolution as a process, eds., J. Huxley, A. C. Hardy and E. B. Ford. pp. 157-180.

Moore, J. A., 1949, Geographic variation of adaptive characters in *Rana pipiens*. Evolution 3: 1-24.

Moore, N. W., 1952, On the so called territories of dragonflies. Behaviour 4: 85-100.

Moreau, R. E., 1944, Clutch size; a comparative study, with special reference to African birds. Ibis 86: 286-347.

Nicholson, A. J., 1957, The self adjustment of populations to change. Cold Spring Harbor Symp. Quant. Biol. 22: 153-173.

Parsons, P. A., 1958, Competition between genotypes in *Drosophila melanogaster*. Nature 182: 271.

Rodd, J. A., 1946, Big trout from big eggs. A Canadian experiment. Salmon and Trout Mag. 116: 32-36.

Sheppard, P. M., 1958, Natural selection and heredity. Hutchinson, London.

Smith, F. E., 1954, Quantative aspects of population growth. *In* Dynamics of growth processes, ed., E. J. Boell. Princeton University Press, Princeton, N. J.

*Svardson, G., 1949, Fish Bd. Inst. Freshwater Res. Drottingholm. Rept. 29: 115-122.

Townsend, J. I., 1952, Genetics of marginal populations of *Drosophila willistoni*. Evolution 6: 428-442.

Waddington, C. H., 1957, The strategy of the genes. Allen & Unwin, London.

Wallace, B., 1958, Average effect of radiation-induced mutations on viability in *Drosophila melanogaster*. Evolution 12: 532-556.

Williamson, W. H., 1958, Selection, controlling factors and polymorphism. Amer. Nat. 92: 329-335.

Wright, S., 1931, Evolution in Mendelian populations. Genetics 16: 97-159.

    1949, Adaption and selection. *In* Genetics, paleontology and evolution, eds, G. L. Jepson, E. Mayr and G. G. Simpson. pp. 365-389.

Wright, S., and Th. Dobzhansky, 1946, Genetics of natural populations. XII. Experimental reproduction of some of the changes caused by natural selection in certain populations of *Drosophila pseudoobscura*. Genetics 31: 125-156.

*Known by reference only.

Experimental Studies on Natural Selection in the Butterfly, *Maniola jurtina*

W. H. DOWDESWELL
Biology Department, Winchester College

Received 12.x.60

ONE of the greatest advances in evolutionary thought during the last decade has been the realisation that, among polymorphic species, selection pressures may occur of far greater magnitude than had hitherto been supposed. Under favourable circumstances, genes conferring beneficial phenotypic effects are thus enabled to spread through populations with remarkable speed. This principle is admirably demonstrated by the advance of industrial melanism in the moth *Biston betularia* (Kettlewell, 1958) where it is clear that, over the last hundred years, selective advantages in favour of the *carbonaria* genotype must have averaged about 30 per cent. per annum.

Extensive studies of the butterfly, *Maniola jurtina*, have shown that the distribution of spots on the hind-wings (ranging from 0 to 5 per wing)—a phenotypic condition evidently under the control of several genes—assumes a variety of equilibria in different parts of Britain, each stabilised at a particular level. Spotting, or rather the characteristics associated with it, thus appears to be subject to the action of natural selection. During our recent investigation of spot-values in *jurtina* on the English Mainland (Creed *et al.*, 1959), we encountered an extraordinary situation in which the female distribution typical of Southern England (unimodal at 0 spots) changed abruptly to an East Cornish stabilisation (bimodal at 0 and 2 spots) near the Devon-Cornish border, in a matter of a few hundred yards. The rapid transition from one spot-phenotype to another has now persisted for four successive years, and there seems no doubt that here we have selection pressures at work of a magnitude at least comparable with those found in polymorphic species. This view is supported by the existence of a " reverse-cline " effect in which the difference between the two populations reaches a maximum as they approach each other closely.

Clearly, there is an urgent need for a more precise analysis both of the magnitude of selective effects and of the agents involved. The following study represents an attempt to achieve this by shielding *jurtina* from the action of natural selection in the laboratory for a period of its life cycle and by comparing the spotting of the resulting adults with that of wild insects subjected to the full force of elimination. The breeding habits of the butterfly are unfortunately not well suited to this sort of experiment, since over-wintering takes place as a minute

Reprinted by permission of The Editors of HEREDITY from
HEREDITY, **16**, Part I, 39–52 (1961).

larva which spends most of its time deep down among the grass tussocks where it is quite inaccessible. However, from late April onwards the caterpillars, now half grown, become active at night and feed on the grass stems. It was from these that our laboratory stocks were derived and from which adults were obtained some seven weeks later for comparison with their wild counterparts.

1. THE MIDDLETON POPULATION OF *MANIOLA JURTINA*

The area chosen for this study is a small patch of chalk downland enclosed within Harewood Forest (41/405455) about 2½ miles due east of Andover (Hampshire). The butterflies are incapable of penetrating dense woodland and the colony is thus totally isolated. The locality is divided into two roughly equal parts by a thick mass of dogwood scrub extending for several hundred yards. Marking experiments showed this to be an effective barrier to *M. jurtina*. Sampling of larvæ and adults was confined entirely to the eastern area comprising approximately 17 acres, and referred to hereafter as Middleton East (Middleton being the name of the nearest village). From rather limited capture-recapture data, it appears that the size of the colony probably fluctuates between 3000 and 10,000 insects.

(i) *Females*

Extensive sampling throughout the season for the last five years has given no indication of any significant seasonal variation in spotting

TABLE 1

Female samples, 1960

Date	Spots						Spot av.	Total
	0	1	2	3	4	5		
9.vii	14	8	4	...	...	...	0·62	26
10.vii	3	4	1	1	...	...	1·00	9
11.vii	13	2	3	2	...	...	0·70	20
19.vii	13	2	3	...	...	...	0·44	18
22.vii	19	5	2	3	...	...	0·52	29
23.vii	11	2	1	1	...	...	0·47	15
18.viii	64	24	10	3	...	...	0·53	101
	137	47	24	10	...	...	0·57	218

$\chi^2_{(5)} = 4\cdot58$; P = 0·5 to 0·3 (values for 1 to 3 spots accumulated).

(see Creed *et al.* (1959) for evidence of intra-seasonal variation elsewhere). However, in both 1959 and 1960 there was a suggestion of higher spot-values in the early samples, but these were far too small to sway a formal test of heterogeneity (table 1). As we shall see later, there is reason to believe that increased spot-averages among females may be a feature of all *jurtina* populations at the beginning of the emergence, but these are difficult to detect with certainty except in very large colonies owing to the small numbers on the wing at that time.

TABLE 2

Total female samples, 1956-1960

Year	Spots						Spot av.	Total
	0	1	2	3	4	5		
1956	93	43	12	...	...	...	0·45	148
1957	126	41	20	3	...	...	0·47	190
1958	158	63	38	8	1	...	0·62	268
1959	157	64	29	3	...	...	0·52	253
1960	137	47	24	10	...	...	0·57	218
	671	258	123	24	1	...	0·54	1077

From an $n \times n$ table, $\chi^2_{(8)} = 11\cdot14$; $P = 0\cdot2$ (values for 2 to 4 spots accumulated).

TABLE 3

Male samples, 1960

Date	Spots						Spot av.	Total
	0	1	2	3	4	5		
26.vi	...	2	8	1	2	...	2·23	13
9.vii	1	5	55	16	3	1	2·23	81
10.vii	...	2	18	5	1	...	2·19	26
11.vii	...	3	16	4	...	1	2·17	24
19.vii	...	1	14	5	...	...	2·20	20
22.vii	...	2	19	2	...	...	2·00	23
18.viii	2	5	30	4	2	...	1·98	43
	3	20	160	37	8	2	2·14	230

$\chi^2_{(3)} = 2\cdot58$; $P = 0\cdot5$ to $0\cdot3$ (values for $0+1+2$ spots and $3+4+5$ spots accumulated; also samples for 26.vi+9.vii ; 10.vii+11.vii ; 19.vii+22.vii grouped together).

A satisfactory feature of the Middleton population has been its remarkable stability of spotting throughout the period of study in spite of the great variations in weather from one year to the next (table 2).

The spot-averages suggest a gradual increase until 1958, after which they levelled off and slightly declined during the two subsequent years.

(ii) *Males*

As in the females, there was a hint of higher spotting among males at the beginning of the season both in 1959 and 1960, but none in the previous three years. However, this was insufficient to influence a χ^2 test (table 3), and there was no appreciable evidence of any intra-seasonal spot-fluctuation. Unlike the females, however, there was strong heterogeneity between the annual samples—$\chi^2_{(6)} = 21 \cdot 22$; $P = 0 \cdot 01$ to $0 \cdot 001$ (values for $0 + 1$ spots and $3 + 4 + 5$ spots accumulated; samples for 1956 and 1957 grouped together (table 4). While

TABLE 4

Total male samples, 1956-1960

Year	Spots						Spot av.	Total
	0	1	2	3	4	5		
1956	2	5	32	8	...	...	1·98	47
1957	7	25	164	37	6	...	2·04	239
1958	6	21	285	91	20	3	2·25	426
1959	4	12	168	56	12	1	2·25	253
1960	3	20	160	37	8	2	2·14	230

maintaining much the same general pattern of variation in spot-average over the five years, the fluctuations among males thus appear to have been more marked than those occurring in the females.

2. COLLECTION AND REARING OF WILD LARVÆ

After hibernation, the larvæ start feeding again in late April, by which time they have attained a length of about 1 cm. Virtually nothing is known of the microclimate in the grass tufts where the animals live, but it is clear that their activity is closely related to temperature and humidity. Thus we found that for successful collecting, a minimum temperature of 50° F. was needed, also a fairly heavy dew. The larvæ are nocturnal and feed on a variety of grasses which at Middleton are chiefly *Helictotrichon pubescens* and *Brachypodium sylvaticum*. Their density is never very high and we found it quite impracticable to collect them by torchlight as is frequently advocated in the entomological literature. The only reasonably efficient collecting device is a sweeping net mounted on a stout stick, but even with this the accumulation of a reasonable sample was a fairly laborious undertaking. Thus four collectors working for an hour and a half after sunset were fortunate if they managed to secure 40 larvæ. The difficulties of collecting are aggravated by the remarkable sensitivity of the caterpillars to touch or even the slightest impact of a net on the grass stems where they are feeding. Their immediate reaction is invariably to curl up and drop down into the herbage below. When sweeping, therefore, the passage of the net must be sufficiently rapid to defeat this alarm reaction.

Rearing the larvæ in captivity presents little difficulty and they thrive in the laboratory on the appropriate grasses grown in pots. Mortality during 1957 and 1958 was relatively low (table 5) and in most instances the cause of death was uncertain. However, in 1959 and 1960 the proportion of fatalities rose steeply to roughly a third. As will be seen from table 5, the reason for this was largely parasitism by the Hymenopteran, *Apanteles tetricus*, of larvæ collected from early June onwards. Although not identified at the time, there now seems little doubt that more than three-quarters of the deaths recorded as due to " parasitisation " among larvæ collected in 1958 after the

TABLE 5

Mortality among reared M. jurtina *from Middleton East, 1957-1960*

Year	Period of collecting	Total larvæ	Mortality of larvæ (per cent.)	Per cent. of mortality due to *Apanteles*	Mortality of pupæ (per cent.)
1957	19.v.-30.v.	39	5·1	...	2·7
1958	8.v.-31.v.	139	8·6	...	9·5
	1.vi.-16.vi	63	14·2	77·8 ?	
1959	9.v.-31.v.	48	10·4	...	6·2
	1.vi.-9.vii	220	31·8	78·6	
1960	26.iv.-31.v.	101	19·8	5·0	10·9
	1.vi.-18.vii	259	39·3	73·5	

beginning of June, were also inflicted by *Apanteles*. The reason for the lack of parasitism in 1957 is clear enough, for no larvæ were collected after the end of May. The isolation of the parasite for identification proved a comparatively simple matter for the fully grown grubs were frequently observed emerging from stricken *jurtina* larvæ and the characteristic white cocoons which they spin prior to pupation were clearly visible on the grass stems or surrounding their dying host. Identification of the emerging adults as *Apanteles tetricus* was kindly undertaken by Mr G. E. J. Nixon of the Commonwealth Institute of Entomology. With a little experience we found it was often possible to tell in the field which larvæ were likely to be parasitised, owing to their inability to curl up in the characteristic manner already described.

Mortality among the pupæ during the four years was consistently at a fairly low level (table 5). The causes of death are unknown but, without exception, failure occurred at the pigmented stage, *i.e.* a day or so prior to emergence. There was no evidence of parasitism carried over from the larval stage.

3. COMPARISON OF REARED AND FLYING ADULTS

(i) *Females*

The samples of reared and flying *M. jurtina* from Middleton East are summarised and compared in table 6.

The most obvious discrepancy concerns the reared insects emerging early which, in all four years, are far more highly spotted than would

TABLE 6

Comparison of reared and flying female M. jurtina *from Middleton East,*
1957-1960

Year	Origin of sample	Date	Spots						Spot av.	Total	Comparison of reared and flying
			0	1	2	3	4	5			
1957	R	22.vi-30.vii	5	6	8	...	...	...	1·16	19	$\chi^2_{(1)} = 11·81$; P<0·001
	F	30.vi-2.ix	126	41	20	3	...	...	0·47	190	
1958	R	3.vii-12.vii	6	4	10	5	1	...	1·65	26	$\chi^2_{(2)} = 27·57$; P<0·001
	R	13.vii-3.viii	14	21	9	2	1	...	1·04	47	$\chi^2_{(2)} = 14·32$; P<0·001
	F	5.vii-16.viii	158	63	38	8	1	...	0·62	268	
1959	R	22.vi-22.vii	15	16	9	1	...	...	0·90	41	$\chi^2_{(2)} = 9·76$; P = 0·01 to 0·001
	R	23.vii-16.viii	41	9	8	...	2	...	0·55	60	$\chi^2_{(2)} = 3·08$; P = 0·3 to 0·2
	F	4.vii-16.viii	157	64	29	3	...	...	0·52	253	
1960	R	20.vi-20.vii	16	11	10	5	...	...	1·10	42	$\chi^2_{(2)} = 11·57$; P = 0·01 to 0·001
	R	21.vii-24.viii	52	31	7	4	...	...	0·61	94	$\chi^2_{(2)} = 4·73$; P = 0·1 to 0·05
	F	9.vii-18.viii	137	47	24	10	...	...	0·57	218	

In column 2, R = reared ; F = flying.

In calculating χ^2 for the 1957 samples, values at 1 to 3 spots have been accumulated. In all the remaining calculations, values for 2, 3 and 4 spots have been grouped together.

have been expected judging by their wild counterparts. As the season proceeded, so the spot-values began to fall, and in both 1959 and 1960 the reared adults emerging from the third week in June onwards showed a spot-distribution similar to that of the flying insects. The situation in 1959 is shown graphically in fig. 1. It will be recalled that early June was the time when the infection of larvæ by *Apanteles* first showed itself. The reared butterflies exhibiting wild-type spotting were thus derived from those caterpillars which managed to remain uninfected.

We are here faced with a remarkable situation, that by selective parasitism, *Apanteles tetricus* plays a major part in controlling spot-distribution in the adult females of *M. jurtina*.

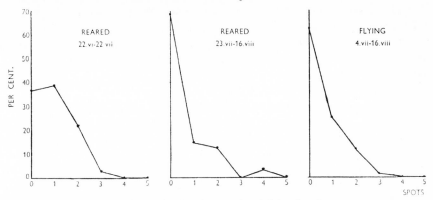

Fɪɢ. ɪ.—Spot-distributions in reared and flying females; 1959.

(ii) *Males*

The result of comparing reared and flying males is less striking than in the females (table 7). Throughout the four years there has

TABLE 7

Comparison of reared and flying male M. jurtina *from Middleton East,*
1957-1960

| Year | Origin of sample | Date | Spots | | | | | | Spot av. | Total | Comparison of reared and flying |
			0	1	2	3	4	5			
1957	R	19.vi-14.vii	...	...	14	2	1	...	2·24	17	$\chi^2_{(1)} = 0\cdot0013$; P = 0·98 to 0·95
	F	18.vi-2.ix	7	25	164	37	6	...	2·04	239	
1958	R	27.vi-3.viii	...	4	57	14	2	3	2·29	80	$\chi^2_{(1)} = 0\cdot31$; P = 0·7 to 0·5
	F	5.vii-16.viii	6	21	285	91	20	3	2·25	426	
1959	R	18.vi-1.viii	...	5	47	10	4	1	2·24	67	$\chi^2_{(1)} = 0\cdot425$; P = 0·7 to 0·5
	F	4.vii-16.viii	4	12	168	56	12	1	2·25	253	
1960	R	20.vi -20.viii	...	2	53	17	4	...	2·30	76	$\chi^2_{(2)} = 5\cdot13$; P = 0·1 to 0·05
	F	26.vi-18.viii	3	20	160	37	8	2	2·14	230	

In column 2, R = reared ; F = flying.

In calculating χ^2 for the 1957, 1958 and 1959 samples, values for 0+1+2 and 3+4+5 spots have been accumulated. In the 1960 data, 0+1 and 3+4+5 spot-values have been grouped together.

31

been no indication of intra-seasonal variation in spotting among reared adults nor any evidence of divergence between them and their flying counterparts. The nearest approach to this was in 1960 but, as will be seen from table 7, the difference did not attain the level of formal significance. The comparison for 1959 provides a typical instance and is presented graphically in fig. 2. The role of *Apanteles* in relation to male spot-values thus remains obscure; but it seems

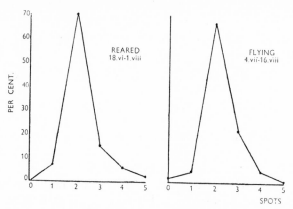

FIG. 2.—Spot-distributions in reared and flying males; 1959.

that the genes controlling spotting must exert different effects in the male from those in the female in influencing susceptibility to *Apanteles* infection.

4. RANDOM SAMPLING OF LARVÆ

Any valid comparison of reared and flying *jurtina* rests on the assumption that a method involving sweeping at night selects the larvæ at random. If spotting in the adult is under genetic control, as it clearly must be (pp. 48-50), the genes concerned could affect some aspects of behaviour as well. For instance, they might determine the tendency of a larva to feed high up on a grass stem thus influencing its liability to capture. Such an arrangement might well account for the excess of high-spotted females obtained at the beginning of the emergence.

To test this hypothesis, larvæ captured in 1959 were divided according to their feeding behaviour in the breeding cages at night into two groups—high feeding and low feeding. The division was obviously rather an artificial one but, as far as was possible, we chose certain arbitrary points on the food plants, to enable us to decide unequivocally into which category each larva should be placed. The cages were examined on four successive nights at a time when collecting at Middleton would have taken place (between 10.0 and 10.45 p.m.). The results are analysed in table 8.

Within the limitations of this rather crude experiment, it seems clear that the majority of larvæ exhibit a fairly consistent form of

32

feeding behaviour under laboratory conditions. Whether this represents faithfully what happens in the wild state is, of course, impossible to say. The spot-distributions of the two resulting groups of adults when compared showed no significant difference between them. For the males $\chi^2_{(1)} = 0.84$ with $P = 0.5$ to 0.3, and in the females $\chi^2_{(1)} = 0.02$;

TABLE 8

Feeding behaviour of larvæ from Middleton East, 1959

Date	Larvæ selected for high feeding				Departure from equality
	Feeding high	Percentage	Total	Standard error	
17.vi	26	79·79	33	±7·11	S.
18.vi	23	69·70	33	±8·00	S.
19.vi	20	74·07	27	±8·43	S.
20.vi	23	65·71	35	±8·03	N.S.

Date	Larvæ selected for low feeding				Departure from equality
	Feeding low	Percentage	Total	Standard error	
17.vi	41	89·13	46	±4·59	S.
18.vi	24	53·30	45	±5·44	N.S.
19.vi	28	77·78	36	±6·93	S.
20.vi	14	51·85	27	±9·62	N.S.

In column 6, S. = significant, and N.S. = not significant.

$P = 0.9$. There thus appears to be good reason for assuming that the sampling of the larvæ in relation to their feeding behaviour was at random in so far as the eventual spotting of the adults was concerned.

5. DISCUSSION

The Middleton population of female *Maniola jurtina* has proved to be ideal for a study of the influence of natural selection on spot-distribution since inter- and intra-seasonal variations in spotting have been virtually absent. By contrast, the imagines reared from wild larvæ have exhibited striking intra-seasonal heterogeneity. As a result of four years' work it is now clear that the emergence of adult females conforms to a distinct pattern. Those appearing from late June to mid-July develop from larvæ unaffected by parasitism and are characterised by a spot-average about double that occurring in the wild state. Thereafter, spotting rapidly declines and, among the adults derived from larvæ which have been subject to a drastic elimination through parasitism by *Apanteles tetricus*, the spot-distribution is identical with that of the flying population. This is well demonstrated by the results obtained in 1959 and 1960 (table 6 and fig. 1).

In 1958 late larval mortality was much reduced compared with the two following years (table 5). As the emergence proceeded the spot-values dropped, but they never resembled those in nature. In 1957, larva collecting was confined to May, so a lack of parasitism and a high level of spotting among the emergent females were to be expected (table 6).

Using an extension of the method described by Woolf (1954), it is possible to calculate the selection pressures operating in nature against " spotted " female *jurtina* emerging early. From the most extensive data available, those for 1959 and 1960, and using 95 per cent. fiducial limits, it appears that the selective elimination of individuals with two spots and over compared with that of unspotted adults in 1959 was 69 per cent. (fiducial limits 87-26 per cent.), and in 1960 attained a value of 74 per cent. (fiducial limits 88-41 per cent.). In other words a larva or pupa whose genotype would cause it to become a female with 2 or more spots, had approximately a 70 per cent. chance of being eliminated by *Apanteles*, or in some other way during the remaining seven weeks or so of pre-imaginal life, compared with one carrying genes which would cause it to become a female at 0 spots. Selection pressures of this order might well account for the abrupt transition in spotting which we have encountered on the borders of Devon and Cornwall.

Information obtained from reared Middleton larvæ provides a ready explanation of the occurrence of " intra-seasonal shift " encountered at Ipswich, Burham Down and elsewhere (Creed *et al.*, 1959). It is noteworthy that in all these localities the trend of spotting, on occasions when it fluctuates intra-seasonally, is invariably from high values at the beginning of the season to lower ones later on, never in the reverse direction. We have seen that at Middleton the *jurtina* population is subject to great selection pressures, so that an excess of high spot-value females never gets a chance of showing itself. However, should the severity of selection be relaxed, it is the early, high-spotted specimens which would benefit out of all proportion. It is perhaps worth noting here that in certain Irish colonies of *jurtina*, selection against high spotting has been even more severe than at Middleton, with the result that values of 2 spots and over seem almost to have been eliminated (Dowdeswell and Ford, 1953).

The situation in the males is more difficult to understand. There is no doubt that " intra-seasonal shift " occurs in some colonies just as it does in the females; there has even been a hint of it at Middleton, but variations there have been too small to attain statistical significance. Like the females, higher spotting at the beginning of the season is invariably the rule in the few wild populations known to fluctuate seasonally elsewhere in England. However, experience with regard to the reared Middleton larvæ shows that spot-values are no higher at the beginning of the summer than they are later on. Moreover, the spot-distribution among reared adults shows no tendency whatever

to depart from that of wild insects. It may well be that other phenotypic effects associated with spotting and subject to selection may
differ in the male from those in the female. Perhaps the system of
polygenes controlling spot-values has varying effects and is differentially selected in the two sexes.

Another aspect of our findings at Middleton bears on the possibility
of explaining spotting in *M. jurtina* on an environmental rather than
a genetic basis, as has often been suggested. We have seen how in
1959 and 1960, the spotting of reared females was extremely different
from imagines caught flying (table 6 and fig. 1), with the exception
of those appearing at the end of the emergence, the survivors of otherwise parasitised larvæ, whose spot-distribution was the same as the
wild insects. Now it might be argued that reared butterflies could
be expected to differ from caught ones, since the two had been bred
in entirely different environments. If this were so, how could the
females emerging late show spotting identical with that in nature?
Admittedly, this might be explained on the assumption that the late
emergers resemble those flying because they are derived from larvæ
found later which have not, therefore, been subject to laboratory
conditions for so long. Alternatively, the late larvæ might differ from
the earlier ones in some way (their lateness being an aspect of this
difference), and therefore fail to react to laboratory conditions in
the same manner. The answer to this argument is to be found in
table 5, where it will be seen that in 1958 the larval mortality due to
parasitism was less than half that in 1959 and 1960. The spotting of
adults emerging late in 1958 bore no resemblance to those flying at
Middleton (table 6).

K. G. McWhirter has pointed out to me a number of other
features of spotting in *M. jurtina* which would be hard to explain on
an environmental basis:

(i) The normal widespread stabilisation of *jurtina* populations
such as has occurred at Middleton and elsewhere.

(ii) The highly significant correlation between the spot-distribution
in male and female populations (McWhirter, 1957).

(iii) The abundant evidence that one sex tends to follow the
other where spot changes do occur, as happened at
Middleton East to a small extent during the years 1956-
1959.

(iv) The rapid change-over from one form of spotting to another
which takes place in the vicinity of the Devon-Cornwall
border.

It is indeed unfortunate that so little is known about the ecology
of *Apanteles tetricus* beyond the bare fact that its attacks seem to be
mainly confined to butterflies of the family Satyridæ. From the

evidence provided by the Middleton larvæ, certain obvious questions arise:

(i) If the parasite infects both male- and female-producing larvæ, as it must, judging by the sex-ratio, why are its effects on spotting so different in the two sexes?

(ii) What enables it to select larvæ destined to give rise to spotted females in preference to those with no spots? Or is the parasite more viable in one kind of body than in another?

(iii) At what stage in the life of a *jurtina* larva does parasitic infection occur?

The fact that parasitism is not evident among the larvæ destined to give rise to the earliest adults suggests a subtle synchronisation of the life cycles of parasite and host to ensure that a supply of adequately grown *jurtina* caterpillars is available by the time the adult *Apanteles* emerge. Clearly, there is an immense field here for further investigation.

Finally, an important genetic question arises in relation to the great selection pressures exerted on spotted females. If the relative elimination rate of female *jurtina* with two spots and over is of the order of 70 per cent., why have not the gene systems concerned disappeared altogether? One explanation seems to be that, while the genes for spotting are advantageous in the male (particularly the 2-spot condition), they are disadvantageous in the female. Thus, as fast as the spot-genotypes are eliminated by *Apanteles* in the female they are reintroduced for the next generation by the males in pairing. Alternatively, the genes for spotting may have advantages balancing the effect of *Apanteles*. Support for an explanation on a selectionist basis is provided on the one hand by the situation in Ireland, where the genes for female spotting have been almost eliminated, and by that in East Cornwall on the other where the high spot-values are at a relative advantage.

Such a mechanism is, in a sense, rather " inefficient " but, as E. B. Ford points out, it is hardly more so than the many polymorphisms which maintain in the heterozygous state genes that are disadvantageous when homozygous. As a result of breeding experiments which we are carrying out at present, we hope before long to be able to analyse such problems further.

6. SUMMARY

1. An isolated colony of the butterfly *Maniola jurtina* at Middleton East, near Andover (Hampshire) has been studied intensively for a period of five years from the point of view of the distribution of individuals with variable numbers of spots on the underside of the hind-wings. This is a character which responds readily to the action of natural selection.

2. By obtaining larvæ from the same locality and rearing them in the laboratory, it was possible to compare spot-values of wild insects with those shielded from the action of selection during the last seven weeks or so of pre-imaginal life.

3. Reared females from larvæ collected in May and early June invariably carried an excess of spots when compared with their free-flying counterparts. Those appearing later on exhibited a spot-distribution similar to the wild type.

4. Evidence is presented to show that the principal selective agent responsible for the reduction in spotting under natural conditions is the Hymenopterous parasite *Apanteles tetricus*. This was found to inflict a high mortality among larvæ collected from about the second week in June onwards.

5. Among male *jurtina*, there is no distinction between the spot-distribution of wild and reared adults. This suggests that the adaptive significance of spotting varies in the two sexes. It may even be under the control of different sets of polygenes.

6. An experiment designed to test the randomness of samples of wild larvæ collected by sweeping with a net at night shows that, on the whole, the larvæ are fairly consistent in their feeding habits. However, there is no indication that a tendency to feed high up on the grass stems and hence to be more easily captured, is in any way related to the spot-distribution of the resulting adults of either sex.

7. Using an extension of a calculation devised by Woolf, it is shown that selection pressures of the order of 70 per cent. operate during the last seven weeks of pre-imaginal life against larvæ and pupæ destined to give rise to females with two or more spots. Such elimination is of the order of magnitude necessary to explain the abrupt transition from a unimodal to a bimodal distribution which is known to occur in the vicinity of the Devon-Cornwall border.

8. The occurrence of an excess of highly spotted females at the beginning of the emergence provides a ready explanation of the phenomenon of " intra-seasonal shift " observed among both sexes in *M. jurtina* populations elsewhere. The reason for such fluctuations in males still remains obscure.

9. It is pointed out that the findings at Middleton render any suggestion that spotting in *M. jurtina* may be under the control of environmental stimuli (as opposed to a genetic mechanism) virtually untenable.

10. Various outstanding problems are considered concerning the mechanism of parasitisation by *Apanteles tetricus*.

11. Suggestions are made of ways in which high-spot female genotypes may be perpetuated in the face of severe adverse selection pressures.

Acknowledgments.—It is a pleasure to be able to record my gratitude to various organisations and individuals who have helped me with this work. To Captain A. S. Wills I am particularly grateful for his permission to work in Harewood

Forest. The Royal Society has kindly contributed financial help for equipment and travelling, while " Shell " Research Ltd. have provided me with a calculating machine. My thanks are also due to Dr E. B. Ford, F.R.S., and Mr K. G. McWhirter for numerous stimulating discussions. Both of them have read the typescript of this paper and have offered many valuable suggestions. Mr McWhirter also kindly assisted me with the calculations. Mr G. E. J. Nixon of the Commonwealth Institute of Entomology was responsible for the identification of *Apanteles tetricus,* and provided me with such references to the literature as were available.

The collection of larvæ and adults of *M. jurtina* in numbers sufficient for work of this kind is a laborious and time-consuming operation, and I am fully aware of the debt I owe to a large body of helpers. In particular I would like to thank my family, numerous members of Winchester College Natural History Society, and my laboratory assistant Mr A. S. Mitchener (and, on occasions, his family as well) for all their valuable contributions. Mr Mitchener took a particularly active part in the larva collecting at night and was largely responsible for the design and construction of the special nets used for the purpose.

7. REFERENCES

CREED, E. R., DOWDESWELL, W. H., FORD, E. B., AND McWHIRTER, K. G. 1959. Evolutionary studies on *Maniola jurtina* : the English mainland 1956-57. *Heredity, 13,* 363-391.

DOWDESWELL, W. H., AND FORD, E. B. 1953. The influence of isolation on variability in the butterfly, *Maniola jurtina. Symposia Soc. Exp. Biol., 7,* 254-273.

KETTLEWELL, H. B. D. 1958. A survey of the frequencies of *Biston betularia* (L.), (Lep.), and its melanic forms in Great Britain. *Heredity, 12,* 51-72.

McWHIRTER, K. G. 1957. A further analysis of variability in *Maniola jurtina. Heredity, 11,* 359-371.

WOOLF, B. 1955. On estimating the relation between blood group and disease. *Ann. Human Genetics, 19,* 251-253.

LARVAL COLOR PATTERN IN *PAPILIO DEMODOCUS*

C. A. CLARKE

Department of Medicine, University of Liverpool

C. G. C. DICKSON

"Blencathra," Cambridge Avenue, St. Michael's Estate, Cape Town

P. M. SHEPPARD

Sub-Department of Genetics, University of Liverpool

Received July 25, 1962

It has been shown by Kettlewell (1956) that natural selection is acting on color pattern in many cryptically colored moths to adjust the appearance of the moth so that it matches its background and is inconspicuous to its enemies, particularly birds. Such selection must have been acting equally strongly on the appearance of many larvae (de Ruiter, 1952). It is therefore of interest that the caterpillars of several species of *Papilio* feeding on *Citrus* and other Rutaceae have very similar color patterns (fig. 1). One of the species, *Papilio demodocus*, has a wide distribution in Africa and feeds on Rutaceae over most of its range, but in parts of South Africa it is also found on Umbelliferae, and here the larva in its final instar is polymorphic, a minority (about 20%) having the normal "citrus" pattern while the remainder has a more complex one (fig. 2). No clear-cut polymorphism is present in the immature larvae. Van Son (1949) maintains that the food of the larvae determines the color pattern in the final instar, larvae feeding on umbellifers developing the umbelliferous pattern, whereas those feeding on *Citrus* develop the citrus pattern. Such a situation is of considerable evolutionary importance, and the present paper discusses some preliminary work on the determination of larval color pattern in this species.

MATERIALS AND METHODS

The living material for the genetic investigations was sent to England by airmail as eggs, larvae, or pupae. Those from Cape Town contained the two forms, whereas those from Natal and Nairobi consisted of the citrus form which is the only type found in these areas. We also obtained the very closely related Asian species, *P. demoleus*, from Ceylon, and the caterpillar of this butterfly is also always of the citrus type. The data from South Africa indicate that the umbelliferous form is confined almost to the Cape Peninsula and to the Cape Province, mainly on the coastal belt but also extending a good way inland on the west. Here the climate is not tropical, but to the east it becomes so well south of Durban and then large-leaved species of Rutaceae become available and the citrus form is characteristic. However, the umbellifer type has been found in the Orange Free State and far inland from Port Elizabeth in the Karroo area.

In England the butterflies used in this investigation were reared in electrically heated greenhouses. Matings were obtained by the hand-pairing technique (Clarke and Sheppard, 1956) and the female butterflies confined in silk organza sleeves on suitable food plants to lay eggs. The larvae usually were reared in the sleeves, but some were transferred to plastic boxes when nearly full grown. Random samples of larvae, used for determining the frequencies of the forms in South Africa, were collected there by one of us (C. G. C. D.) both from *Citrus* and from umbellifers.

RESULTS

Breeding Results

Relation of food plant to larval pattern. —Our first experiment was carried out to test Van Son's assertion that the larval

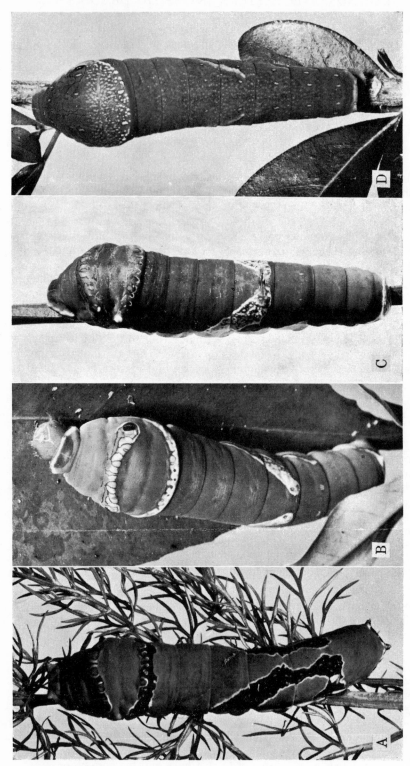

Fig. 1. Final instar larvae of four *Citrus*-feeding *Papilios*. A, *P. demodocus*, citrus form; B, *P. polytes*; C, *P. memnon*; D, *P. bianor*. Note the similarity of pattern of the various species, all of which feed on shiny-leaved members of the Rutaceae.

Fig. 2.   Left, Full umbellifer form of *P. demodocus* larva, final instar. Right, Intermediate form of *P. demodocus* larva, final instar.

pattern was determined by the type of food plant, and table 1 gives the data and the analysis on two of the broods. The broods were divided in half as soon as the larvae hatched and one-half fed on fennel (*Foeniculum vulgare* Mill.) and one-half

on *Citrus*. As will be seen from table 1 the breeding results give no evidence that the color pattern of the larvae is determined by its food, there being segregation for patterns in broods fed on *Citrus* and also in those fed exclusively on umbellifers.

TABLE 1.   P. demodocus. *Color pattern of larva in relation to food plant*

Brood number	Locality and larval pattern of parents where known	Larval pattern and food plant of offspring			
		Citrus pattern reared on *Citrus*	Umbellifer pattern reared on *Citrus*	Citrus pattern reared on fennel	Umbellifer pattern reared on fennel
2269	Cape Town, wild	3	2	5	5
2403	Cape Town citrus pattern ♀ 2269 × umbellifer pattern ♂ 2269	2	3	0	4
Totals		5	5	5	9

The table gives no evidence that the food plant affects the larval pattern. *P* > 0.3.

TABLE 2. P. demodocus. *Genetics of larval color pattern*

Brood number	Locality and larval pattern of parents where known	Larval pattern of offspring			P[1]
		Umbellifer	Intermediate	Citrus	
2269	Cape Town, wild	7	0	8	–
2390	Cape Town, umbellifer form 2269 ♀ × umbellifer form 2269 ♂	25	0	3	> 0.10
2403	Cape Town, citrus form 2269 ♀ × umbellifer form 2269 ♂ same as 2390	7	0	2	> 0.10
2411	Race cross of ♀ 2269 umbellifer form × ♂ citrus form from Nairobi	5	6	9	> 0.80
5216	Race cross of ♀ citrus form from Natal × ♂ umbellifer form from Cape Town, wild	6	14	17	> 0.50
5254	Cape Town, wild	6	3	0	–

[1] Probabilities of obtaining these departures from the expected Mendelian ratios.

Moreover, the distribution of patterns within broods, some of whose members were fed on *Citrus* and some on fennel, shows no evidence that the citrus form survived better on *Citrus* or the umbellifer form on fennel.

In Cape Town, where the two principal forms occur, there are also intermediate forms (fig. 2) which again do not appear to be produced by one or the other food plant. These intermediates, in general, much more closely resemble the umbellifer than the citrus type. It must be emphasized that in the breeding work we scored the larvae for the three forms only when they had reached their final instar, since we did not feel that we could make an accurate assessment before. However, Van Son (1949) considers that the citrus and the umbellifer forms are distinguishable at all instars. More observations, therefore, seem to be required on this point.

Having established the facts shown in table 1, we next found that in England all the larvae, whatever their pattern, did better on fennel than on *Citrus*, the early larval mortality in particular being much less.

Genetics of larval color pattern.—As the larval patterns were shown not to be controlled environmentally by the food, we next decided to investigate in what way they were inherited, and it was soon found

that there was segregration within broods which could be explained on Mendelian lines. Thus "umbellifer" appeared to be dominant to "citrus," though it was clear from an examination of the broods that dominance was not always complete. The relevant data are now considered in more detail.

It will be seen (table 2) that the wild brood 2269 from Cape Town segregated into 7 umbellifer and 8 citrus forms, and that when two of the former were sibmated the resulting offspring segregated into 25 umbellifer and 3 citrus forms (brood 2390). Furthermore, when the same male was mated (brood 2403) to a citrus-type sister there was segregation into 7 umbellifer- and 2 citrus-type larvae. These results clearly suggest that the umbellifer is dominant or semidominant to the citrus pattern and that 2269 was a backcross, 2390 a mating between two heterozygotes, and 2403 another backcross. The other broods in table 2 are also consistent with this hypothesis.

In the race crosses (2411 and 5216) there are good fits to a 1:1 ratio if the intermediates and the umbellifer patterns are classed together. Intermediates occur more often in race crosses, but brood 5254 shows that they also can appear in wild Cape Town material.

One F_2 brood (5281) was obtained, this

FIG. 3. Some F₁ generation larvae of the species cross *P. demoleus* ♀ × *P. demodocus* ♂ in which the *demodocus* was a heterozygote for the citrus pattern. Note the extreme variability of the four intermediate forms.

being a sibmating of the race cross 5216. It produced 3 umbellifer-type larvae, 28 intermediates, 12 citrus-type, and 12 black larvae of a form not previously observed. A somewhat similar type of black larva was also found in the species cross (brood 5356) of a female *P. demoleus* from Ceylon and a male *P. demodocus* heterozygous for the umbellifer form. This brood segregated into 15 intermediates of very variable type (fig. 3), 13 citrus, and 7 black larvae. It is clear from this brood that the black forms cannot be of the homozygous umbellifer type, and it seems probable that they are some new combination of the intermediate form. If this is so, brood 5281

becomes a good 3:1 ratio and brood 5356 not significantly different from a 1:1 (table 3).

The data generally, therefore, strongly suggest that the difference between the umbellifer and citrus pattern is determined in the main by a single pair of genes with the umbellifer form dominant or semi-dominant. Crosses between "Cape" and Nairobi stocks suggest that dominance is less complete in this cross than in offspring from pure "Cape" material, or even in those between "Cape" and Natal. There is also evidence that the "Cape" gene complex modifies the citrus pattern itself, since larvae from this area have a citrus pattern

TABLE 3.   *F₂ of Natal × Cape Town race cross, and species cross of* P. demoleus × P. demodocus

Brood number	Locality and description of parents' larval pattern where known	Larval pattern of offspring				P
		Umbellifer	Intermediate	Black	Citrus	
5281 (F₂ brood)	♀ 5216 × ♂ 5216 (race cross between Natal and Cape Town. Both parents intermediate)	3	25	12	12	> 0.70
5356	♀ *P. demoleus* from Ceylon × *demodocus* ♂ umbellifer form 5205[1] from Cape Town	0	15	7	13	> 0.10

[1] An all umbellifer-type brood, but clearly containing some heterozygotes.

more like the umbelliferous one than do Nairobi or Natal stock. The Nairobi larvae have a citrus pattern almost identical with that of the Asian species, *P. demoleus*. Moreover, the *P. demoleus* × *P. demodocus* cross using "Cape" material gives offspring which are more intermediate between the umbelliferous and citrus pattern than are "Cape"/Nairobi heterozygotes. They are also much more variable. These findings suggest that there are modifiers in the "Cape" race which improve the dominance and which are lacking in areas where only the citrus form is found.

Samples of Larvae Collected at Random in the Wild (Cape Town)

One of us (C. G. C. D.) collected a random sample of larvae in the wild from the Cape Town area, where both umbellifers and *Citrus* are plentiful, the latter having been cultivated for the past three centuries. Some of these larvae were in their final instar when found, and some were at an earlier stage. The proportion of heterozygotes which are intermediate in appearance could be calculated by obtaining the gene frequency in the random samples from the proportion of the citrus form, estimating the expected number of heterozygotes and comparing it with the number of intermediate forms found. However, a comparison of the samples found on umbellifers and on *Citrus* both for the mature and immature larvae demonstrates that the samples are "biased" for reasons to be discussed later, and therefore, the degree of dominance can be judged only from the breeding results.

Predation

It is clear that if, as seems probable, the citrus pattern is more inconspicuous on *Citrus* than on fennel, and (less obviously) the umbellifer type is less conspicuous on fennel, there might then be differential predation and the proportions of the two forms found in the final instar might be different from those found if the larvae were collected at an early age and bred in captivity. We have evidence on this point (table 4). It will be seen that of the few larvae collected in the final instar none (out of five) found on *Citrus* were umbelliferlike; on the other hand, out of the 25 final instar larvae found on fennel, 23 were umbelliferlike or intermediate, and only two were citruslike. These figures are significantly different from those found when younger larvae were taken and reared in captivity.

Moreover, if one examines the 2 × 2 contingency table of umbellifer pattern on umbellifer, umbellifer pattern on *Citrus*,

TABLE 4.   *Random sample in relation to food plant on which larvae were found*

	Umbellifer form on umbellifer	Umbellifer form on *Citrus*	Intermediate form on umbellifer	Intermediate form on *Citrus*	Citrus form on umbellifer	Citrus form on *Citrus*	Totals
Collected in final instar	14	0	9	0	2	5	30
Collected before final instar	36	13	1	10	4	9	73

citrus pattern on umbellifer, and citrus pattern on *Citrus,* one finds a highly significant ($P = 0.00015$) discrepancy from a random distribution in favor of umbellifer patterns being more frequent on umbellifers and citrus patterns on *Citrus* in mature larvae. Examining the same classes in those larvae collected when immature (when there is no clear distinction between the two forms), the discrepancy from a random distribution is much reduced ($P > 0.05$). This suggests that, when the adult pattern is manifest, there is selection for the citrus pattern on *Citrus* and the umbellifer pattern on umbellifers. This hypothesis is strengthened by an examination of the frequency of intermediates (presumably heterozygotes) that appeared from the sample of immature larvae. On umbellifers there was one intermediate among the 37 non-citrus patterned larvae, whereas on *Citrus* there were 10 in 23, the difference being significant ($P = 0.00013$). If the inappropriate patterns are eliminated as suggested, and if the females tend to lay on the food plant on which they were reared, then most non-citrus larvae on *Citrus* must be heterozygotes since their female parent will have tended to be a citrus homozygote. However, on fennel the reverse will be true and therefore a smaller proportion of heterozygotes (intermediate larvae) will be expected, which is apparently what is found. It is known that some female insects do in fact tend to choose the food on which they were reared to lay their eggs (Thorpe, 1956).

That predation can occur is demonstrated by the results obtained by transferring 12 umbellifer and "intermediate" larvae from umbelliferous plants to a small rutaceous tree (*Calodendron capense*) which is a natural food plant of the species in eastern South Africa. Within 24 hours all the larvae had disappeared. In another experiment 9 final instar larvae, 3 of which were umbelliferlike, 2 intermediate, and 4 citrus, were placed on a small lemon tree, and Cape robins were observed to remove them within a few hours. The fact that all

forms were removed may have been due to the birds having been attracted initially by those larvae which were on an unsuitable background.

However, more detailed experiments would need to be carried out before any conclusions could be drawn about the degree of protection afforded by the background.

SUMMARY

(1) *Papilio demodocus* is a butterfly whose larvae feed on both *Citrus* and umbellifers in parts of South Africa. Elsewhere, this and closely related species feed on *Citrus* and have a distinctive larval color pattern, different from that of most of the larvae on umbellifers.

(2) The breeding results give no evidence that the color pattern of larvae is determined by food, there being segregation for pattern both in broods fed on *Citrus* and in those fed on umbellifers. There is also no evidence that the citrus form survives better on *Citrus* or the umbellifer form on fennel.

(3) Breeding results agree with the hypothesis that the difference between the citrus and the umbellifer patterns is determined in the main by a single pair of genes, with the umbellifer form dominant or semidominant. Thus, only a proportion of the heterozygotes can be recognized.

(4) Race crosses, and a species cross with *P. demoleus,* show that the dominance of the umbellifer pattern can be broken down. This argues that there are modifiers in the South African population which affect the dominance, indicating the evolution of dominance in this area due to the accumulation of modifiers. There is also evidence that the "Cape" gene complex modifies the citrus pattern itself, since larvae from this area have a citrus pattern more like the umbelliferous one than do Nairobi and Natal stock.

(5) In an F_2 mating a black form of larva was produced which was not found in the parents or their sibs. This black form is probably some modification of the

intermediate class and may be the result of modifiers in the homozygous state.

(6) The different proportion of the forms among full-grown larvae and immature ones collected on the two hosts in the wild and reared in the laboratory suggests that there is strong selection against the umbellifer pattern on *Citrus* and possibly against the citrus pattern on umbellifers. Evidence is adduced showing that birds may be responsible for the selection.

ACKNOWLEDGMENTS

We are indebted to Mr. Gowan C. Clark of Port Elizabeth for his helpful comments on the paper and for allowing us to see his watercolor paintings of all stages of the larvae of *P. demodocus*. We are also grateful to Mr. H. E. Irving for useful information about the distribution of the umbellifer form of larva in the Orange Free State. Our thanks are due to the Nuffield Foundation for its generous support, without which the work would not have been possible.

LITERATURE CITED

CLARKE, C. A., AND P. M. SHEPPARD. 1956. Hand pairing of butterflies. Lepid. News, **10**: 47–53.

DE RUITER, L. 1952. Some experiments on the camouflage of stick caterpillars. Behavior, **4**: 223–232.

KETTLEWELL, H. B. D. 1955. Selection experiments on industrial melanism in the Lepidoptera. Heredity, **9**: 323–342.

THORPE, W. H. 1956. Learning and instinct in animals. Methuen, London.

VAN SON, G. 1949. The butterflies of southern Africa. Part 1. Papilionidae and Pieridae. Transvaal Museum, Pretoria.

House Sparrows:
Rapid Evolution of Races
in North America

Richard F. Johnston*
Robert K. Selander†

A number of workers have attempted to demonstrate evolutionary changes in the house (English) sparrow (*Passer domesticus*) in North America since its introduction from England and Germany in 1852 (*1*). Several early studies based on small samples of specimens produced results (*2*) which were negative or statistically unreliable. In an investigation which has been widely cited (*3*) as evidence for slow rates of evolution of avian races, Lack (*4*) found no unequivocal evidence of divergence in bill and wing dimensions of the North American and Hawaiian populations from the Old World stock. However, Calhoun (*5*), using larger samples and employing refined methods of analysis, was able to show that average wing length in populations of the eastern and central United States increased slightly more than 1 mm between the time of introduction and 1930. He also demonstrated geographic variation in average length of wing, femur, and humerus correlated with regional differences in duration and severity of freezing temperatures in the United States. Recently, the possibility that New World populations exhibit regional color differences has been suggested by Keve (*6*).

To assess the full extent of variation in characters of color and size, series of 100 to 250 specimens of house sparrows

Reprinted by permission of R. F. Johnston and the publisher from SCIENCE, **144**, 548–550 (May 1, 1964). Copyright 1964 by the American Association for the Advancement of Science.

FIGURE 1. Map of North America showing distribution of house sparrow (shaded area) and localities where specimens were taken (dots).

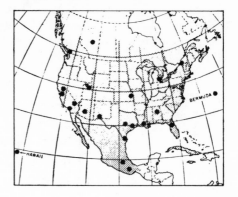

in fresh plumage were taken by us in October and November, 1962 and 1963, at various localities in North America and in the Hawaiian Islands, Bermuda, England, and Germany (Fig. 1). This extensive material clearly demonstrates the existence of pervasive geographic variation in a large number of characters in the North American and Hawaiian populations. Each New World population sampled has differentiated to greater or lesser degree from any other and from the Old World stock. Preparation and analysis of this material is still in process, but the preliminary findings presented here provide a general indication of the surprising extent to which selection has produced morphologic differentiation in a small number of generations. We have not as yet undertaken studies of the developmental basis of the morphologic characters of the house sparrow populations, but, in view of extensive evidence for comparable racial characters in other species of birds and in mammals (7), we are safe in assuming that the geographically variable characters of color, pattern, size, and body proportions are in fact genetically controlled and are either directly adaptive in themselves or represent selectively neutral or weakly nonadaptive correlates of other adaptive characters.

In analyzing individual and geographic variation in color, as well as in size, we have found it useful to segregate our specimens into adult and first-year age groups, since many of the characters studied exhibit significantly different means and variances in the two age groups.

In general, geographic variation is more pronounced in characters of color than in those of size. Specimens from northern and Pacific coastal localities and from the Valley of Mexico (Mexico City) are darkly pigmented, and those from Vancouver, British Columbia, are especially dark. Sparrows from collecting stations in the arid southwestern United States from southern California east to southern and central Texas are relatively pale in color, with extremes of pallor being achieved in samples from Death Valley, California, and Phoenix, Arizona. Samples from Salt Lake City, Utah, Lawrence, Kansas, and other localities in North America can be categorized broadly as intermediate in color. Specimens from Zachary, Louisiana, and Oaxaca City, Mexico, have a conspicuous yellow wash on the posterior under parts which is absent or only weakly indicated in birds from other North American localities.

Geographic variation in color of the breast in female house sparrows from Honolulu, Hawaii, and several localities in North America is shown in Figure 2, which presents spectral reflectance curves (8) for five specimens from each locality.

The overall geographic pattern of color variation in North American house sparrows conforms with Gloger's ecogeographic rule, which relates color to regional variation in temperature and humidity (9). Students of geographic variation in warm-blooded vertebrates a priori expect native North American species to be darker along the northwestern coast and paler in the arid southwest. The fact that house sparrows manifest this pattern of variation is evidence for the selective action of the same environmental factors that are assumed to be significant for native species.

Sparrows from Oahu, Hawaiian Islands, are very distinctive in color, being unlike specimens from English, German, and North American localities. They are characterized by a reduced value of the dark markings of the plumage, a general absence of fine streaks on the under parts, and an overall rufous-buff color which is especially intense on the breast and flanks. The legs and feet tend strongly to be pale buff in color rather than dark brown as in continental birds. The unusually strong differentiation of the sparrows of the Hawaiian Islands is not surprising in view of their geographic isolation and the fact that they have had an evolutionary history apart from North American populations. Sparrows were introduced to the islands in 1870 or 1871 from a New Zealand stock, which in turn had been brought to New Zealand from England in the years 1866–1868 (10).

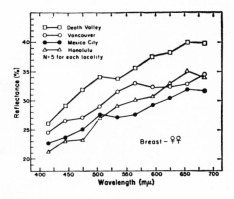

FIGURE 2. Spectral reflectance curves for the breast of female house sparrows from Honolulu, Hawaii, and several North American localities.

We emphasize the fact that geographic variation in color in New World house sparrows does not consist merely of subtle average differences among the samples, with broadly overlapping ranges of variation. On the contrary, in many cases the color differences between samples are both marked and consistent, permitting 100 percent separation of specimens from the two localities. For example, we have observed no overlap in color of the pileum (top of the head) in females between samples from Oakland, California, and Progreso, Texas, or between those from Death Valley, California, and Vancouver, British Columbia. Again, specimens of either sex from the Hawaiian Islands and any of the North American localities are consistently separable on the basis of color.

Geographic variation occurs as regularly in size as in color, and for the most part parallels trends which are generally characteristic of indigenous species. The pattern of variation in size is largely clinal: in the United States and Canada the largest individuals are from the more northerly localities sampled, the smallest are from the desert southwest, and birds from other stations are of intermediate sizes. Some indication of the degree of geographic variation in wing length in North America is provided by data for adult males of three popula-

FIGURE 3. Individual and geographic variation in wing length in adult male house sparrows from three localities. Vertical line: mean; horizontal line: observed range; solid rectangle: 2 standard errors on either side of mean; open rectangle: one standard deviation on either side of mean.

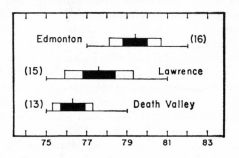

FIGURE 4. Individual and geographic variation in bill length (from nostril) in adult male house sparrows from four localities. See Figure 3 for an explanation of the graph.

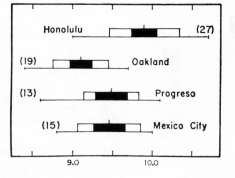

tions shown in Figure 3. Variation in bill length in four representative populations is shown in Figure 4. Note that the bill averages longer in the sample from Honolulu than in the continental populations. This was previously suggested by Lack's data (4), which had been considered equivocal because of uncertainties concerning seasonal variation in his material (11).

For reasons not important to the exposition here, wing length in house sparrows tends to vary independently of body size. Body weight is a good index of size, provided weights are taken from specimens having similar relative amounts of body fat, a character known to vary seasonally with the gonadal condition of the individual (12). Our samples are strictly comparable, since all were taken when the birds had just completed the annual molt and were in the same condition gonadally and physiologically; all specimens show uniformly moderate degrees of sub-cutaneous lipid deposition.

In Figure 5, mean body weights of adult males from 17 localities in North America are plotted against isophanes of the localities. Isophanes are calculated from latitude, longitude, and altitude of the localities and hence reflect gross climatic features (13). For localities north of southern Texas a simple relationship is evident, and a straight line fitted to the points by the method of least squares has the equation $Y = 24.1 + 0.12X$. The regression coefficient is highly significant (99.9 percent confidence interval = 0.02 to 0.21), and 93 percent of the variability is attributable to the linear regression effect. The observed relationship, which was predictable on the basis of Calhoun's geographically more restricted study (5) of linear dimensions, exemplifies the ecogeographic rule of Bergmann, which describes adaptive trends in body size as they relate to problems of heat flow and temperature regulation (9). Birds of larger body size occur at localities having high isophane numbers, reflecting boreal climates with severe winter cold; and those of smaller body size are from stations with low isophane numbers, reflecting mild or austral climates, occasionally with severe summer heat. A similar relationship between body size and climate is found in many native species of birds.

South of latitude 28°N in North America, other selective factors tend to override the effects of selection for body size as described by Bergmann's ecogeographic rule. Although mean body weight in the sample from Oaxaca City does not fall far from an expected position along the regression line based on data from samples taken in the United States and Canada, birds from Mexico City are surprisingly light in weight and those from Progreso, Texas, are unexpectedly heavy. That these differences reflect real variation in body size and not merely nongenetic variation in level of fat deposition is indicated not only by examination of the fat condition of the specimens but also by data on the length of the tarsus, which in house sparrows is closely correlated with body weight.

Current taxonomic practice gives formal nomenclatural recognition,

51

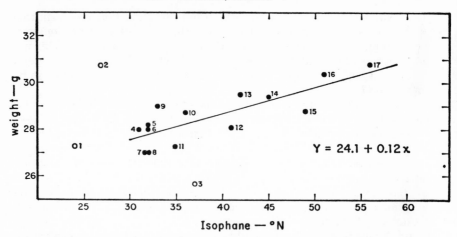

FIGURE 5. Mean body weights of adult male house sparrows plotted against isophanes (see text for explanation). Localities: 1, Oaxaca City, Mexico; 2, Progreso, Tex.; 3, Mexico City, Mexico; 4, Houston, Tex.; 5, Los Angeles, Calif.; 6, Austin, Tex.; 7, Death Valley, Calif.; 8, Phoenix, Ariz.; 9, Baton Rouge, La.; 10, Sacramento, Calif.; 11, Oakland, Calif.; 12, Las Cruces, N.M.; 13, Lawrence, Kan.; 14, Vancouver, B.C.; 15, Salt Lake City, Utah; 16, Montreal, Quebec; 17, Edmonton, Alberta. The regression line is based on data from localities 4 to 17.

at the subspecific level, to morphologically definable geographic segments of species populations. And it is obvious that the levels of differentiation achieved by the introduced house sparrow in the Hawaiian Islands and in a number of areas in North America are fully equivalent to those shown by many polytypic native species. Although application of subspecific trinomials to certain New World populations of sparrows would be fully warranted, we are not convinced that nomenclatural stasis is desirable for a patently dynamic system. Nomenclatural considerations aside, the evolutionary implications of our findings are apparent. Current estimates of the minimum time normally required for the evolution of races in birds range upward from about 4000 years (*14*), and nowhere is there a suggestion that such conspicuous and consistent patterns of adaptive evolutionary response to environments as we have found in New World house sparrows are to be expected within a period covering not more than 111 generations. Actually, much of the differentiation in North American populations must have occurred in the present century, since sparrows did not reach Mexico City until 1933 (*15*), and they were not present in Death Valley before 1914, or in Vancouver before 1900. Our findings are consistent with recent evidence of evolutionary changes in some other groups of animals, including mammals and insects (*16*), within historical times. Clearly, our thinking must not exclude the possibility of animals attaining to extremely rapid rates of evolution at the racial level.

ABSTRACT

Conspicuous adaptive differentiation in color and size has occurred in the house sparrow (*Passer domesticus*) in North America and the Hawaiian Islands since its introduction in the middle of the 19th century. Patterns of geographic variation in North America parallel those shown by native polytypic species, in conformity with Gloger's and Bergmann's ecogeographic rules. Racial differentiation of house sparrow populations may require no more than 50 years.

January 27, 1964

REFERENCES AND NOTES

* Museum of Natural History, University of Kansas.

† Department of Zoology, University of Texas.

1. W. B. Barrows, *U.S. Dept. Agr. Div. Econ. Ornithol. Mammal. Bull.* 1 (1889); L. Wing, *Auk* 60, 74 (1943).

2. C. W. Townsend and J. Hardy, *Auk* 26, 78 (1909); J. C. Phillips, *ibid.* 32, 51 (1915); J. Grinnell, *Am. Naturalist* 53, 468 (1919); _____, *Proc. Calif. Acad. Sci.* 13, 43 (1923).

3. E. Mayr, *Systematics and the Origin of Species* (Columbia Univ. Press, New York, 1942), p. 60; J. Huxley, *Evolution: The Modern Synthesis* (Harper, New York, 1943), p. 519; B. Rensch, *Evolution above the Species Level* (Columbia Univ. Press, New York, 1960), p. 91.

4. D. Lack, *Condor* 42, 239 (1940).

5. J. B. Calhoun, *Am. Naturalist* 81, 203 (1947).

6. A. Keve, *Proc. XII Intern. Ornithol. Congr., Helsinki,* pp. 376–95 (1960).

7. L. R. Dice and P. M. Blossom, *Carnegie Inst. Wash. Publ.* 485, 1 (1937); W. F. Blair, *Contrib. Lab. Vert. Biol.* 25, 1 (1944); _____, *ibid.* 36, 1 (1947); F. B. Sumner, *Bibliog. Genetica* 9, 1 (1932); J. Huxley, *Evolution: The Modern Synthesis* (Harper, New York, 1943), p. 433.

8. Reflection was measured with a Bausch and Lomb Spectronic 20 colorimeter equipped with a color analyzer reflectance attachment. Readings were taken at 30-mμ intervals and a magnesium carbonate block was used as a standard of 100-percent reflectance. See R. K. Selander, R. F. Johnston, T. H. Hamilton, *Condor,* in press, for further explanation.

9. C. L. Gloger, *Das Abändern der Vögel durch Einfluss des Klimas* (Breslau, 1833); C. Bergmann, *Gött. Stud.* 1, 595 (1847); B. Rensch, *Arch.Naturgesch N. F.* 7, 364 (1938); _____, *ibid.* 8, 89 (1939); E. Mayr, *Evolution* 10, 105 (1956); T. H. Hamilton, *ibid.* 15, 180 (1961).

10. D. Summers-Smith, *The House Sparrow* (Collins, London, 1963), p. 182.

11. J. Davis, *Condor* 56, 142 (1954).

12. R. K. Selander and R. F. Johnston, unpublished.

13. A. D. Hopkins, *U.S. Dept. Agr. Misc. Publ.* 280 (1938).

14. R. E. Moreau, *Ibis* (ser. 12) 6, 229 (1930); E. Mayr, *Animal Species and Evolution* (Harvard Univ. Press, Cambridge, 1963), p. 579.

15. H. O. Wagner, *Z. Tierpsychol.* 16, 584 (1959).

16. E. H. Ashton and S. Zuckerman, *Proc. Roy. Soc. London, Ser. B* 137, 212 (1950); E. C. Zimmerman, *Evolution* 13, 137 (1960); E. O. Wilson and W. L.

Brown, Jr., *ibid.* **12**, 211 (1958); R. M. Lockley, *Nature* **145**, 767 (1940); J. N. Kennedy, *Bull. Brit. Ornithol. Club* **33**, 33 (1913); F. C. Evans and H. G. Vevers, *J. Animal Ecol.* **7**, 290 (1938); Th. Dobzhansky, *Evolution* **12**, 385 (1958); _____, *ibid.* **17**, 333 (1963); E. B. Ford, *Cold Spring Harbor Symp. Quant. Biol.* **20**, 230 (1955); P. M. Sheppard, *Advan. Genet.* **10**, 165 (1961); H. B. D. Kettlewell, *Heredity* **10**, 287 (1956).

17. Supported by NSF grants GB 240 and GB 1739.

Selection Response and Genetics of Parathion Resistance in the Pacific Spider Mite, *Tetranychus pacificus*[1]

Lloyd A. Andres and Timothy Prout,[2] *University of California, Riverside*

Abstract

Parathion resistant and parathion susceptible strains of the Pacific spider mite, *Tetranychus pacificus* McG., were derived from certain field populations and established as laboratory colonies.

The two colonies were characterized by dosage-mortality curves for the effect of parathion and also Aramite® (2-(*p-tert*-butylphenoxyl)-1-methylethyl 2-chloroethyl sulfite).

One generation selection experiments for parathion resistance and for Aramite resistance were performed on the susceptible colony. The colony responded to both acaricides. The colony responded to selection for parathion resistance by not only an increase in LC-50 but also by producing a population partitioned into susceptible and resistance classes, thus providing evidence for the existence of a major gene for resistance.

The latter genetic hypothesis was then tested by performing conventional crosses between the original susceptible and resistant colonies. The results of these crosses produced further strong evidence for a major mendelian dominant with resistance to parathion dominant to susceptibility.

The development and occurrence of resistance to various acaricides in several members of the mite family Tetranychidae is continuing to prove itself a problem not only to the grower and pest control operator but also to the research worker. It has re-emphasized the complexity of the organism with which he is dealing and the difficulties that are inherent in regulating their numbers. The solution of this problem will require not only the development of basic information regarding resistance but also basic biological and ecological studies of the organisms involved. Herein are presented the results of several tests designed to increase the understanding and delimitation of the mite resistance problem. The work consisted of a brief selection program to develop a resistant mite strain from a field-collected susceptible strain and the mating of resistant and nonresistant mites to study the mechanism by which resistance is inherited.

Materials and Methods.—In the summer of 1956 several strains of the Pacific spider mite, *Tetranychus pacificus* McG., one from cotton in the San Joaquin Valley suspected of resistance to organophosphorous compounds and several from alfalfa fields grown for seed in which no control difficulties had been encountered, were brought into the laboratory and maintained separately on Henderson dwarf lima bean plants. On the basis of preliminary tests the mites from the several fields of alfalfa were found to have a similar LC-50 response to parathion and thus were consolidated into one colony. The dosage mortality curves of this colony and the one suspected of resistance collected from cotton were determined in the following way. Infested leaves were selected from the colonies and pinned onto the primary leaves of young bean plants with roots placed in bottles of water. After the mites had transferred to the new plants (14 to 16 hours) these leaves were removed and the petioles of the newly infested leaves banded with lanolin. These infested leaves along with uninfested plants bottled in a similar manner were then carefully dipped in the test solution

[1] Accepted for publication February 8, 1960.
[2] The authors wish to acknowledge the help of Mr. Roy L. Hale during the laboratory phase of the work.
[3] Alkylated aryl poly-ether, manufactured by Rohm and Haas Co., Philadelphia, Pennsylvania.

Table 1.—Parathion dosage–mortality response of original field-collected susceptible (S) and resistant (R) colonies of *Tetranychus pacificus*.

MORTALITY IN CHECK (%)		PARATHION DOSE (PER CENT SOLUTION)											
		0.0001	0.0003	0.0005	0.00075	0.001	0.0015	0.0025	0.0035	0.03	0.05	.1	.3
		Susceptible—S											
3.4	Mortality (%)[a]	2.7	43.7	71.3	87.2	93.2	96.1	98.9	95.5				
	No. tested	250	250	550	300	850	600	300	300				
		Resistant—R											
3.1	Mortality (%)									3.3	20.9	61.5	98.9
	No. tested									175	175	225	210

[a] Corrected for natural mortality.

and allowed to dry. Immediately upon drying, healthy adult female mites from the infested leaves were transferred to the also treated uninfested leaves. The number of females transferred were recorded. These plants were held 24 hours at 80° to 85° F. after which the number of live mites remaining were counted. Each dosage was replicated on two to four leaves and was repeated on several different days. The results of these tests appear in table 1, represented by the average mortality over all leaves and days, corrected for natural mortality. This information is also graphically presented in figure 1. Hereafter the susceptible and resistant strains will be referred to as S and R, respectively.

The solutions used in these tests were prepared by mixing an amount of technical parathion, 99.9%, or Aramite®, 90.5% (2-(*p-tert*-butylphenoxyl)-1-methylethyl 2-chloroethyl sulfite) with a given amount of water plus 2 drops of Triton X-100[3] in a Waring Blendor for several minutes. This solution was then aliquoted into a series of beakers containing an amount of water to produce the appropriate dilutions. Two drops of Triton X-100 were added to each beaker per 100 cc. of dilutions. The check solution contained only Triton X-100 and water. All solutions were prepared just prior to testing.

The selection experiments were carried out as follows: Several thousand female mites from the S colony were transferred to bottled plants and treated in the previously

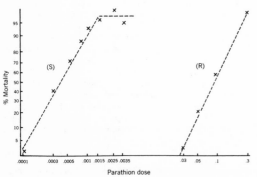

FIG. 1.—Dosage-mortality curves of field-collected resistant (R) and susceptible (S) strains of *Tetranychus pacificus* in response to parathion.

described manner. Several hundred of these mites were transferred to uninfested leaves immediately following treatment to estimate the per cent mortality while the remainder were left on the treated plants. After 24 hours, the adult female survivors were selected and placed in a new colony. The progeny of these surviving females was later tested for their dosage-mortality response to the selecting chemical. The dosages used for selection were based on the original dosage mortality curve of the S colony.

The crossing experiments were conducted as follows: Reciprocal crosses between S and R colonies were made by placing together a single female deutonymph with two males of the opposite strain on a portion of excised bean leaf maintained on wet cotton. After the females had emerged and mated each mite pair was transferred to the leaflet of a bottled bean plant isolated with a band of lanolin around the petiole. After 3 to 5 days of egg laying the females were removed to new leaflets. The parent females lived about 8 to 12 days and produced approximately 30 to 40 female young. The F_1 progeny were allowed to develop on the leaflets until sufficient females had matured to permit testing. The female progeny from each parent cross were then divided into three or four groups, each group being placed on one of two primary leaflets of a bottled bean plant. These mites were permitted to feed 14 to 16 hours after which both the infested and uninfested leaflets in each pair were treated in the previously described manner. Upon drying, the surviving adults were transferred from the infested to the uninfested leaflet in each pair and held 24 hours. The number of live females was then counted. It was observed that adult females 2 to 3 days old were optimum for testing. Backcrosses were made between F_1 females placed with males from the S colony. Again the progeny of each female was maintained separately and handled as above. The dosage mortality curves of the F_1 and backcross female progeny were then determined. A conventional F_2 progeny is difficult to obtain since this is an arrhenotokous organism.

RESULTS AND DISCUSSION.—*Statistics.*—The dosage-mortality information of the original S and R populations (table 1; fig. 1) was examined statistically by calculating a number of heterogeneity chi squares to determine the reliability of the data produced by the above techniques. Leaf to leaf replicates for a given day and dose were found to be homogeneous while a small amount of heterogeneity was detected operating between days for a given

Table 2.—Parathion dosage–mortality response of various populations of *Tetranychus pacificus* resulting from selection and crossing experiments.

Colony	Mortality in Check (%)		Parathion Dose (Per Cent Solution)											
			0.0001	0.0003	0.0005	0.001	0.003	0.005	0.01	0.03	0.05	0.1	0.2	0.3
Selected for resistance. Survivors of one treatment, 99% mortality dose	12.4	Mortality (%)[a]	0	14.9	41.8	60.8	64.0	66.9	49.4	44.5	52.6	71.8	96.1	98.6
		No. tested	100	200	300	300	200	100	300	675	200	575	500	375
Selected for resistance. Survivors of one treatment, 90% mortality dose.	10.8	Mortality (%)		3.8	19.3	61.3	72.3	77.6	58.5	68.2	81.5	91.7		100
		No. tested		200	200	200	300	100	300	275	200	175		100
F₁ ♀ progeny from R ♀ ×S ♂	4.4	Mortality (%)							15.7		47.7	92.3		
		No. tested							72		74	68		
F₁ ♀ progeny from S ♀ ×R ♂	4.9	Mortality (%)							17.7		19.9	92.6		
		No. tested							46		42	43		
Backcross of F₁ ♀ from R ♀ ×S ♂ parents with S ♂	8.9	Mortality (%)	7.2	30.9		49.3			46.5	46.3	62.2	92.6		
		No. tested	71	70		46			39	45	32	30		
Backcross of F₁ ♀ from S ♀ ×R ♂ parents with S ♂	7.0	Mortality (%)	0	46.9		53.5			58.5	58.1	77.7			
		No. tested	32	81		74			57	41	29			

[a] Corrected for natural mortality.

dose. The data were then combined and fitted to the logistic function, and good fits were obtained. The S population (excluding the two highest doses) yielded a chi square testing goodness of fit equal to 2.14 which having 4 degrees of freedom corresponds to a probability of approximately 0.74. The same chi square for the R population equaled 2.81 which with 2 degrees of freedom corresponds to a probability of approximately 0.25. Thus, considerable reliability can be placed on a curve, the points of which were determined on the same day. On the other hand, because of the day to day heterogeneity, small discrepancies between experiments done at different times should be viewed with caution.

Selection Experiments.—Two single selections of resistant individuals from the S colony were made with parathion, one at the 90% and the other at the 99% mortality level. The progeny from these survivors were maintained in separate colonies and their dosage-mortality response determined (table 2; fig. 2).

Both intensities of selection produced populations clearly composed of two discrete classes: individuals as susceptible as those of the S colony and individuals apparently as resistant as those of the R colony.

Estimating from the level of the plateaus, selection at the 90% mortality level produced a population with approximately 34% resistant individuals while the more intense selection (99% mortality) produced a population with approximately 46% resistant individuals.

The abrupt appearance of these two classes suggests that the selection process has either brought into high frequency a major gene for resistance which was already present or possibly created a high probability of occurrence of a simple gene combination capable of conferring high resistance. The former possibility is made more likely by the fact that the original S colony showed signs of possessing some rare individuals of unusually high resistance (figure 1, see responses to doses 0.0025 and 0.0035).

The results of a single selection for Aramite resistance are shown in figure 3, and table 3. In this case rather than a partitioning of the population into distinct classes there

appeared to be a general increase in resistance accompanied by a possible increase in individual variability. The fact that there was a response to selection indicates that Aramite resistance has a genetic basis but the data give little reason to believe that individual resistance is not continuously distributed and under polygenic control.

Crossing Experiments.—As already indicated, families from each mating pair were tested separately. However, because of the small number of individuals per family it was found that little information would be lost by combining the data. This procedure was justified when for most doses and most crosses no interfamily heterogeneity was found.

F₁ females from both reciprocal crosses showed LC-50's in the general region of the parent R population. This would suggest the near complete dominance of resistance over susceptibility.

Backcrossing the F₁ females with susceptible males (table 2; fig. 4) gave a clear partition of the backcross progeny into resistant and susceptible classes. Consider-

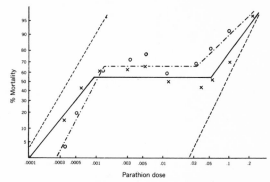

FIG. 2.—Dosage mortality curves of progeny derived from mites of the S colony which had survived with parathion at the 90% mortality level (o and –·–·–·–) and 99% mortality level (x and ————). Dashed lines – – – – represent original R and S strains.

Table 3.—Aramite dosage–mortality response of the original parathion-resistant colony and of an Aramite resistance selected colony of *Tetranychus pacificus*.

MORTAL-ITY IN CHECK (%)		ARAMITE DOSE (PER CENT SOLUTION)										
		0.00075	0.001	0.0015	0.0025	0.0035	0.005	0.0075	0.01	0.025	0.035	0.05
					Susceptible—S							
9.8	Mortality (%)[a]	0	2.8	6.9	58.2	91.9	93.3	99.9				
	No. tested	200	300	200	600	300	400	400				
			Selected for resistance survivors of one treatment 99.5% mortality dose									
13.9	Mortality (%)		1.3	11.7	47.3		77.0	73.9	84.3	96.5	97.1	100
	No. tested		100	100	500		600	600	400	600	200	100

[a] Corrected for natural mortality.

ing the values from the plateaued part of the curves, one backcross gave 46.8% individuals in the susceptible class and the other backcross gave 56.2% individuals in the susceptible class. Neither of these values differs significantly from 50%. These two facts, the partitioning of the backcross progeny into two classes and the incidence of the two classes approximating 50%, provide strong evidence that resistance is under the control of a major mendelian dominant.

The rather pronounced (significant) non-linear arrangement of the F_1 points suggests that in addition to this dominant factor, there may be some sort of modifying factor or factors involved. This disturbance could easily be explained by the segregation of modifiers in the S population which only act in the presence of the major gene for resistance. For example, figure 5 shows one of

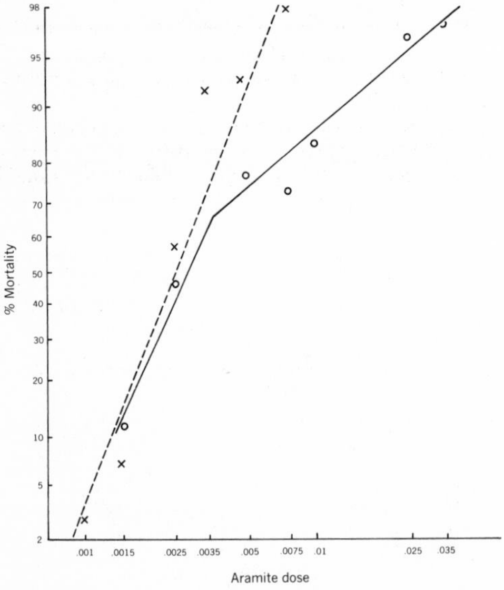

many model systems of modifier-major gene interaction which would yield a set of theoretical curves giving good fits to all the empirical curves of the crossing experiments. Elucidation of such systems would require further experimentation such as the establishment and genetic investigation of a series of inbred lines derived from the S population. The question of modifiers, however, should not obscure the fact that there still remains good evidence for a single major gene for resistance.

In some previous studies of the genetics of resistance it has been the practice to choose a single dose, which would give a high mortality in the susceptible stock and a low mortality in the resistant stock, and then apply this single dose to F_2 and backcross progeny. Taylor & Smith (1956), using this technique with *Tetranychus telarius* (L.), obtained mendelian ratios from the crossing of resistant and susceptible mites, similar to those reported here. It should be emphasized, however, that the production of mendelian ratios by a single dose is necessary but by no means sufficient evidence for a major gene. The dose used could well be truncating a continuous distribution of resistance at levels numerically equivalent to mendelian ratios.

Therefore, it is also necessary to demonstrate that the

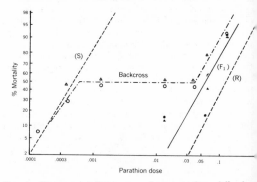

FIG. 4.—Dosage-mortality curves of progeny from following crosses.

F_1, R ♀ ×S ♂
F_1, S ♀ ×R ♂
Backcross, F_1 (R ♀ ×S ♂)×S ♂
Backcross, F_1 (S ♀ ×R ♂)×S ♂
P_1's, R ♀ and S ♀

FIG. 3.—Dosage-mortality curves of susceptible (S) mites and the progeny of survivors of a dose of Aramite equivalent to the 99.5% mortality level. x and – – – – represent (S) strain, and o and ———— represent selected strain.

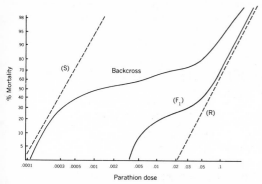

FIG 5.—Theoretical curves of P_1, F_1 and backcross results expected assuming a major gene for resistance (R, r) and a hypostatic modifier (M, m) which acts such that R-, mm has full resistance R-, M- has a lower level of resistance and any other genotype is susceptible. Further assumptions necessary for fitting to data were: Resistant strain homozygous RR, mm and susceptible strain homozygous rr but segregating for M, m with frequency of M equal to 0.20.

segregating progeny (backcross or F_2 where possible) is partitioned into discrete resistance classes and for this purpose at least four appropriately chosen doses (rather than one) are required for establishing the existence of a plateau in the dosage-mortality curve. The demonstration of both discrete classes and the occurrence of these classes in mendelian proportions as has been done in this case may then be taken as good evidence for simple mendelism. However, such information is still not sufficient, for as Crow (1957) has indicated, a polygenic system underlying a phenotypic threshold could "mimic" simple mendelism.

Thus, it appears that the determination of the exact mechanism of inheritance in the material reported here as well as in the work of some others will require still further experimentation involving not only studying inbred lines as already suggested but also possibly a system of backcrossing as suggested by Crow (1957, p. 234).

Finally it might be mentioned that the above results considered in connection with others may constitute a case contrary to the current view that different populations of the same species or of different species will respond with different genetic mechanisms when subjected to selection for the same phenotype (King 1955). In the work reported here on *T. pacificus*, a single mendelian dominant for resistance has apparently arisen twice: once "naturally" in parathion-treated cotton fields and once by artificial selection in the laboratory. In addition the work of Taylor & Smith (1956) indicates parathion resistance in a different species, *T. telarius*, may also be under the control of a simple mendelian dominant and the inference that this is the same gene is given some support by the fact that a comparison of LC-50 values indicates the same magnitude of resistance in the two species. Also the work on another species, *T. atlanticus* McG., by Andres & Reynolds (1958) indicates the same magnitude of resistance. In this latter case, however, no genetic evidence is available.

Similar findings have been obtained by Kikawa (1958) in his studies of *Drosophila* where parathion resistance is apparently under the control of the same simple mendelian factor in strains of such diverse origin as Japan and Sweden.

The above genetic evidence indicates that future biochemical investigations of the mechanism of parathion resistance might possibly reveal a wide ranging system of homologous genes such as that being found for insect eye pigment synthesis (Ward & Hammen 1957).

REFERENCES CITED

Andres, L. A., and H. T. Reynolds. 1958. Laboratory determination of organophosphorus insecticide resistance in three species of *Tetranychus* on cotton. Jour. Econ. Ent. 51(3): 285–7.

Crow, James F. 1957. Genetics of insect resistance to chemicals. Ann. Rev. Ent. 2: 227–46. Annual Reviews Inc., Palo Alto, Calif.

King, James C. 1955. Evidence for the integration of the gene pool from studies of DDT resistance in Drosophila. Cold Spring Harbor Symposium on Quant. Biol. Bol. 20: 311–17.

Kikawa, H. 1958. Genetic analyses of resistance to parathion in a Swedish strain of *D. melanogaster*. Drosophila Inform. Ser., 32: 130.

Taylor, E. A , and F. Smith. 1956. Transmission of resistance between strains of two-spotted spider mites. Jour. Econ. Ent. 49(6): 858–9.

Ward, C. L., and C. S. Hammen. 1957. New mutations affecting Tryptophan-derived eye pigments in three species of insects. Evolution 11(1): 60–4.

REGIONAL DIFFERENTIATION IN PLANT SPECIES[1]

JENS CLAUSEN, DAVID D. KECK AND WILLIAM M. HIESEY

DIVISION OF PLANT BIOLOGY, CARNEGIE INSTITUTION OF WASHINGTON,
STANFORD UNIVERSITY

GENERAL RELATIONS BETWEEN PLANT AND CLIMATE

MANY species complexes of plants have an extremely wide vertical or horizontal distribution. Such complexes show a remarkable diversity of form and reactions that must be understood before a proper classification can be presented, and, more important, before the organization of the living world can be fully interpreted. Examples of such complexes are *Potentilla glandulosa, Achillea millefolium* and *Artemisia vulgaris,* all of which cover a large part of California from near sea level to around 11,000 feet altitude, and in addition have representatives circling the Northern Hemisphere.

The climates in which their California members live range from warm temperate to arctic-alpine. The weather graphs in Fig. 1 describe the climatic differences in such a transect across central California. The lowermost graph describes the climate in the mild, warm temperate, coastal region, where freezing temperatures occur only during a very limited period and continuous growth is possible for many herbaceous species. The center graph gives similar information for a locality midway up the western slope of the Sierra Nevada, at 4,600 feet altitude, where winters are cold enough to force most plants into dormancy for five or six months of the year. The uppermost graph presents data from a station near the crest of the Sierra Nevada at 9,600 feet altitude, and although it does not represent the extreme conditions found among the peaks, it does give an idea of the climate in the high mountains.

Plants of the same or closely related species from cli-

[1] Read at the Seattle symposium by Dr. Keck.

Reprinted by permission of W. M. Hiesey and the publisher
from THE AMERICAN NATURALIST, 75, 231–250 (1941).

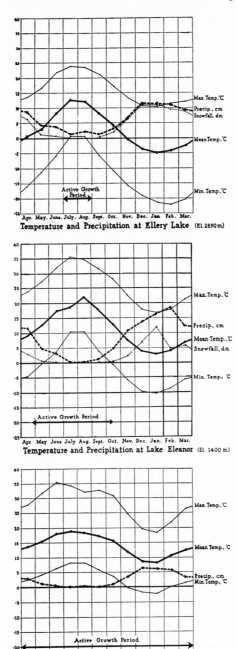

FIG. 1.   Weather data from three stations on a transect across central California.

mates so unlike as the California coast and the high Sierra Nevada are very different in appearance and reactions. The alpines generally differ from their lowland relatives in size and other morphological characters, and also in their rate of growth, earliness, frost-resistance and other ways physiological. Series of intermediate forms connect the extremes.

Many questions arise concerning the nature of climatic forms: Are they due to the direct impact of the environment, and hence to be regarded as modifications, or are they hereditary in nature? Is it possible to change lowland forms into alpines by transferring them to the alpine environment as Bonnier (1895, 1920) reported, or do lowland and alpine forms remain distinct when grown side by side in a uniform environment as Kerner (1891) and Turesson (1925) found? If the differences are hereditary, what is their nature? Are they purely morphological, or are physiological characters also involved? If so, is each climatic belt populated with a race especially fitted to survive there? Finally, cytologists and geneticists raise other questions concerning possible chromosomal differences in such forms, the possibility of free exchange of genes in offspring of crossings between plants native to contrasting environments and the vigor of any such offspring.

In order to clarify such questions as these, the Carnegie Institution of Washington undertook an investigation in which experiment stations were established in three very unlike climates in central California. The principal station is located on the San Francisco peninsula, near sea level, at Stanford University. The second is at Mather, near the western boundary of Yosemite National Park, at 4,600 feet elevation, and the third is situated near Timberline just east of the crest of the Sierra Nevada, at 10,000 feet elevation, in Mono County. The contrast between the climates at the three stations is striking, as shown by the weather graphs of Fig. 1, which were constructed from U. S. Weather Bureau data obtained near the three experiment stations. At Stanford, the growth period for plants is ordinarily continuous the year around; at Mather, it is approximately six months long; while at Timberline, it is shortened to approximately three months. At the alpine station snows usually persist in the gardens until the first of July, and there are but three to six weeks of relatively frost-free weather.

Into the gardens of these three stations representatives of many climatic races from the Pacific Coast region were brought for an analysis of their reactions. Species from a wide range of plant families were used. Perennials only were employed, for this made it possible to propagate them asexually and grow parts of one individual simultaneously at the three climatically very unlike stations. This permitted a two-way comparison. Genetic variation was eliminated by comparing divisions of one individual grown in three contrasting environments, so the differences observed were due to environmental modification alone. On the other hand, by bringing races of the same or related species from contrasting environments into a uniform garden at one station, gross environmental differences were eliminated, and the hereditary differences between them could be compared. Systematic records in the form of yearly herbarium specimens, measurements and notes made it possible to study the plants in detail through a number of consecutive years. An analysis of these experiments, which were inaugurated by the late Dr. H. M. Hall, has recently appeared (Clausen, Keck and Hiesey, 1940).

From these experiments it is clear that the variations which one observes in wild plants are of two sorts: those due to hereditary differences and those due to environmental modifications. Both contribute to the complex differences observed, not only in comparisons between climatic or geographic races, but also between competing individuals of the same population.

Each species of wide distribution consists of an assemblage of biotypes and races, some local, others of higher order and regional. Species are usually broken up into intermittent populations because of environmental conditions. Each population consists of minor local variants or biotypes, but its members as a whole share characteristic morphological traits that frequently serve to distinguish this population from others of the same species The frequent development of the local population into a recognizable morphological-geographical unit is probably the result of partial geographic isolation alone. The local differentiation appears to be of no major importance for survival in a given habitat, for individuals from different populations in one climatic belt follow the same general pattern of reactions and survival when transplanted to the different climates of the transplant stations. However, plants from the same population have been found to show slight individual differences in their reactions to these contrasting environments.

A very different situation is uncovered when representatives of races native to climatically different belts are analyzed by the transplant method. Such races do not react alike at the transplant stations. They differ much in their periods of activity, time of flowering and capacity to survive at the stations. These reactions are correlated with the environment in which they are native, and plants of different families but from the same general climatic belt show basically similar reactions.

By classifying the plants as to their reactions in the different climatic gardens, it is possible to recognize several major or regional climatic races that recur with frequency in various genera and families. These correspond roughly to the major life zones, which are, of course, a biotic expression of climatic differences. It takes about five to seven major climatic races of a species to occupy the entire climatically diverse region across central California.

Like the life zones, regional climatic races replace one another in the territory occupied by the species. They are most homogeneous toward the center of their distribution, but frequently intergrade through hybridization where they meet or even overlap. Sometimes observed differences in reaction between races can be correlated with morphological differences, thus providing markers for delimiting the climatic races quickly in herbaria after such a correlation has been established by experiment.

POTENTILLA GLANDULOSA

An example of a species differentiated into climatic races is shown in Figs. 2 and 3. This is *Potentilla glandu-*

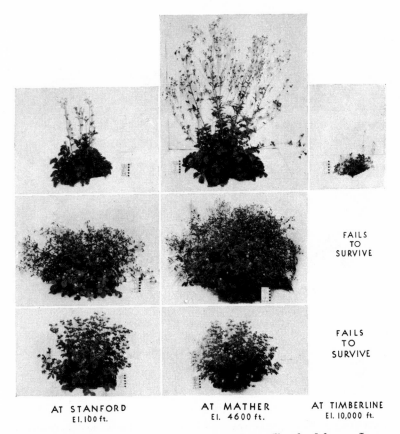

| AT STANFORD | AT MATHER | AT TIMBERLINE |
| El. 100 ft. | El. 4600 ft. | El. 10,000 ft. |

Fig. 2. Clones of three climatic races of *Potentilla glandulosa*. *Lower row*: plant of the Coast Range race, ssp. *typica*, from 600 ft. altitude; *center row*: the Sierran foothill race, ssp. *reflexa*, from 2,500 ft.; *upper row*: the mid-Sierran meadow race, ssp. *Hanseni*, from 4,600 ft. Horizontal rows show modifications of one individual at three transplant stations. Vertical rows show differences between races at any one station.

losa Lindl., of the rose family, whose California representatives are distributed from near the seacoast to about 11,000 feet elevation in the Sierra Nevada. The horizontal rows in the two figures represent divisions (clonemembers) of individuals transplanted to the three stations. The differences seen between members of one clone are modifications imposed by the contrasting environments. The five individuals in the two figures were native at different elevations, as follows.

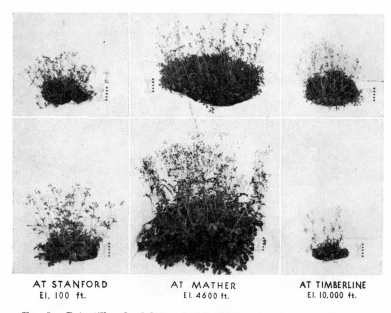

AT STANFORD   AT MATHER   AT TIMBERLINE
El. 100 ft.   El. 4600 ft.   El. 10,000 ft.

Fig. 3. *Potentilla glandulosa:* clones of the subalpine race, from 5,800 ft. altitude (lower row), and alpine race, from 10,000 ft. (upper row), both referable to ssp. *nevadensis*, showing modifications and racial differences at the three transplant stations.

The lower row of Fig. 2 is the clone of a plant representing the climatic race native in the Coast Ranges of California. This race grows well both near sea level at Stanford and at Mather at 4,600 feet, but it fails to survive at Timberline. Although it grows somewhat larger at Stanford than at Mather, it survives equally well in both environments. In its mild, native climate and in the garden at Stanford it is in active but slow growth almost the entire year. It is sufficiently cold-resistant not to be injured by the frosts during the winters at Stanford. The more severe winters at Mather, however, force it into dormancy for some six months, thus delaying its entire seasonal development, but not interfering with its capacity to flower and produce ripe seed. Most of the plants of this species in the California Coast Ranges from 600 to 5,000 feet altitude are referable to this climatic race, for in spite of considerable individual variation, they have fundamental morphological and physiological characteristics in common by which they may be distinguished from all other races. Also, they react basically the same in the experiments regardless of the elevation of their native habitats. This climatic race is recognized taxonomically as subspecies *typica*.

In the warm, western foothills of the Sierra Nevada up to mid-altitudes, there is another regional race of the same species. The Stanford and Mather modifications of a typical plant of this race are shown in the central horizontal row of Fig. 2. Like the Coast Range race, it is unable to survive at Timberline. But unlike the representatives of that race, this plant grows taller and more vigorously at the mid-Sierran station than at Stanford. It flowers and produces seed successfully at both stations. Its leaves are susceptible to even light frosts, causing the plants to become dormant even at Stanford, with its mild winters, whereas the Coast Range race is active at this time. Consequently, at Stanford, its first spring flowers appear approximately two weeks after those of the Coast Range plants. At Mather, however, where both are forced into dormancy for approximately the same period, they flower almost together, as shown by the graph in Fig. 4.

The Sierran foothill race, known as subspecies *reflexa*, occurs from about 700 to 6,800 feet elevation, but at the higher levels it is found exclusively on the warmest slopes. Its natural populations vary considerably, but a series of morphological and reactional characteristics readily dis-

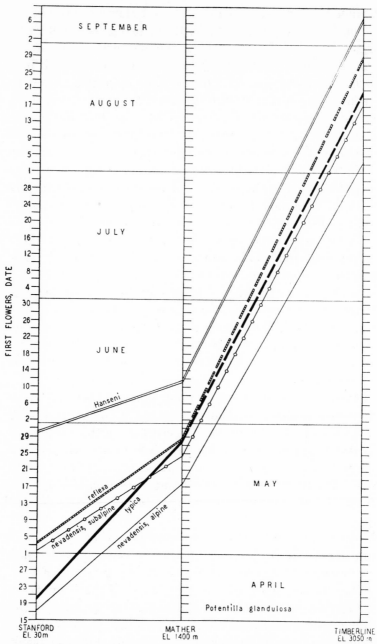

FIG. 4.   Differences in dates of first flowers of climatic races of *Potentilla glandulosa* at three altitudes.   Graphs represent 3-year averages of 134 clones, namely, 24 of *typica*, 47 of *reflexa*, 6 of *Hanseni*, 26 of subalpine, and 31 of alpine *nevadensis*.

tinguish it from the Coast Range race. Many plants from
the upper altitudinal limits of its range are somewhat
reduced in size, but otherwise show no unique differences
in reactions at the three stations, and die equally promptly
at Timberline.

In middle altitude meadows in the Sierra Nevada another race is found. It differs from the foothill race not
alone in its preference for moister, cooler habitats, but in
a number of other characters and in its reactions. Three
modifications of this mid-Sierran meadow race are shown
in the upper row of Fig. 2. It is definitely most vigorous
in the mid-altitude environment. Unlike both the foothill
and the Coast Range races, members of the meadow race
are able to survive not only at lower elevations but also
at Timberline. Although greatly reduced in size and
vigor, the clone-member at Timberline has been able to
withstand the rigors of the alpine climate for ten years.
It produces flowering stems there, but because of the
shortness of the season, it is unable to produce ripe seed.
At Stanford, the meadow race tends to die out of the cultures more frequently than the foothill form. It is the
most modifiable of all the races of *Potentilla glandulosa*,
yet close comparison reveals the fundamental identity in
structure of clone-members at the three stations.

The Sierran foothill and meadow races overlap in altitudinal distribution although the meadow race rarely
descends below 4,000 feet. But a rather clear-cut ecological separation is maintained between the two, for the
meadow race never grows on dry hillsides, and the foothill race very rarely invades the meadows. Hybrids
between them are occasionally found near their parents
on meadow borders. The meadow race is distinguished
taxonomically as subspecies *Hanseni*.

Two race-complexes of *Potentilla glandulosa* are found
in the Sierras above 6,000 feet. These form an intergrad-
ing series morphologically so that it is impractical to
separate them taxonomically. Together they compose
subspecies *nevadensis*. By their reactions, however, it

is possible to distinguish both subalpine and alpine races. This has been done, as in the other cases, by assembling a large number of individuals from a number of different habitats and elevations and observing their reactions. Representatives of these races and their modifications at the transplant stations are shown in Fig. 3. Both races survive at Timberline, but the alpine tends to be the more vigorous there. Both grow best and attain their largest size at Mather, where they are able to survive indefinitely. Neither does as well at Stanford, showing reduced stature, increased susceptibility to disease and reduced flowering, although both survive moderately well. The subalpine flowers better than the alpine at the lowland station. Both become dormant during the winter at all three stations; even at the lowland station they are dormant for two to three months.

The alpine race is one or two weeks earlier in flowering at all three stations, as shown by the graphs in Fig. 4. This difference in earliness is sufficient to permit it to produce ripe fruit consistently in the very short growing season at Timberline, whereas the subalpine plants can ripen seed only in the most favorable years. The alpine plants are so rapid in their development that, in spite of their winter-dormancy, even at Stanford they are able to flower before the Coast Range races. Moreover, the alpine plants are more frost-resistant than the subalpines, a difference which is most accentuated at Timberline. In the Sierra Nevada, plants reacting like subalpines are found at altitudes between 5,000 and 8,000 feet, and alpine-reacting types may occur between 7,500 and 11,000 feet.

Morphologically, subspecies *nevadensis*, with its subalpine and alpine races, stands out as a very distinct unit. Moreover, it is self-sterile, whereas the others are self-fertile. But the physiological differentiation within the subspecies, separating an early-flowering, dwarfish and alpine race from a later-flowering, taller, subalpine one, may be just as important as the differences distinguishing this subspecies from the others.

Close study of modifications, such as are illustrated in Figs. 2 and 4, discloses that the climatic races retain their morphological and physiological individuality in the three very different environments in spite of striking modifications in general appearance. Structural features such as habit of branching and density of inflorescences, shape, venation and general texture of leaves, character and density of pubescence, distribution of glands, presence or absence of anthocyanin in stems, size, color and shape of flowers, size and color of seeds, and similar characters serve to identify each climatic race, and even each individual. On the other hand, such characters as size of vegetative parts, number of stems and vigor of growth may be profoundly modified in different surroundings, although these also are characteristics of the various races. Moreover, the manner in which a given climatic race or individual is modified is as much a part of its character as a morphological feature. Each climatic race appears particularly adjusted to thrive in its native environment, although with competition removed, it may be even more vigorous in another environment. The entire cycle of development of each climatic race appears to be fitted to the environment in which the race is native.

Modifications resulting from exposure to changed environments are quickly reversible when plants are returned to their original environment. From these transplanting experiments there is no evidence that modifications have a durable effect on the plant, even after continuous exposure to a new environment for as long as eighteen years.

Many plant groups of different families from central California were investigated and likewise found to be composed of ecologic races. Those races from the same kind of environment often show morphologic similarities as well as parallel reactions in different environments. Such correlations point to the conclusion that we are dealing with a basic principle governing the ecological differentiation of plants. Moreover, they confirm the findings

71

of Turesson (1922, 1925), who found in more northern latitudes in Europe the same general type of climatic differentiation in other groups of plants.

These facts naturally lead to further inquiry as to the basis of climatic differentiation. It has been experimentally demonstrated that climatic races have a genetic basis. Their hereditary differences may be either purely genic or associated with differences in chromosome number, depending upon the evolutionary history of the forms in question. In the case of *Potentilla glandulosa,* all of the races have seven pairs of chromosomes, and no genetic barriers have been found between them. For example, the foothill and alpine races (the most unlike within the species morphologically and physiologically) hybridize without any difficulty and their hybrids are fully fertile. A large second generation has segregated nearly every conceivable recombination of both morphological and physiological traits, although there is considerable linkage, as would be expected with the low chromosome number. Nearly every morphological character was found to depend upon a small series of genes, each of minor but cumulative effect. Furthermore, traits that appear to have an adaptive value, like earliness of flowering, duration of dormancy, frost resistance, growth rate and self-fertility, segregate too, indicating a genetic basis for them as well as for the others.

We find, therefore, in *Potentilla glandulosa* a remarkable differentiation into major ecologic races fitted to occupy very contrasting environments. This differentiation depends upon a multiplicity of genes in a few chromosomes, but these genes are interchangeable without upsetting the physiological balance of the offspring. The apparent absence of genetic barriers within this group indicates that all these climatic races belong within one species.

ACHILLEA

A different pattern of regional differentiation is found in the western yarrow of the *Achillea millefolium* com-

plex. Its members have an even wider distribution than
Potentilla glandulosa, and cover many climatic zones with
different races. However, a difference in chromosome
number separates the West American representatives
into two large groups. Plants from mid-elevations on
the west slope of the Sierra Nevada eastward across the
crest of the range, the Great Basin and the Rocky Mountains have 18 pairs of chromosomes. Those west to the
coast have 27 pairs. Since these differences in chromosome number impose a definite barrier to interbreeding,
at least two species are involved. The coastal species is
Achillea borealis Bong., the interior one is *A. lanulosa*
Nutt., and in each there has been ecologic differentiation
into races fitted to different climates.

The change in chromosome number in *Achillea* has
offered no complication to the formation of climatic races
across California very parallel to those found in the
Potentilla. Some of these are illustrated in Figs. 5 and 6.
The reactions of two races of *A. borealis* at the transplant
stations are shown in Fig. 5. The upper row shows clone-

AT STANFORD   AT MATHER   AT TIMBERLINE
El. 100 ft.   El. 4600 ft.   El. 10,000 ft.

FIG. 5. Clones of two latitudinal races of *Achillea borealis* at three altitudes. Both are hexaploid, $n = 27$. *Above:* plant from Seward, Alaska;
below: plant from Berkeley, California; both from near sea level but separated by 22° of latitude.

members of a plant from coastal Alaska as they appear at the three transplant stations, while the lower row shows corresponding clone-members of a plant from the central California coast, 22 degrees of latitude farther south. The Alaskan race is able to live at all three stations and is early flowering, but its stems are very susceptible to

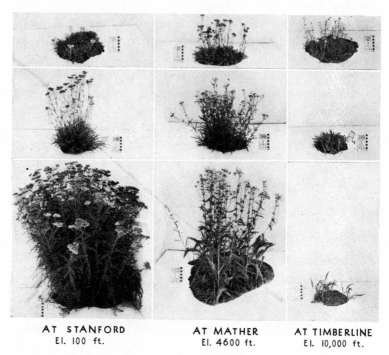

AT STANFORD   AT MATHER   AT TIMBERLINE
El. 100 ft.   El. 4600 ft.   El. 10,000 ft.

FIG. 6. Clones of three altitudinal races of *Achillea lanulosa* at three altitudes. All are tetraploid, $n = 18$. *Top:* an alpine, from 10,700 ft. altitude; *center:* a subalpine, from 7,100 ft.; *bottom:* a mid-Sierran plant, from 4,675 ft.; all from the Sierra Nevada along the station transect.

frost and are killed at Timberline before they are able to ripen seeds. By far its best growth is attained at the mid-Sierran station. The southern race, on the other hand, cannot survive at Timberline, and it even suffers a loss of vigor at the mid-Sierran station. It grows most successfully at Stanford, near its native habitat. At both stations it is in flower a month and a half later than the Alaskan plant.

Three altitudinal races of *A. lanulosa* of the Sierra Nevada are illustrated in Fig. 6. The reactions of clone-members of a mid-Sierran individual (lower row), a subalpine (center row) and an alpine (upper row) are shown at Stanford, Mather and Timberline stations. The mid-Sierran race (from 4,675 feet) survives only two or three years at Timberline and seldom is able to develop more than a few basal leaves there. At Stanford, however, it develops even more vigorously than in its native habitat at Mather, but it is far more vigorous at Mather than the coastal form. The subalpine race, from 7,100 feet elevation, survives well at all three stations, but is unable to ripen fruit at Timberline because the stems are frost-killed before maturity, as shown in the figure. The alpine race, on the other hand, thrives at all three altitudes, but grows more vigorously at both mountain stations than at Stanford; it is early and frost-resistant enough to be able to mature in its native environment in favorable years. The most frost-resistant race (not illustrated) comes from the Great Basin, east of the Sierra Nevada. It is a fairly tall form, which remains green and active at the alpine station long after the other plants are frost-killed, but is so slow in its development there that it is unable to mature fruit.

Accordingly, in *Achillea,* as in *Potentilla glandulosa,* the regional races appear to be well adapted to their natural environments, although they do not always make their maximum growth in the climate in which they are native.

OTHER SPECIES

A summary of a survey of regional differentiation in several groups of widely distributed California plants is presented in Fig. 7. The diagrammatic profile at the top indicates the elevations in a transect across central California. The approximate distribution of regional races of various plant groups is shown below the profile and also their differences in chromosome number. It will be seen that some of the plant groups are distributed across

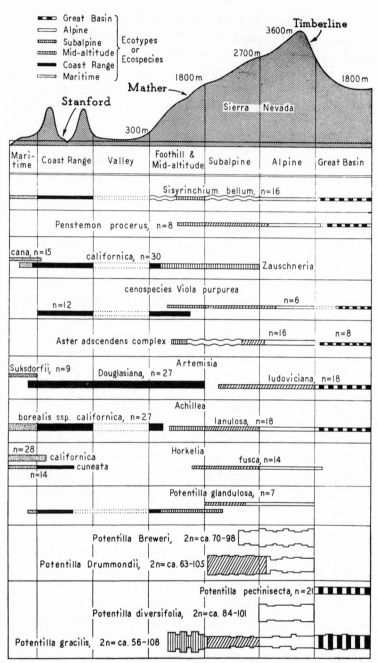

FIG. 7. Distribution of major climatic races within species complexes in a transect across central California. The width of the symbols roughly indicate the degree of polyploidy. Further explanation in text.

the entire transect, while others occur on only a part of it. Almost all are absent from the San Joaquin Valley, an expanse populated primarily by annuals.

Of the eleven complexes shown, three have effected their differentiation without change in chromosome number, namely, *Sisyrinchium bellum*, *Potentilla glandulosa* and *Penstemon procerus*. The remainder have simple or complex differences in chromosome number within them. The *Potentilla* species of the two complexes shown at the bottom of Fig. 7 are the antithesis of *Potentilla glandulosa* cytologically. In contrast to the extreme regularity of the latter, these species present differences in chromosome number even among the individuals of one population (as suggested by the varying widths of the symbols in the graph), and all plants have many unpaired chromosomes. These groups probably reproduce asexually through apomixis. Yet despite this great variability in chromosome number and lack of pairing at meiosis, they have developed climatic races very parallel to those found in *P. glandulosa*.

In the remaining six cases in the graph the chromosome number changes somewhere along the transect. The component races of almost all these complexes are so closely related that at one time or another they have been combined in one species. However, the differences in chromosome numbers produce genetic barriers that prevent free interbreeding, and these differences are usually correlated with differences in morphology. This makes it possible to recognize the chromosomal groups as taxonomic species. Closely related species differing in chromosome number usually do not overlap very much in distribution, but replace one another in different climates.

There is no observable correlation between degree of polyploidy and environment, for in some complexes the forms with low chromosome numbers are at high altitudes, in others, at low altitudes, in some, near the sea, in others, inland. Irrespective of what the chromosome number is, however, or where it changes, each complex has developed a series of climatic races of parallel reaction, fitted to the climates in which they are native. An exception to this rule is found in *Artemisia Douglasiana,* for no well-defined climatic race has been discovered in this species, which, nevertheless, covers a rather wide range of environments. There is some evidence that this species may be an amphidiploid of comparatively recent origin, produced by the addition of the chromosomes of the maritime *A. Suksdorfii* with those of *A. ludoviciana* from the interior mountains and desert plateaus. The combination of chromosomes from such ecologically different species should produce a form capable of inhabiting a wide variety of environments.

Conclusions

This survey and the one conducted by Turesson in Europe indicate that the genetic-physiologic differentiation of a plant group is correlated with the climatic zones it occupies. This follows from the fact that the same kinds of environments are occupied by races that have similar patterns of reaction, even though they belong to unrelated genera or families. This is found to hold irrespective of whether or not the regional forms differ in chromosome number.

The usual pattern of differentiation is purely genetic, with relatively few major steps involved; but superimposed upon this one often finds a cytological differentiation, with one or two changes in chromosome number across the California transect. However, the effects of increases in chromosome number must have been far overshadowed by the selective influence of the environment in determining the appearance and reactions of plants. From these considerations it appears that it is the genes in the chromosomes, and not the number of chromosomes, which determine the climatic adaptation.

From the point of view of fitness to the environment it is evident that the ecologically important unit is not the species, but the regional climatic race, or, to adopt Turesson's term, the *ecotype*. Several of these may combine to form a species, or a single ecotype may develop an isolating genetic barrier to form a monotypic species, such as *Zauschneria cana, Artemisia Suksdorfii* and *Horkelia californica*, in Fig. 7. Such monotypic species occupy a narrow climatic belt and show little variation and adaptability. However, it makes little difference whether a given area is populated by a series of ecotypes belonging to one species, or by a series of monotypic species belonging to one species complex, or by a combination of both. The evolutionary past and future differ, however, in the three instances.

Evolutionary processes have left plants arranged in groups of various order and separation, such as populations, ecotypes, species and species complexes. These groups indicate stages in evolutionary differentiation, and they have evolved only where there is a diversity of environments.

There are many mechanisms by which living things can increase their hereditary variation, but regional differentiation requires the discriminating selection offered by unlike environments. We have no evidence that the direct influence of environment produces fundamental hereditary changes in species, but major alterations in environments provide new habitats and refuges for the products of nature's continual experimentation among all the plant species that populate a given area.

LITERATURE CITED

Bonnier, G.
    1895. *Ann. des sci. nat., Botanique,* 7th ser., 20: 217–358.
    1920. *Rev. gén. de botanique,* 32: 305–326.
Clausen, J., David D. Keck and William M. Hiesey
    1940. *Carnegie Inst. Wash. Publ.* 520. vii + 452 pp.   Washington.
Kerner von Marilaun, A.
    1891. "Pflanzenleben."   Vol. 2.   viii + 896 pp.   Leipzig.
Turesson, G.
    1922. *Hereditas,* 3: 211–350.
    1925. *Hereditas,* 6: 147–236.

TAXONOMIC AND EVOLUTIONARY IMPLICATIONS OF LAWN RACES IN PRUNELLA VULGARIS (LABIATAE)[1]

Andrew P. Nelson

Department of Biological Sciences, Dartmouth College, Hanover, New Hampshire

The North American population of *Prunella vulgaris* L. contains representatives of both subsp. *vulgaris* and subsp. *lanceolata* (Bart.) Hultén (Nelson 1962). The former, which occurs as a weed of fields, roadsides, forest margins, and especially lawns, is native to Europe and presumed to be introduced in North America (Nelson 1962). The latter, a plant of open woods, stream sides, meadows, and similar habitats, may well be an indigenous North American plant (Nelson 1962).

Lawn inhabiting strains of subsp. *vulgaris* are generally of a low-growing, dwarf form and have been given recognition in the proposal of a number of taxa. Included among these are var. *pallida* Gilmour (1933), f. *nana* Clute (1902), var. *dunensis* Druce (cited in Gilmour 1933), var. *parviflora* (Poir.) DC. (1848), and var. *parviflora* (Gilib.) Moore (1950). It appears that these taxa all deal with the same dwarf, lawn-inhabiting form. If so, the valid name is *P. vulgaris* subsp. *vulgaris* var. *parviflora* (Gilib.) Moore.

Some authors have not recognized this taxon. Fernald, in his treatment of *P. vulgaris* subsp. *vulgaris* (as var. *vulgaris*), states that, "When repeatedly mowed, cropped or trampled the plants become densely matted, depressed and small-leaved." (Fernald 1950, p. 1225). Howell, Raven, and Rubtzoff, though recognizing var. *parviflora* (Poir.) DC., state that, "This plant may not be varietally distinct from typical *P. vulgaris* of Europe." (Howell et al. 1958, p. 120).

Cultivation experiments reported by Witte in 1906 (cited in Turesson 1922) indicate that some dwarf forms of *P. vulgaris* are merely phenotypic modifications called forth by the environment. However, Clute (1933) reported that dwarf plants taken from lawns retained their distinctive habit and morphology in garden culture.

The following experiments, done in the context of a study of variation in Californian *P. vulgaris* (Nelson 1962), suggest an explanation for the contrasting experimental results reported by Witte and Clute. They supply basic information about the plants currently designated as var. *parviflora* and suggest that the problem of whether or not this taxon should be recognized may have implications which go beyond the specific case in *P. vulgaris*.

MATERIALS AND METHODS

Response to the lawn environment. Materials for this experiment consisted of 160 plants from naturally occurring populations of subsp. *lanceolata* and subsp. *vulgaris* in Europe, Michigan, and California (Table 1). These plants were propagated by cuttings, each about three inches long and including a terminal bud, in December, 1960. In order to hasten root growth, the cuttings were treated with Rootone (Anchem Products, Inc.) and placed under a 12 hr. photoperiod.

The rooted cuttings were divided into three sets; A, B, and C. Each set contained one ramet of each of the 160 clones. Near the end of January, 1961, the ramets of sets A and B were transplanted to a lawn at the Botanical Garden in Berkeley.

[1] Based on portions of a dissertation submitted to the Department of Botany, University of California, Berkeley. The research was directed by H. G. Baker and supported, in part by the National Science Foundation (graduate fellowship 21252). Most of the cultivation experiments were carried out at the Botanical Garden, University of California, Berkeley. Additional work has been supported by NSF Grant GB-1564.

TABLE 1.   Materials of *Prunella vulgaris* used in lawn experiment

Collection*	No. of Plants	Subspecies	Origin
P 1	10	lanceolata	Natural habitat, Champion, Michigan
P45	9	vulgaris	Natural habitat, Rouen, France
P70	10	vulgaris	Natural habitat, Minsk, USSR
P84	7	vulgaris	Natural habitat, Lisbon, Portugal
P92	6	vulgaris	Natural habitat, Ashkhabad, USSR
P95	9	vulgaris	Natural habitat, Solaspils, LSSR
P97	6	vulgaris	Natural habitat, Cluj, Romania
588	6	lanceolata	Natural habitat, Copco Lake, California
618	9	lanceolata	Natural habitat, Zenia, California
620	8	lanceolata	Natural habitat, Weott, California
627	5	lanceolata	Natural habitat, Eagle Point, California
629	9	vulgaris & lanceolata	Natural habitat, Scotia, California
635	10	lanceolata	Natural habitat, Eureka, California
639	1	vulgaris	Lawn, San Francisco, California
645	4	vulgaris	Lawn, Berkeley, California
646	17	vulgaris & lanceolata	Natural habitat, Pitkin Marsh, California
660	9	lanceolata	Natural habitat, Mt. Palomar, California
670	6	vulgaris	Lawn, Berkeley, California
675	9	lanceolata	Natural habitat, Quaking Aspen Camp, California
683	5	vulgaris	Lawn, Berkeley, California
684	5	vulgaris	Lawn, Berkeley, California

* P numbers obtained (as seed) through botanic gardens; other numbers indicate living plants collected by author.

Each set occupied half of the lawn, and the ramets of each set were arranged in a random sequence in a 4-foot grid. At the same time, the ramets of set C were transplanted to a cultivated garden plot where they were arranged in a 3-foot grid in a random sequence duplicating that of set B.

Ecological variation within the lawn containing sets A and B was evident at the initiation of the study. The lawn was on a moderately sloping hillside and was subject to marginal shading from adjacent trees and shrubs. Weedy dicotyledonous plants present were not evenly distributed nor was drainage uniform throughout the lawn. Grasses, mostly *Festuca rubra* L., were the primary constituent of the lawn flora. Prominent introductions were *Achillea* sp., *Bellis perennis* L., *Cerastium vulgatum* L., *Dichondra repens* Forst. et Forst. f., *Nasturtium officinale* R. Br. (confined to a single, poorly drained strip of the lawn), *Oxalis corniculata* L., *Taraxacum officinale* Wigg., and *Veronica serpyllifolia* L. A very few plants of *Picris echioides* L. and *Rumex* sp. were also present.

Recognition of ecological variation within the lawn prompted replication of experimental materials (i.e., inclusion of two sets, A and B) in the lawn. The data presented below suggests that differences noted between A and B ramets of the same clones were largely self-compensating or insignificant relative to the total comparison between lawn and garden grown materials.

Observations on sets A, B, and C were made periodically throughout the growing season of 1961. During this period, the lawn containing sets A and B received normal treatment which included moderate trampling, periodic watering (as often as once a day during the summer) from a built-in sprinkling system, and mowing to a height of about two cm every week or two.

Data from this experiment are used below to evaluate the effect of the lawn environment on plants of *P. vulgaris* and to compare the response of plants of subsp. *lanceolata* and subsp. *vulgaris* to this environment. Two of the samples used (*629* and *646*) were collected from populations which contained individuals of both subsp. *vulgaris* and subsp. *lanceolata* (Table 1). Introgressive hybridization of a limited nature has been suggested between the two subspecies in population *646* (Nelson 1964). Although the two subspecies can be differentiated by morphological features of leaf shape, corolla size, and galea pubescence in these mixed populations (Nelson 1964), the nature and amount of possible introgression of physiological features affecting reactions to lawn and garden culture has not been determined. Therefore, these two mixed samples have been excluded from group comparisons between the two subspecies (e.g., Table 5). However, an apparently typical response on the part of a plant identifiable by morphology as a member of one subspecies is noted if consistent with the response of other members of that subspecies from pure populations.

Nature of lawn-inhabiting plants. Collections from four Californian lawn populations (*645, 670, 683,* and *684*) included mature seed as well as living plants. In the collection of seed, a conscious effort was made to obtain seed from as many different individuals of each population as possible with the recognition that spread of a single clone by vegetative propagation might be particularly effective in the lawn environment.

Plants were grown from seed of collections *683* and *684* in Berkeley, California, in 1961. Plants from seed of all four of these collections were grown in Hanover, New Hampshire, in 1963. The seeds were germinated on moist filter paper in petri dishes in February, 1961, and March, 1963. As soon as the cotyledons were free, the seedlings were planted in flats in the greenhouse. The young plants were transplanted to a cultivated garden plot in early April in Berkeley, and in early June in Hanover.

Quantitative data collected from these materials were subjected to statistical analysis as discussed below. In most cases, photographic records of qualitative comparisons were made as a supplement to written records. Specimens collected from the original populations and from plants which flowered in the experimental garden at Berkeley have been deposited with the herbarium of the University of California, Berkeley.

RESULTS

Response to the lawn environment. Only 17 of the 160 clones flowered in the lawn (six in set A, nine in set B, two in both A and B), while 112 flowered in the garden (set C). All of those which flowered in set A or set B flowered vigorously in set C. Some ramets of set C (garden) flowered in all samples except *618*. All of the ramets which flowered in the lawn belonged to clones identified as subsp. *vulgaris* (from samples *P45, P84, 629, 645, 683,* and *684*). The clones which flowered in the lawn overwintered in garden culture (set C) by means of repent mats of basal shoots. Most Californian plants of subsp. *lanceolata* and many types of subsp. *vulgaris* from Europe and from non-lawn sites in California overwinter in garden culture as pulvinate to caespitose rosettes (Böcher 1949, Nelson 1962). All of the clones with flowering A or B (lawn) ramets formed much reduced, often cleistogamous flowers on the lower shoots late in the season in garden culture (set C). These reduced flowers were the only type formed by the ramets in the lawn. In the lawn plants, inflorescences were very small and seed formation was limited.

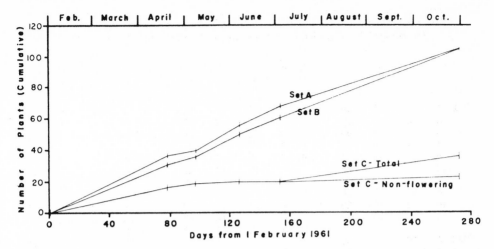

Fɪɢ. 1. Comparison of mortality in clones of *Prunella vulgaris* in lawn (sets A and B) and garden (set C) culture at Berkeley, 1961.

The plants in the lawn experienced a much higher total mortality than those in the garden (Fig. 1, Table 2). The mortality rate in the lawn was relatively constant throughout the period of observation (Fig. 1). In the garden, mortality in non-flowering plants was negligible after 97 days (8 May) (Fig. 1). However, 13 plants which had flowered succumbed in the period from 6 June to 30 October (Fig. 1). There were only five clones in which the C ramet died and both the A and the B ramet survived (Table 2). In each of these cases, the C ramet died only after flowering strongly (over 100 inflorescences) in the garden.

In 152 of the 160 clones, the C (garden) ramet attained a maximum diameter exceeding that attained by either the A or the B ramet of the same clone by from 8 to 88 cm (Table 3). In all but one of the eight cases in which the A ramet, the B ramet, or both equaled or exceeded the C ramet of the same clone in size, all three ramets reached their maximum diameter early in the season and were dead before 3 July. The greatest diameter attained by any ramet in the lawn (40 cm, plant *P45-9A*) was exceeded by 94 ramets in the garden (Table 3).

On the basis of a paired individual statistical analysis (Snedecor 1956), the difference in maximum diameter between ramets in sets A and B (lawn culture)

Tᴀʙʟᴇ 2. Mortality of *Prunella vulgaris* in lawn (sets A, B) and garden (set C) cultures (1 Feb through 30 Oct 1961).

Clones eliminated in set:	Number	Percent
A only	25	16
B only	23	14
C only	5	3
A and B	52	32
A and C	1	1
B and C	3	2
A, B, and C	27	17
A total	105	66
B total	105	66
C total	36	22

TABLE 3. Maximum diameter (cm) attained by plants of *Prunella vulgaris* in lawn (A, B ramets) and garden (C ramet) culture (1 Feb through 30 Oct 1961).

Clone	Ramet A	B	C	Clone	Ramet A	B	C	Clone	Ramet A	B	C
P 1- 1	—*	5	20	7	15	15	61	12	7	10	78
2	3	5	42	8	5	12	75				
3	—	11	43	10	16	14	46	635-1	7	4	55
4	4	7	3	11	17	5	47	3	—	—	—
5	4	—	31	P97- 1	3	17	63	4	3	—	—
6	—	—	38	2	10	16	57	5	—	—	28
7	4	—	43	3	5	4	80	6	4	6	90
8	16	6	46					7	—	3	—
10	8	5	30	8	17	4	70	11	3	2	47
11	—	10	28	9	7	16	57	12	—	3	80
				10	6	3	73	13	—	—	33
P45- 5	10	5	42					14	7	7	62
7	6	2	54	588-1	4	8	29				
8	20	8	82	2	6	6	33	639-1	5	9	17
9	40	25	90	3	14	4	33				
10	19	16	86	4	6	4	48	645-2	23	15	57
18	25	33	78	5	5	3	40	3	28	—	41
27	20	20	72	6	4	5	25	4	3	13	48
29	24	31	79					9	7	4	68
30	6	24	97	618-1	3	4	23				
				2	—	—	—	646-1	10	6	61
P70- 2	9	10	55	4	—	3	25	2	12	19	60
4	13	14	82	5	—	—	30	3	15	10	50
8	—	—	63	6	—	—	—	4	5	13	65
15	4	5	45	7	—	—	17	5	10	5	52
16	20	6	37	8	3	9	26	6	16	8	45
18	14	9	50	10	—	—	—	7	8	7	61
20	12	13	46	11	2	3	31	8	8	7	37
25	2	12	28					9	6	12	83
27	6	12	46	620-7	3	—	—	10	3	—	32
29	5	7	32	8	3	3	32	11	4	6	25
				9	—	—	—	12	—	17	85
P84- 2	33	8	73	10	—	—	—	13	19	—	89
3	4	10	70	12	—	—	—	15	—	4	49
4	5	8	40	13	—	—	—	16	4	3	40
5	3	10	46	14	—	1	—	18	4	3	33
6	4	12	63	16	—	—	30	21	2	3	60
7	25	2	51	627-4	—	—	—				
8	9	4	75	6	2	—	—	660-1	—	—	38
				9	—	—	—	2	4	12	23
P92- 3	4	6	45	17	8	2	83	3	4	4	26
4	8	9	56	20	—	3	1	4	3	5	22
6	10	5	42					5	3	7	32
7	8	4	58	629-1	—	7	60	6	2	—	26
8	9	10	31	2	24	20	59	7	4	4	42
9	4	3	46	3	26	7	64	9	10	7	26
				4	19	26	90	12	4	4	20
P95- 2	14	6	83	5	—	—	56				
3	8	20	73	6	12	19	54	670-1	4	22	54
4	18	28	62	8	3	6	45	4	7	12	72
5	20	11	74	10	3	23	62	5	4	5	63
6	4	20	62					6	6	14	64

* Missing data due to death of ramet between transplanting and first measurement of diameter 78 days after transplanting.

TABLE 3. (Cont.)

Cone	Ramet			Clone	Ramet			Clone	Ramet		
	A	B	C		A	B	C		A	B	C
7	4	5	61	8	—	—	—	9	6	14	74
8	4	8	51	10	10	2	29	10	—	7	82
				12	—	—	15				
675–2	4	3	27	14	3	4	24	684–1	8	6	30
3	4	5	25					5	12	2	75
4	3	3	33	683–1	6	5	69	7	9	6	80
5	—	—	—	2	7	14	68	9	12	9	100
6	—	3	3	4	16	20	46	11	8	5	80

were not significant while the differences between ramets in sets A and C and in sets B and C (comparison of lawn and garden culture) showed equal and high statistical significance (Table 4).

On the basis of a paired group analysis (Snedecor 1956) plants of subsp. *vulgaris* attained a significantly greater average maximum diameter than those of subsp. *lanceolata* in both lawn and garden culture (Table 5). Thus the fact that plants which attained diameters of 20 cm or more in lawn culture (sets A and B, Table 3) were identifiable as members of subsp. *vulgaris* may be correlated with a generally greater potential for diameter growth in subsp. *vulgaris* than in subsp. *lanceolata*.

Nature of lawn-inhabiting plants. Comparison of the two samples grown from seed in Berkeley shows that lawn-inhabiting plants of subsp. *vulgaris* are not of a uniform type. Plants of sample *684* were distinctly taller and broader than those of sample *683* during the first year of growth (Figs. 2a, 2b). By the beginning of the second season, the difference in diameter had largely disappeared (Fig. 3b) but the difference in height was still apparent (Fig. 3a). In addition to differences in size, these two samples showed striking differences in pattern of development. Plants of sample *683* first developed a compact, repent mat of freely rooting basal shoots from which procumbent to weakly ascending flowering shoots later developed. In Berkeley, these plants ceased flowering and died back to a basal mat

TABLE 4. Comparison of maximum diameters attained by paired ramets of *Prunella vulgaris* in lawn (sets A, B) and garden (set C) cultures using a paired individual statistical design and "t" test of significance (Snedecor 1956).

	B minus A	C minus A	C minus B
N*	116 pairs	122 pairs	126 pairs
Sample mean difference ($\bar{d}$)	1.0	43.8	43.7
Range of difference	$-23 - +25$	$-1 - +91$	$-4 - +91$
Standard deviation of difference (S)	7.46	18.94	19.40
Standard error of difference ($S_{\bar{d}}$)	0.69	1.71	1.73
t $((\bar{d}-0)/S_{\bar{d}})$	1.394	25.570	25.292
Probability of a higher value of t (P)**	17.0%	<0.1%	<0.1%
95% confidence interval for population mean difference ($\mu_{\bar{d}}$)	$\bar{d} \pm 1.4$	$\bar{d} \pm 3.4$	$\bar{d} \pm 3.4$

* Number of clones in which both ramets survived until the first observation date.
** A probability of 5% or less is generally accepted as grounds for rejecting the null hypothesis.

TABLE 5. Comparison of maximum diameters attained by clones of *Prunella vulgaris* subsp. *vulgaris* and *P. vulgaris* subsp. *lanceolata* in lawn (sets A, B) and garden (set C) culture using a paired group statistical design and "t" test of significance (Snedecor 1956). Clones collected from mixed populations containing both subsp. are excluded from this comparison (see text).

	Set A	Set B	Set C
N vulgaris*	66	66	68
N lanceolata*	37	34	49
Sample mean difference ($\bar{d} = \bar{x}_v - \bar{x}_1$)	6.0	6.3	27.5
Pooled variance (S_p^2)	44.83	35.97	307.65
Standard error of difference ($S_{\bar{d}}$)	1.37	1.26	3.29
t (($\bar{d} - 0$)/$S_{\bar{d}}$)	4.376	4.964	8.380
Probability of higher value of t (P)**	<0.1%	<0.1%	<0.1%
95% confidence interval for population mean difference ($\mu_{\bar{d}}$)	$\bar{d}\pm2.7$	$\bar{d}\pm2.5$	$\bar{d}\pm6.5$

*Number of clones surviving on fiist observation date.
** A probability of 5% or less is generally accepted as grounds for rejecting the null hypothesis.

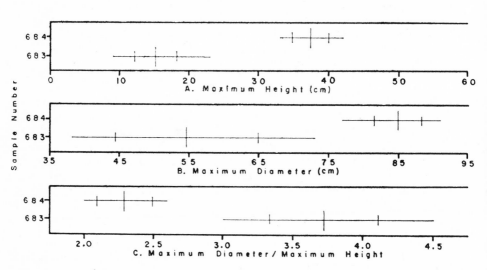

FIG. 2a,b,c. Size of plants from lawn-inhabiting populations of *Prunella vulgaris* subsp. *vulgaris* grown from seed and flowering in Berkeley, 1961. Horizontal lines indicate range of variation within samples, long verticals indicate sample means, short verticals indicate the 95% confidence limits for the means. $N_{683} = 9$, $N_{684} = 10$.

in late August, September, or early October. In the Berkeley garden, plants of sample *684* developed rapidly and directly to a flowering condition. The flowering shoots were strongly ascending and showed little tendency to root at the base until late in the season. Modification for overwintering was accomplished by the production of basal shoots toward the end of the summer. The mat subsequently formed by these basal shoots was of a repent nature. These plants continued to flower intermittently into the winter months. The differences in habit resulting from differences in developmental pattern in samples *683* and *684* are reflected in differing diameter/height ratios for the two samples (Fig. 2c).

Data obtained from plants of collections *683* and *684* grown from cuttings in the

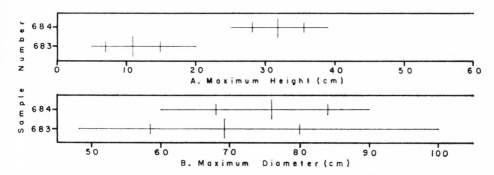

Fig. 3a, b. Size of plants from lawn-inhabiting populations of *Prunella vulgaris* subsp. *vulgaris* grown from seed in Berkeley as measured in May, 1962. Symbols as in Fig. 2 $N_{683.684} = 10$.

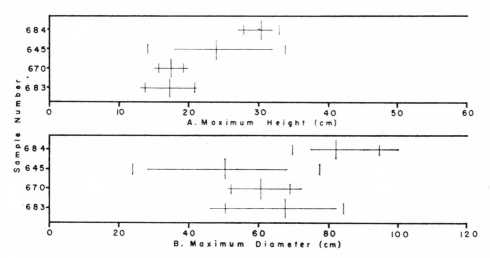

Fig. 4a, b. Size of plants from lawn-inhabiting populations of *Prunella vulgaris* subsp. *vulgaris* grown from cuttings in Berkeley, 1961. Symbols as in Fig. 2. $N_{683} = 5$, $N_{670} = 6$, $N_{645} = 4$, $N_{684} = 5$.

garden at Berkeley (set C of the lawn experiment discussed above) agree with the second-season data on plants grown from seed (Figs. 3, 4). The difference in maximum diameter between the two samples does not appear to be particularly significant but the difference in maximum height is (Fig. 4). Coupled with this height difference were differences in developmental pattern and habit consistent with those described above for plants grown from seed of the two collections. Plants grown from cuttings (set C) of collection *670* were comparable to those from collection *683* in developmental pattern and height (Fig. 4). The C ramets of collection *645* resemble those of collection *684* in developmental pattern but were intermediate between *684* and *683* in height (Fig. 4).

All samples grown in Berkeley had a uniformly high percentage of flowering in the first and second seasons of growth (Table 6). In Hanover, the percentage of flowering during the first season in samples *645*, *670*, and *683* was uniformly quite low and significantly lower than the percentage of flowering in sample *684* (Table 6). The relatively rapid development to flowering of plants in sample *684*, as illustrated in the Berkeley garden, may account for their ability to flower during

TABLE 6. Percent flowering in samples of *Prunella vulgaris* subsp. *vulgaris* from lawn populations.

	Sample 645		Sample 670		Sample 683		Sample 684	
	N	%	N	%	N	%	N	%
Grown from cuttings:								
Berkeley, 1961	4	100	6	100	5	100	5	100
Grown from seed:								
Berkeley, 1961					10	90	10	100
Berkeley, May 1962*					10	100	10	100
Hanover, 1963*	15	20	14	21	7	14	15	93

* As determined by percentage of sample forming flower buds.

the first year in Hanover's shorter growing season. All flowering in Hanover ceased abruptly with the first heavy frost on 23 September 1963.

As with the Berkeley data, differences in diameter among the samples grown in Hanover appeared to have relatively low significance (Figs. 5b, 6b). Flowering plants of sample *684* were distinctly taller than those of samples *683* and *670* (Fig. 5a). Flowering plants of sample *645* tended to be closer to those of *684* in height but the statistical significance of the mean value in *645* is questionable (Fig. 5a), apparently due to the limited number of flowering plants in the sample.

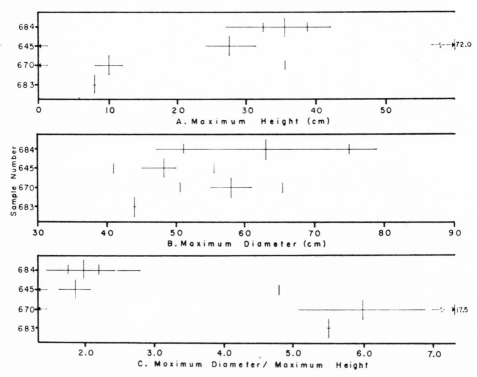

Fig. 5a, b, c. Size of plants from lawn-inhabiting populations of *Prunella vulgaris* subsp. *vulgaris* which flowered in Hanover in 1963. Symbols as in Fig. 2. $N_{683} = 1$, $N_{670} = 2$ (3 in b), $N_{645} = 2$ (3 in b), $N_{684} = 12$ (14 in b).

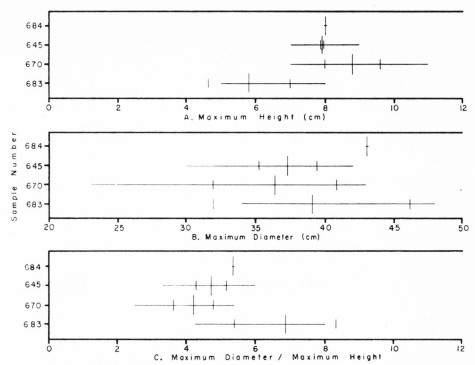

Fig. 6a, b, c. Size of plants from lawn-inhabiting populations of *Prunella vulgaris* subsp. *vulgaris* which did not flower in Hanover in 1963. Symbols as in Fig. 2. $N_{683} = 6$, $N_{670} = 11$, $N_{645} = 12$, $N_{684} = 1$.

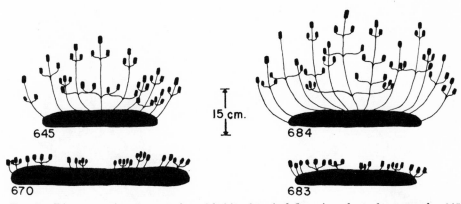

Fig. 7. Diagrammatic representation of habit of typical flowering plants from samples *645*, *684*, *670*, and *683* derived from photographs of plants grown in the Berkeley and Hanover gardens and measurements made on plants grown in Hanover.

In the Hanover garden, flowering plants of samples *684* and *645* had a rather different developmental pattern than that seen in the Berkeley garden. The production of repent basal shoots was initiated much earlier in the sequence of development in Hanover and actually coincided with the development of flowering shoots. Thus the single non-flowering plant of sample *684* did not differ in developmental

Fig. 8.   Lawn plants of *Prunella vulgaris* subsp. *vulgaris* from nature and from garden culture. A. Specimens from collection *683*.   B. Branch of a plant grown from seed of collection *683* in Berkeley.   C. Specimens from collection *684*.   D. Branch of a plant grown from seed of collection *684* in Berkeley.

pattern from flowering plants of the same sample except for the absence of flowering shoots. The two flowering plants of sample *645* were essentially similar in shape and appearance to flowering plants of sample *684* (Fig. 7), accounting for the close correspondence between the two samples in diameter/height ratios for flowering plants (Fig. 5c).

Non-flowering plants of sample *683* and flowering plants of *683* and *670* in Hanover developed in a manner essentially similar to that noted for these samples in Berkeley. Some non-flowering plants of samples *645* and *670* formed a low, pulvinate rosette rather than a repent mat of shoots in the Hanover garden. This accounts for the discrepancy between samples *683* and *670* in height and in diameter/height ratio for non-flowering plants (Figs. 6a, 6c).

In their original lawn environment, plants of lawn populations were quite uniform in their expression of a creeping habit, dwarf leaves, flowers and inflorescences, and low flowering shoots (e.g., Fig. 8). In all garden cultures, plants from these populations were noticeably different in morphology and habit from specimens collected directly from lawns (e.g., Fig. 8). Lawn-grown materials do express variation in leaf texture, inflorescence pigmentation, and pubescence but more extensive field and garden studies are necessary before it can be determined whether this variation is correlated with the variation in habit, development, and growth potential described above for cultivated samples from lawn populations.

In summary, two extreme types might be described among the lawn samples. The first, illustrated by sample *683*, includes plants which, in garden culture, develop into low, spreading mats of vegetative shoots from which short, procumbent to weakly ascending flowering shoots ultimately develop (Fig. 7). In Berkeley, a high percentage of these plants flowered during the first season of growth while in Hanover a low percentage succeeded in flowering (Table 6). In the second type, illustrated by sample *684*, early developmental sequences generally lead directly to tall, ascending flowering shoots. In Berkeley, there was a period of continued development of new flowering shoots before the initiation of a basal mat of vegetative shoots. In Hanover, the development of ascending floral shoots and repent basal shoots was more or less coincident. Flowering plants of this second type were much taller, relative to their breadth, than those of the first type (Figs. 2, 5, 7). There was a high percentage of flowering during the first season of growth both in Berkeley and in Hanover in this second type.

For the most part, sample *670* corresponded to the type illustrated by sample *683* (Figs. 4, 5, 7; Table 6). Sample *645* was generally similar to *684* (Figs. 5, 7) but conformed to *683* in potential for flowering in the first season of growth in Hanover (Table 6) and was somewhat intermediate in height of ramets in set C in Berkeley (Fig. 4). Some non-flowering plants of samples *645* and *670* departed to a degree from both of the two types described above in terms of habit (diameter/height ratio) in the Hanover garden (Fig. 6).

As stated above (Table 1), the five lawn populations included in this study consisted of plants identifiable as subsp. *vulgaris*. At the present time, 44 different population samples of Californian subsp. *lanceolata*, 3 non-lawn samples of Californian subsp. *vulgaris*, and 8 European samples of subsp. *vulgaris* have been observed in garden culture either in Berkeley or Hanover. The combinations of developmental and morphological features which typify the two types of plants found in the Californian lawn populations have not been found in plants of subsp. *lanceolata*, whether comparisons be made on field or garden grown materials. Garden grown plants of two European samples (*P45* and *P84*) and one non-lawn Californian sample of subsp. *vulgaris* (P115)[2] conform to the type illustrated by garden grown materials of the lawn sample *684*. There is some suggestion that this type may be equivalent to the "therophyte race" described by Böcher (1940, 1949) as particularly common in southern Europe (Nelson 1962). Except for the lawn samples themselves, none of the Californian or European samples so far cultivated conform to the type illustrated by sample *683*. However, Böcher's (1949) data on European subsp. *vulgaris* in garden culture includes ten samples which, by height and diameter/height ratio, could be classed with sample *683*. A repent growth habit is recorded for 15 of Böcher's 147 samples and he suggests a correlation between the repent habit and moist habitats as well as a concentration of populations with this growth habit from meadows in central Europe (Böcher 1949). Böcher gives no indication that any of his samples came directly from lawn habitats (Böcher 1949).

DISCUSSION

The results presented above clearly show that survival, vegetative growth, and flowering of *P. vulgaris* are severely limited in the lawn environment. There is a strong suggestion that some strains of the species are more capable of adaptation to the conditions of the lawn environment than others. Even among these types, successful establishment, growth, and reproduction in lawns may be a difficult and infrequently occurring event. Instances of flowering and the highest growth rates in lawn-grown experimental materials were restricted to clones of subsp. *vulgaris* suggesting that the highest degree of adaptability to the lawn environment is contained within this subspecies.

The types of plants found in samples from naturally occurring lawn populations were not found in samples of Californian subsp. *lanceolata* but do occur in samples of European subsp. *vulgaris* from habitats other than lawns. This suggests that the Californian lawn populations studied were not derived from local materials of subsp. *lanceolata* but are probably the direct or indirect result of the introduction of European materials of subsp. *vulgaris*.

The differences which were noted between the features of plants of *P. vulgaris* in cultivation and the characteristics of the same plants in their natural habitats are consistent with observations which have been made in genecological studies from the early works of Turesson (1922) to the present. This principle is admirably expressed in the recent data of Gregor and Watson (1961) on *Plantago lanceolata* L. and *Agrostis* spp. and serves to emphasize the fact that "... 'characters' are produced by the joint action of genotype and environment." (Waddington 1961, p. 258).

A second generalization of genecological investigations is implicit in the observation that plants which are phenotypically similar in their natural habitats may show considerable variation in cultivation. In terms of low-growing, dwarf forms in species other than *P. vulgaris*, this tendency is evident in Turesson's (1922) studies of *Succisa pratensis* Moench and *Centaurea jacea* L. and in Gregor's (1938) work on *Plantago maritima* L. Such observations suggest that an environment may exert a stabilizing effect which induces phenotypic conformity among the genetically different organisms capable of occupying it.

The nature of the variation observed between garden-grown plants from lawn-inhabiting populations of subsp. *vulgaris* is of particular interest in relation to the recognition and typification of var. *parviflora*. To the extent that a low, spreading growth habit in both vegetative and flowering phases may be viewed as a reasonable or logical adaptation to existence in the lawn environment, the type of plant seen in garden culture of samples *670* and *683* (Fig. 7) is consistent with the supposition

---

[2]Rubtzoff 4784 (CAS, UC), Sonoma County, California.

of specific genetic adaptation to the lawn habitat. In contrast, it is difficult to accept the tall, strongly ascending flowering shoots seen in garden culture of plants of samples *645* and *684* (Fig. 7) as features of a genetically adapted lawn-inhabiting race. If plants such as those of sample *683* may be designated as a genetically determined lawn type for this species, plants of the type seen in sample *684* may be designated as phenocopies inasmuch as they exhibit far greater resemblance to the lawn type under lawn conditions than under garden conditions.

Environmentally induced variation in the degree to which plants of sample *684* resemble those of sample *683* implies a greater potential for variation in the developmental sequences which lead to the phenotype in plants of the sort seen in sample *684*. This high potential for variation is evident in the tendency of plants from samples *645* and *684* to exhibit a developmental pattern in the garden in Hanover which differs noticeably from that observed in the Berkeley garden. It might be noted that in both gardens these plants developed in such a manner as to achieve maximum reproduction without negating the possibilities of perennation. It appears that plants of the lawn type (samples *670* and *683*) were inherently incapable of significant alteration of the developmental pattern expressed in Berkeley and thus completed only those early phases of development concerned with the production of perennating organs (the basal shoots) during the first growing season in Hanover.

Any attempt at classification of forms such as the one discussed here must deal with the phenomenon of phenocopies and the potential for phenotypic variation which may be associated with them. For practical reasons, taxa must be so constituted that their members are recognizable despite vagaries of the environment and that they reproduce themselves in kind. In the present instance, this requires that typification of var. *parviflora* be initiated by a decision to include or exclude the phenocopy by search for and utilization of appropriate, stable, phenotypic characteristics. If it may be postulated that classification, by virtue of its phylogenetic basis, should reflect a coherent and comprehensible picture of phytogeography, genetic relationships, and evolution of the members of a taxon, the decision as to whether the phenocopy should or should not be included in var. *parviflora* must rest on an informed evaluation of the evolutionary potential of the phenocopy.

The phenocopy might be viewed as a highly plastic form in potential equilibrium with a wide variety of environments. If so, it might be assumed that adaptation of this form to the lawn environment by direct phenotypic response to stimuli inherent in the environment is as effective as the genetic adaptation shown by the lawn form. Thus the phenocopy would be no more likely to undergo evolutionary change in this environment than the lawn type. Under these conditions a stable phylogenetic classification recognizing var. *parviflora* might be realized by excluding the phenocopy from the variety.

On the other hand, Waddington (1961) has shown that in certain organisms which exhibit a direct response to strong environmental stimuli, such a response may become stabilized or fixed over a period of many generations as a result of the selective advantage enjoyed by individuals in which the response is expressed with relative ease. Should this situation apply in the present case, the phenocopy might be viewed as a type in the process of stabilization as a genetically adapted lawn form similar or even identical in adaptive and typifying characteristics to the present lawn type. In this case, a relatively stable phylogenetic classification including var. *parviflora* could only be realized by including the phenocopy in the variety.

Information on which to assess the probability of one or the other of these two evolutionary possibilities for the phenocopy is not currently available. Such information might be gained through breeding experiments and long term cultivation experiments involving the observation of successive vegetative and sexual generations of the lawn type and its phenocopy in various environments. At the present time, it can only be concluded that var. *parviflora* as currently typified (Moore 1950) is not a stable, uniform taxon with members recognizable under all environmental conditions. It might be suggested that the problem posed by var. *parviflora* may be of relevance in many instances where groups of organisms show greater variation under experimental conditions than in their natural environments.

LITERATURE CITED

Böcher, T. W. 1940. Introductory studies on variation and life-forms in *Brunella vulgaris* L. Dansk Bot. Ark. **10**(3): 1–15.

——————. 1949. Racial divergences in *Prunella vulgaris* in relation to habitat and climate. New Phytol. **48**: 285–314.

Candolle, A. de. 1848. Prodromus Systematis Naturalis Regni Vegetabilis. Masson, Paris.

Clute, W. N. 1902. A new form of *Brunella*. Am. Bot. **3**: 11.

——————. 1933. *Prunella vulgaris nana*. Am. Bot. **39**: 129–130.

Fernald, M. L. 1950. Gray's Manual of Botany. 8th ed. American Book Co., New York.

Gilmour, J. S. 1933. New variety of *Prunella vulgaris*. Jour. Bot. **71**: 320–321.

Gregor, J. W. 1938. Experimental taxonomy II. Initial population differentiation in *Plantago maritima* L. New Phytol. **37**: 15–49.

——————— & Watson, P. J. 1961. Ecotypic differentiation: observations and reflections. Evolution **15**: 166–173.

Howell, J. T., Raven, P. H. & Rubtzoff, P. 1958. A Flora of San Francisco, California. The University of San Francisco, San Francisco.

Moore, J. W. 1950. Studies of Minnesota flowering plants with notes on addition to the flora. Rhodora **52**: 54–60.

Nelson, A. P. 1962. A Genecological Study in *Prunella vulgaris* L. (Labiatae). Ph.D. Thesis, University of California, Berkeley.

——————. 1964. Relationship between two subspecies in a population of *Prunella vulgaris* L. Evolution **18**: 43–51.

Snedecor, G. W. 1956. Statistical Methods, 5th ed. Iowa State College Press, Ames.

Turesson, G. 1922. The genotypical response of the plant species to the habitat. Hereditas **3**: 211–350.

Waddington, C. H. 1961. Genetic assimilation. Advances Genet. **10**: 247–293.

SECTION II

The Origin of Species

BLAIR, W. FRANK, and MURRAY J. LITTLEJOHN. 1960. Stage of speciation of two allopatric populations of chorus frogs (*Pseudacris*). Evolution **14:** 82–87.

ALEXANDER, RICHARD D., and ROBERT S. BIGELOW. 1960. Allochronic speciation in field crickets, and a new species, *Acheta veletis*. Evolution **14:** 334–346.

BROWN, W. L., JR., and E. O. WILSON. 1956. Character displacement. Syst. Zool. **5:** 49–64.

STONE, WILSON S., WILLIAM C. GUEST, and FLORENCE D. WILSON. 1960. The evolutionary implications of the cytological polymorphism and phylogeny of the *virilis* group of *Drosophila*. Proc. Nat. Acad. Sci. U.S. **46:** 350–361.

LEWIS, HARLAN, and MARGARET R. ROBERTS. 1956. The origin of *Clarkia lingulata*. Evolution **10:** 126–138.

WHITAKER, THOMAS W., and W. P. BEMIS. 1965. Evolution in the genus *Cucurbita*. Evolution **18:** 553–559.

Diversification is the inevitable result of the evolution of populations, and the processes involved in "speciation" are precisely those responsible for the changes described in papers in the first section. Historically, however, people have focused separately on the splitting process. In particular, considerable attention has been paid among zoologists to the question of the degree of physical isolation (allopatry) necessary before populations can diverge. The paper by Blair and Littlejohn* on *Pseudacris* is a good example of a study of populations diverging allopatrically. A similarly illuminating study with plant materials is that of Kruckeberg (1957) on the annual serpentine endemic *Streptanthus glandulosis.* In contrast, Alexander and Bigelow* describe a situation in which divergence may have occurred in the absence of geographic isolation, but with seasonal isolation instead. Brown and Wilson* present now widely accepted explanations of why populations of similar animal species seem more highly differentiated physically or ecologically from one another in areas where they overlap than in areas where they occur separately. When previously isolated populations come together, hybrids between them may have lowered fitness. This means that individuals which tend to hybridize will be selected against or, conversely, any mechanism which tends to prevent hybridization (e.g., enhancement of recognition characters, or of ecological differences) will be favored. Less certain is the role played by selection related to reduction of interspecific competition in promoting ecological divergence (Birch and Ehrlich, 1967).

The paper by Stone, Guest, and Wilson* shows a way in which the complexity of relationships among natural populations at several levels of differentiation may be untangled by cytological analysis. In the botanical literature, a number of examples can be cited of the elegant cytogenetic analyses of the evolutionary relationships between closely similar species, some recent papers being those of Lewis and Roberts;* Lewis and Raven (1958); and Kyhos (1965). Lewis (1962) has generalized the results of some of these studies into a theory of catastrophic selection along the margins of range of a relatively widespread species, which leads to the formation of local derivatives.

Variability in crossing relationships is reported by Stone *et al.,* among strains of *Drosophila montana* and other species of the *Montana* subgroup. The wide variety of crossing relationships among *Drosophila* entities has long been known (e.g., see Patterson and Stone, 1952, and Dobzhansky and Spassky, 1959). Besides the crossing experiments, some of the most interesting studies of animal speciation have dealt with what are now usually called "rings of races." These (e.g., Brown and Stebbins, 1964) involve a linear series of populations, among which there is assumed to be gene flow at points of contact along the

* Paper included in this section.

series. Should the ends of the series come to overlap, there is little or no exchange of genes.

In general, however, evolutionists working with animals have paid relatively little attention to the complexities of relationships around what taxonomists think of as the species level. This lack of emphasis is unfortunate, for it has hindered our understanding of the process of speciation in animals. Evolutionists working with plants have illuminated this complexity in many instances. The paper by Whitaker and Bemis* is an example of the type of study which has formed the background of our understanding of plant diversification. An excellent summary of research dealing with a number of different groups of plants is given by Clausen (1951). Other examples involve reticulate evolution and are included in Section III.

BIBLIOGRAPHY

BIRCH, L. C., and P. R. EHRLICH. 1967. Evolutionary history and population biology. Nature **214**: 349–352.

BROWN, C. W., and R. C. STEBBINS. 1964. Evidence for hybridization between the blotched and unblotched subspecies of the salamander *Ensatina eschscholtzi*. Evolution **18**: 706–707.

CLAUSEN, J. 1951. *Stages in the Evolution of Plant Species*. Cornell University Press, Ithaca, N.Y.

DOBZHANSKY, TH., and B. SPASSKY. 1959. *Drosophila paulistorum*, a cluster of species *in statu nascendi*. Proc. Nat. Acad. Sci. **45**: 419–428.

KRUCKEBERG, A. R. 1957. Variation in fertility of hybrids between isolated populations of the serpentine species, *Streptanthus glandulosis* Hook. Evolution **11**: 185–211.

KYHOS, D. W. 1965. The independent aneuploid origin of two species of *Chaenactis* (Compositae) from a common ancestor. Evolution **19**: 26–43.

LEWIS, H. 1962. Catastrophic selection as a factor in speciation. Evolution **16**: 257–271.

———, and P. H. RAVEN. 1958. Rapid evolution in *Clarkia*. Evolution **12**: 319–336.

PATTERSON, I. T., and W. S. STONE. 1952. *Evolution in the Genus Drosophila*. The Macmillan Co., New York.

STAGE OF SPECIATION OF TWO ALLOPATRIC POPULATIONS OF CHORUS FROGS (*PSEUDACRIS*)[1]

W. Frank Blair and Murray J. Littlejohn [2]

The University of Texas

Received July 8, 1959

The best estimate of the course of geographic speciation comes from analysis of disjunct, allopatric populations in respect to their differentiation in attributes that might function as isolating mechanisms, and in morphological characters. Various east-west disjunct populations of vertebrates on the Gulf coastal plain of the southern United States, with presumed Pleistocene origins (Blair, 1958b), afford excellent material for such an analysis. The present report deals with two geographically separate populations of chorus frogs. One, *Pseudacris ornata,* occurs on the coastal plain of the southeastern United States and has its western distribution limited at the Mississippi Embayment. The other, *P. streckeri,* occurs in the broad forest—grassland ecotone just west of the deciduous forest in Texas and Oklahoma and has its eastern distribution limited by the forest. Relict populations of *P. streckeri* occur in Illinois and Missouri.

For these two allopatric species we have obtained a measure of the morphological differentiation, of the differentiation in mating call and certain other attributes that might affect interbreeding if the populations should become sympatric, and of the discrimination by ripe females of one of the species when exposed to the calls of males of both.

Materials and Methods

The morphological comparisons are based on museum specimens of 91 male and seven female *Pseudacris ornata* from northern Florida and southern Georgia, and 483 male and 52 female *P. streckeri* from Texas and Oklahoma. All specimens of the latter species are in the Texas Natural History Collection at The University of Texas.

The comparisons of mating calls are based on tape recording of 10 individuals of *ornata* and 26 of *streckeri*. All these recordings except those of three *ornata* borrowed from Cornell University are on file in the bioacoustical laboratory at The University of Texas. Analyses of the calls have been made by use of a sound spectrograph (Sona-Graph) which portrays frequency, intensity, and time.

The female *streckeri* used in the discrimination experiments were obtained in central Texas. The simple apparatus used in the experiments consists of an enclosure with a speaker at each end so that choices of recorded calls can be presented to a female. This apparatus is modeled after that described by Martof and Thompson (1958) and has been described in detail by Littlejohn and Michaud (1959). The recorded calls are played through two 2.5 inch diameter loudspeakers, one at each end of the tank, using repeating loops of tape. The work is done in a temperature-controlled room at $19.5 \pm 2.0°$ C.

Acknowledgments

We are indebted to Arnold B. Grobman for the loan of the specimens of *Pseudacris ornata* in the Florida State Museum.

[1] This work was assisted by National Science Foundation Grant No. G-4956 to the senior author.

[2] Work done while recipient of a Hackett Studentship from the University of Western Australia and a Fulbright Travel Grant. Present Address: Department of Zoology, University of Melbourne, Carlton, Victoria, Australia.

Paul Kellogg kindly made available recordings of the calls of *P. ornata* in the Cornell University Library of Natural Sounds. The sound spectrographic work was done by Wayne H. McAlister and M. J. Fouquette, and the latter made the morphological measurements and did the statistical analyses.

Morphological Differentiation

Frogs of the two allopatric populations are rather similar, but there are subtle and subjectively describable differences as well as differences in size and proportions. The color pattern is variable in both, but *streckeri* tends more to spot-like bars of dark pigment on the dorsum, while *ornata* tends more to have two dark longitudinal dorsal bars. The dark bars or spots may be greatly reduced in individuals of either species. The ventral surface appears more granular in *streckeri* than in *ornata*. In general terms, *ornata* is more slender, with more pointed snout and longer and more slender arms and legs; *streckeri* is short, fat, squatty, with shorter, broader snout and short, broad arms and legs (Wright and Wright, 1949). Comparison of the measurements of the available specimens (table 1) provides support for the statement of these general differences between the two species. The larger size of *streckeri* is reflected in the significantly greater snout-urostyle length, although the greater robustness of this frog cannot be shown by this linear measurement. The relatively longer head of *ornata* is indicated by the ratio of head length to head width. The head is significantly longer in male *streckeri* in relation to snout-urostyle length than in male *ornata*. There is no significant difference in this respect between the females, but the sample of female *ornata* is inadequate. Both the tibia and foot (including toes) are significantly longer in relation to snout-urostyle length in *ornata* than in *streckeri*.

The adaptive significance of the obvious morphological differences between the two populations of frogs can only be hypothesized at present. Circumstantial evidence suggests that the differences in size and proportions are probably adaptive to the rather different environments of these two frogs. The larger, more robust body of *streckeri*, with less surface area in relation to mass, would presumably have a selective advantage in terms of water conservation in the more xeric western distribution area of this frog. At least two other complexes of anurans with eastern and western differentiates (*Acris gryllus—A. crepitans; Bufo woodhousei fowleri* and *B. w. woodhousei*) show larger body size in the western member and smaller in the eastern one. The situation of longer legs (and feet) in the eastern, low-coastal-plain population and shorter ones in the more western population is paralleled in *Acris*. The significance of this is obscure, although it could be a surface to mass phenomenon related to water conservation.

Potential Isolating Mechanisms

Time and place of breeding

These are both winter-breeding frogs that spawn in temporary pools after winter

TABLE 1. *Comparisons of external morphological measurements of* Pseudacris streckeri *and* P. ornata

Characters	Males Means and standard errors		Females Means and standard errors	
	streckeri (N = 483)	*ornata* (N = 91)	*streckeri* (N = 52)	*ornata* (N = 7)
Snout-urostyle length	31.93 ± 0.11	29.36 ± 0.14	33.87 ± 0.17	30.97 ± 0.25
Head length/head width	0.876 ± 0.002	0.940 ± 0.005	0.873 ± 0.006	0.931 ± 0.017
Head length/snout-urostyle	0.338 ± 0.001	0.330 ± 0.001	0.336 ± 0.001	0.328 ± 0.004
Tibia/snout-urostyle	0.433 ± 0.001	0.457 ± 0.002	0.426 ± 0.003	0.449 ± 0.006
Foot/snout-urostyle	0.707 ± 0.002	0.778 ± 0.003	0.688 ± 0.005	0.775 ± 0.012

TABLE 2. *Measurements of mating calls of* Pseudacris ornata *and* P. streckeri

Species and locality	N	Air temp. °C.	H₂O temp. °C.	Mean dominant freq. (cps)	Mean duration (sec)	Mean interval (sec)
P. ornata—Newton, Ga.	7	18.0	16.5	2750	.04	.34
P. ornata (Cornell record)	3	—	—	2830	.04	.40
P. streckeri—Austin, Tex.	1	22.0	19.0	2350	.06	.24
P. streckeri—Austin, Tex.	17	21.5	18.0	2300	.05	.35
P. streckeri—Luling, Tex.	3	19.0	21.3	2225	.04	.35
P. streckeri—Brenham, Tex.	5	23.0	22.0	2430	.04	.21

rains. The breeding season of a *streckeri* population at Austin, Texas, has been carefully observed over a period of four years. The beginning of the breeding season, as evidenced by calling males, varied from October 22 to January 23. These variations were influenced largely by rainfall and to a lesser degree by temperature. The end of the breeding season varied from March 2 to April 29. The breeding season of *ornata* in Florida has been stated (Carr, 1940) as extending from November 3 to March 2. The close approximation of their breeding seasons and their habits of breeding in temporary pools indicate that if these two populations became sympatric there would be no initial restriction on interbreeding through habits of breeding at different times or places.

Genetic incompatibility

Mecham (1957) obtained normal-appearing, viable F₁'s in the cross of ♀ *streckeri* × ♂ *ornata*. One hybrid male, in an attempted backcross to a *streckeri* female, fertilized no eggs and appeared to be producing no viable sperm. Mecham (1959) made the reciprocal cross and obtained only sterile males.

It would appear, therefore, that these populations in isolation have differentiated sufficiently that there is a sterility barrier to their interbreeding, although there is no proof at present that the barrier is complete.

Mechanical incompatibility

The difference in robustness and body size must be considered as a possible isolating mechanism. However, the difference is less than that between *Bufo woodhousei woodhousei* and *B. w. fowleri* which apparently interbreed freely in a narrow zone of secondary contact (Meacham, 1958).

Mating call

The call in both of these species is a short, finely tuned whistle that derives most of its energy from a dominant frequency band between 2,000 and 3,000 cps and from the first higher harmonic of this band at 4,000 to 6,000 cps. This call is repeated in sequence, with a silent interval between calls of about one-third of a second. Comparison of the available sound spectrograms of calls (table 2) shows that there is no significant difference between the two species in duration of the call or in interval between calls (measured as the silent period). The only apparent difference in call is in the frequency. The dominant frequency band rises about 200 cps from beginning to end, and for purposes of comparison the dominant frequency has been measured at approximately the middle of the call. As may be seen from table 2, the dominant frequency averages about 500 cps higher in *ornata* than in *streckeri* and twice that in the harmonic. The range of variation in the two species barely overlaps, as one of the 10 *ornata* and one of the *streckeri* had a dominant frequency of 2,500 cps.

Call discrimination

Discrimination experiments were run, by methods referred to earlier, in order to test whether the rather slight differences in mating call might serve as species

TABLE 3. *Details on calls used in discrimination experiments*

Species and locality	Recording temperatures, °C.		Duration (seconds)	Dominant frequency (cps)
	Air	Water		
P. streckeri				
6 miles S.S.E. of Luling, Texas	19.0	21.3	0.04	2280
P. ornata				
Newton, Georgia	18.0	16.5	0.03	2640

identification cues for the females in going to the calls of the males. Gravid *streckeri* females, collected in amplexus, were released in the test tank, and their orientation toward the loudspeakers from which the calls of *ornata* and *streckeri* were being played was noted. The particular calls between which the females were given a choice differed in that the call of the *ornata* had dominant frequency of 360 cps higher and a duration 0.01 seconds shorter than that of the *streckeri* (table 3).

In the test runs, contacts with a loudspeaker were scored if a female fulfilled any one of the following conditions:

1. circled the speaker at a distance of 4–10 inches;
2. jumped at the speaker, making a transient contact with it, then passing on for about 6–10 inches;
3. sat about 2 inches away from the speaker;
4. made deliberate contact with the speaker by jumping or climbing over it or sitting on or against it.

Only one contact was scored for a sequence involving orientation which could include two or more of the above conditions. However, if a frog stopped circling and moved away, then returned again, or if a frog moved more than 6 inches away after fulfilling conditions 2–4, and returned again, then subsequent contacts were also scored.

Frogs were initially released at the center of the tank, either two or three being tested at the same time. After the frogs had contacted a speaker, connections were switched so that the calls now came from opposite ends. Such exchanges of calls were sometimes made several times during the testing of a particular frog and at least once for each individual. The interval between changes is referred to as a trial (Littlejohn and Michaud, 1959).

The results given in table 4 are from 29 frog-trials involving a total of nine female *streckeri,* eight from Travis County, and one from Lee County, Texas. As can be seen, 35 contacts were scored with the *streckeri* speaker and four with the *ornata* speaker. Two of the latter occurred directly after release and could have resulted from random movement; three were made by the same frog, and all occurred during one test run involving three frogs.

A reactive frog moved decisively and accurately toward the sound source of the *streckeri* call and ultimately contacted the speaker. On several occasions females after contacting the *streckeri* speaker moved to within about a foot of the *ornata* speaker, paused, faced it for a few seconds, then turned and swam back to the *streckeri* speaker, usually to make another contact. On three occasions females clasped other females in front of the

TABLE 4. *Summary of contacts made with loudspeakers by 9* P. streckeri *females.* See text for explanation. ? refers only to the category into which the contact should be placed.

Loudspeaker	Class of contact				
	1.	2.	3.	4.	Total
P. streckeri call	1	1	13+?1	19	35
P. ornata call	0	1	?1	2	4

Chi^2 = 24.6, P less than 0.001.

streckeri speaker. These lasted from about 15 seconds up to three minutes. Times taken for females to move from the release point at the center of the tank to contract the *streckeri* speaker some 42 inches away ranged from 3.17 to 5.50 minutes (mean = 4.78), and for the total distance between the speakers of about seven feet from 0.25 to 8.50 minutes (mean = 2.54).

On one occasion two females were offered only the calls of *ornata* through one of the speakers over a six minute period. During this time they came within two inches of the speaker five times but were never actually observed to make direct physical contact (types 2 and 4) with it. When *streckeri* calls were started at the opposite end, the two frogs immediately left the vicinity of the *ornata* speaker and moved directly to the *streckeri* speaker, contacting it by persistently jumping against it. They then assumed a position of amplexus. All this activity occupied about one minute from the starting of the *streckeri* calls.

The results of these tests indicate decisively that the female *streckeri* are attracted to the calls of male *streckeri* but not to the slightly different calls of the male *ornata*. The females generally respond to the calls of the male of their own species by making physical contact (with the loudspeaker in the experimental situation), which in these frogs normally elicits clasping by the male. Blair (1958a) regarded the relatively slight difference in call of these two species as being insignificant as an isolating mechanism. The results of the present experiments indicate that this opinion was unjustified.

DISCUSSION

This pair of disjunct, allopatric species provides an excellent opportunity for assessing the process of geographic speciation. The time element must remain uncertain in the absence of a fossil record, but the fragmentation of the ancestral range is reasonably attributable to the effects of Pleistocene climatic change (Blair, 1958b). The disjunction could have come as recently as the beginning of the Wisconsin, but it cannot be proved that it did not come earlier.

Differentiation in the various attributes discussed above presumably came after geographic isolation of the two populations, but there is no way of knowing how much intraspecific geographic variation in morphological and ecological characters existed prior to the time of the disjunction. Nevertheless, the two populations are now sufficiently different in morphology that they have been regarded as distinct species by taxonomists. The most notable differentiation (in body size and robustness) seems probably to have come from differential selection in different moisture environments. The two populations have differentiated genetically to the extent that genetic incompatibility, expressed in sex-ratio disturbance and sterility of the F_1 would certainly limit and possibly block gene transfer between the populations if they should ever become sympatric.

The two populations have remained essentially undifferentiated in respect to breeding season (winter) and the kinds of water (temporary rainpools) in which spawning occurs. The mating call, with a primary function in each population of aggregating the sexes for reproduction, has differentiated slightly, and apparently as a byproduct of the adaptive differentiation in body size and robustness. As a general rule, the dominant frequency varies inversely with body size in anurans (Blair, 1958a). The relatively slight differentiation in mating call, which we have shown, however, to be adequate for species discrimination, and which apparently came about incidental to adaptive differentiation of the two populations, exists as a potential isolating mechanism of great significance if the populations should ever establish contact.

We construct the speciational history of these frogs, then, as being initiated by geographic separation, followed by adaptive differentiation that led indirectly to the acquisition of an important pre-mating isolating mechanism (call difference) and possibly along with genetic drift, to the acquisition of an important post-isolating mechanism (genetic incompatibility). This case history closely parallels the one reported for the *Peromyscus maniculatus—P. polionotus* complex (Blair and Howard, 1944) where there is strongly adaptive differentiation in color pattern, interspecific discrimination, and partial genetic incompatibility between disjunct, allopatric species of presumed Pleistocene origin. Both of these cases fit the often termed "Mullerian" model of geographic speciation (Muller, 1940).

In closing, however, we would like to emphasize that these cases represent only one of the possible pathways of geographic speciation and should not be the basis for any broad generalization. Pre-mating isolating mechanisms may evolve without concomitant genetic incompatibility; populations may establish sympatry and undergo reinforcement of less completely effective isolating mechanisms than the ones under discussion here would appear to be (Blair, 1958a).

Summary

The allopatric chorus frogs (*Pseudacris ornata* and *P. streckeri*) of the southern United States are analyzed in respect to their morphology, breeding habits, genetic compatibility, and mating call. The populations have presumably been separate since some time in the Pleistocene. The most noticeable morphological differentiation is in body size and proportions, with the larger size of *streckeri* being possibly adaptive to a more xeric environment than that of the smaller *ornata*. The two populations have not differentiated in time of breeding or in the kinds of waters (temporary pools) used for spawning. The two species on available evidence show genetic incompatibility of a degree that would restrict and possibly prevent gene exchange if they should become sympatric. The mating call is moderately differentiated in frequency (about 500 cps in the dominant and 1,000 cps in its first harmonic), but the differentiation is sufficient for female *streckeri,* at least, to discriminate between calls of their own species and those of *ornata.*

These two allopatric populations have differentiated sufficiently, presumably while geographically isolated, that they should behave as separate species if they should become sympatric. Differentiation in mating call, which appears to be the most significant attainment of these populations in respect to their evolution into separate species, is possibly a byproduct of their adaptive differentiation in body size.

Literature Cited

Blair, W. F. 1958a. Mating call in the speciation of anuran amphibians. Amer. Nat., **92**: 27–51.

——. 1958b. Distributional patterns of vertebrates in the southern United States in relation to past and present environments (in *Zoogeography,* A. A. A. S. Pub. No. 51).

——, and W. E. Howard. 1944. Experimental evidence of sexual isolation between three forms of mice of the cenospecies *Peromyscus maniculatus.* Contrib. Lab. Vert. Biol., Univ. Mich., 26: 1–19.

Carr, A. F. 1940. A contribution to the herpetology of Florida. Univ. Florida Publ., Biol. Sci. Ser. 3: 1–118.

Littlejohn, M. J., and T. C. Michaud. 1959. Mating call discrimination by females of Strecker's chorus frog (*Pseudacris streckeri*). Tex. Jour. Sci., 11: 86–92.

Martof, B. S., and E. F. Thompson. 1958. Reproductive behavior of the chorus frog, *Pseudacris nigrita.* Behaviour, 13: 243–258.

Meacham, W. R. 1958. Factors affecting gene exchange between two allopatric populations in the *Bufo woodhousei* complex. Unpub. doctoral dissertation, The University of Texas.

Mecham, J. S. 1957. Some hybrid combinations between Strecker's chorus frog, *Pseudacris streckeri,* and certain related forms. Tex. Jour. Sci., 9: 337–345.

——. 1959. Experimental evidence on the relationship of two allopatric chorus frogs of the genus *Pseudacris.* Tex. Jour. Sci. (in press).

Muller, H. J. 1940. Bearing of the "Drosophila" work on systematics (in Huxley's *The New Systematics,* Oxford Univ. Press: 185–268).

Wright, A. H., and A. A. Wright. 1949. Handbook of Frogs and Toads of the United States and Canada. Comstock, Ithaca, N. Y.

ALLOCHRONIC SPECIATION IN FIELD CRICKETS, AND A NEW SPECIES, *ACHETA VELETIS*

RICHARD D. ALEXANDER AND ROBERT S. BIGELOW

Museum of Zoology and Department of Zoology
The University of Michigan, Ann Arbor

and

Department of Entomology and Plant Pathology
MacDonald College, Quebec

Received January 25, 1960

McNeill (1889) was apparently the first investigator to recognize that the most abundant and widely distributed field cricket in northeastern North America is actually composed of two populations, one overwintering as a late instar nymph and maturing in spring and one overwintering in the egg stage and maturing in middle or late summer. McNeill also noted (1) that the adult males of the nymph-overwintering population more often occupy burrows and are characteristically more solitary and more aggressive than those of the egg-overwintering population, and (2) that the ovipositors of the females in the nymph-overwintering population are usually shorter in relation to the length of the body than those of the females in the egg-overwintering population. Later investigators, such as Blatchley (1903, 1920), Walker (1904), Criddle (1925), Urquhart (1941), Cantrall (1943), Fulton (1952), Alexander (1957), and Bigelow (1958) have corroborated and refined McNeill's observations on these two populations without materially altering his conclusions. It is surprising that in spite of the confusion in field cricket taxonomy, the relationships of this pair of populations have been fairly well understood by field biologists for about seventy years.

Prior to Fulton's work, various names had been applied to these two forms, either as binomials or as trinomials. Fulton, Alexander, and Bigelow did not separate the two populations with formal nomenclature. Fulton remained quite uncertain as to their status, being able to deal only with the southernmost fragments of their ranges in the northwestern part of North Carolina. Alexander, puzzled by the apparent identity of the two populations in song, habitat, and distribution, noted that most females could be separated on the basis of ovipositor length, and stated (p. 592), "These two broods may interbreed in mid-summer, or possibly in fall in the southern part of their range, or it may be that they have been isolated such a short time that no noticeable differences have yet appeared between them. Certainly more investigation is needed to clarify their relationship." Bigelow, on the basis of differences he had discovered in the developmental rates of the two populations, and the differences in diapause stage, stated (p. 147), "The distinctive differences between these two populations are more likely to become further consolidated than they are to break down through any future gene exchange. Therefore, these two populations should be regarded as distinct species, however similar they might be morphologically."

Recently, we have pooled our information on these populations and have concluded that a more detailed discussion of their relationships, and their recognition as distinct species, is in order. We believe that these species have become reproductively isolated through a seasonal separation of adults initially imposed by elimination of all but two widely separated overwintering stages in the ancestral population; there is no evidence that spatial isolation has ever existed, and no necessity for its postulation. The term "allochronic speciation" is used because it seems appropriate to include all speciation resulting initially from temporal separation (cyclic as well as linear) under "allochronic speciation" and all speciation resulting initially from spatial separation (micro-geographic as well as macro-geographic) under "allopatric speciation." "Sympatric speciation" seems to us an inappropriate label because it refers only to spatial relationships which play no more role in the process suggested here than synchrony plays in allopatric speciation.

Acheta pennsylvanicus (Burmeister)
The Northern Fall Field Cricket

The name *Acheta pennsylvanicus* (Burmeister) has most often been used for the nymph-overwintering species, apparently because Scudder (1862) used it for a cricket which he distinguished primarily on the basis of a short ovipositor. As Blatchley (1903, p. 438) pointed out, none of the early American workers gave evidence of having seen Burmeister's types, and the original description (only a sentence) included no measurements. Examination of the types shows that the name was actually applied by Burmeister to the much more frequently collected egg-overwintering species. Measurements of types and examination of descriptions also show that *Gryllus luctuosus* Serville (1839), *G. abbreviatus* Serville (1839), *Acheta nigra* Harris (1841), *Gryllus angustus* Scudder (1862), *G. neglectus* Scudder (1862), and *G. arenaceous* Blatchley (1903) were all applied to the egg-overwintering species (cf. fig. 2 and Alexander, 1957), and are thus synonyms of *A. pennsylvanicus* (Burmeister). This is not surprising in view of the confusion among early taxonomists with regard to this group, and the much greater abundance of fall adults in collections. As shown in figure 2, a single female in Scudder's series of *neglectus* cotypes falls just inside the range of variation of the nymph-overwintering species in the ratio of ovipositor length to body length. Because there is no date on the label, and because this specimen cannot be assigned with any degree of confidence to the nymph-overwintering species, another specimen from this series which is obviously from the egg-overwintering species is here selected as lectotype (fig. 2) to avoid the possibility of name changes at some later date.

Acheta veletis, n. sp.
The Northern Spring Field Cricket

We designate the nymph-overwintering species as *Acheta veletis* in reference to its aggressive behavior. This species can be distinguished from *A. pennsylvanicus* by life history, ovipositor, and behavioral differences, and from other North American field crickets by song, distribution, morphology, and other characteristics (Alexander, 1957).

Holotype male: Collected by Alexander in Piatt County, Illinois, Sangamon Township, 17 June 1954, under a stone in a bluegrass pasture. Head, pronotum, and abdomen black; tegmina and cerci dark brown; hind femora nearly black with a reddish patch extending along the basal one-third of the outer ventral margin; other appendages dark brown or black; pronotum slightly wider anteriorly; head full and rounded, nearly as wide as widest part of pronotum; tegmina reaching to end of abdomen; hind wings reaching to basal margin of third abdominal segment anterior to base of cerci, and completely hidden by tegmina in resting position. Other distinguishing morphological characteristics are not known, except for body measurements given below and shown in figures 2–5.

Allotype female: Collected with holotype; same as holotype except legs a little lighter and more reddish in color, and hind wings reaching just past basal margin of fourth abdominal segment anterior to base of cerci; ovipositor a fairly uniform dark brown.

Measurements of holotype and allotype (in millimeters, made with ocular micrometer in binocular microscope): body length, ♂, ♀, 22.0; pronotal length, ♂, 4.3, ♀, 4.5; greatest pronotal width, ♂, 6.9, ♀, 6.7; head width, ♂, 6.9, ♀, 6.4; length of hind femur, ♂, 11.9, ♀, 13.0; length of tegmina, ♂, 13.0, ♀, 12.8; length of hind wings, ♂, 9.0, ♀, 9.5; length of ovipostor, 14.3.

The types are located in the University of Michigan Museum of Zoology. Variations in morphology and in the calling song are discussed by Alexander (1957) under the name, *Acheta pennsylvanica*[1] (Burmeister), spring brood." The different sounds of the males are described and illustrated by Alexander (1957a) under the name "mountain cricket," and appear on a record (Alexander, in press). The calling song consists of 3- to 5-pulse chirps delivered at 120–370 per minute at 85° F. The pulse rate (wingstroke rate) at this temperature is about 25 per second. Aggressive sounds are made by increasing the chirp length, and the courtship song consists of multi-pulse, noise-like phrases delivered at about four per second with a sharp "tick" terminating each prase. There appear to be no differences between the sounds of *veletis* and those of *pennsylvanicus,* suggesting that the breeding populations of the two species have never been in contact on a large scale. No other sympatric species of Orthoptera with identical acoustical behavior are known to us.

There is no evidence of habitat separation of these species; where one is found,

the other is also present, and often individual *pennsylvanicus* males are located in the same spots that *veletis* males occupied earlier in the season (Alexander, 1957; Bigelow, 1958). The only known difference in geographic distribution is that *pennsylvanicus* extends into Nova Scotia, while *veletis* apparently does not (Piers, 1918; V. R. Vickery, personal communication). These two species occur over most of the northeastern North America from southern Canada to Maryland and Virginia, down the Appalachian Mountains into western North Carolina and northern Georgia, and west across northern Alabama, Tennessee, and northern Arkansas. The western limits are not known, though they seem likely to angle northwest from about the Oklahoma-Arkansas line following the general line of the Missouri River. Both species may extend to Washington and Oregon, but we have no biological information or song records to confirm the identity of preserved specimens from the northwestern states.

EVIDENCE OF REPRODUCTIVE ISOLATION

Morphology and behavior. The chief deterrent to recognition of *veletis* and *pennsylvanicus* as distinct species has been the absence of non-overlapping morphological differences, coupled with a lack of information as to reproductive barriers between *pennsylvanicus* and late surviving or occasional second-generation *veletis.* Nearly every worker has noted the slight overlap of adults (fig. 1), apparent because there are no nights during mid-summer when a few singing males cannot be heard.

Morphological comparisons become confusing whenever specimens from all over the geographic ranges of the species are lumped together for the evaluation of individual characters. Both species are quite variable in most of the characters we have studied, but except for a general decrease in size northward, there is little

---

[1] It has since been pointed out to Alexander by Dr. A. B. Gurney (in correspondence) that *Acheta* is a Greek word, masculine in gender, and the feminine endings used in 1957 for *A. firmus* (Scudder) and *A. pennsylvanicus* (Burmeister) were erroneous.

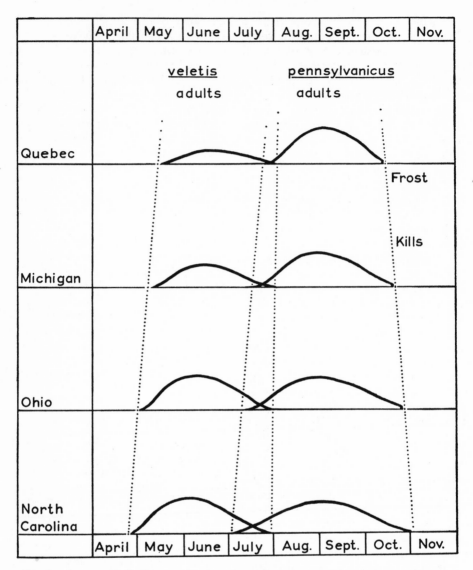

Fig. 1. A generalized diagram showing changes on a north-south plane in the relative sizes of adult populations of *Acheta veletis* and *A. pennsylvanicus,* and in the amount and time of overlap of adults of the two species.

indication of consistent geographic or clinal variation. Specimens from sandy areas (such as beaches around the Great Lakes and along the Atlantic Coast, and inland locations along the Illinois River and in the Kankakee Basin in Illinois and Indiana) have consistently longer ovipositors and are lighter-colored than specimens from other areas. Local populations are often distinctive; for example, a *veletis* population with unusually pale tegmina occurs at Fort Hill in Jackson County, Ohio, and Appalachian populations of either species are apt to be uniformly large and almost entirely black. Occasional Canadian and New England specimens are even smaller than *A. vernalis* (Blatchley), although they retain

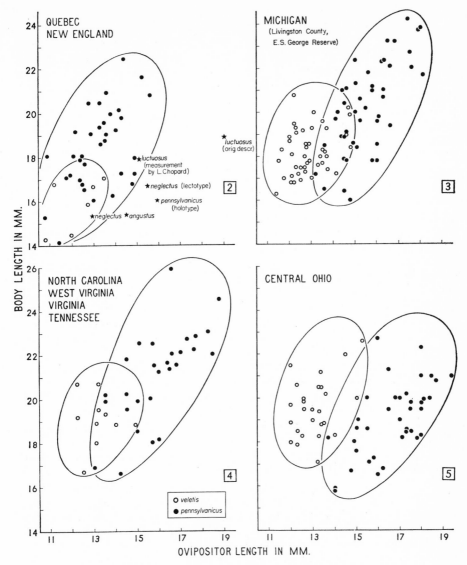

FIGS. 2–5. The relationship of ovipositor length to body length in females of *Acheta veletis* and *A. pennsylvanicus* from various locations within their ranges.

the characteristic body conformation of *veletis* and *pennsylvanicus*.

Figures 2–5 show the relationship of body length to ovipositor length in females of the two species from the four areas considered in figure 1. The species were separated on the basis of collection date, and all specimens available from each of the four areas involved were used, with the exception of the few taken in July which could have been either species. Although there is overlap in each scatter-diagram, a high percentage of specimens can be separated, except on the northern border of the ranges.

Selection for longer ovipositors in *pennsylvanicus* has probably occurred because this species overwinters in the egg stage. It has also occurred in both species in sandy areas, and one might expect *pennsylvanicus* females to have longer ovipositors in the north than in the south. This is not the case; the *pennsylvanicus* females from Canada and New England have ovipositors that are shorter in relation to body length than those in any other population we have studied. Possibly the more consistent cold weather during winter in northern localities is less dangerous to overwintering eggs than the fluctuating temperatures in southern localities.

The ease with which body length is distorted by mounting techniques, and the difficulty in measuring it accurately, led us to search for other characters which would enhance the difference in ovipositor length. However, all those tested (such as femoral length, ovipositor width, and width and length of the head and pronotum) either were valueless or tended to obscure rather than to enhance the difference in ovipositor length. Since there is no reason to assume other than random error in measurement of body length, we believe it is satisfactory for the use to which we have put it. The specimens in figure 5 were pinned and dried, all in the same manner, those in figure 3 were preserved in alcohol, and both kinds of specimens were used in figures 2 and 4.

As mentioned earlier, several workers have noted a general difference between these species in gregariousness and aggressiveness, especially of the adult males, and in the tendency of older nymphs and adults to burrow or to occupy niches and crevices of various sorts. *A. veletis* has thus been described as a sedentary, solitary, aggressive, burrow-inhabiting cricket, while *pennsylvanicus* has been described as a gregarious cricket often found in groups and less often observed in burrows or displaying aggressive behavior. These behavioral differences appear to be fairly consistent in the field, at least in northern latitudes, and this has led to the supposition that they are genetic in origin. However, while differences in these characteristics are apparent among different species of *Acheta,* they can also

be produced to some degree between individuals of the same species by varying the situations in which the crickets are reared (Alexander, in prep.). Isolation increases aggressiveness and encourages burrow construction and territorial behavior, and observable differences in these respects between field-collected Michigan males of the two species have been erased in the laboratory by subsequent isolation of *pennsylvanicus* and crowding of *veletis*. Nymphs of *veletis* spend several months in the last three instars, when aggression and burrowing are just beginning to be evident, and are likely to disperse and become isolated. Nymphs of *pennsylvanicus,* on the other hand, mature directly from egg to adult in a few months, and also they do not pass through the periods of cool weather which might be partly responsible for *veletis* nymphs more often occupying crevices and beginning the process leading to solitary, aggressive behavior. Finally, *pennsylvanicus* nymphs are generally more abundant than *veletis* nymphs, and it is significant that the above behavioral differences have been emphasized exclusively by workers in northern latitudes where the difference in population size is most evident. At this point, we must conclude that there is no clear evidence of genetically based behavioral differences of any sort between these two species.

Diapause. Under laboratory conditions, diapause in *pennsylvanicus* and *veletis* is expressed by extensive delay in development in the egg stage and in the late nymphal instars, respectively. At 80–85° F., non-diapause field cricket eggs usually hatch within three weeks; the eggs of *pennsylvanicus* rarely hatch in less than 60 days, and several months may be required. Under the same conditions, non-diapause nymphs usually reach maturity within two months after hatching; in *veletis* and other nymph-diapausing species, a small percentage matures without apparent delay, but most require several months.

The diapause difference between *veletis*

and *pennsylvanicus* has persisted in spite of temperature, season, and light-dark ratio fluctuations in successive generations of laboratory-reared strains at MacDonald College. All of the many thousands of *veletis* eggs successfully incubated in the laboratory have hatched within 47 days, even at temperatures as low as 68° F, while less than one per cent of the *pennsylvanicus* eggs have hatched in less than 40 days, even at temperatures as high as 82 ± 2° F. All *veletis* nymphs were greatedly retarded at temperatures below 73° F, and even at 82° F, about 25 per cent were retarded. The last two or three instars persisted in some cases for three to five months.

The diapause differences between these two species appear to be fundamental. They are infallible in tagging individuals as belonging to one species or the other, they are a direct cause of temporal isolation between the species, and they may be even more directly involved in isolation if differences in the eggs and embryos are involved in the physiological incompatability demonstrated below.

Crossing experiments. It is difficult to obtain adults of *veletis* and *pennsylvanicus* at the same time; in order to do so the normal developmental rate of one species or the other must be altered in the laboratory. Both *pennsylvanicus* and *veletis* seem to require a period of low temperature conditions (in the egg and nymphal stages, respectively) if the vigor and fecundity that exist normally in the field are to be maintained. Consequently, laboratory-reared specimens must be used in controls whenever they are used in tests if the results of the crosses are to be conclusive.

The following experiments were carried out by Bigelow at MacDonald College. The adults were left together in each case until death; in the few cases of premature death, the individuals were replaced.

1. Laboratory-reared Quebec *pennsylvanicus* and *veletis*.

Test	Replications	Offspring
1 vel. ♂ × 3 vel. ♀ ♀	2	many
1 penn. ♂ × 3 vel. ♀ ♀	3	none
1 vel. ♂ × 3 penn. ♀ ♀	2	none
1 penn. ♂ × 3 penn. ♀ ♀	2	many

2. Field-collected Quebec *pennsylvanicus* and laboratory-reared Quebec *veletis*.

Test	Replications	Offspring
6 penn. ♂ ♂ × 12 penn. ♀ ♀	1	many
6 penn. ♂ ♂ × 12 vel. ♀ ♀	1	none
6 vel. ♂ ♂ × 12 penn. ♀ ♀	1	none
6 vel. ♂ ♂ × 12 vel. ♀ ♀	1	many

3. Field-collected *veletis* from Danbury, North Carolina, Culpepper, Virginia, Frederick, Maryland, and Quebec, and laboratory-reared *pennsylvanicus* from Quebec and Dutchess County, New York. Every combination of *veletis* individuals from different localities was tested, and every test produced many offspring; the same was true of *pennsylvanicus* matings involving Quebec × New York individuals. No offspring were produced in the two crosses attempted: 2 penn. ♂ ♂ (NY) × 3 vel. ♀ ♀ (Va) and 3 penn. ♂ ♂ (NY) × 4 vel. ♀ ♀ (Q).

Eggs were laid frequently in the crosses listed above, copulation was observed once between a *pennsylvanicus* female and a *veletis* male, and the spermatheca of a single *veletis* female examined was found to contain *pennsylvanicus* sperm. Clearly, some effective barrier exists; if hybrids are present in the field they must be exceedingly rare, and actual exchange of genes is even less likely.

ALLOCHRONIC SPECIATION

In the vast majority of cases, speciation in sexually reproducing animals probably takes place as outlined by Mayr (1942, 1947) and others. Populations become geographically isolated and diverge through differential selection imposed by their respective environments, and additionally through the accumulation of chance differences in mutations and recombination. If these differences happen to make the two populations physiologically, morphologically, or behaviorally incompatible, or if they merely make exchange of genetic materials sufficiently deleterious prior to the resumption of geographic contact, then the two populations are irrevocably isolated. With resumption of geographic contact, the resultant interaction between such newly formed species should operate to maximize the efficiency of their isolation and enhance the accelerating and re-inforcing factors operative in their continuing divergence.

Basic to this process is the presence of an extrinsic barrier to gene flow between the two populations with at the same time a sufficiently broad avenue of gene flow within each population to allow consolidation of characteristics leading (eventually) to incompatibility. In sexually reproducing animals these requirements largely eliminate (with certain exceptions—cf. Dethier, 1954) the possibility of speciation along the lines of ecological divergence, which is essentially speciation in the absence of an initial extrinsic barrier to gene flow (Mayr, 1947).

One is faced with certain problems in attempting to reconstruct the evolution of *veletis* and *pennsylvanicus* on the basis of previous allopatry. First, there is no evidence that these species have ever been allopatric; indeed, their wide range, their apparent identity in ecological distribution, and the fact that their geographic limits appear to coincide everywhere but in the north tend to support the opposite suggestion—that they have never differed in geographic distribution more than they do today. The fact that only *pennsylvanicus* occurs in Nova Scotia appears to be more likely a result of the difference in overwintering stage than a reflection of difference in distributional history, and this is supported by the north-south change in the relative abundance of the two species (fig. 1), which indicates that *veletis* nymphs are less likely to survive severe winters than *pennsylvanicus* eggs.

If one postulates that *veletis* and *pennsylvanicus* acquired their present incompatability while geographically separated, he is left with the problem of how they developed such widely different overwintering stages without diverging in other ecological respects. The difference in breeding season cannot easily be explained as a result of interaction after hybridization had become disadvantageous, for the identity in all phases of acoustical behavior and the ability to cross-copulate strongly suggest that the breeding populations of the two species have not been in significant contact since their separation. Further, the lack of difference in ecological distribution reduces the likelihood that the difference in breeding season arose in association with other environmental factors favoring the presence of particular stages at particular times.

But extrinsic barriers need not involve geographic or spatial separation. Bigelow (1958) discussed the possibility that *veletis* and *pennsylvanicus* have speciated without geographic separation through a seasonal isolation of breeding populations. All of the information we have been able to gather with respect to the relationships of these species and the pertinent characteristics of related Orthoptera has reinforced this hypothesis. Three relatively simple steps are involved: (1) the repeated elimination during successive winters of all stages but late juveniles and eggs, with a concomitant reduction or elimination of gene flow between the resulting populations, (2) subsequent increases in the winter-hardiness of the two overwintering stages, culminating in the development of obligate diapauses and (3) the eventual appearance of reproductive incompatibility.

The first step in the above sequence is obviously the most important one, and the one which must be clearly understood if this process can be accepted. How can a species be divided into two populations which exchange genes on a very much reduced basis or not at all, simply by a differential elimination of overwintering stages? How could this sort of separation persist long enough to allow consolidation of intrinsic isolating mechanisms, and in what sorts of climates could such a phenomenon take place?

An animal susceptible to splitting through the kind of allochronic speciation suggested here for *veletis* and *pennsylvanicus* would be required to possess the following characteristics: (1) a consistent developmental rate producing fewer than two generations per year, (2) a narrow breeding season or a short adult life, and (3) a duality in winter-hardiness, with the two stages involved widely separated on the life history cycle. All of the approximately 85 species of native Gryllidae and Tettigoniidae in northeastern North America possess the first two of these characteristics, and the eight species of Gryllinae there possess all three. North of the 38th parallel, none of these 85 species produces more than a single generation per year. The adults live about six weeks, or less than half the available season, and they generally mature together, producing for each species either a spring or a fall adult population. Only two overwintering stages are represented—late juveniles and eggs—and no species overwinters north of about the 38th parallel in more than a single stage, with the exception of the European house cricket, *Acheta domesticus,* living in artificially warmed situations, and the possible exception of the ant nest inhabitant, *Myrmecophila pergandei.* Two cone-headed grasshoppers, *Pyrgocorypha uncinata* and *Neoconocephalus triops,* overwinter after their final molt, but even these "adults" must be considered immature, for sexual behavior does not begin until the following spring, even in adults kept in the laboratory. Seventy species overwinter as eggs and the rest as late juveniles; all of the latter are burrowing crickets except for the two cone-headed grasshoppers, which apparently spend the winter deep in the bases of clumps of thick vegetation, and which reach northward only to the vicinity of the 38th parallel. One southern field cricket, *Acheta firmus,* reaches to about the 38th parallel and overwinters as both eggs and late instar nymphs there, while breeding more or less continuously and overwintering in all stages farther south.

Duality in winter-hardiness is obviously not unusual in Orthoptera, and it would appear that the burrowing behavior which begins in late juvenile crickets is closely associated with the ability to overwinter. Evidently, nymphs are somewhat less winter-hardy than eggs, even after diapause has appeared, for *veletis* is the most northern nymph-overwintering orthopteran in North America; the other two strictly nymph-overwintering field crickets, *A. vernalis* and *A. fultoni,* which incidentally are much less active burrowers than *veletis,* reach only to the vicinity of the 40th parallel.

All of the native Gryllidae and Tettigoniidae in northeastern North America exhibit obligate diapauses in the overwintering stage, completing development only after considerable delay or after passing through a cold period. These diapauses have an important function in addition to their association with winter-hardiness; they synchronize the appearance of the short-lived adults and are thus responsible for producing a definite breeding season which can be relatively short and yet highly efficient. The cone-headed grasshoppers which overwinter as adults and are not triggered into sexual behavior until spring are important examples. It seems a fair assumption that selection for diapause in connection with synchronizing the appearance of adults in climates such as prevail in northeastern North America is at least as intense as selection for diapause in connection with winter-hardiness.

The nymph-overwintering Gryllinae, including species of *Miogryllus* and *Anurogryllus* as well as *Acheta,* almost inevitably diapause in the second instar from adulthood. The reasons for this rather precise limitation are not clear, but nymphal diapause has certainly appeared more than once in these crickets, suggesting that this particular stage is unusually susceptible to its development. This is important information, for it strengthens our speculation that nymphal diapause must have appeared independently many times across the range of the nymph-overwintering population that gave rise to *veletis,* as well as egg diapause probably many times within the egg-overwintering population that gave rise to *pennsylvanicus.* There is no reason to believe that this could not have happened while a considerable amount of gene flow was still going on between the ancestral populations of *veletis* and *pennsylvanicus;* whenever and wherever diapause appeared, either in *veletis* nymphs or in *pennsylvanicus* eggs, it surely decreased to a great extent the likelihood of subsequent amalgamation of the two populations.

We would hypothesize the evolution of *veletis* and *pennsylvanicus* as follows. The ancestral population probably inhabited an area of mild winters and bred more or less continuously there. Either an increase in the rigorousness of winters or the isolation of a northern segment of this population (or some combination of such events) produced a population in which all stages but late juveniles and eggs were decimated during each winter. The eggs survived initally because they were buried in the soil, and the nymphs survived initially because of their beginning to actively burrow about three instars from adulthood. We might expect that overwintering nymphs would frequently mature before spring under these conditions, but adults which matured late in the fall would be unlikely to survive until spring because of the short adult life and the tendency of the adults to be active in connection with sexual behavior.

A reasonably consistent developmental rate would now produce a population of spring adults and a population of fall adults. There would undoubtedly be a reduction in gene flow between these two populations, and this condition could persist indefinitely under proper climatic conditions in the absence of genetic differences between the two populations.

Under these conditions, the appearance of diapauses increasing winter-resistance in the already resistant stages and synchronizing the appearance of adults in spring and fall would be advantageous to each of the two partially isolated populations. Wherever such diapauses appeared and were retained, they would further reduce gene flow between the two populations, at the least through emphasizing the appearance of adults only in spring and in fall. The gradual consolidation of diapause in the two different overwintering stages could lead only to more stringent isolation, eventually allowing development of the intrinsic isolating mechanisms present today. As noted, the diapauses themselves may involve morphological or physiological characteristics which produce incompatability. Hybridization at any time during the above sequence would probably be disadvantageous, early in the sequence simply because it would tend to occur in the middle of the season and thus to produce individuals that were likely to be in the wrong stages at the onset of winter, and late in the sequence because almost any manner of inheritance of diapause characteristics would likely cause hybrids to be at a disadvantage additional to that accruing from being in the wrong stage at the wrong time.

The beach cricket, *Acheta firmus,* is especially important in this reconstruction, not only because it illustrates how the process could take place, but also because it may actually be involved in this particular case. This species occurs along the Gulf Coast and the Atlantic Coast from Louisiana to Delaware. In southern Florida, it appears to breed more or less continuously; in the northern parts of its range it becomes an egg-over-wintering species producing a single generation per year, but with a few individuals there getting "out of step with the main population" (Fulton, 1952, p. 289), overwintering as juveniles and maturing in May and June. Not only does this species illustrate duality in winter-hardiness without significant nymphal dispause, but should a northern population become isolated in the area where the species now overwinters only as eggs and as late juveniles, then the separation of that northern population into two species according to the process suggested here for *veletis* and *pennsylvanicus* would be very easy to visualize. It is quite possible that this is exactly what did happen in the past, and that *firmus* represents the southern remnant of the ancestral population which also gave rise to *veletis* and *pennsylvanicus*. Today, *firmus* is clearly more closely related to *veletis* and *pennsylvanicus* than any other North American field cricket, showing close similarity in acoustical behavior, morphology, and developmental rate. The chief difference in morphology among these species is that *firmus* females have very long ovipositors, undoubtedly evolved in association with the beach habitat.

Allochronic speciation as outlined above is a simple and reasonable hypothesis, and the only one which satisfactorily explains all facets of the present characteristics and relationships of *veletis* and *pennsylvanicus*. It is doubtful that the possibility of allopatric speciation could ever be completely ruled out, but the evidence suggests that geographic isolation is both unlikely and unnecessary in this particular case.

DISCUSSION

Speciation through initial seasonal or other cyclic isolation is not a new idea, but the actual process by which it might occur has not previously been outlined in detail for a particular group of animals. Emerson (1949) summarized most of the investigations dealing with this possibility, and more recently Ghent and Wallace have hypothesized speciation through a seasonal separation caused by overwintering in both egg and pupa in sawflies (Hymenoptera). The greatest problem has been in visualizing the initial step; in the process as suggested here, no genetic difference is required, either for the initial separation of populations or for the long-time maintenance of their separation.

A great deal of biological information will have to be acquired before the significance of temporal isolation in helping to account for the prolificness of speciation in insects can be determined. A cyclic phenomenon similar to that discussed here occurs in many insects when populations of species in which the life cycle requires more than a year become isolated by maturing on different years. This happens in many cicadas, most notably between sympatric broods of periodical cicadas, and between those species with 17-year and 13-year life cycles. It may be a more common occurrence than is suspected in other insects as well. Gabbutt (1959), for example, found that *Nemobius sylvestris* (Bosc.), a European ground cricket, has a two-year life cycle, each individual diapausing as an egg one year and as a nymph the next year. The only possibility of gene exchange between populations maturing on different years is through stragglers, and in cicadas, in which the presence of adults can easily be detected because of their loud songs, stragglers are known to be extremely unusual. In such cases, temporal isolation can be as effective as complete allopatry.

The characteristics of animals susceptible to allochronic speciation are obviously not restricted to the Orthoptera; rather they are widespread among invertebrates in temperate climates, especially among metamorphosing insects. Without the hypothesis of allochronic speciation we would continue to be puzzled by the hundreds of cases in which dichotomy in overwintering stages has become established within groups of closely related species. Such dichotomies have surely arisen many times without speciation, either through the chance appearance of greater winter-hardiness in an unusual stage or through selection for the appearance of the breeding population during a particular season. But when two closely related, sympatric species are found to overwinter in stages which are widely separated on the life history cycle, when there is no evidence for earlier allopatry, and when the two species also maintain brief, non-overlapping periods of reproductive maturity without evidence of previous interaction with respect to characters involved in sexual selection, then it would appear that the possibility of allochronic speciation should not be ruled out without careful study.

Summary

Analysis of what has seemed to be a single species of field cricket, abundant and widely distributed in northeastern North America, shows that it is actually composed of two closely related species which are distinguished as follows: (1) they diapause only in the late nymphal instars and in the egg stage, respectively, (2) they are unable to produce viable eggs in controlled crossing experiments in the laboratory, and (3) most females from the same locality can be separated by ovipositor length. Breeding populations of these two species are seasonally isolated because of the difference in overwintering stage and the short adult life of four to eight weeks. Ecologically and geographically the two species have always been found together, with the exception that *Acheta pennsylvanicus* (Burmeister), the egg-overwinterer, occurs in Nova Scotia, while *A. veletis,* n. sp., the nymph-overwinterer,

does not. All of the communicative sounds of the two species appear to be identical, indicating that there has been no interaction with respect to characters involved in sexual selection. It is suggested that these species have become isolated through a seasonal separation of breeding populations imposed by a duality in winter-hardiness originally due to the deposition of the eggs below the soil surface and the burrowing of late juveniles. This initial isolation is then believed to have been re-inforced by the appearance of genetically-based diapauses which not only increased winter-hardiness but also aided in synchronizing the appearance of the adults. The term "allochronic speciation" is applied because of the role of temporal isolation; it is suggested that various forms of cyclic isolation may have been important factors in initiating speciation among insects in temperate climates.

Acknowledgments

This study was supported by grants awarded to Alexander by the Horace H. Rackham School of Graduate Studies of The University of Michigan, and to Bigelow by The National Research Council of Canada. We are indebted to Drs. Theodore H. Hubbell, Thomas E. Moore, and Irving J. Cantrall, and to Mr. Kenneth C. Shaw, all of The University of Michigan Museum of Zoology, for suggestions concerning the manuscript. Dr. Edward S. Thomas of The Ohio State Museum has allowed us to use excerpts from his extensive notes concerning the distribution and abundance of Orthoptera. The specimens from the E. S. George Reserve, Livingston County, Michigan (fig. 3) were all collected by Dr. Irving J. Cantrall.

Literature Cited

ALEXANDER, R. D. 1957. The taxonomy of the field crickets of the eastern United States (Orthoptera: Gryllidae: *Acheta*). Ann. Ent. Soc. Amer., **50** (6): 584–602, 19 fig., 1 tab.

——. 1957a. Sound production and associated behavior in insects. Ohio Jour. Sci., **57** (2) : 101–113, 13 fig., 1 text fig.

ALEXANDER, R. D. (in press). Sound communication in Orthoptera and Cicadidae. (*In* A. I. B. S. Symposium Series, *Animal Sounds*).

ALEXANDER, R. D. (in prep.) Aggressiveness, territoriality, and sexual behavior in field crickets.

BIGELOW, R. S. 1958. Evolution in the field cricket, *Acheta assimilis* Fab. Canadian Jour. Zool., **36** (1958) : 139–151, 3 tab.

BLATCHLEY, W. S. 1903. The Orthoptera of Indiana. 27th Ann. Rept. Ind. Dept. Geol. and Nat. Resources : 123–471, 122 fig.

——. 1920. Orthoptera of Northeastern America. 784 pp., 246 fig. Indianapolis, Ind., The Nature Publ. Co.

CANTRALL, I. J. 1943. The ecology of the Orthoptera and Dermaptera of the George Reserve, Michigan. Univ. Mich. Mus. Zool. Misc. Publ., **54**: 1–182, 3 fig., 2 maps, 16 tables, 10 pl.

CRIDDLE, N. 1925. Field crickets in Manitoba. Canadian Ent., **57** (4) : 79–84.

DETHIER, V. G. 1954. Evolution of feeding preferences in phytophagous insects. EVOLUTION, **8** (1) : 33–54, 1 fig.

EMERSON, A. E. 1949. Ecology and Isolation. (Pp. 605–630 in *Principles of Animal Ecology* by Allee et al., xii + 837 pp., 263 fig., 54 tables. Philadelphia and London: W. B. Saunders Co.).

FULTON, B. B. 1952. Speciation in the field cricket. EVOLUTION, **6** (3) : 283–295, 4 fig.

GABBUTT, P. D. 1959. The bionomics of the wood cricket, *Nemobius sylvestris* (Orthoptera: Gryllidae). Jour. Animal Ecol., **28** (1) : 15–42.

GHENT, A. W. AND D. R. WALLACE. 1958. Oviposition behavior of the Swaine jackpine sawfly. Forest Science, **4** (3) : 264–272, 2 fig., 1 table.

HARRIS, T. W. 1841. A treatise on some of the insects injurious to vegetation. Orange Judd and Co., New York. xi + 640 pp., numer. fig.

HEBARD, M. 1931. A revision of the North American species of the genus *Myrmecophila* (Orthoptera: Gryllidae: Myrmecophilinae). Trans. Amer. Ent. Soc., **46**: 91–111, 1 fig.

MAYR, E. 1942. Systematics and the Origin of Species. New York: Columbia Univ. Press. xiv + 334 pp., 29 fig., 14 tables.

——. 1947. Ecological factors in speciation. EVOLUTION, **1** (4) : 263–288, 1 fig.

McNEILL, J. 1889. Notes upon Gryllus and Oecanthus. Entomologica Americana, **5**: 101–104.

PIERS, H. 1918. The Orthoptera (cockroaches, locusts, grasshoppers and crickets) of Nova Scotia; with descriptions of the species and notes on their occurrence and habits. Trans. Nova Scotia Inst. Sci., **14** (3) : 201–356, 4 pl., 27 fig.

SCUDDER, S. H. 1862. Materials for a monograph of the North American Orthoptera, including a catalogue of the known New England species. Bost. Jour. Nat. Hist., **7**: 409–480.

——. 1877. New forms of saltatorial Orthoptera from the southern United States. Proc. Bost. Soc. Nat. Hist., **19**: 35–41.

——. 1902. The species of *Gryllus* found in the United States east of the Sierra Nevadas. Psyche, **9** (309) : 291–296.

SERVILLE, M. A. 1839. Histoire naturelle des insectes Orthoptères (dans les suites à Buffon). Paris, Roret, 1–776 pp., 22 fig.

URQUHART, F. A. 1941. The Blattaria and Orthoptera of Essex County, Ontario. Contrib. Roy. Ontario Mus. Zool., 1–32 pp., 4 fig.

WALKER, E. M. 1904. The crickets of Ontario. Canadian Ent., **36** (7) : 181–188.

Character Displacement

W. L. BROWN, JR. and E. O. WILSON

IT IS the purpose of the present paper to discuss a seldom-recognized and poorly known speciation phenomenon that we consider to be of potential major significance in animal systematics. This condition, which we have come to call "character displacement," may be roughly described as follows. Two closely related species have overlapping ranges. In the parts of the ranges where one species occurs alone, the populations of that species are similar to the other species and may even be very difficult to distinguish from it. In the area of overlap, where the two species occur together, the populations are more divergent and easily distinguished, i.e., they "displace" one another in one or more characters. The characters involved can be morphological, ecological, behavioral, or physiological; they are assumed to be genetically based.

The same pattern may be stated equally well in the opposite way, as follows. Two closely related species are distinct where they occur together, but where one member of the pair occurs alone it converges toward the second, even to the extent of being nearly identical with it in some characters. Experience has shown that it is from this latter point of view that character displacement is most easily detected in routine taxonomic analysis.

By stating the situation in two ways, we have called attention to the dual nature of the pattern: species populations show displacement where they occur together, and convergence where they do not. Character displacement just might in some cases represent no more than a peculiar and in a limited sense a fortuitous pattern of variation. But in our opinion it is generally much more than this; we believe that it is a common aspect of geographical speciation, arising most often as a product of the genetic and ecological interaction of two (or more) newly evolved, cognate species during their period of first contact. This thesis will be discussed in more detail in a later section.

Character displacement is not a new concept. A number of authors have described it more or less in detail, and a few have commented on its evolutionary significance. We should like in the present paper to bring some of this material together, to illustrate the various aspects the pattern may assume in nature, and to discuss the possible consequences in taxonomic theory and practice which may follow from a wider appreciation of the phenomenon.

Two Illustrations

An example of character displacement outstanding for its simplicity and clarity has been reviewed most recently by Vaurie (1950, 1951). This involves the closely related rock nuthatches *Sitta neumayer* Michahelles and *S. tephronota* Sharpe. *S. neumayer* ranges from the Balkans eastward through the western half of Iran, while *S. tephronota* extends from the Tien Shan in Turkestan westward to Armenia. Thus, the two species come to overlap very broadly in several sectors of Iran (Fig. 1). Outside the zone of overlap, the two species are extremely similar, and at best can be told apart only after careful examination by a taxonomist with some experience in the complex (Vaurie, personal communication). Both species show some geographical variation, and it seems clear from Vaurie's account (1950, Table 5, pp. 25–26) that such races as bear names have been raised for character discordances in various combinations. It therefore appears safe to ignore the subspecies analysis as such and to concentrate on the variation of the independent characters themselves.

Reprinted by permission of E. O. Wilson and The Society of Systematic Zoology from SYSTEMATIC ZOOLOGY, **5,** 49–64 (1956).

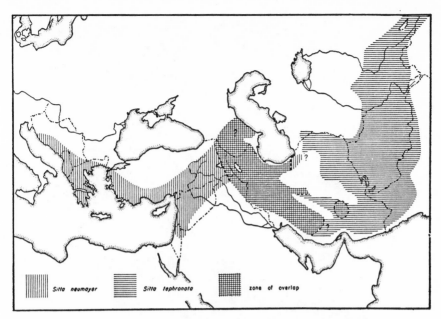

FIG. 1. Distribution of *Sitta neumayer* and *S. tephronota*. (After Vaurie.)

These show quite remarkable displacement phenomena in the Iranian region of overlap between the species, where the two species apparently usually occur in more or less equal numbers (see Fig. 2). In this region, *S. neumayer* shows distinct reductions in overall size and bill length, as well as in width, size, and distinctness of the facial stripe. *S. tephronota,* on the other hand, shows striking positive augmentation of all the same characters in the overlap zone, so that it is distinguishable from sympatric *neumayer* at a glance. Vaurie concludes, we think quite correctly, that the differences within the zone of overlap constitute one basis upon which the two species can avoid competition where they are sympatric. The case of these two nuthatches has already received considerable attention both in the literature and elsewhere, and it bids fair to become the classic illustration of character displacement.

A more complicated case involving multiple character displacement is seen in the ant genus *Lasius* (Wilson, 1955). Where they occur together, in forested eastern North America, the related species *L. flavus* (Fabr.) and *L. nearcticus* Wheeler show differences in the following seven characters: antennal length, ommatidium number, head shape, degree of worker polymorphism, relative lengths of palpal segments, cephalic pubescence, and queen size. In western North America and the Palaearctic Region, where *nearcticus* is absent, *flavus* is convergent to it in all seven characters. In this shift, each character behaves in an independent fashion; e.g., scape length becomes exactly intermediate between that of the two eastern populations, ommatidium number increases in variability and overlaps the range of the two, and queen size changes to that of *nearcticus*. In North Dakota, at the western fringe of the *nearcticus* distribution, the *flavus* population is at an intermediate level of convergence (Fig. 3).

There is some evidence that this dual displacement-convergence pattern is associated with competition and ecological

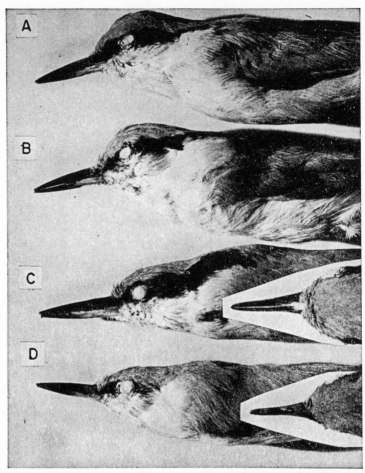

Fig. 2. Size and shape of the bill and facial stripe in *Sitta neumayer* and *S. tephronota*: *A, S. neumayer* from Dalmatia; *B, S. tephronota* from Ferghana; *C, S. tephronota* and *D, S. neumayer*, both from Durud, Luristan, in western Iran. (After Vaurie.)

displacement between the two species. So far as is known, they have similar food requirements. But in eastern North America, where they occur together, *flavus* is mainly limited to open, dry forest with moderate to thin leaf-litter, while *nearcticus* is found primarily in moist, dense forest with thick leaf-litter. There is little information available on the western North American and Asian *flavus* populations, but in northern Europe this species is known to be highly adaptable, preferring open situations, but also occurring commonly in moist forests.

Some Additional Examples

In the following paragraphs we wish to present a number of cases selected from the literature (with two additional unpublished examples) which we have interpreted as showing character displacement. In so doing we are trying to document the thesis that character displacement occurs widely in many groups of animals and in a range of particular patterns. But at the same time we are obliged to give warning, perhaps unnecessarily for the critical reader, that most of these cases in-

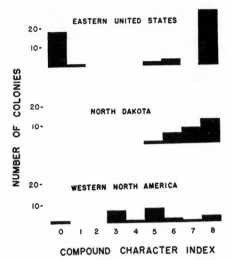

FIG. 3. Frequency histograms of the compound character index of the ants *Lasius nearcticus* (0–1) and *L. flavus* (3–8) in three broad geographic samples. For each colony typical *nearcticus* characters are given a score of 0, typical eastern *flavus* characters a score of 2, and intermediate characters a score of 1. The four characters most clearcut in the eastern United States are used: maxillary palp proportions, antennal scape index, compound eye ommatidium number and head shape. Thus, completely typical *nearcticus* colonies score a total of 0 and completely typical eastern *flavus* 8, with the various ranks of intermediates falling in between (after Wilson, 1955).

volve discontinuously distributed populations, that as a result the species status of these populations with respect to one another has not been ascertained with complete certainty, and that explanations alternative to character displacement are therefore assuredly possible. We ask only that the reader bear through and consider our interpretation in each case.

Birds of the Genus Geospiza. A striking case of character displacement has been described by David Lack in his classic, *Darwin's Finches* (1947). Lack has shown that in the Galapagos certain species of *Geospiza* are often absent on smaller islands, in which case their food niche is filled by other species of the genus. The populations of the latter tend to converge in body size and beak form to the absent species, so much so as to make placement of these populations to species difficult. Lack has demonstrated that body size and beak form are generally important in *Geospiza* in both food getting and species recognition. The dual displacement-convergence pattern we are interested in occurs, at least once, in the following situation. The larger ground-finch *Geospiza fortis* Gould and the smaller *G. fuliginosa* Gould differ from each other principally in size and beak proportion. On most of the islands, where they occur together, the two species can be separated easily by a simple measurement of beak depth, i.e., a random sample of ground-finches (excluding from consideration the largest ground-finch *G. magnirostris* Gould) gives two completely separate distribution curves in this single character. But on the small islands of Daphne and Crossman a sample of ground-finches gives a single unimodal curve exactly intermediate between those of *fortis* and *fuliginosa* from the larger islands. Analysis of beak-wing proportions has shown that the Daphne population is *fortis* and the Crossman population is *fuliginosa;* according to Lack's interpretation each has converged toward the other species, filling the ecological vacuum its absence has created.

Birds of the Genus Myzantha. Among the Australian honey-eaters of the genus *Myzantha*, a light-colored species, *M. flavigula*, occupies the greater part of the arid inland. Toward the wet southwestern corner of the continent, *flavigula* blends gradually into a darker population, usually referred to as "subspecies *obscura*." In southeastern Australia, in higher-rainfall country, *flavigula* is replaced by two forms—*M. melanocephala*, mostly in the wettest districts, and *M. melanotis* of the subarid Victorian-South Australian mallee district. The southwestern (*obscura*) and one of the southeastern populations (*melanotis*) are extremely similar, differing by what are described as trifling characters of plumage shading, so that some authors consider them conspecific.

The members of an ornithological camp-out in the Victorian mallee, however, have found that *melanotis* there nests sympatrically with both *melanocephala* and *flavigula,* and that at this place the three behave as distinct species without intergradation. Thus we find the two morphologically very similar forms, *obscura* and *melanotis,* flanking the much more widely distributed and differently colored species, *flavigula,* but showing exactly opposite interbreeding reactions with *flavigula. Obscura* appears to represent merely the terminus of a cline for melanism produced by *flavigula* in the southwest, where, it may be noted, there is no other competing dark form of the same species group (Fig. 4).

Judging by the findings of the mallee observers, *melanotis* is clearly to be regarded as a species distinct from *flavigula,* including the southwestern *obscura* population. In this we follow Condon (1951), and not Serventy (1953), though

the latter has furnished the most comprehensive analysis of the situation.

Serventy's dilemma is keyed by his statement that ". . . it would be unreal to treat *melanotis,* obviously so akin to south-western *obscura,* as a separate species from it. . . ." Here one plainly sees the conflict between two species criteria: one based on morphological similarity, and one on interbreeding reaction in the zone of sympatry.

From the data presented, we interpret the *Myzantha* situation as a case of character displacement. *M. flavigula* tends to produce, in the less arid extremities of its range, populations with darker plumage. In the southwest, it has done just this; presumably, melanism is connected adaptively in some way, directly or indirectly, with increased moisture ("Gloger's Rule"), or plant cover, or both. In the southeastern mallee, however, the melanistic tendencies presumed to be latent or potential in *flavigula* toward the wetter extremes of its range are suppressed in the presence of the darker species *melanotis* (and possibly also *melanocephala*). It would be interesting to know more about

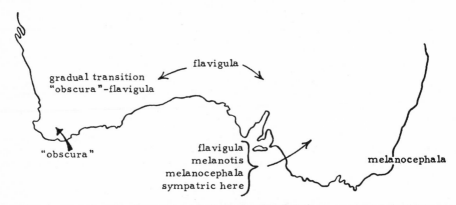

Fig. 4. Map showing the geographical relationships of three species of the bird genus *Myzantha* in southern Australia, based on the discussion of Serventy, 1953. *M. flavigula,* the light-colored bird of arid central Australia, grades into a darker population ("race *obscura*") in southwestern higher-rainfall districts. In southeastern Australia, in the Victorian mallee belt, transitional and mixed ecological conditions allow three non-intergrading species to breed side by side: *M. flavigula; M. melanotis,* a species characteristic of the mallee scrub; and *M. melanocephala,* a southeastern bird of the higher-rainfall districts. *M. melanotis* and the *"obscura"* population are extremely similar, and have been considered synonymous or at least conspecific in the past.

the ecological distribution, food, and habits of the three *Myzantha* species within the region where they occur together.

Parrots of the Genus Platycercus. Serventy (1953) also reviews, among other cases that may involve character displacement, the situation in the rosellas of southeastern Australia (Fig. 5). The crimson rosella (*Platycercus elegans*) is a species of the wooded eastern areas—mostly those with higher rainfall nearest the coast. On Kangaroo Island, off the coast of South Australia, occurs a crimson population that appears to be *elegans* from a strictly morphological viewpoint. Beginning on the mainland opposite Kangaroo Island is a cline connecting the crimson form to an inland, arid-country yellow form (*P. flaveolus*) inhabiting the red gums of the rivers and dry creeks in

FIG. 5. Map showing the approximate distribution of color forms of the rosellas (parrots) of the *Platycercus elegans* complex in southeastern Australia. The heavy pecked line indicates roughly the inland margin of the southeastern highlands and the higher-rainfall districts, and also the inland limit of the range of the crimson-trimmed *P. elegans*. Inside this line, along the upper reaches of the Murray-Darling river systems, the closely related *P. flaveolus,* a yellow-trimmed form, approaches and may even meet the range of *P. elegans* at some points without producing intergrades. Downstream, *P. flaveolus* grades through a series of intermediately-colored populations culminating in the crimson-trimmed flocks of Kangaroo Island, which are apparently outwardly indistinguishable from those of the true eastern *elegans*. (Adapted from Cain, 1955.)

the Murray-Darling Basins. However, in the Albury district of the upper Murray River and elsewhere up the other rivers, *flaveolus* overlaps or closely approaches the true southeastern *elegans* along a wide front without interbreeding (for a recent detailed account, see Cain, 1955).

It is interesting to note that the cline from yellow to crimson in South Australia follows broadly the regional increase in moisture and luxuriance of forest vegetation; both rise to peaks in the ravines at the western end of Kangaroo Island. We suggest that the South Australian clinal population on the mainland, and probably even the crimson populations of Kangaroo Island, are referable to *flaveolus,* which can here produce a wet-adapted crimson form free of displacement pressure from *elegans.*

Birds of the Cape Verde Islands. Bourne (1955) in his review of the birds of the Cape Verde Islands, has presented several cases of character displacement so concisely and pointedly that we can quote him directly:

The two shearwaters [breeding in the Cape Verde Islands], Cory's shearwater *Procellaria diomedea* and the Little Shearwater *Procellaria baroli,* take similar foods (fish and cephalopods) differing only in size; competition for food between the two species is reduced by the development of different breeding seasons. Elsewhere in its range *Procellaria diomedea* breeds at the same stations as the medium Manx Shearwater *Procellaria puffinus,* which takes similar foods but breeds slightly earlier. There is a dramatic difference in size, and particularly the size of bill, between those races of *Procellaria diomedea* which breed with *Procellaria puffinus* and the form [*P. diomedea*] *edwardsi* which breeds alone at the Cape Verde Islands, the latter having a bill exactly intermediate in size between that of the northern races and that of *Procellaria puffinus.* It seems likely that *edwardsi* takes the food that is divided between both species elsewhere. It may be remarked that one race of *Procellaria puffinus, mauretanicus* of the Balearic Islands, avoids competition with *Procellaria diomedea* by breeding unusually early and leaving the area when the larger species prepares to nest; it is significant that this is the only race of the species which has a large bill resembling that of *P. d. edwardsi*. It would appear that the bill-size and the breeding seasons of these shearwaters vary with the amount of competition occurring between different species breeding at the same site. . . .

Where the two kites *Milvus milvus* and *Milvus migrans* occur together the latter is the species which commonly feeds over water. The race of *Milvus milvus* found in the Cape Verde Islands closely resembles *Milvus migrans* in the field, and very commonly feeds along the shore and over the sea. It may replace *Milvus migrans*, but it seems likely that with the Raven *Corvus corax*, which also abounds along the shore, it replaces the gulls *Larus* spp. which usually scavenge along the shore elsewhere but have failed to colonize the barren coast of the islands.

Bourne's opinion concerning which species are replaced is a little confusing in this case, since elsewhere *Milvus*, notably *M. migrans* in India, often tends to replace or at least dominate the gulls in scavenger-feeding situations around seaports (Brown, personal observation). The absence of *migrans* seems to us the probable chief reason for the convergence characteristics in the Cape Verde Islands populations of *milvus*.

Bourne cites one additional case:

The Cane Warbler *Acrocephalus brevipennis* [a species precinctive to the Cape Verde Islands] is closely related to large and small sibling species *Acrocephalus rufescens* and *A. gracilirostris* which occur together in the same habitats on the [African] mainland. Where the ranges of these two species overlap they are sharply distinct in size and voice; where they occur apart these distinctions are less marked (Chapin, 1949). *A. brevipennis* is probably related to the larger species, *A. rufescens*, but in the absence of the smaller species it is exactly intermediate in all its characters except the bill, which is large, resembling that of *A. rufescens*. The large bill may be part of the general trend seen on islands, or a consequence of competition for food with the smaller *Sylvia* warblers.

Birds of the Genus Monarcha. Mayr (1955 and personal communication) has described a case of displacement in the monarch flycatchers of the Bismarck Archipelago. *Monarcha alecto* and *M. hebetior eichhorni* occur together through the main chain of the Bismarcks, from New Britain north onto New Hanover, but beyond, on isolated St. Matthias, *M. hebetior hebetior* occurs alone; this last is an ambiguous variant combining several features of *alecto* and *eichhorni*. Mayr suggests the following evolutionary scheme: *hebetior* differentiated from *alecto* as an isolate on St. Matthias and later reinvaded the range of *alecto* on New Britain and New Ireland, where it diverged further under displacement pressure from the latter until it became the present *eichhorni*.

It seems to us that this situation can be more simply explained by assuming that the Bismarcks were first populated by a stock which evolved within the Archipelago and became the species *hebetior*. The later entry of *alecto* into the chain was followed by the displacement of *hebetior* as far as the sympatry extended, leaving the St. Matthias isolate to represent the undisplaced relict of the original *hebetior*.

Fishes of the Genus Micropterus. The two basses *Micropterus punctulatus* and *M. dolomieu* have ranges which include a large part of the eastern United States and are mostly coextensive (Hubbs and Bailey, 1940). Of the two, however, only *punctulatus* is known to occur in Kansas, western Oklahoma, and the Gulf States south of the Tennessee River drainage system. In the Wichita Mountains of western Oklahoma there is a population, described as *M. punctulatus wichitae*, which is intermediate between typical *punctulatus* and *dolomieu*. Its affinity to *punctulatus* is shown by the fact that in a number of characters it grades without a break into *punctulatus*, so that some specimens are indistinguishable from typical *punctulatus*, and in its agreement with *punctulatus* in the critical character of scale-row counts. Hubbs and Bailey seem to favor the theory of a hybrid origin for *wichitae*, but they consider this "no more plausible than the view that the similarities between *wichitae* and *dolomieu* are caused by parallel development, or the view that *wichitae* is a relict of a generally extinct transitional stage between *punctulatus* and *dolomieu*." We, of course, are inclined to favor parallel development, resulting specifically from the absence of the displacing influence of *dolomieu*, as the simplest and most plausible explanation.

Away to the south, many of the Texas populations of *punctulatus* are peculiar in showing converging trends toward *dolomieu*, but less strongly, so that Hubbs and Bailey consider them as possible intermediates between *punctulatus* and *wichitae*. In northern Alabama and Georgia there is a form described as a distinct species (*M. coosae*), which combines some of the characters of *punctulatus* and *dolomieu*, besides showing some peculiar to itself. *Coosae* is completely allopatric to *dolomieu*, and there is some evidence that it may hybridize extensively with the sympatric *punctulatus*. We should like to suggest the possibility here that *coosae* is conspecific with *punctulatus* and represents a section of the *punctulatus* population tending to converge toward *dolomieu* where that species is absent.

In summary, it appears to us likely that *wichitae*, the Texas populations, and possibly even *coosae*, each of which shows intermediate characters, are not products of introgressive hybridization, but may instead represent true *punctulatus* stocks that have tended to converge toward *dolomieu* in the absence of displacing influence from that species.

Frogs of the Genus Microhyla. W. F. Blair (1955) concludes from his study of two North American frogs of the genus *Microhyla:*

The evidence now available shows that there are geographic gradients in body size in both *Microhyla olivacea* and *M. carolinensis.* The former species shows a west to east decrease in body length, while the latter shows an east to west increase. The clines are such, therefore, that the largest *carolinensis* and the smallest *olivacea*, on the average, occur in the overlap zone of the two species. This pattern of geographic variation in body size parallels the pattern of geographic variation in mating call reported by W. F. Blair (1955) [in press] in which the greatest call differences in frequency and in length occur in the overlap zone. One of these call characteristics, frequency, probably is directly related to body size, for smaller anurans of any given group tend to have a higher pitched call than larger ones of the same group. The other, length of call, appears unrelated to size.

The differences in body size, like those in mating call, belong to a complex of isolation mechanisms (W. F. Blair, 1955) which tends to restrict interspecific mating in the overlap zone of the two species. The existence of greatest size differences as well as the greatest call differences where the two species are exposed to possible hybridization supports the argument (*op. cit.*) that these potential isolation mechanisms are being reinforced through natural selection.

Frogs of the Genus Crinia. A most interesting case in the Australian genus *Crinia* has recently been called to our attention by A. R. Main (*in litt.*). Where they occur together in Western Australia, as around Perth, the two species *C. glauerti* and *C. insignifera* have markedly different calls. *C. glauerti* has a rattling call resembling "a pea falling into a can and bouncing"; oscilloscope analysis shows this to consist of evenly spaced single impulses at the rate of about 16 per second. *C. insignifera* produces a call "similar to a wet finger being drawn over an inflated rubber balloon . . . we refer to this call as a 'squelch.'" Oscilloscope analysis shows the squelch to have a duration of about 0.25 second and to consist of impulses crowded together. Around Perth and in other localities where it is sympatric with *insignifera*, *glauerti* individuals are occasionally heard to produce the beginnings of the "squelch" by running 12–15 impulses together, but this occurrence is extremely rare. Along the south coast of Western Australia, however, where *glauerti* occurs alone, the call is commonly modified by running 30 or more single impulses together to produce a squelch almost identical to the ear with that of *insignifera*. Thus, in effect, where this species occurs alone it has extended the variability of its call to include the sounds typical of both species. According to Main, the two species show color differences in the breeding males and different ecological preferences; laboratory crosses show reduced F_1 viability. It seems evident to us (Brown and Wilson) that displacement in this case is associated with the reinforcement of reproductive barriers, the breakdown of which would result in inferior hybrids. This aspect will be discussed more fully in a later section.

Ants of the Genus Rhytidoponera. The ants of the Australian *Rhytidoponera metallica* group (revised by Brown, ms.) are widespread and often among the dominant insects of given localities. The common greenhead (*R. metallica*) is the most successful species—a metallescent green or purple ant adapted to a variety of habitats ranging from desert to warm, open woodland, and the only species of the group at all abundant across the dry interior of Australia. In the southeastern and southwestern ("Bassian") corners of

the continent, where the rainfall is higher and luxuriant forests occur, *metallica* is replaced by similar species of the same group that nearly or quite completely lack metallic coloration (Fig. 6).

In the east, two such species make the replacement, *R. tasmaniensis* Emery and *R. victoriae* André. *R. tasmaniensis* is the larger of the two, has the fine gastric sculpture of *metallica*, and is usually reddish brown, with bronzy-brown gaster. It is virtually identical with *metallica*, except for color. *R. victoriae* is smaller, more blackish, and has relatively coarser gastric striation. *R. tasmaniensis* is found in a variety of woodland situations, but apparently is excluded from the very wettest forests, which are occupied by *victoriae*. Nevertheless, the two species exist in abundance side by side over large parts of southeastern Australia without a sign of interbreeding. At some points, such as on the moist temperate grasslands west of Melbourne, both species occur together with *metallica*, but maintain their distinctness.

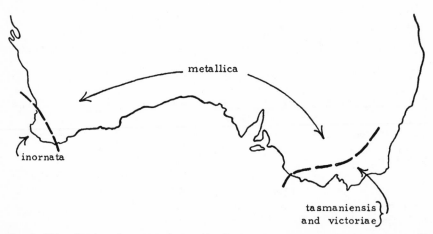

FIG. 6. Map showing the approximate distribution in southern Australia of four closely related common species of ants of the *Rhytidoponera metallica* group. *R. metallica* is nearly or quite the only representative of its group in the more arid central regions, and occurs in open situations in the southeast and southwest as well. In the moister forests of the southeast, *metallica* is replaced by the small, dark *R. victoriae* and the larger, more reddish *R. tasmaniensis*, which frequently occur side by side in the same localities. In the mesic wooded areas of the extreme southwestern corner of Australia, *metallica* is replaced by *R. inornata*, a distinct species which in size and color resembles closely, and broadly overlaps in variation, the two eastern forest species.

In the southwestern corner of Australia, *metallica* is replaced in the wetter parts of the region by non-metallescent *R. inornata* Crawley (though the two species overlap in the Darling Range and undoubtedly elsewhere). The interesting feature here is that *R. inornata* varies in size and color so as to cover the variation in these attributes of both southeastern non-metallic species, *tasmaniensis* and *victoriae*. In fact, one might speak of the two southeastern forms as mutually-displacing equivalents of the southwestern *inornata,* the latter being nearest the generalized type of the group because it has never suffered close competitive pressure and the character displacement that helps to relieve that pressure. This example illustrates the existence of a dual character-displacement pattern where the convergent population is clearly at, or above, the species level.

Slave-making Formica *Ants.* A simpler case in the ants involves the famous Holarctic slavemakers of the *Formica sanguinea* group. In a recent revision (Wilson and Brown, 1955) only three really distinct species are recognized in the group: *F. sanguinea* Latreille, widely distributed through temperate and northern Eurasia, where it is the only species; *F. subnuda* Emery, of boreal and subboreal North America; and *F. subintegra* Emery, ranging through temperate North America and overlapping the range of *subnuda* in the northern United States and along the Rocky Mountain chain.

The two most different forms are *subnuda* and *subintegra,* which can be separated on several external characters. *F. sanguinea* is closely related to *subnuda* in form and habits and is treated as a separate species only arbitrarily, on the basis of slight morphological discontinuities. At the same time, *sanguinea* has pilosity intermediate between that of the two American species, and its clypeal notch, a second important diagnostic character, is more like that of *subintegra* than like that of *subnuda*. We have interpreted this

pattern to represent a displacement of *subnuda* away from *subintegra* where these two species meet and interact, while the Palaearctic equivalent of *subnuda* (i.e., *sanguinea*) has tended to converge toward *subintegra* as a consequence of its filling the "adaptive vacuum" which a companion species might otherwise occupy. Of course in this case, as in all others under present consideration, there is no way of determining how much "displacement" has occurred as a process in the sympatric populations as opposed to "convergence" in the unispecific one. The final pattern observed may in fact be the result of one of these two processes alone.

American Scarabaeid Beetles. Howden (1955, p. 207) discusses the status of two geotrupine beetles considered by him to represent subspecies of the species *Eucanthus lazarus* (Fabricius). His *E. l. lazarus* is stated to range widely over the United States, but records from the Gulf States, excepting Florida, are scanty. *E. l. subtropicus* Howden, on the other hand, is restricted to the southeastern states, and is best represented in Florida, Georgia, Alabama and neighboring states.

Howden is puzzled by the apparent fact that "intermediates" between the two forms came from areas "not bordering the Gulf of Mexico," despite the circumstance that it is in this region that the main overlap falls. Intergrades came from areas "on the East Coast," and from Miami, Florida, and, "Occasional northern specimens appear to exhibit most of the characters of *subtropicus.*" However, in particular limited localities, presumably near or in the zone of overlap, Howden was able to name the populations one way or the other with little difficulty.

Although the situation in the Florida Peninsula is not clear from Howden's account, the "intermediate" and more typical-appearing *E. l. lazarus* occurring together with *subtropicus* in the Miami area may really represent undisplaced populations of *subtropicus*. If this is the case, then we would favor Howden's alternative interpretation, and consider *lazarus* and *subtropicus* as closely related but distinct species.

Crabs of the Genus Uca. Jocelyn Crane (in Allee *et al.*, 1950, p. 620) notes that in fiddler crabs of the genus *Uca* differentiation in behavior and often in the coloration of the male is greater if the species are found together than if they are found in different habitats or regions.

The Evolution of Character Displacement

Divergence between two species where they occur together, coupled with convergence where they do not, is a pattern that strongly suggests some form of interaction in the evolutionary history of the pair. The usual case may be one in which the members of the pair are cognate (derived from the same immediate parental population) and have recently made secondary contact following the geographical isolation that has mediated their divergence to species level. In such cases, the "terminal" populations, to which overlap does not yet extend, are not affected by the contact and remain closely similar to each other. But where contact has been made, there are two important ways in which the sympatric populations can interact to augment their initial divergence.

The first type of interaction might best be termed *reinforcement* [1] of the reproductive barriers. It may happen that the species continue to interbreed to some extent, and either the resulting inseminations are ineffectual, or the hybrids produced are inviable or sterile, resulting in what geneticists have termed "gamete wastage." Consequently, any further ethological or genetic divergence reducing this wastage will be strongly favored by natural selection (Dobzhansky, 1951; Koopman, 1950; Kawamura, 1953).

Of conceivably equal or greater importance is the process of *ecological displacement*. It seems clear from an *a priori*

---

[1] *Reinforcement* is a familiar term in psychology that has been applied to speciation processes (Blair, 1955).

basis that any further ecological divergence lessening competition between the overlapping populations will be favored by natural selection if it has a genetic basis (Mayr, 1949). That such a process actually occurs is suggested by abundant indirect evidence from ornithology (Lack, 1944), as well as the cases already cited above.

It seems unnecessary to go into a detailed discussion of these previously elaborated concepts, except to point out that secondary divergence of this nature inevitably entails phenotypic "characters" of the type employed in ordinary taxonomic work. Character displacement therefore may be considered as merely the aspects of such divergence that are recognizable to the taxonomist and some other favored organisms. It is interesting to note that the tendency toward displacement of characters is opposed by the pressure for mimicry. One can imagine some elaborate interactions between the two tendencies, particularly in the evolutionarily fertile tropics.

Competition

The concept of competition has been the focus of much important disagreement among ecologists and other biologists, and it deserves close and persistent investigation. However, were it not that Andrewartha and Birch (1954) criticize the use of the concept by Lack and others to explain distribution and variation of birds and other animals, we might well have avoided discussing it here altogether. Andrewartha and Birch (p. 25) seem to consider that competition is an idea of lesser, perhaps even negligible, importance in biology. They think that the tendency for closely related species to inhabit different areas or exploit different ecological niches (as reported, for instance, by Lack) may conceivably have originated from causes "quite different" from competition. They do not offer alternatives that seem to us anything like as satisfactory as Lack's hypotheses.

Andrewartha and Birch make a point

when they ask for more direct evidence for the action of competition, but it is clear that they have failed to appreciate the amount of evidence that does exist in the literature. However, interspecific competition of the direct, conspicuous, unequivocal kind is apparently a relatively evanescent stage in the relationship of animal individuals or species, and therefore it is difficult to catch and record (just as is the often parallel crisis in the rise of reproductive barriers between two newly diverging species). What we usually see is the result of an actually or potentially competitive contact, in which one competitor has been suppressed or is being forced by some form of aggressive behavior to take second choice, or in which an equilibrium has been established when the potential competitors are specialized to split up the exploitable requisites in their environment. A third possible result is the dispersion of potential competitors in space (Lack, 1954). Surely the cases of character displacement we have considered above, especially those for which we have some ecological data, are pertinent examples of correlation between sympatry (with the possibility of competition) and genetic fixation of specializations resulting in the avoidance of competition. The respective convergent unispecific populations outside the sympatric zones are the "controls" for these observations.

The case in which Lack (1944) cites the distribution of the chaffinches (*Fringilla*) in the Canary Islands is held up to special criticism by Andrewartha and Birch. Lack demonstrates that *F. teydea,* endemic to the islands of Gran Canaria and Tenerife, occupies only the coniferous forests at middle altitudes. On the same islands there also occurs a form of the widespread *F. coelebs,* presumably a relatively recent arrival from the Palaearctic mainland, but this bird occurs only in the tree-heath zone above, and in the broadleaf forests below, the coniferous belt. On the island of Palma, however, *F. teydea* is absent, and there a form of *F.*

coelebs occupies the coniferous forest as well as the broadleaf zone. Andrewartha and Birch conclude that, "So far as the case is stated, there is no direct evidence that the two species could not live together if they were put together." It is obvious from this that Lack's critics are not going to be satisfied by any ordinary kind of evidence.

What emerges starkly from contemporary discussion of "competition" is the great variation in the meanings with which different authors freight the word. Andrewartha and Birch, while differing with Nicholson (1954) on most important points, do manage to agree with him that the correct kernel of meaning of competition is contained in the expression "together seek." We would adopt the part of their definition that deals with the common striving for some life requisite, such as food, space or shelter, by two or more individuals, populations or species, etc. This seems to us to be close to the definitions preferred by the larger dictionaries we have consulted.

But Andrewartha and Birch, following many other writers, allow their competition concept to include another idea—that expressing direct interference of one animal or species with the life processes of another, as by fighting. On the surface, this inclusion of aggression as an element of competition may seem to some familiar and reasonable, but we wonder whether the concept of competition could not be more useful in biology if it were more strictly limited to "seeking, or endeavoring to gain, what another is endeavoring to gain at the same time," the first meaning given in *Webster's New International Dictionary, Second Edition, Unabridged.* It is noteworthy that competition as defined by this dictionary fails to include the idea of aggression in any direct and unequivocal way.

It may therefore be more logical in the long run to regard the various kinds of aggression between potential competitors (the outcome of which is so often predictable) as another method, parallel with character displacement and dispersion—and genetically conditioned in a similar fashion—by which organisms seek to lessen or avoid competition. Surely it is significant that aggressive behavior often seems most highly developed in cases where a conspecific, or closely related, potential competitor occurs with the aggressor, yet shows little or no displacement in behavior or form. In contrast are the many cases of complete mutual tolerance shown by closely related organisms that live side by side and are differentially specialized in behavior or form.

Character Displacement versus Hybridization

Since both divergent and "intermediate" populations are involved in the displacement patterns we have been describing, it is clear that the convergent populations might easily be mistaken as representing products of interspecific hybridization between the two species displacing each other. This is especially true if the convergent populations are small and isolated, or if only a single one is developed. Lack, for instance, in an early paper (1940) interpreted the Daphne and Crossman populations of *Geospiza* as being of hybrid origin, changing his mind only after he had begun to consider more fully the influence of competition on speciation (in *Darwin's Finches,* 1947).

To take another possible example, Miller (1955) describes what he calls a "hybrid" between the woodpeckers *Dendrocopos scalaris* and *D. villosus.* This specimen, a female, was shot in the Sierra del Carmen, Coahuila, Mexico, at about 7000 feet altitude, near the lower limits of the coniferous belt capping the Sierra. Up to, or near, this altitude, Miller found the Sierra to support a population of *scalaris,* but despite intensive collecting, he found no sign of occupancy by the other putative parent species, *villosus. D. scalaris* reaches a higher point in these mountains than it usually does in the neighboring regions of desert scrub and bottomland—its habitat wherever it has been studied—

in Mexico, Arizona, New Mexico and parts of Texas. In general, the *villosus* populations of this part of North America are restricted to the higher coniferous belts, but *villosus* and *scalaris* are in contact at some stations where pinyon-oak-juniper meets coniferous forest. Presumably *scalaris* extends farther vertically in the Sierra del Carmen because *villosus* is not present to limit its upward expansion. According to Miller, *villosus* probably does not occur within 200 miles of the Sierra at the present time.

The specimen, thoroughly described and figured by Miller, is indeed intermediate in many respects between the *scalaris* and *villosus* of northern Mexico. However, there seems to be nothing in the information presented to prevent one's interpreting this as a large, unusually dark specimen of *scalaris,* instead of as a hybrid. There is no good reason to deny the possibility that *scalaris* can produce somewhat *villosus*-like variants at the upper limits of its range when *villosus* is absent.

Other examples we have already cited in the present paper show the difficulty in deciding between displacement and hybridization where the species involved are incompletely known. This situation adds considerable complication to the analysis of interspecific hybridization in nature, for it is clear that the alternative explanation of displacement should at least be taken into account.

One thing seems certain; the "hybrid index," better called "compound character index," can by itself be no sound indication that the situation plotted really involves hybridization. This leads us to ask whether even such elaborate and beautifully documented studies of "hybrid" situations as that made by Sibley (1950, 1954) on the towhees of southern Mexico (*Pipilo erythrophthalmus s. lat.* and *P. ocai*) are not really just illustrations of character displacement. In some of the higher mountains of the southeast (Orizaba, Oaxaca), the two very differently colored forms (species) meet but remain distinct. Farther west are found various populations that apparently grade between the extreme *erythrophthalmus* form and the *ocai* form to various degrees of intermediacy, as expressed by Sibley in his "hybrid index."

Some of the *ocai*-form populations at the western end of the range (*P. ocai alticola*) are stated to be distinct from the other races of *ocai* by a characteristic melanization of the head region, which Sibley thinks is due to introgression from *erythrophthalmus* populations found to the north in the Sierra Madre Occidental. Despite this indication of introgression, the western populations at the *ocai* end of the gradients studied are indexed at, or extremely close to, zero, the figure indicating a population of "pure" *ocai*. Aside from what seems to be a variation in "purity" standards for *ocai* here, it is interesting to note that the western populations and those others among the apparent intermediates of the southern Plateau Region can all conceivably, on present evidence, be interpreted as *erythrophthalmus* that have converged toward *ocai* in the absence of the "true" *ocai* form represented by the upland, sympatric southeastern samples.

It seems possible that some strong selective pressure may be acting in the southern Plateau region to produce an *ocai* coloration-type in finchlike birds, and that *erythrophthalmus* may yield to this pressure wherever the true *ocai* is absent in this area. A very *ocai*-like bird of a related genus, *Atlapetes brunneinucha*, reaches the northern limit of its range in the southern Plateau area, and it is possible that the striking similarity marks some adaptive relationship to which both it and the *Pipilo* stock respond. It might even be that mimicry is involved between the sympatric *Atlapetes* and *Pipilo* stocks, although this is nothing more than the sheerest speculation in view of our very incomplete knowledge of the relative distribution of the two forms and other aspects of their biology and their environment, including their predators. At any rate, character displacement must for the time being be considered a reasonable alternative explanation of the variation of southern Mexican *Pipilo* in this group.

It may perhaps be argued that the "hybrid" populations of *Pipilo* are more variable than the presumed parental populations, and that this in itself is a strong indication of hybridization. We do not believe, however, that the case should be decided on this kind of evidence. To start with, tailspot length, the one character used in Sibley's study that has also been analyzed at length in other populations of *P. erythrophthalmus*, shows very considerable variation in areas far removed from the likely influence of *ocai*. According to the data of Dickinson (1953), the Florida population ("race *alleni*") has a coefficient of variation in this character of about 22 in the male; the range of variation is from 6.1 to 27.5 mm. The northeastern (nominate) race shows a corresponding coefficient of about 12, with a range of variation of from 24.0 to 55.0 mm. Furthermore, the chestnut-tinted pileum characteristic of *ocai-erythrophthalmus* "hybrids" occasionally crops up in the eastern North American samples of *erythrophthalmus*. But even if it were true that variation in the direction of *ocai* could be demonstrated only in the *ocai* "area of influence," this could not be taken as proof of hybridization, because an increase in variation is also a common quality of the "convergent" populations in character displacement patterns.

Character Displacement and Taxonomic Judgment of Allopatric Populations

Foremost among the problems of taxonomic theory today is the tantalizing conundrum concerning the status of the allopatric (isolated) population. Few authors hesitate to assign such populations either subspecific or specific rank, and most, it is hoped, appreciate the fact that their decisions are essentially arbitrary. As Mayr (1942) says, "The decision as to whether to call such forms species or subspecies is often entirely arbitrary and subjective. This is only natural, since we cannot accurately measure to what extent reproductive isolation has already evolved." There does not seem to be any definable threshold between polytypic species composed of such subspecific "units" and the superspecies composed of allopatric sister species. However, it is entirely possible that by the time an isolated population attains an ascertainable level of character concordance, it has already passed the species line; i.e., the more sharply defined an isolated subspecific population is by conventional standards, the less likely it is to be infraspecific in reality.

The phenomenon of character displacement should be borne heavily in mind in considering this matter of allopatric populations. If the present conception is correct, related sympatric species will generally show more morphological differences than similarly related allopatric ones. Hence the degree of observed difference between sympatric species cannot be considered a reliable yardstick for measuring the real status of related allopatric populations, nor can the differences among the latter be taken too seriously as indications of their relationships. In fact, the morphological standards set for determining which completely allopatric populations have reached species level may be much too strict in current practice. Despite impressions that might be gained from recent literature, many systematists have realized that in different allopatric populations (of the same species-group or genus), the degree of morphological divergence may be poorly correlated with the amount of reproductive isolation holding between them (Moore, 1954; Kawamura, 1953). In other words, where there is any question whatsoever about the objective species status of two closely related but geographically separated populations, morphology alone cannot be expected to answer it definitely.

Unfortunately, allopatric species or "subspecies" designated as such on a purely morphological basis frequently enter into theoretical discussions as though they were objectively established realities, when in fact they are usually no more than arbitrary units drawn for curatorial convenience.

Summary

Character displacement is the situation in which, when two species of animals overlap geographically, the differences between them are accentuated in the zone of sympatry and weakened or lost entirely in the parts of their ranges outside this zone. The characters involved in this dual divergence-convergence pattern may be morphological, ecological, behavioral, or physiological. Character displacement probably results most commonly from the first post-isolation contact of two newly evolved cognate species. Upon meeting, the two populations interact through genetic reinforcement of species barriers and/or ecological displacement in such a way as to diverge further from one another where they occur together. Examples of the phenomenon, both verified and probable, are cited for diverse animal groups, illustrating the various aspects that may be assumed by the pattern.

Character displacement is easily confused with a different phenomenon: interspecific hybridization. It is likely that many situations thought to involve hybridization are really only character displacement examples, and in cases of suspected hybridization, this alternative should always be considered. Displacement must also be taken into account in judging the status (specific *vs.* infraspecific) of completely allopatric populations. It is clear that, in the case where the species are closely related, sympatric species will tend to be more different from one another than allopatric ones. Thus, degrees of difference among related sympatric populations cannot be used as trustworthy yardsticks to decide the status of apparently close, allopatric populations.

Acknowledgements

We are grateful for information, advice and other aid received from numerous colleagues in the course of preparing this contribution. Especially to be thanked are J. C. Bequaert, W. J. Bock, W. J. Clench, P. J. Darlington, A. Loveridge, A. R. Main, E. Mayr, A. J. Meyerriecks, K. C. Parkes, R. A. Paynter, and E. E. Williams. Dr. C. Vaurie kindly offered the use of his figures to illustrate the *Sitta* case and gave us the benefit of some unpublished observations. Our acknowledgement is not meant to imply that any of those listed necessarily support the arguments we advance.

REFERENCES

ALLEE, W. C., EMERSON, A. E. and others. 1950. Principles of animal ecology. W. B. Saunders Co.

ANDREWARTHA, H. G., and BIRCH, L. C. 1954. The distribution and abundance of animals. Univ. Chicago Press.

BLAIR, W. F. 1955. Size differences as a possible isolating mechanism in *Microhyla*. *Amer. Naturalist*, 89:297–301.

BOURNE, W. R. P. 1955. The birds of the Cape Verde Islands. *Ibis*, 97:508–556, cf. 520–524.

CAIN, A. J. 1955. A revision of *Trichoglossus haematodus* and of the Australian platycercine parrots. *Ibis*, 97:432–479, cf. 457–461, 479.

CONDON, H. T. 1951. Notes on the birds of South Australia: occurrence, distribution and taxonomy. *S. Aust. Ornith.*, 20:26–68.

DICKINSON, J. C. 1952. Geographical variation in the red-eyed towhee of the eastern United States. *Bull. Mus. Comp. Zool. Harv.*, 107:273–352.

DOBZHANSKY, TH. 1951. Genetics and the origin of species. 3rd Ed. Columbia Univ. Press.

HOWDEN, H. F. 1955. Biology and taxonomy of the North American beetles of the subfamily Geotrupinae . . . *Proc. U. S. Nat. Mus.*, 104:159–319, 18 pls.

HUBBS, C. L., and BAILEY, R. M. 1940. A revision of the black basses (*Micropterus* and *Huro*) with descriptions of four new forms. *Misc. Publ. Zool. Univ. Mich.*, No. 48, 51 pp.

KAWAMURA, T. 1953. Studies on hybridization in amphibians. V. Physiological isolation among four *Hynobius* species. *J. Sci. Hiroshima Univ. (B, 1) 14*:73–116.

KOOPMAN, K. F. 1950. Natural selection for reproductive isolation between *Drosophila pseudoobscura* and *Drosophila persimilis*. *Evolution*, 4:135–148.

LACK, D. 1940. Evolution of the Galapagos finches. *Nature, 146*:324–327.

——— 1944. Ecological aspects of species formation in passerine birds. *Ibis*, 86:260–286.

——— 1947. Darwin's finches. Cambridge Univ. Press.

——— 1954. The natural regulation of animal numbers. Oxford Univ. Press.

MAYR, E. 1942. Systematics and the origin of species. Columbia Univ. Press.

——— 1949. Speciation and selection. *Proc. Amer. Phil. Soc.*, 93:514–519.

——— 1955. Notes on the birds of northern Melanesia. *Amer. Mus. Novitates*, No. 1707: 1–46, cf. p. 29.

MOORE, J. A. 1954. Geographic and genetic isolation in Australian amphibia. *Amer. Naturalist*, 88:65–74.

MILLER, A. H. 1955. A hybrid woodpecker and its significance in speciation in the genus *Dendrocopos*. *Evolution*, 9:317–321.

NICHOLSON, A. J. 1954. An outline of the dynamics of animal populations. *Australian J. Zool.*, 2:9–65.

SERVENTY, D. L. 1953. Some speciation problems in Australian birds . . . *Emu*, 53:131–145, with further references.

SIBLEY, C. G. 1950. Species formation in the red-eyed towhees of Mexico. *Univ. Calif. Publ. Zool.*, 50:109–194.

——— 1954. Hybridization in the red-eyed towhees of Mexico. *Evolution*, 8:252–290.

VAURIE, C. 1950. Notes on Asiatic nuthatches and creepers. *Amer. Mus. Novitates*, No. 1472:1–39.

——— 1951. Adaptive differences between two sympatric species of nuthatches. *Proc. Xth Internat. Ornith. Congr., Uppsala, June 1950*:163–166, 3 figs.

WILSON, E. O. 1955. A monographic revision of the ant genus *Lasius*. *Bull. Mus. Comp. Zool. Harv.*, 113:1–205, ill.

WILSON, E. O., and BROWN, W. L., JR. 1955. Revisionary notes on the *sanguinea* and *neogagates* groups of the ant genus *Formica*. *Psyche*, 62:108–129.

WILLIAM L. BROWN, JR. is Associate Curator of Insects at the Museum of Comparative Zoology, Harvard University. EDWARD O. WILSON is a Junior Fellow of the Society of Fellows of Harvard University.

THE EVOLUTIONARY IMPLICATIONS OF THE CYTOLOGICAL POLYMORPHISM AND PHYLOGENY OF THE VIRILIS GROUP OF DROSOPHILA*

By Wilson S. Stone, William C. Guest,† and Florence D. Wilson

GENETICS FOUNDATION, DEPARTMENT OF ZOOLOGY, THE UNIVERSITY OF TEXAS

Communicated by J. T. Patterson, January 11, 1960

In 1938 Professor J. T. Patterson embarked on a very intensive collection of Drosophila species because preliminary investigations had convinced him that this fauna was very rich, comparatively unknown, and most suited for the study of the evolution of a genus. The investigations of these species fully justified his conviction (Patterson and Stone[1]). Two of the species groups he and his colleagues investigated extensively were the virilis and the repleta groups of the subgenus Drosophila. Both of these groups have added and continue to add greatly to our understanding of evolution. Flies such as Drosophila leave no fossil record, except for a few recognizable specimens in amber. Mutations are repetitive so the presence of the same allele in different species is hard to prove or to evaluate. However, Professor T. S. Painter's[2] demonstration of the characteristics of the chromosomes of the salivary gland cells of Drosophila and their unique usefulness in analyses of chromosomal abnormalities gave us a tool to analyze the direction and degree of cytological change. With this tool the chromosome phylogeny and variability can be determined and compared to the genetic changes within a species group.

Materials and Methods.—A recently described species, *Drosophila ezoana* (Takada and Okada[3]), and new strains of *Drosophila montana* were available for our study. Genetic and cytological analyses were made by crosses within and between strains of a species together with crosses between different species. The details are to be found in Guest's[4] manuscript and will be published in full later. This paper will present the critical features of the cytological evolution and diversity of this species group, and only a few crosses showing the genetic differences will be presented. The cytological differences between species and the cytological polymorphism within strains were determined in the heterozygotes or hybrids or by comparison to the standard maps of *Drosophila virilis* by Hsu[5] and the standard *Drosophila montana* by Moorhead.[6] Strains of all the species of the virilis group were used in the crosses. In some cases two strains of a species were crossed and the F_1 tested to a third species in the hope that viable offspring would be more probable from the heterotic F_1. The new members of the *montana* species were compared to the standard and giant *montana* for size.

Results.—The new strains of the *montana* from Alaska and Canada proved approximately the same size [estimated using length from head through folded wing tip (mean 4.9 mm, ♀)] as standard *montana* (mean 4.8 mm, ♀) and smaller than giant *montana* (mean 5.3 mm, ♀). Moorhead[6] showed that giant *montana* (which might have been designated a new subspecies) was larger than standard *montana* but did not otherwise differ phenotypically from the standard except for the inversion pattern. The new strains from Alaska and Canada do not differ appreciably from standard in size or other phenotypic characteristics but might be classed as a different subspecies on inversion pattern differences.   Table 1 shows tests to the closely related species of the *montana* complex, *Drosophila lacicola, D. borealis* and *D. flavomontana*.   The Alaskan and Canadian strains were test mated to the other members of the virilis group including *Drosophila littoralis* (the F_1 female hybrids between the latter and the Smithers' strain were fertile).   The variations in fertility are similar to those found by Patterson,[7, 8] by Moorhead,[6] and reported from earlier work by Patterson and Stone.[1]

Drosophila ezoana proved quite unusual in that it is by far the most effectively genetically isolated species in the group.   Reciprocal crosses were made with all other members of the group (involving over 20,000 pairs of each sex, including over 6,000 with *Drosophila virilis* and 4,000 with *D. littoralis*).   Only four offspring, all F_1 from *littoralis* males to *ezoana* females, survived even as far as large larvae. Table 2 shows that insemination also occurred in the reciprocal cross, and that *virilis* females were more frequently inseminated by *ezoana* males than *ezoana* females were by *littoralis* males (in this cross the alien *ezoana* sperm remained motile in the seminal receptacles of the *virilis* females ten days after the flies were placed together).

The cytological variation in the *virilis* species group including these new forms

TABLE 1

CROSSES OF STRAINS OF *Drosophila montana* FROM ALASKA AND CANADA WITH OTHER SPECIES OF THE MONTANA SUBGROUP

| | U. T. No. 2501.2a Yukon | | | U. T. No. 2503.1 Alaska | | | U. T. No. 2514.1 Smithers | | |
	No. of Pairs	No. of Offspring ♀ ♂	Fertility of F_1	No. of Pairs	No. of Offspring ♀ ♂	Fertility of F_1	No. of Pairs	No. of Offspring ♀ ♂	Fertility of F_1
borealis ♀	130	25 31	Fertile	120	2 1	Sterile	120	0 0	..
borealis ♂	120	0 0	..	130	0 0	..	120	2 0	Sterile
lacicola ♀	150	2 6	Fertile	120	0 0	..	120	8 8	Fertile
lacicola ♂	190	256 283	Fertile	150	108 94	Fertile	120	230 248	Fertile
flavomontana ♀	120	25 23	Sterile	110	0 0	..	120	40 43	Fertile
flavomontana ♂	120	0 0	..	120	0 0	..	120	0 0	..

All crosses were made in small mass matings of 10 pairs per vial.

proved most informative (Fig. 1 and Table 3).   The *montana* complex which evolved from Primitive III, Figure 1, in North America consists of the three subspecies or forms of *Drosophila montana*, standard, giant, and the Alaskan and Canadian forms, plus three species descended from standard *montana: D. lacicola, D. flavomontana*, and *D. borealis*.   Unfortunately, many of the changes in gene sequence in the X-chromosome in descendants of Primitive III have not been analyzed.   We do not know the basic sequences of genes in the X-chromosomes of *ezoana, littoralis, montana*, or *lacicola*.   It would seem probable that five or more inversions were present in hybrids between *ezoana* and *littoralis, littoralis* and *montana, montana* and *lacicola*, and *montana* and *virilis*.   Therefore the total number of inversions analyzed, 92, plus the unanalyzed inversions in the X chromosome, would mean a total of perhaps 120 known in the evolution of members of this species group.   The inversions in *Drosophila novamexicana* and the two subspecies *D. americana americana* and *D. americana texana* were worked out especially by Hsu,[5] who also studied *littoralis*, basic *montana, lacicola, flavomontana*, and *borealis*, and proposed the three primitive types, modified slightly in Figure 1, to account for the cytological phylogeny of the group.   The cytological analysis of the giant *montana* strains was made by Moorhead.[6] Since no rearrangements were found in chromosome 6, it will not be referred to further.

The chromosome phylogeny including the postulated primitive types is shown in Figure 1 and Table 3. In these illustrations we have indicated the inversions at their origin (in a primitive type, a species, or a subspecies) by capital letters. Lower case letters indicate that the inversion occurred in an ancestral form, while letters in italics indicate that the inversion is not fixed but is heterozygous in some individuals. For sample, a particular inversion, B, in the 2 chromosome would be written $2B$, 2B, 2b, or $2b$. We have used overlapping inversions where they occur to give direction to the phylogeny as did Sturtevant and Dobzhansky,[9] Dobzhansky and Sturtevant,[10] and Dobzhansky,[11] who reviewed the extensive work done by him and his colleagues. These are not sufficient to establish all relations and we have used the presence of added new inversions, heterozygous and especially homozygous, to establish the direction of cytological evolution. Hsu[5] and Patterson and Stone[1] have presented convincing evidence that *D. virilis* (or Primitive I) was ancestral to the group. The present paper places *D. ezoana* as an intermediate between Primitive III and *D. littoralis*, very close cytologically to the former. The arrows on Figure 1 indicate the direction or more probable

TABLE 2

INSEMINATION OF FEMALES IN CROSSES OF *Drosophila ezoana* WITH OTHER SPECIES OF THE VIRILIS GROUP

♀	♂	Number of Females Mated*	Number of Females Dissected	Number Inseminated	Number with Motile Sperm
ezoana	×	virilis	500	100	0	0
virilis	×	ezoana	500	100	29	14
ezoana	×	littoralis	260	50	2	0
littoralis	×	ezoana	260	50	2	0
ezoana	×	montana	260	50	0	0
montana	×	ezoana	140	50	0	0

* Crosses made in small mass matings of about 20 pairs each.

direction of cytological evolution. There is no reason to think that we have found all the inversions in any species—for example, the few strains of *D. montana* from Alaska and Canada had 7 new inversions heterozygous. We know 43 inversions which are fixed in one or more species, 41 which originated in a species or the Primitive form which gave rise to it, and 2 which were only heterozygous at their origin but were fixed in a descendant form (2f and 4h). There are additional inversions fixed in X_E, X_{Li}, X_M, and X_{Lc}. Because the complexities of these inversions have so far defied analysis, we can only estimate that there are perhaps 20 to 30 additional inversions fixed in these X chromosomes. Furthermore, there are 51 new inversions heterozygous in the species in which they first occurred. as well as 8 inversions carried over from an ancestral form but still heterozygous.

All of these 92 (+ unanalyzed X inversions) are paracentric except the one pericentric in chromosome 2 which occurred in Primitive III and is present in all descendants of that form. In addition there are present in these species three centric fusions (see Patterson and Stone[1] for summary of analysis): the 3–4 fusion of *D. littoralis*, the 2–3 fusion of *D. americana americana* and *D. americana texana*, and the X–4 fusion of *americana* not found in *texana* except by gene interflow in their overlap zone. No other translocations and only a few minor shifts in

TABLE 3
CHROMOSOME VARIABILITY AND PHYLOGENY OF THE VIRILIS GROUP

Species	Chromosomes and Elements					Inversions	
	X A	2 E	3 D	4 B	5 C	Homozygous New/Old	Heterozygous New/Old
virilis	..	..	..	..	..	0	0
Primitive I	..	A	..	..	..	1/0	0
Primitive II	A B	a	..	..	..	2/1	0
novamexicana	a b C	a B C	A	A	B	6/3	0
texana	a b c	a	..	a b	A b	0/3	1/4
americana	a b c D	a b c	a	a B C	a b	0/3	3/6
Primitive III	..	a D E F	..	D E F	..	0/3 5/1	4/6 1/0
ezoana	X_E	a d e f	..	d e f	I	1/6 (+X_E)	0/1
littoralis	X_{Li}	a d e I	H I	d e f M N	H i J	5/7 (+X_{Li})	2/0
montana— standard	X_M	a d e f G H J K L	B C D	d e f H G I L O U W	C D	8/7 (2f) (+X_M)	9/0
montana— giant	X_M J K L	a d e f g h j k S T	b c d L	d e f h g i l R S T u V w X Y Z	c d O	0/7 (+8) (+X_M)	14/0
montana— Alaska- Canada	X_M k N	a d e f g h j k U V W X	b c M	d e f h g i l u w x z	c d o P	0/7 (+8) (+X_M)	7/0
						8/7	30/0
lacicola	X_{Lc}	a d e f g h j k O P Q R	b c J K	d e f h P Q	c d K L M N	4/15 (+X_{Lc})	8/1 (4h)
flavomontana	X_M E F G	a d e f g h j k N	b c E	d e f h J K	c d E	6/16 (4h) (+X_M)	2/0
borealis	X_M H I	a d e f g h j k M	b c F G	d e f h	c d F G	3/16 (4h) (+X_M)	4/0
Homozygous	8 + X_E, X_M, X_{Li}, X_{Lc}	11	7	9	8	41 + X_E, X_M, X_{Li}, X_{Lc} new inver- sions + 2f and 4h old inversions	
Heterozygous	5	13	6	17	8	49 + 2f, 4H new in- versions + 8 old inversions	
Total	13 + X_E, X_M, X_{Li}, X_{Lc}	24	13	26	16	92 + X_E, X_M, X_{Li}, X_{Lc}	

All forms are compared to *Drosophila virilis*, the cytological standard form. Each chromosome has a series of inversions which are given letters, following the system of Hsu.[5] New inversions are indicated by capital letters; inversions brought in from an ancestral form by lower case letters; and inversions that are not fixed in a species but occur heterozygous in part of the individuals by italicized letters. The accumulation and correlation of inversions show relations and give direction to the phylogeny.

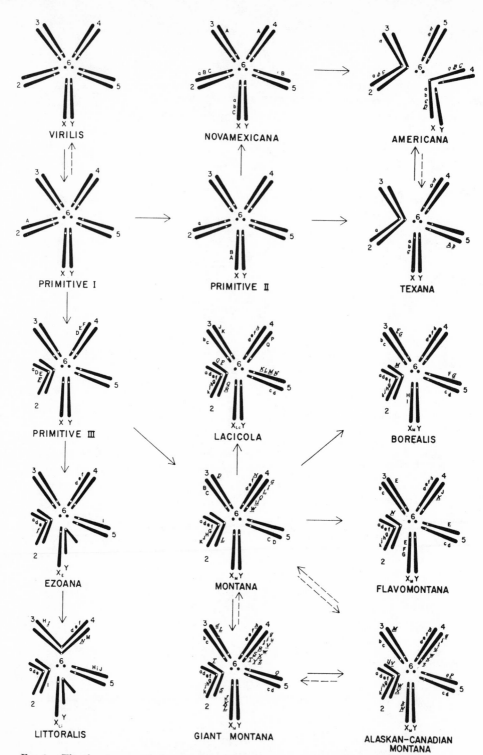

FIG. 1. The chromosome phylogeny and variability of the virilis species group.
Each inversion in a chromosome is given a separate letter. Capital letters mark the origin of an inversion in a species, subspecies, or primitive form; lower case letters indicate the inversion originated in an ancestral form; letters in italics (underscored in the figure), whether capital or lower case, show that the inversion is heterozygous, at least in some individuals. The arrows indicate the more probable evolutionary phylogeny, while arrows each way indicate gene flow between subspecies.

heterochromatin are known. It is interesting to note that the X-4 fusion without a Y and 4 fusion gives *americana* a multiple sex chromosome complex. Nevertheless this is fixed in *americana* and absent from the subspecies *texana* except for gene exchange along the band of overlap of the two subspecies, while no one of the many new paracentric inversions is fixed in one subspecies and absent in the other—Xc of *americana* approaches it most closely. Another interesting observation is that 2F occurred only heterozygous in Primitive III (this is the only modification we found necessary in the primitive types as first postulated by Hsu[5]), remains heterozygous in *D. ezoana*, was lost in the evolution of *D. littoralis*, but was fixed in the other line of descent of Primitive III in standard *montana* and its descendants.

Discussion.—Sturtevant and Dobzhansky[9, 10] first used a chromosome phylogeny to establish the sequence relationships in the 3 chromosome of *Drosophila pseudoobscura* and *D. persimilis*. They also indicated that the 3 chromosome of *D. miranda* was related to the other sequences through their hypothetical sequence which differs from the Standard gene sequence by one inversion. Many other inversion differences are present between these three species. Dobzhansky[12] has compared the chromosomes of *Drosophila willistoni* and three of its sibling species and Carson[13] has compared three other members of this species group. Stone[14] has reviewed the studies of chromosome polymorphism in the genus Drosophila and listed most of the extensive investigations up to that time. Despite these many investigations only two real phylogenies that represent major analyses of the chromosome evolution of large species groups exist—the virilis group as discussed here and earlier by Hsu[5] and Patterson and Stone,[1] and the repleta group investigated especially by Wasserman[15] and Wasserman and Wilson.[16] The reason for the success in these two groups and relative lack of success elsewhere is not hard to determine. The inversion changes often involve small inversions, the number of inversion differences between closely related forms is small, nearly the full series of intermediate forms is still in existence, and finally these are quite good species groups for laboratory studies including cytological analysis. For example, comparing *pseudoobscura* and *persimilis* with *miranda* is like attempting to compare *novamexicana* and *texana* with giant *montana* without the known intervening forms. By far the most remarkable chromosome phylogeny is that of the repleta group. Wasserman and Wilson[16] reported the analysis of 22 species of this group. More recently Wasserman[17] has extended the analysis so that he has the cytological phylogeny of 39 species of the more than 60 in the group. Furthermore, he has been able to show the cytological evolution of 7 other species not at present included in the group from the common cytological stem gene sequence. The ancestor(s) of the repleta group achieved some basic adaptation to desert conditions which led to a tremendous multiplication of species in the sparsely populated Southwest and especially Mexico. In these species genetic evolution was rapid, cytological evolution was not. For example, Wasserman has now recognized 100 inversions in chromosome 2, which is homologous to element E and hence to chromosome 2 of the virilis group; in the latter, consisting of nine species plus three subspecies or separate varieties, there are 24 inversions in this chromosome. The general problem of chromosome homologies in Drosophila was developed by Muller,[18] and Sturtevant and Novitski.[19] Inversion phylogenies have a unique advantage in that they show the steps, but not the number of species in the steps, in the evolution of a group even if members and their steps are missing.

The chromosome variability in the genus has been reviewed by Stone[14] so only a few added comparisons with the data on the virilis group will be given. Most of the inversion variability in *pseudoobscura* is in chromosome 3, element C. This element is not especially variable in the virilis group. There are 50 known inversions found heterozygous in *willistoni* alone and one individual was heterozygous for 16 of them, (da Cunha, Dobzhansky, Pavlovsky, and Spassky[20]). These authors point out that there are now known the following heterozygous inversions in this species, given by chromosome arm and element: $XL(A) = 11$, $XR(D) = 7$, $2L(B) = 8$, $2R(C) = 6$, $3(E) = 18$. The most variable species of the virilis group, *montana*, consisting of three varieties or subspecies, has the following series of heterozygous inversions, given by chromosomes and elements to facilitate comparison: $X(A) = 4$, $4(B) = 14$, $5(C) = 2$, $3(D) = 3$, $2(E) = 7$, total $= 30$. The three sibling species of *montana* are also quite variable, as are the sibling species of *willistoni*. The largest number of heterozygous inversions present in one strain (perhaps involving more than one pair as parents) of giant *montana* was 8 (Moorhead[6]) in contrast to 16 in one individual in *willistoni*. Da Cunha *et al.*[20] repeat their deduction that chromosomal polymorphism of paracentric inversions exists because of selective advantage. With this conclusion we must agree. The simplest general observation supporting it is the paucity of pericentric inversions and translocations (even the relatively innocuous centric fusions) which like paracentric inversions are two-break rearrangements and should therefore occur in as great numbers. However, the infrequent and absent types are known to have varying degrees of disadvantage when heterozygous (and they would originate heterozygous) because most of them produce aneuploid gametes at meiosis (Patterson and Stone[1]). Even paracentric inversions involving the heterochromatin which so often gives rise to position effect mutations that are often detrimental are very rare in Drosophila. The theoretical basis was developed by Fisher[21] over twenty years ago, who pointed out that slightly less than 2 per cent of unique mutational events would survive even with 1 per cent selective advantage, while no mutation without selective advantage would survive indefinitely from a single occurrence.

Da Cunha *et al.*[20] state: "The question which unavoidably presents itself, is, what causes some populations to be so much more polymorphic than others? Da Cunha, Burla, and Dobzhansky (1950)[22] advanced the working hypothesis that the chromosomal polymorphism is adaptive, and the populations which exploit a greater variety of ecological niches in the territory which they inhabit are more polymorphic than populations restricted to a narrow range of ecological opportunities."

It might be well to state the relations somewhat differently. Regions with many varied ecological niches have these filled in time by living systems, sometimes by several species and sometimes by one with great adaptive capacities which may depend on genetic polymorphism, whereas regions with serious ecological restrictions must impose similar restrictions on the variability of the genotypes. Furthermore, genotypes from a marginal restricted habitat might be able to invade an area with rich and varied ecological niches much more effectively than a genotype from a rich area could invade an area of much more restricted and intense selection, despite population pressure which causes major migrations from densely populated centers to peripheral regions.

Carson[23] (and earlier publications) has suggested that marginal populations are homozygous because homozygosity allows maximum recombination. This is undoubtedly true but certain additional facts must be considered. For example, the restriction of crossingover in some chromosome regions by heterozygous inversions has repeatedly been demonstrated to increase recombination in others, Schultz and Redfield.[24] Furthermore, the mere effect of difference in population size must have an effect. In a very large central population the number of individuals with any chromosome or large segment of a chromosome homozygous must be very much larger than in the peripheral populations. Therefore, the number of recombinations will be much greater in the central population (although not as great a per cent), than in peripheral areas. In fact, if these new combinations are especially beneficial and dominant in their effect, they may be multiplied as inversion heterozygotes protected from immediate breakdown by crossingover until they can build up in frequency. J. F. Crow (personal communication) pointed out a second and more important reason for questioning the greater importance to survival of homozygosity of peripheral populations. The importance of a sexual system and of recombination over an asexual system increases with population number. Further consideration stresses the importance of the role of selection against the ill-adapted migrants from the population centers in establishing the genotypes of the peripheral populations. The evidence that necessarily peripheral populations connected to parent populations give rise to new forms and species does not seem sufficient. As Carson pointed out, *Drosophila robusta* does not have such budded-off species. Rather it seems that isolation plus restricted population size are both necessary. This has been discussed and the genetic effects elaborated and illustrated in bird evolution by Mayr[25] and for insects and invertebrates in general by White.[26] Both of these seem to be necessary factors in the evolution and elaboration of the repleta species group in Drosophila in addition to the desert adaptation of the ancestral form. Probably most of the more than 60 species in the repleta group evolved in the desert and semidesert conditions of Mexico and the Southwest, an environment where both isolation and initial restriction in size would occur frequently.

There are some interesting conclusions to be drawn from comparisons of the cytological evolution and polymorphism of different species groups with very different population distributions and densities. Wharton[27] made the first extensive analysis of the role of fusions, pericentric inversions and changes in heterochromatin in the genus. Further adequate discussions are to be found in Patterson and Stone[1] and Stone.[14] We shall deal with the role of paracentric inversions, both fixed and heterozygous, in the evolution of the species group. Wasserman[15–17] has investigated the repleta group, particularly in the southwest United States, Mexico, and Central and South America and the Antilles around the Caribbean Sea. These are usually small populations, particularly in the desert areas, where most of them occur. The 39 analyzed members of the group are characterized by relatively few inversion differences between species. Even so, there are decidedly more inversion differences fixed between species than occur as heterozygotes within species. The virilis group includes species with very small populations (e.g., *novamexicana*), those which are small, and *virilis* which in Asia seems to have large populations. This last species and the most restricted species, *novamexicana*, seem to be cytologically homozygous, whereas the others are variable. Spieth[28] demonstrated that *lacicola* and *borealis*, which are sympatric in northern Minnesota, live in a restricted high humidity belt around lakes. Other members of the group found in North America are also restricted to banks of streams and lakes. Along desert streams of the southwest the collections of *novamexicana* have been few so we must defer final decision—so far it is homozygous for gene arrangements although the three populations investigated for heterotic properties by Stone, Alexander, and Clayton[29] prove to have some very interesting genetic differences.

Drosophila pseudoobscura and *persimilis* have more inversions heterozygous in their populations than the number of fixed inversion differences. However, the restricted species with comparatively small populations, *Drosophila miranda*, differs from these two by many more fixed inversions than the total of variable inversions in the three species. Unfortunately for an analysis, the species of the willistoni group are too diverse cytologically to determine the number of inversion differences fixed between them. The species *willistoni* has one of the larger if not the largest population distribution in the genus, perhaps being the largest species in numbers and large population distribution of any amenable to genetic analysis.

Perhaps the most significant finding is that there is no direct correlation between number of individuals in a species and number of heterozygous (unfixed) inversions in a species. *Drosophila pseudoobscura*, with a widespread distribution and large populations in western North America, has somewhat fewer inversions heterozygous than *montana*, although the latter species is at present characterized by small linear populations spread over a considerable area. A guess, which certainly overestimates the relative number of *montana*, would estimate their ratios as *montana: pseudoobscura: willistoni* $= 1:10^4:10^8$. Nevertheless there are known only 50 heterozygous inversions in the latter species but 30 in *montana*, even though *willistoni* has been sampled much more extensively. Perhaps this is good evidence that the difficulties discussed by Haldane,[30, 31] in terms of the conditions for coadaptation in polymorphism for inversions together with the cost of natural selection, limit the number of cumulatively heterotic gene combinations associated with inversions that may be expected in a population. Dobzhansky and Pavlovsky[32] claim that the inversions in certain populations of *pseudoobscura* are heterotic because of genes with *specific combining ability*, and that different populations differ in this respect so that the same inversions are not necessarily successfully interchangeable between populations. This can hardly be the case in the tremendous populations of *willistoni* with a number of inversions heterozygous in each chromosome for da Cunha *et al.*[20] point out that individuals with the same set of inversions are rare. In *willistoni* inversions must be retained by heterotic genes which have *general* and *cumulative combining ability*. This seems to be the case also in *montana*. Several inversions may be heterozygous in a strain but we do not find consistent heterozygotes between certain gene sequences in a population, so far as our more limited sampling allows us to determine.

The effective uniqueness of each inversion and its loss if it lacks selective advantage (Fisher[21]) allows us to make some interesting calculations about the number of inversions which has been utilized in the evolution of the genus and also the number which occurred but was lost. Stone[14] estimated the number of inversions fixed in the evolution of the genus using the number fixed per species in the virilis and repleta groups compared to the number heterozygous in those and other groups. The number of variable (heterozygous) inversions then numbered 592 in the 42 species which had been studied. The virilis and repleta groups differ in ratio of fixed to heterozygous inversions from 1.2:1 for the former to 2:1 for the latter, as now determined by Wasserman.[17] The number of species in the genus was earlier estimated at 650 but M. R. Wheeler now estimates that there are two to three times that number. On the basis of the 650 species, the number of inversions fixed in the evolution of the genus was estimated at between 6,100 and 36,500. This was a very conservative estimate as no additional allowance was made for greater cytological differences between than within species groups or subgenera. With the larger number of species now proposed for the genus, the number of paracentric inversion differences fixed in its evolution is probably between 22,000 to 56,000, while perhaps 18,000 to 28,000 are now heterozygous in the many populations around the world. If we assume that the selective advantage of the inversions in their initial struggle to be established was one per cent, this would mean that from 1.1 to 2.8 million inversions with this much selective advantage occurred, but the remainder were eliminated. This leaves the vast majority of inversions, conservatively ten or one hundred times as many, which did not have selective advantage, or were disadvantageous, that also were eliminated. When we remember that inversions are relatively unique events whereas mutations occur and recur time and again, we get some further idea of the tremendous numbers of trials of rearrangements and mutations in different combinations and sequences which have gone into the evolution of even this small genus. These repeated and varied trials with natural selection and time enough to absorb the cost (Haldane[31]) make evolution inevitable, as Fisher[21] pointed out. Wright[33] has reviewed his concepts of the necessity of a balanced array of forces (mutation, selection, population structures, etc.) and of the importance of complex balanced genotypes and their shifts to higher selective peaks. We have presented some evidence on the results of variations in population structure and the tremendous array of variability available through time to make possible the changes necessary to reach more highly adapted genotypes.

Summary.—The virilis group of the genus Drosophila has been revised and extended. Strains of *Drosophila ezoana* from Hokkaido and new strains of *Drosophila montana* from Alaska and Canada have been tested and compared to earlier tests with members of the group. *D. ezoana* is isolated genetically more than any other member of the group. Cytologically it is very close to the postulated Primitive III in gene arrangement and in part validates this postulated ancestral form. The strains of *montana* from Canada extend the known range and cytological variability of this species. The several strains proved to be genetically diverse as had other strains of *montana*. The virilis group consists of nine species. The chromosome phylogeny has been worked out so that we know the lines of evolution and the necessary primitive forms (cytologically) to fill out the phylogeny, Figure 1. *Drosophila virilis* has been demonstrated to be both genetically and cytologically nearest the primitive ancestor of the group. In addition to the normal *virilis* arrangement of genes in the X and the four major autosomes, there are 92 known and analyzed heterozygous or homozygous inversions in this group (plus 20 to 30 more which are fixed, i.e., homozygous, in the X chromosomes of *Drosophila ezoana, montana, lacicola, and littoralis*). There are 43 analyzed plus these added X chromosome inversions which have been fixed in the evolution of one or another member of this species group. There are now known 49 inversions which are present sometimes in some species but not fixed (plus 2f and 4h which are variable in some species but fixed in others). The amount of cytological variability cannot be predicted from the present population of a species since more unfixed, sometimes heterozygous, inversions occur in *montana* than in *pseudoobscura* but less than in *willistoni*. *Drosophila montana* is much less frequent than the other two species and, like other members of the virilis group, is restricted to the high humidity belt along streams or lakes.

There exist now two extensive chromosome phylogenies in the genus Drosophila where the direction and extent of cytological variation in the evolution of the species has been thoroughly established. These are the virilis group discussed here, consisting of 9 species plus 3 subspecies or varieties (Figure 1) and in addition, there is the remarkable repleta group and its relatives which has been analyzed, particularly by Wasserman. He will soon publish a revised phylogeny which includes now 39 species in the repleta group plus 7 species in closely related groups. The extensive genetic evolution but very conservative cytological evolution has made this possible.

It is most remarkable that only 100 years after Darwin published *The Origin of Species* we have established so many of the genetic mechanisms involved in evolution. Perhaps it is even more remarkable that we have been able to establish the direction and extent of cytological changes in the well-established cytological phylogeny of 9 species in one species group and 46 species in a complex involving several other species groups.

We wish to thank Dr. Eizi Momma who brought us the strains of *Drosophila ezoana* from Hokkaido; Dr. D. D. Miller and Mr. Chris Dahlie, who collected the strains of *Drosophilia montana* in Canada and Alaska; Dr. Marvin Wasserman, who allowed us to include some of his unpublished data on the repleta group; Dr. M. R. Wheeler, who discussed these general problems and checked the manuscript; and Dr. J. F. Crow, who read the manuscript and made several suggestions. Professor J. T. Patterson began the work on the virilis group with us and continues to contribute inspiration and interest in these problems.

* This work was supported by grants from the Rockefeller Foundation, the U.S. Public Health Service, and a contract with the Atomic Energy Commission.

† Present address: Department of Biology, University of Alabama, University, Alabama.

[1] Patterson, J. T., and W. S. Stone, *Evolution in the Genus Drosophila* (New York: The Macmillan Co., 1952).

[2] Painter, T. S., *J. Hered.*, 25, 465 (1934).

[3] Takada, Haruo, and Toyoki Okada, *Jap. J. Zoo.*, 12, 133 (1958).

[4] Guest, William C., Unpublished Ph.D. dissertation (1959).

[5] Hsu, T. C., Univ. Texas Pub., No. 5204 (1952), p. 35.

[6] Moorhead, Paul S., Univ. Texas Pub., No. 5422 (1954), p. 106.

[7] Patterson, J. T., Univ. Texas Pub., No. 5204 (1952), p. 7.

[8] *Ibid.*, p. 20.

[9] Sturtevant, A. H., and Th. Dobzhansky, these PROCEEDINGS, 22, 448 (1936).

[10] Dobzhansky, Th., and A. H. Sturtevant, *Genetics*, **23**, 28 (1938).

[11] Dobzhansky, Th., *Genetics and the Origin of Species* (New York: Columbia University Press, 1951, Third revised edition).

[12] Dobzhansky, Th., *J. Hered.*, **41**, 156 (1950).

[13] Carson, Hampton L., *Evolution*, **8**, 148 (1954).

[14] Stone, W. S., *Cold Spring Harbor Symposia on Quant. Biol.*, **20**, 256 (1955).

[15] Wasserman, Marvin, Univ. Texas Pub. No. 5422 (1954), p. 130.

[16] Wasserman, Marvin, and Florence D. Wilson, Univ. Texas Pub. No. 5721 (1957), p. 132.

[17] Wasserman, Marvin, Unpublished data (1959).

[18] Muller, H. J., in *New Systematics*, ed. Julian Huxley (Oxford, Clarendon Press, 1940), p. 185.

[19] Sturtevant, A. H., and E. Novitski, *Genetics*, **26**, 517 (1941).

[20] Da Cunha, A. Brito, Th. Dobzhansky, O. Pavlovsky, and B. Spassky, *Evolution*, **13**, 389 (1959).

[21] Fisher, Ronald A., *The General Theory of Natural Selection* (New York: Dover Publication, Inc., 1958, 2nd revised edition).

[22] Da Cunha, A. Brito, H. Burla, and Th. Dobzhansky, *Evolution*, **4**, 212 (1950).

[23] Carson, Hampton L., *Cold Spring Harbor Symposia on Quant. Biol.*, **23**, 291 (1958).

[24] Schultz, Jack, and Helen Redfield, *Cold Spring Harbor Symposia on Quant. Biol.*, **16**, 175 (1951).

[25] Mayr, Ernst, in *Evolution as a Process*, ed. Julian Huxley (London: Allen and Unwin, 1954), p. 157.

[26] White, M. J. D., *Australian J. Sci.*, **22**, 32 (1959).

[27] Wharton, Linda T., Univ. Texas Pub. No. 4313 (1943), p. 282.

[28] Spieth, Herman T., *Science*, **113**, 232 (1951).

[29] Stone, Wilson S., Mary L. Alexander, and Frances E. Clayton, Univ. Texas Pub. No. 5422 (1954), p. 272.

[30] Haldane, J. B. S., *J. Gen.*, **55**, 218 (1957).

[31] *Ibid.*, **55**, 511 (1957).

[32] Dobzhansky, Th., and Olga Pavlovsky, *Evolution*, **7**, 198 (1953).

[33] Wright, Sewall, *Cold Spring Harbor Symposia on Quant. Biol.*, **20**, 16 (1955).

THE ORIGIN OF CLARKIA LINGULATA

Harlan Lewis and Margaret R. Roberts [1]

University of California, Los Angeles

Received June 23, 1955

An unusual *Clarkia* was discovered in 1947 in the canyon of the Merced River, California, by the senior author. It appeared to be a simple variant, with un-lobed petals, of *C. biloba* (Dur.) Nels. & Macbr., a species which occurs abundantly in the same canyon. Examination of microsporocytes showed, however, that this variant had genomes of 9 chromosomes, rather than the 8 characteristic of *C. biloba*. Furthermore, the hybrid between them was nearly sterile. Consequently, the new entity was described as a species, *C. lingulata* (Lewis and Lewis, 1953).

The purpose of this paper is to compare these two species phenotypically and cytogenetically in order to ascertain the factors which led to speciation.

Distribution and Breeding Habit

Clarkia lingulata is known only from two sites in the Merced River Canyon. One population is on the east and north-facing slopes at the junction of the Merced River with its South Fork; the other population is on a steep north-facing slope about two miles farther down the canyon. Other populations may occur, but the deep and steep-sided canyons of the Sierra Nevada are difficult to explore, except where roads or trails exist. On the other hand, *C. lingulata* may be endemic to a very small area and is perhaps confined to the two known colonies. Each of these colonies is morphologically homogeneous and consists of several thousand flowering individuals in an ordinary season.

Clarkia biloba, on the other hand, is a polytypic species with an area of distribution which extends for about 150 miles along the Sierra Nevada foothills from

[1] Present address: Amherst College, Amherst, Mass.

Butte County to the Merced River. It is frequent throughout this area and occurs in more or less discrete colonies of various size. A few colonies are also found in a disjunct area near San Francisco Bay (fig. 1).

The southern limit of distribution of *C. biloba* coincides with the restricted distribution of *C. lingulata* and colonies of the two species occur within 100 yards of each other, although no mixed colonies are known. This absence of mixed colonies, despite the close proximity of the two species, suggests a difference in ecological preference. However, the sites occupied by adjacent colonies of the two species appear to be comparable in all respects and a closely related species, *C. dudleyana*, grows with both species in this area. Furthermore, under uniform cultural conditions no differences in response between *C. biloba* and *C. lingulata* have been detected. Nevertheless, effective ecological differences between the species are not precluded, even though our observations show no gross differences.

Both species are insect pollinated. The anthers mature before the stigma is receptive and the stigma is held well above the anthers. Consequently, out-crossing is the rule, but individuals of both species are self-compatible and self-pollination can occur from insect visits to more than one flower on the same plant. The seeds have no special mechanism for dissemination and are generally dropped close to the parent plant.

Morphological Studies

Clarkia biloba consists of three geographical races designated as subspecies *brandegeae, biloba* and *australis* (fig. 1),

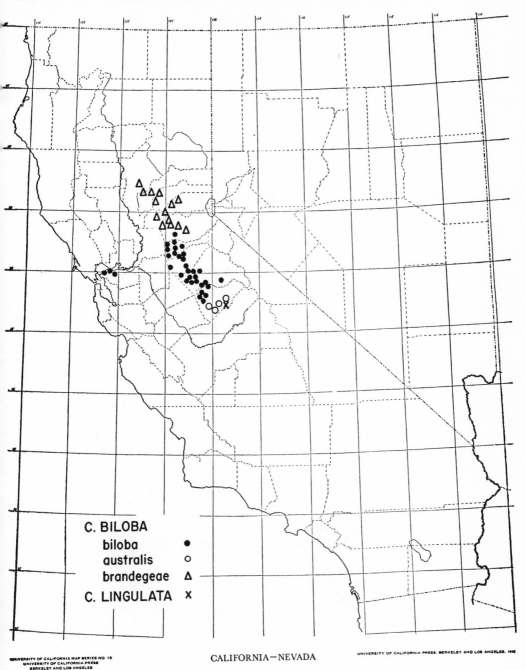

C. BILOBA
   biloba   ●
   australis   ○
   brandegeae   Δ
C. LINGULATA   ✕

CALIFORNIA—NEVADA

FIG. 1. Distribution of *Clarkia biloba* and *C. lingulata*

which we shall refer to without specific epithet. These subspecies differ from one another most conspicuously in petal shape and color, although vegetative differences are also discernible (Roberts and Lewis, 1955). Measurements of the more conspicuous morphological traits are summarized in table 1. From this table it will

TABLE 1. *Morphological characters of* Clarkia lingulata *and* C. biloba

Species	Petal length/breadth	Petal sinus depth/petal length	Petal color	Sepal length (mm.)	Leaf breadth (mm.)	Leaf margin	Stem tip
C. lingulata	1.9 (2.51) 3.1*	.00 (.00) .08	magenta	7 (9.0) 10	3 (4.9) 8	subentire	recurved
C. biloba							
australis	1.4 (2.23) 3.3	.18 (.23) .31	magenta	7 (9.1) 11	3 (4.4) 6	subentire	recurved
biloba	1.2 (1.71) 2.4	.22 (.34) .52	pink to lavender	6 (11.5) 17	5 (5.9) 8	subentire	recurved
brandegeae	1.2 (1.69) 2.3	.09 (.15) .22	lavender to orchid	9 (12.4) 15	5 (7.1) 8	denticulate	strongly recurved

* Minimum, mean, and maximum are indicated for ratios and measurements.

FIG. 2. *Clarkia biloba australis* (left) and *C. lingulata* (right) grown simultaneously under the same cultural conditions.

be seen that the range of variation of *C. lingulata* with respect to vegetative characters as well as petal color and proportion falls within that of *australis*, the southernmost subspecies. In fact, *C. lingulata* differs from this subspecies in external morphology only by the degree to which the petals are lobed, as shown in figure 2.

CHROMOSOME STUDIES

Meiosis has been studied in squash preparations of microsporocytes of thirty-seven individuals of *C. lingulata* and one hundred fourteen individuals of *C. biloba*, including all of the subspecies (Roberts and Lewis, 1955). All of the individuals of *C. lingulata* were found to have 9 pairs of chromosomes at first metaphase, whereas the individuals of *C. biloba* consistently had 8. Seven of the nine pairs in *C. lingulata* usually form ring bivalents, with chiasmata in both arms; the other two pairs usually do not. In *C. biloba* only six of the eight pairs usually form ring bivalents. This suggests that the genomes of the two species differ by a chromosome that normally forms chiasmata in both arms and, hence, has a submedian centromere. This conclusion is further substantiated by the chromosome configurations found in the F_1 hybrids discussed below.

Mitotic chromosomes of the two species have been studied in root-tip sections. Individual chromosomes could not be distinguished but careful measurement of the entire metaphase complement indicates that the somatic complement of *C. lingulata* differs from that of *C. biloba* by two chromosomes of average length (Lewis, 1954).

INTERSPECIFIC HYBRIDIZATION

A total of sixty crosses have been made between *C. lingulata* and the three subspecies of *C. biloba*. The results are shown in table 2. The seed set resulting from crosses between *C. lingulata* and *australis* was as high as the norm for the parents, but was lower in crosses with the other two subspecies, particularly *brandegeae*. All of the seeds from these original crosses and subsequent hybrid progenies germinated equally well.

The F_1 hybrids are morphologically intermediate in all respects. The fertility of these hybrids is low, as indicated by the percentage of visibly good pollen and by seed set. The percentage of good pollen in the parental plants was in all instances above 90, and usually above 95 per cent. In contrast, good pollen did not exceed 15 per cent in hybrids between *C. lingulata* and *australis*. Similar results were obtained for hybrids with *biloba*. On the other hand, the hybrids with *brandegeae* consistently showed a higher percentage of good pollen (table 2). Comparable results were obtained with respect to seed set. The hybrids with *australis*, when self-pollinated, set only one capsule containing one seed, despite 33 pollinations; the hybrids with *biloba* did but little better. In contrast, the hybrids with *brandegeae* produced as many as 9

TABLE 2. *Fertility of the* F_1 *hybrids between* Clarkia lingulata *and the three subspecies of* C. biloba

C. lingulata ✕C. biloba	australis			biloba			brandegeae		
	n	M	X̄	n	M	X̄	n	M	X̄
seed set—original cross	39	73	39.6	3	30	22.0	8	25	18.6
per cent good pollen—F_1	23	15	9.4	3	14	12.0	18	27	16.3
seed set—F_1✕self	33	1	<1	18	3	<1	12	9	5.0
seed set—F_1✕parent	55	19	2.2	29	13	1.5	30	32	9.5

seed set: n = number of pollinations; M = maximum number of seeds per capsule; X̄ = mean number of seeds per capsule.

per cent good pollen: n = number of plants; M = maximum; X̄ = mean per plant.

seeds per capsule and nearly every pollination resulted in a capsule. When backcrossed, the hybrids with *brandegeae* again proved to be conspicuously more fertile than the hybrids with the other two subspecies. An explanation of these results is to be found, at least in part, from a study of meiosis in the hybrids.

Meiosis in the hybrids between *C. lingulata* and each of the three subspecies of *C. biloba* will be discussed in turn. In all instances squash preparations of microsporocytes were used. In contrast to the parents, the meiotic chromosomes of the hybrids and subsequent progenies tend to be "sticky" which frequently makes an analysis of configurations difficult.

Five hybrids between *C. lingulata* and *australis* have been examined. The parents were obtained from two different colonies of each. Since meiosis was found to be comparable in each hybrid, the data obtained have been combined. The configurations at first metaphase could be

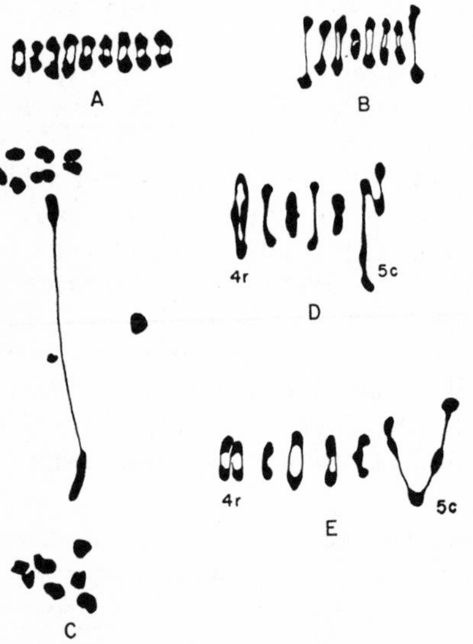

A

B

4r

5c

D

4r

5c

E

C

Fig. 3. Meiotic chromosomes of *Clarkia lingulata, C. biloba australis,* and their F₁ hybrid.

A. *C. lingulata*, metaphase I; B. *C. biloba australis*, metaphase I; C. F₁ hybrid, anaphase I, showing a bridge, fragment, and lagging chromosome; D. and E. F₁ hybrid, metaphase I, showing four pairs, a ring of 4, and a chain of 5.

examined with certainty in 94 microsporocytes. The maximum association was found to be 4 pairs, a ring of 4, and a chain of 5 chromosomes (fig. 3 d, e).

Four pairs of chromosomes were present in every cell and always separated in a regular manner. This suggests that each of these pairs may be comprised of structurally homologous chromosomes. If so, these four pairs do not contribute to the observed reduction in fertility of the hybrid.

The ring of 4 chromosomes indicates that the parental plants differ by a reciprocal translocation involving large parts, if not entire arms, of two pairs of chromosomes. In addition to a ring of 4, these chromosomes form a chain of 4 or two pairs. The observed frequency of these configurations was 74, 16, and 10 per cent respectively. In no instance was a chain of 3 and an unpaired chromosome observed. When a ring of chromosomes is formed it may separate disjunctionally at anaphase, with adjacent chromosomes moving to opposite poles (fig. 3e), or it may separate nondisjunctionally, with adjacent chromosomes moving to the same pole (fig. 3d). In nearly all cases of nondisjunction, the ring was observed to be oriented in such a manner that two chromosomes on opposite sides of the ring were toward the poles, with the other two chromosomes more or less on the equator. Sixty five per cent of the rings were observed to separate nondisjunctionally (table 3), and these would not be expected to produce viable genotypes. When a chain rather than a ring was formed, it was observed to separate nondisjunctionally in about half of the cells. When two separate pairs are formed, they are presumably oriented independently, and half of the time would not be expected to produce viable genotypes. In total, then, one would expect approximately 62 per cent of the meiotic products of the cells observed to be nonfunctional because of the translocation alone. However, the cells that could be analysed cytologically may not represent a random

TABLE 3. *Chromosome configurations in microsporocytes of* F_1 *hybrids between*
Clarkia biloba *and* C. lingulata

T								Total number of cells
aust x ling.	45	25	7	6	2	0	9	94
brand. x ling.	50	31	6	1	0	1	9	98

L											Total number of cells
aust. x ling.	21	18	6	2	2	0	1	13	25	0	6	94
brand. x ling.	1	1	2	0	1	1	1	65	15	1	10	98

T = translocation configurations. L = configurations involving the "ninth" chromosome of *C. lingulata*. aust. = *C. biloba australis*. brand. = *C. biloba brandegeae*. ling. = *C. lingulata*.

sample. Consequently, the fertility of backcross hybrids, discussed below, that are presumably structurally homozygous except for this translocation probably affords a better measure of its effect upon fertility.

The 5 chromosomes that form a maximum configuration of a chain of 5 obviously include the additional, ninth, chromosome of *C. lingulata*. This maximum configuration was observed in 53 per cent of the cells. These same 5 chromosomes were observed to form a chain of three and a pair, or two pairs and an unpaired chromosome in 41 and 6 per cent of the cells respectively (table 3). In one cell a chain of 4 and an unpaired chromosome was found, but the position of the unpaired chromosome suggested that it may have separated precociously from the chain of 4.

The various metaphase associations of these 5 chromosomes are most easily explained by the assumption that the additional chromosome of the *C. lingulata* genome is homologous, at least so far as the pairing segments are concerned, with parts of two chromosomes that are common to the genomes of both *C. lingulata*

and *australis* (fig. 4). With this interpretation, one would expect the completely homologous chromosomes to be regularly associated at meiotic first metaphase in the hybrid; the additional chromosome from *C. lingulata* would be unpaired, or more frequently, would be associated with one or the other pairs, with which it is partly homologous, to form a chain of 3; or it would join the two pairs together to form a chain of 5.

The chain of 5 chromosomes is oriented in various ways (table 3). Some orientations would be expected to dissociate in such a manner as to result in viable products, whereas others certainly would not. Since we do not know the frequency with which nondisjunction and elimination of chromosomes may occur for some of these orientations we cannot estimate with any degree of accuracy the reduction in fertility that would be expected. However, the data obtained from backcross progeny, discussed below, indicate that the reduction in fertility from the dissociation of these five chromosomes is appreciable and probably sufficient, when combined with the effects of the translo-

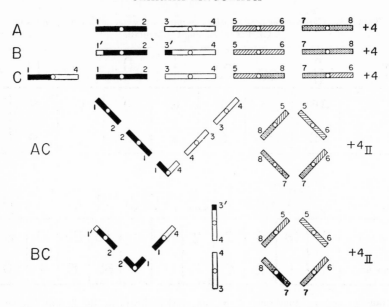

Fig. 4. Diagram of the structural and quantitative relationship of the genomes of (A) *Clarkia biloba australis* and *C. biloba biloba,* (B) *C. biloba brandegeae,* and (C) *C. lingulata.*

An inversion, not shown, differentiates genomes A and B from C but the chromosome in which it is located is not known.

cation, to account for the observed reduction in fertility of the hybrid.

A bridge and an accompanying fragment was observed at first anaphase in one hybrid cell (fig. 3c), indicating that the genomes concerned differ by a paracentric inversion. Since the same configuration is also occasionally found in cells from other hybrid progenies it seems probable that the two species differ consistently by at least one paracentric inversion. However, because of the low frequency with which crossing over apparently occurs within the inversion, its effect upon fertility is probably negligible.

Meiosis in hybrids between *C. lingulata* and *biloba* was found to be comparable in all respects to meiosis in the hybrids between *C. lingulata* and *australis.* The same configurations appear in both and in comparable frequencies.

It has been shown elsewhere (Roberts and Lewis, 1955) that the two subspecies, *biloba* and *australis,* are completely interfertile and that hybrids between them regularly form 8 bivalents. Consequently,

the earlier conclusion that these two subspecies have structurally comparable genomes is further substantiated by the similarity of behavior of their genomes and comparable reductions in fertility in hybrids with *C. lingulata.*

Meiosis has been studied in two hybrids between *C. lingulata* and *brandegeae.* A total of 98 cells have been analysed. The maximum chromosome association was found to be 4 pairs, a ring of 4, and a chain of 5 chromosomes, exactly as in the hybrids discussed above. The ring of 4 was found in approximately the same percentage of microsporocytes and showed a comparable frequency of nondisjunctional separations (table 3). The conclusion seems justified that the ring has the same structural basis in all of the hybrids and that its effect in reducing fertility is essentially the same in each. On the other hand, a chain of 5 chromosomes was found infrequently (table 3). In most of the microsporocytes these 5 chromosomes formed a chain of 3 and a pair, and, in the remainder, two pairs and an unpaired chromosome. One explanation of the low frequency with which a chain of 5 is formed would be that a structural rearrangement is involved which greatly restricts chiasma formation between two particular chromosome arms.

We have shown elsewhere (Roberts and Lewis, 1955) that hybrids between *brandegeae* and each of the other two subspecies of *C. biloba* are approximately 50 per cent sterile, although eight pairs of chromosomes are regularly formed at meiosis. We have suggested, as a possible explanation, that they may differ by a translocation of a sort that, in heterozygotes, greatly restricts chiasma formation in the chromosome arms involved. The result would be that two pairs rather than a ring of 4 chromosomes would usually be formed and the independent orientation of these pairs would lead to deficiencies in half of the products. Should this presumed translocation include the

same chromosomes that comprise the additional chromosome in the genome of *C. lingulata,* a chain of 3 and a pair, rather than a chain of 5, would be the normal maximum association in the hybrid with *brandegeae.*

The structural relationship of the genomes of *C. lingulata* and the three subspecies of *C. biloba,* suggested by their behavior in hybrid combinations, is diagramed in figure 4. The evidence indicates that the genome of *C. lingulata* is structurally more similar, and hence more closely related to that of subspecies *australis* and *biloba* than it is to *brandegeae.* Nevertheless, as we have shown above, hybrids with the latter are the most fertile. The explanation of this anomalous situation probably lies in the frequency with which chains of 5 chromosomes are formed in the different hybrids. Additional evidence that this is indeed the case

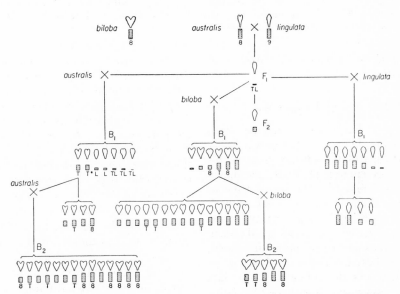

Fig. 5. Tracings of representative petals of *Clarkia lingulata, C. biloba australis,* their F₁ hybrid, *C. biloba biloba,* and the indicated progenies.

Progenies derived from self-pollination are shown by a direct line from the parent. Fertility is indicated by bar diagrams. Known chromosome complements are indicated by the following symbols: 8—structural homozygotes with 8 pairs of chromosomes; 9—structural homozygotes with 9 pairs of chromosomes; T—heterozygous for a reciprocal translocation; L—heterozygous for the "ninth" chromosome of *C. lingulata;* *—17 chromosomes but not heterozygous for the "ninth" chromosome of *C. lingulata.*

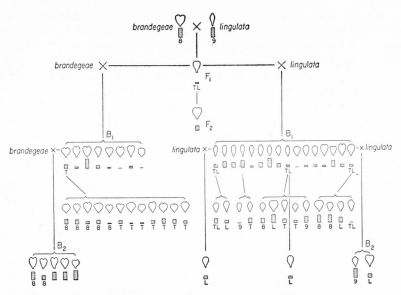

Fig. 6. Tracings of representative petals of *Clarkia lingulata, C. biloba brandegeae,* their F₁ hybrid, and the indicated progenies.

Progenies derived from self-pollination are shown by a direct line from the parent. Fertility is indicated by bar diagrams. Known chromosome complements are indicated by the following symbols: 8—structural homozygotes with 8 pairs of chromosomes; 9—structural homozygotes with 9 pairs of chromosomes; T—heterozygous for a reciprocal translocation; L—heterozygous for the "ninth" chromosome of *C. lingulata.*

comes from the progenies obtained from backcrossing.

Backcross Progenies

Progenies have been obtained from backcrossing hybrids between *C. lingulata* and each of the subspecies of *C. biloba.* Representative progenies are shown in figures 5 and 6. The petal shape of each individual is shown, together with a bar diagram indicating fertility, measured as the per cent of visibly good pollen. The chromosome constitution, if known, is also indicated. The size of the progenies shown is determined by the data available and is not indicative of relative fertilities.

Petal shape falls into two classes in the progeny obtained from backcrossing *C. lingulata* × *australis* hybrids to the *australis* parent. One group of individuals is intermediate between the two original parents; the other group is indistinguishable from *australis.* The available data indicate that the former are heterozygous for the additional chromosome from the *C. lingulata* genome whereas the latter do not have this chromosome. Furthermore, the progeny obtained from selfing a B₁ individual that did not have the additional chromosome, showed no evidence of the petal shape of *C. lingulata,* nor did the B₂ from the same individual. At the same time, these progenies did show segregation for the translocation that distinguishes the genomes of the original parents.

These data indicate that the genetic factor, or factors, determining the difference in petal shape between *C. lingulata* and *australis* is probably associated with the additional chromosome of *C. lingulata* and is certainly not associated with the translocation.

The F₁ hybrid from which the above progenies were derived was also crossed to *biloba* (fig. 5). The resulting progeny and its derivatives were variable in petal shape but a distinction can not be made between the variation resulting from recombination of the factors responsible for the differences between the two subspecies of *C. biloba* and those attributable to *C. lingulata*.

Progenies derived from the hybrid between *C. lingulata* and *brandegeae* vary greatly in petal shape (fig. 6). Furthermore, this variation is in large measure independent of segregation not only of the translocation but also of the additional chromosome from *C. lingulata*. This indicates that the factors determining the differences in petal shape between the two original parents are several or perhaps many in number and are distributed on several and perhaps all of the chromosomes.

Segregation for fertility also follows a different pattern in the progenies from different hybrids. We have indicated above that the genomes of *australis* and *biloba* are structurally homologous and have shown that they produce hybrids of comparable fertility when crossed to *C. lingulata*. Consequently, progenies involving these two subspecies will be considered together, as regards fertility, in contrast to the progenies involving *brandegeae*.

The progenies derived from F_1 hybrids between *C. lingulata* and *australis* or *biloba* fall into a few more or less distinct classes with regard to fertility, and these show a close correspondence to the chromosome complement.

Twelve individuals of hybrid derivation shown in figure 5 regularly formed 8 pairs of chromosomes at meiosis, and these individuals were as fertile as the original parents, with two exceptions. The lower fertility in these two instances may have been due to any one of several reasons affecting the health of the plant and not to genetical or chromosomal differences. On the other hand, all of the individuals known to be heterozygous for the translocation or the additional chro-

mosome of *C. lingulata* were conspicuously less fertile than the original parents. Twelve individuals were heterozygous for the translocation but did not have the additional chromosome from *C. lingulata*. These individuals were remarkably similar in fertility for the mean percentage of visibly good pollen, for each individual fell between 55 and 70, and most frequently near 65 per cent. These figures probably afford a much better estimate of the effect of heterozygosity for this translocation on fertility than do the figures obtained from observations of meiosis. Two individuals that had the additional chromosome from *C. lingulata* but were not heterozygous for the translocation had means of 20 and 25 per cent visibly good pollen. These figures can be taken as indicative of the effect of this additional chromosome on fertility. The validity of the estimates of the effects of the additional chromosome on fertility as well as heterozygosity for the translocation is further substantiated by the fertility of individuals that are heterozygous for both. The fertility of these individuals is comparable to that of the F_1.

The chromosome complement of one of the B_1 individuals deserves special comment. It was heterozygous for the translocation and had a total of 17 chromosomes. However, the additional chromosome was in no instance associated with a chain of 5 but at most a chain of 3 and usually was found as a univalent. In this respect, the chromosome association was comparable to that in the primary trisomics of *C. unguiculata* (Vasek, 1955) and like them had little, if any, effect on fertility. Consequently, we believe that this plant is a primary trisomic of the sort that would be expected from certain of the gametes resulting from the dissociation of the chain of 5 in the F_1 (i.e. 1-2, 3-4, 3-4, or 1-2, 1-2, 3-4).

The restoration of complete fertility in hybrid derivatives that regularly form 8 pairs of chromosomes, together with the constancy of the reduction in fertility associated with each of the two major chromosomal differences indicates beyond reasonable doubt that the level of fertility of the F_1 hybrid and subsequent progenies is attributable to the two gross chromosomal differences between the genomes of the parents.

Derivatives of the F_1 hybrid between *C. lingulata* and *brandegeae* (fig. 6) are much more variable in fertility than the progenies discussed above and furthermore bear no simple relationship to the observed chromosomal differences between individuals. Heterozygosity for the translocation probably has a comparable effect upon fertility wherever it occurs. Consequently, the greater variability of these hybrids is probably due, in considerable measure, to the structural differences in the 5 chromosomes that usually form a chain of 3 and a pair rather than a chain of 5. Assuming that the structural relationships indicated in figure 4 are correct, functional gametes from the hybrid between *C. lingulata* and *australis* that include two of these chromosomes will be structurally identical (i.e., 1-2, 3-4), whereas those with three will be at most of 3 sorts (i.e., 1-2, 3-4, 1-4; 1-2, 3-4, 3-4; or 1-2, 1-2, 3-4). On the other hand, the corresponding 5 chromosomes in the hybrid between *C. lingulata* and *brandegeae* can produce two kinds of functional gametes with two of these chromosomes and seven presumably viable combinations of three chromosomes. The fertility of the individuals resulting from these nine classes of gametes will vary, depending upon the meiotic behavior and genotypes of the combinations concerned. The progenies would, consequently, be expected to be more variable in fertility and to have fewer individuals recovering full fertility, as indeed is the case. However, all of the variability in fertility in these progenies is apparently not attributable to the structural and quantitative differences we have been considering. Many of these derivatives show various degrees of asynapsis, which in the most extreme cases results in a high degree of sterility, and probably ac-

counts for most, but not necessarily all, of the instances in which the derivatives are more sterile than the F_1 hybrid. We believe that this asynapsis results from genetic recombination rather than from structural or quantitative differences. Genetic recombination may also modify fertility in other ways in these hybrid derivatives.

DISCUSSION

We have shown that only the shape of the petal distinguishes the external morphology of *C. lingulata* from *C. biloba australis*. Nevertheless, their respective genomes differ quantitatively by one chromosome that is homologous to parts of two chromosomes in the normal complement of both entities. The fertility of the hybrid between them is low, which we regard as a consequence of the dissociation at meiosis of the translocation ring and of the chain involving the additional chromosome. The genetical basis for the difference in petal shape is also probably associated with this additional chromosome.

The genomes of subspecies *australis* and *biloba* are apparently structurally homologous in all respects and when combined with a genome from *C. lingulata* yield hybrids of comparable fertility. However, *biloba*, in contrast to *australis*, differs from *C. lingulata* by several morphological traits, the inheritance of which is not associated with the additional chromosome of *C. lingulata*.

In addition to the differences that distinguish the genome of *C. lingulata* from those of *australis* and *biloba*, the genomes of *C. lingulata* and *brandegeae* probably differ by a translocation. This translocation involves the chromosomes from which the added chromosome of *C. lingulata* was derived. Our data also indicates that the morphological differences between *C. lingulata* and *brandegeae* are determined by genes distributed throughout the genome and that genetic recombination, as well as structural differences in the genomes, is probably responsible for a reduction in fertility of some of the hybrid derivatives. Nevertheless, the F_1 hybrids between *C. lingulata* and *brandegeae* are more fertile than those with *australis* or *biloba;* at the same time, hybrids with *brandegeae* are more difficult to obtain.

The difficulty of obtaining the hybrid between *C. lingulata* and *brandegeae* reflects, we believe, the degree of genetic difference between the two parents. On the other hand, the greater fertility of the hybrid is due, paradoxically, to greater structural difference in the genomes which leads to more simple chromosome configurations at meiosis, and which, in turn, results in a greater number of functionable gametes in the F_1. However, the backcross progenies, in contrast to those involving *australis* or *biloba,* include a far lower percentage of individuals that recover full fertility.

Considering both morphological and cytogenetical evidence, there can be no doubt that *C. lingulata* is most closely related to the subspecies of *C. biloba* that grows adjacent to it. Let us now speculate on the way they became differentiated.

The quantitative difference between the genomes of *C. lingulata* and *australis* indicates that the former is derived from a genome of 8 by the addition of one chromosome. We know that chromosomes in excess of the basic number, particularly in *Clarkia,* do not necessarily disturb normal development (Lewis, 1954). Furthermore, other evidence also indicates that in *Clarkia* genomes of 9 have been derived from those with 8, which in turn are derivatives of an original basic number of 7 (Lewis, 1953b).

The genome of *C. lingulata* is assuredly derived from one comparable to that of *australis* for at present they apparently have 6 chromosomes in common that have not become differentiated structurally, except perhaps for an inversion, nor genetically to any apparent extent. Furthermore, the reciprocal translocation by which two pairs of chromosomes have become differentiated is not associated with any detected phenotypic dif-

ference. Consequently, the genetic differentiation between these two entities is associated primarily, if not entirely, with the additional chromosome in the genome of *C. lingulata.*

This additional chromosome may have originated as a tertiary trisomic of *australis* from which a constant tetrasomic condition was then derived. The alternative would be that the additional chromosome was derived from another, closely related, species. Two species closely related to *australis* grow with or near it, namely, *C. dudleyana* and *C. modesta.* One of these, *C. modesta,* has a petal shape suggestive of *C. lingulata.* However, we have been unable, after innumerable attempts, to obtain a hybrid between *australis* and *C. modesta* or *C. dudleyana.* In the absence of positive evidence of an interspecific origin of the additional chromosome, we are inclined to favor the first hypothesis. Furthermore, evidence from another species supports this view. A tertiary trisomic was found among the self progeny of an individual of *C. unguiculata.* The parent had the normal number of chromosomes but was heterozygous for a translocation (Lewis, 1954). However, this particular trisomic had no distinctive morphological traits.

Differentiation in petal shape between *C. lingulata* and *australis* was probably coincident with the establishment of the additional chromosome. Certainly the morphological differentiation did not preceed this establishment, although it may be due to subsequent mutation.

The translocation which differentiates the genomes of *australis* and *C. lingulata* may have become fixed before or after the difference in chromosome number but the sequence can not be determined. However, the paracentric inversion, by which these genomes differ, probably had its origin in *C. lingulata,* or a population destined to become that species, subsequent to the establishment of one or both of the chromosomal alterations which restrict genetic exchange between populations. On the other hand, the colonial habit of these plants, of itself, may form a highly effective barrier to gene exchange, even when the distance between colonies is small (Lewis, 1953a).

The relative adaptedness of the altered genotypes that ultimately resulted in the differentiation of *C. lingulata* may have been an important factor in speciation although fixation by chance may also have played a major role. The colonial habit and the capacity for self-pollination are undoubtedly factors that would tend to promote the latter. In any event, the transition from one species to the other seems to have been a rapid process which depended only upon the fixation of one or perhaps two chromosomal alterations, which also led to a morphological and perhaps ecological difference. We are inclined to believe in the present case that the stage was set for subsequent differentiation and speciation by the single step of adding a chromosome to the genome of *australis*.

The close relationship of the genomes of *C. lingulata* and *australis,* the geographical juxtaposition the two taxa, and the restricted distribution of the former, suggests to us not only a rapid but also a relatively recent origin of *C. lingulata* from *C. biloba australis.*

Summary

Clarkia lingulata has been compared phenotypically and cytogenetically with each of the three subspecies of the closely related species *C. biloba.*

Clarkia lingulata is distinguishable in external morphology from *C. biloba australis,* which grows adjacent to it, only by the shape of the petal. Their genomes differ quantitatively by a chromosome, and structurally by a translocation and a paracentric inversion. Fertility of the hybrid between them is low, a consequence of the meiotic behavior associated with heterozygoscity for the translocation and

the additional chromosome. The morphological difference is apparently also associated with this additional chromosome.

The genomes of *C. biloba australis* and *C. b. biloba* are structurally homologous. Consequently, their hybrids with *C. lingulata* are comparable in fertility. However, *C. b. biloba* differs to a greater extent from *C. lingulata* in external morphology.

Clarkia biloba brandegeae, which is geographically most remote from *C. lingulata,* shows the greatest difference both in chromosome arrangement and external morphology. Nevertheless, the hybrids between *C. lingulata* and *C. b. brandegeae* are more fertile than those involving the other two subspecies. The explanation lies in the more simple meiotic configurations resulting from a greater structural difference in the chromosomes. This explanation is substaniated by the fertility of the B_1 and subsequent progenies.

The conclusion is reached that *C. lingulata* evolved in comparatively recent time from *C. biloba australis* by a rapid process whereby a chromosome homologous with parts of two others was added to the genome of the latter.

Literature Cited

Lewis, H. 1953a. The mechanism of evolution in the genus *Clarkia*. Evolution, **7**: 1–20.

——. 1953b. Chromosome phylogeny and habitat preference of *Clarkia*. Evolution, **7**: 102–109.

——. 1954. Quantitative variation in wild genotypes of *Clarkia*. International Union of Biol. Sci. Symposium, Ser. B (15), 114–125.

Lewis, H., and Margaret Lewis. 1953. New species and changes in nomenclature in the genus *Clarkia*. Madroño, **12**, 33–39.

Roberts, Margaret R., and H. Lewis. 1955. Subspeciation in *Clarkia biloba*. Evolution **9**: 445–454.

Vasek, F. C. 1955. Aneuploidy in *Clarkia unguiculata*. Ph.D. Thesis (unpub.). Univ. of California, Los Angeles, Library.

EVOLUTION IN THE GENUS *CUCURBITA*

Thomas W. Whitaker and W. P. Bemis

U. S. Department of Agriculture, ARS, Crops Research, La Jolla, California,
and Department of Horticulture, University of Arizona, Tucson, Arizona

Accepted July 6, 1964

For the study of evolution the genus *Cucurbita* offers several unique advantages: (a) *Cucurbita* is a comparatively small closed system composed of about two dozen species concentrated in a relatively small land mass. Because of their conspicuous vines and fruits, it is unlikely that more than one-half dozen species are yet to be discovered, although a few new species might be expected from Baja California, the west coast of Mexico opposite the peninsula of Baja California, and in southern Mexico and Central America. These are areas that have not yet been thoroughly explored by botanists. (b) All species have 20 pairs of chromosomes. For this reason species differentiation must be largely genic or cytoplasmic, rather than dependent upon gross chromosomal rearrangements. (c) There are both wild and cultivated species in the genus. This situation presents an opportunity to compare the evolution of closely related species under cultivation contrasted with the evolution of species in nature. (d) From archaeological remains it is possible to trace man's association with these plants backward in time for a maximum of 10,000 years.

Evolution in the Wild Species

The center of distribution of the genus is the tropical or semitropical region south of Mexico City extending as far south as the Mexico–Guatemala border. There are a number of annual and perennial species from this area (table 1). These species are uniformly mesophytic lowland plants, with dark green or grayish-green foliage, normally with slender runners, mostly annual with a long, hard taproot, but one species (*C. radicans*) producing perennial tubercles.

As species of the genus migrated northward they entered an area characterized by extreme aridity and high temperatures. About eight species are found in the huge area that stretches from Baja California on the west to the Gulf of Mexico on the east, and extends as far north as the southwestern United States.

North of Mexico City the species are characteristically xerophytic (except for *Cucurbita okeechobeensis*), and adapted to cope with the rigors of an arid or semiarid desert environment. Species indigenous to this area are able to withstand prolonged periods of drought and high temperatures without desiccation. The xerophytic species have light grayish-green foliage, and are usually coarse, rank-growing plants. Their most characteristic feature is the large, perennial storage roots that range in size from 5 to over 150 pounds depending upon the species. Like many other xerophytic species these plants produce vegetative and reproductive structures rapidly after the infrequent rains. Some may delay vegetative growth for several years until there is sufficient moisture to produce aerial organs. Dittmer and Roser (1963) suggest that the periderm which is comparatively thick in the xerophytic species aids in the retention of water, enabling the plants to survive long periods of drought.

The xerophytic species are relatively uniform because of their method of asexual reproduction. Colonies have been observed to develop from a central plant by the production of adventitious roots at the nodes of the larger runners during periods of favorable growth. The adventitious roots eventually develop into a long tuberous root that can withstand low temperatures and prolonged drought, yet produce new vine growth under favorable conditions. Colonies established in this manner forestall the need for intervention of a sexual generation.

TABLE 1. *The distribution, growth, and moisture habit of the cultivated and wild species of* Cucurbita. *Compiled from Bailey (1948) and others*

	Species	Distribution	Annual	Perennial	Xerophytic	Mesophytic
Cultivated	pepo L.	Northern Mexico, southern U. S.	x			
	*texana Gr.	Central Texas				
	mixta Pang.	Mexico, Central America, southwestern U. S.	x			
	moschata Poir.	Mexico, Central America	x			
	maxima Duch.	Argentina, Bolivia, Chile	x			
	*andreana Naud.	Argentina, Bolivia				
	ficifolia Bouché	Mexico, Central America, northern South America		x		
Wild	sororia Bailey	Guerrero, Oaxaca	x			x
	fraterna Bailey	Tamaulipas	x(?)			x
	kellyana Bailey	Jalisco	x			x
	okeechobeensis Bailey	Florida	x			x
	mooreii Bailey	Hidalgo	x			x
	martinezii Bailey	Vera Cruz	x			x
	radicans Naud.	Mexico City		x		x
	lundelliana Bailey	Guatemala, British Honduras		x		x
	pedatifolia Bailey	Quaretaro		x(?)		x
	palmeri Bailey	Culiacan, Sinaloa		x(?)	x(?)	
	gracilior Bailey	Mexico (state)		x(?)		x(?)
	cordata Wats.	Baja California		x	x	
	cylindrata Bailey	Baja California		x	x	
	digitata Gr.	New Mexico, Arizona		x	x	
	palmata Wats.	S. California		x	x	
	californica Torr.	S. California, Arizona		x	x	
	galeottii Cogn.	Oaxaca		x(?)	x(?)	
	scabridifolia Bailey	Northeastern Mexico, southern Tamaulipas		x	x	
	foetidissima HBK	Nebr., Mo., Kansas, Colo., Utah, Nev., Texas, Ariz., N. Mex., Calif., southern Mexico to Guanajuato		x	x	

* Non-cultivated feral species.

RELATIONSHIP OF THE XEROPHYTIC SPECIES TO THE MESOPHYTIC SPECIES

The results obtained to date show that the xerophytic, perennial species of *Cucurbita* are incompatible with the mesophytic wild species. For example, the xerophytic species *C. digitata*, *C. palmata*, *C. cylindrata*, and *C. foetidissima* failed to set fruit when repeatedly pollinated by *C. lundelliana*, *C. sororia*, and *C. radicans* (Bemis and Nelson, 1963). When used as pollinators the four xerophytic species did set fruit in matings with *C. lundelliana*, but there was no evidence of embryo development in the seeds of such fruits (fig. 1).

Cucurbita radicans failed to set fruit when pollinated by the four xerophytic species, with the exception of a single fruit obtained by using pollen from *C. palmata*; but there was no evidence of embryo development in seeds from this fruit. In other test, reciprocal crosses of *C. cylindrata* × *C. lundelliana* and *C. cylindrata* × *C. okeechobeensis* failed to set fruit. Present evidence suggests that the two groups, mesophytic and xerophytic, are well separated genetically and geographically.

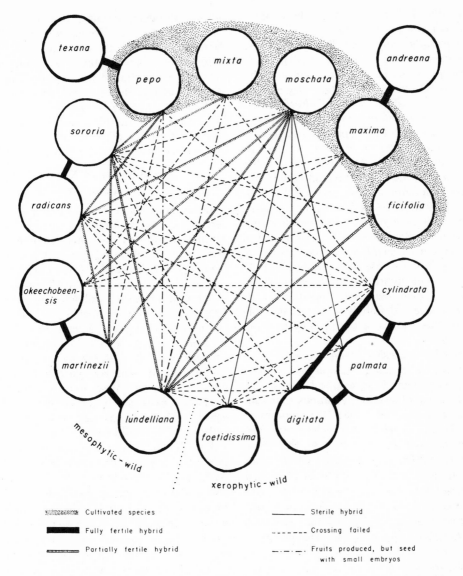

FIG. 1. Crossability diagram of different species of *Cucurbita*. The interrelationships among the cultivated species are not shown.

RELATIONSHIPS AMONG THE XEROPHYTIC SPECIES OF *CUCURBITA*

Experimental hybridization among the xerophytic species is not complete, but the work thus far suggests they can be sorted into two groups: (a) *Cucurbita palmata*, *C. digitata*, and *C. cylindrata*; and (b) *C. foetidissima*. The three species of group (a), when hybridized, produced fertile F_1 and F_2 populations. The most striking visual difference between them is the shape of the leaves; *C. digitata* has narrow digitate leaves; *C. palmata* has palmately lobed leaves; and *C. cylindrata* has cordate–ovate leaves. The leaves are about the same size in each species, but those of *C. palmata* and *C. cylindrata* have a light-grayish cast. The leaves of *C. digitata* are normally darker green that those of C. palmata or C. cylindrata.

Cucurbita californica Torrey ex Wats., considered by some to be a variant of C. palmata Wats., most likely belongs to this group. Likewise, C. cordata Bailey appears to be closely allied to C. cylindrata Bailey.

Cucurbita foetidissima stands apart from the other xerophytic species both genetically, and by the remarkable extent of its geographic range. Attempts to hybridize C. foetidissima with other species in the xerophytic group were unsuccessful. Although fruit were set in reciprocal crosses, there was no sign of embryo development. Similarly, Bemis (1964) has observed colonies of C. foetidissima growing side by side with C. digitata in nature but with no evidence of hybridization between them. Thus, present evidence suggests that C. foetidissima is definitely cross-incompatible with other species of the xerophytic group (fig. 1).

Hurd and Linsley (1964), in an exhaustive and penetrating study of bees belonging to the genera Peponapis and Xenoglossa, have recorded some observations that substantiate the idea that the xerophytic species of Cucurbita can be separated into two or more groups. Bees of the above genera exhibit a preferential selection for the pollens of certain species of Cucurbita in some instances. Hurd and Linsley state: "Thus P. pruinosa, whose females appear to use only the pollen of the native C. foetidissima, readily gather the pollen of the various domestic Cucurbita, but apparently are unable to use the pollens of the native C. digitata and C. palmata even though these plants occur abundantly within the geographic range of P. pruinosa. Similarly, P. timberlakei, which apparently does not collect pollen from flowers of the domestic Cucurbita, appears to be limited to the pollens of the native C. digitata and C. palmata. Our present evidence suggests that P. timberlakei cannot use the pollen of C. foetidissima even when that plant occurs within its range."

Cucurbita foetidissima ranges from Nebraska, through Missouri, Kansas, Colorado, and west into Texas, New Mexico, Arizona, Utah, Nevada, and California. It is found in northern Mexico extending as far south as the state of Guanajuato. There seems to be considerable variability within C. foetidissima, notably in leaf lobing and leaf shape. A careful taxonomic survey might disclose the need to distinguish several forms or varieties.

RELATIONSHIP OF THE XEROPHYTIC SPECIES TO THE CULTIVATED SPECIES

Information about the relationship of the xerophytic species to the cultivated ones is confined mostly to the reactions obtained using a single cultivated species, Cucurbita moschata. Grebenščikov (1958) was successful in hybridizing C. foetidissima and C. moschata, but the F_1 plants were sterile. Bemis (1964) has obtained F_1 hybrids by pollinating Butternut, a cultivar of C. moschata, with pollen from C. digitata, C. palmata, and C. foetidissima. F_1 plants were produced using embryo culture techniques; however, they were completely sterile but extremely vigorous once established. These plants did not produce pollen, and seeds did not develop.

The F_1 plants from the crosses of Cucurbita moschata with C. digitata, C. palmata, and C. foetidissima have tuberous root systems, indicating dominance of this character derived from the xerophytic species. These F_1 plants can be maintained indefinitely by asexual means for further study. Bemis (1964) states that pollination of xerophytic species with non-xerophytic species other than C. moschata has resulted in failure of fruit set and embryo development. Additional work supports this observation. In reciprocal pollinations, C. cylindrata did not set fruit when crossed with either C. andreana, C. mixta, or C. pepo (fig. 1). A viable embryo, however, was cultured from the triple species cross (C. moschata × C. lundelliana) × C. foetidissima. This hybrid was sterile, and similar in appearance to the F_1 hybrid from the cross C. moschata × C. foetidissima.

Following the breeding and other evidence, we are suggesting (1) that *C. moschata* is more closely related to the xerophytic species than the other cultivated species or the non-xerophytic wild species; (2) the xerophytic species represent specialized terminal types that are not in the mainstream of evolution from which the present-day cultivated species were derived.

In their studies of the solitary bees of the genera *Peponapis* and *Xenoglossa*, Hurd and Linsley (1964) report data that suggest *Cucurbita foetidissima* is more closely allied to the domestic *Cucurbita* than either *C. digitata* or *C. palmata*. They state: "It appears significant that all species of *Peponapis* and *Xenoglossa* which use pollen of the native *C. foetidissima* are also able to freely utilize the pollen of domestic *Cucurbita*. This relationship suggests that *C. foetidissima* may be closely related to the domestic *Cucurbita*. The fact that *P. timberlakei* is apparently unable to utilize the pollen of the domestic *Cucurbita* seems to strengthen this view." Our data are not sufficiently critical to accept or reject this suggestion. If, however, *C. foetidissima* is closely allied to the cultivated group, it must be through *C. moschata* because reciprocal crosses between *C. foetidissima* × *C. maxima*, and a single cross between *C. foetidissima* × *C. pepo*, failed to set fruit (fig. 1).

RELATIONSHIP OF CULTIVATED SPECIES
TO EACH OTHER

The relationship of the cultivated species to each other has recently been examined in detail (Whitaker, 1961; Whitaker and Davis, 1962). The conclusions that emerge can be stated as follows: (1) F_1 hybrids are obtained from most interspecific pollinations in this group. The hybrids, however, are usually sterile because of the inability of the F_1 plants to produce functional pollen. (2) *Cucurbita ficifolia*, the single perennial species, is well separated from the annual species. The fig-leafed form of this species is probably allied with *C. pepo* or *C. maxima*. Likewise, the form

with moschata-like leaves is perhaps closely related to *C. moschata*. The breeding data suggest that the four annual species are arranged like a wheel, clustered around *C. moschata* which serves as the hub. (3) There is no evidence for spontaneous hybridization among the cultivated *Cucurbita*, although they have been grown side by side in fields and gardens for many generations.

It is a curious fact that at least three of the cultivated species are associated with feral species whose breeding reactions correspond almost exactly with their cultivated counterpart. The two feral species, *Cucurbita andreana* Naud. and *C. texana* Gray, will exchange genes readily with their cultivated counterparts, *C. maxima* and *C. pepo* (Whitaker, 1951 and unpublished data). Furthermore, there is no loss of fertility in the F_1, F_2, and following generations. We have grown several collections of an unidentified wild species that is similar in vegetative, fruit, and seed characters to *C. mixta*. The relationship between these three pairs of species, i.e., *C. andreana* with *C. maxima*, *C. pepo* with *C. texana*, and *C. mixta* with an unidentified wild species, is such as to suggest that the feral species may be escapes, well adapted for survival in their present environment. It should be remembered, however, there is no critical evidence to support this judgment. The reverse could be true, i.e., the so-called feral species might be the ancestors of the cultivated forms.

RELATIONSHIPS AMONG THE MESOPHYTIC
SPECIES

Experimental work to determine the relationships among the mesophytic species is not complete, but enough has been learned to suggest that they are a more or less homogeneous group. The group is composed of the following species: *Cucurbita lundelliana*, *C. martinezii*, *C. sororia*, *C. radicans*, and *C. okeechobeensis*. It is probable that *C. kellyana*, *C. mooreii*, and *C. pedatifolia* also belong to this group, but we have no breeding data to substantiate this suggestion. With the exception of

C. okeechobeensis, indigenous to a restricted area along the shores of Lake Okeechobe, Florida, the species are from central and southern Mexico (table 1).

We have not been able to fully explore the compatibility status of this group chiefly because seed collections of most species are not available for culture. *Cucurbita sororia* will hybridize with *C. lundelliana* producing fertile F_1 and F_2 populations, if *C. lundelliana* is used as ♀ parent. *Cucurbita martinezii* will hybridize reciprocally with *C. lundelliana* with no loss of fertility in the individuals of the F_1 and F_2 populations; also *C. martinezii* will hybridize with *C. okeechobeensis*, and *C. sororia* with *C. radicans* produce nearly similar results (fig. 1).

RELATIONSHIPS OF THE MESOPHYTIC SPECIES TO THE CULTIVATED SPECIES

The peculiar compatibility relationships between *Cucurbita lundelliana* and the cultivated species of *Cucurbita* were reported in detail (Whitaker and Davis, 1962). In summary, *C. lundelliana* is compatible with all five cultivated species, producing fruit and seeds. In matings with three of the cultivated species (*C. moschata, C. maxima,* and *C. ficifolia*), viable F_1, F_2, and backcross progenies are produced, mostly with reduced fertility. In matings with *C. pepo* and *C. mixta* the seeds have small embryos that will not germinate using conventional cultural methods, but they have responded to embryo culture techniques (Chinn, unpublished data).

The remainder of the mesophytic species used will cross with one or more of the cultivated species, but their spectrum of affinity is not as broad as that of *Cucurbita lundelliana*. For example, *C. sororia* will hybridize with *C. pepo* and *C. mixta*, but no fruit are set from pollinations of *C. moschata* or *C. ficifolia*. *Cucurbita okeechobeensis* hybridizes with *C. moschata* but not with *C. maxima, C. mixta,* or *C. ficifolia*. *Cucurbita martinezii* will hybridize with *C. moschata*, but not with *C. pepo*. *Cucurbita radicans* will hybridize with *C.*

moschata and *C. pepo,* but not with *C. maxima* (fig. 1). While these are the results of many attempts at hybridization, it is possible that further work using different cultivars or strains of the same species would produce hybrids which could not be obtained with the seed stocks available at present.

From the above results it is most likely that the origin of the cultivated *Cucurbita* is to be sought in the mesophytic complex of gourds indigenous to southern Mexico and the northern portions of Central America. *Cucurbita lundelliana* appears to be the most promising candidate as a choice for the putative ancestor of the cultivated species. Not only is *C. lundelliana* widely compatible among the cultivated species, it will also hybridize readily with most of the species in the mesophytic group.

DISCUSSION

In tracing the origin of the cultivated *Cucurbita*, a survey of the evidence indicates that *C. moschata* is the indispensable cog through which the species of *Cucurbita* are related. Its compatibility reactions suggest relationships with the cultivated species, as well as the xerophytic and mesophytic ones. The archaeological record attests to the antiquity of *C. moschata* as a cultivated plant. From the huge midden of Huaca Prieta on the north coast of Peru, Whitaker and Bird (1949) identified seeds and rinds of *C. moschata* with a date of about 3000 B.C. Likewise, in the area near Tehuacán, Puebla, Mexico, Cutler, Whitaker, and MacNeish (1964) identified seeds of *C. moschata* dated at 5200–3500 B.C.

Cucurbita lundelliana is the most interesting species among the non-cultivated groups. Its relationships to the mesophytic species, and its apparently close relationship to the cultivated species, particularly *C. moschata*, suggest that it may have been involved in the ancestry of the cultivated species.

If we assume that *Cucurbita lundelliana* is concerned in the ancestry of the cultivated types, evolution from wild to cultivated forms has probably followed the course suggested below. Generally each mutation or series of mutations has made the cultivated forms more and more dependent upon man for their survival.

from Wild	to Cultivated
annual, but some perennial	annual
adventitious roots at stem nodes	absence of adventitious roots at nodes
small leaves, many slender runners	large leaves, few coarse runners
numerous, small fruits	few, large fruits
fruits with durable rind	fruits with non-durable rind
fruits with many small seeds	fruits with few and larger seeds
fruits mostly green-striped or mottled, turning yellow at maturity	fruits varicolored, green, tan, gray, white, orange, etc.
greenish-white, fibrous flesh, usually bitter	orange or whitish flesh, mostly non-fibrous, seldom bitter

SUMMARY

1. The xerophytic species of *Cucurbita* are specialized types isolated both genetically and geographically from the wild mesophytic species.

2. The breeding data indicate the xerophytic species can be divided into two incompatible groups: (1) *Cucurbita cylindrata, C. digitata,* and *C. palmata*; (2) *C. foetidissima.* This separation is supported by the studies of Hurd and Linsley with the solitary bees of the genus *Peponapis.*

3. The xerophytic species appear to be more closely related to *Cucurbita moschata* than to other species in the cultivated group.

4. The compatibility pattern of the cultivated species suggests that *Cucurbita moschata* is the axis through which they (the cultivated species) are related to each other.

5. The mesophytic species are genetically a more or less homogeneous group. Those available for study were mostly compatible within the group. In this group, *Cucurbita lundelliana* is the key species. It has a wide spectrum of compatibility with the mesophytic species, and is compatible with the cultivated species.

ACKNOWLEDGMENTS

The manuscript was read by Drs. Edgar Anderson, G. W. Bohn, Hugh C. Cutler, Paul Hurd, Jr., G. Ledyard Stebbins, Jr., and Dean Harlan Lewis. We are grateful for their helpful comments and suggestions. The authors, however, are responsible for any errors that may occur and for the interpretation.

LITERATURE CITED

BAILEY, L. H. 1943. Species of *Cucurbita*. Gentes Herb., **6**: 266–322.

BEMIS, W. P. 1964. Interspecific hybridization in the *Cucurbita*. II. *C. moschata* Poir. × xerophytic species of *Cucurbita*. J. Hered., **54**: 285–289.

—— AND J. M. NELSON. 1963. Interspecific hybridization with the genus *Cucurbita*. I. Fruit set, seed and embryo development. J. Ariz. Acad. Sci., **2**: 104–107.

CUTLER, H. C., THOMAS W. WHITAKER, AND R. S. MACNEISH. 1964. Cucurbits from the Tehuacán Caves. Ann. Rep. Tehuacán Arch.-Bot. Project (in press).

DITTMER, H. J., AND MARGARET L. ROSER. 1963. The periderm of certain members of the Cucurbitaceae. Southwestern Nat., **8**: 1–9.

GREBENŠČIKOV, I. 1958. Über Zwei *Cucurbita*-Artkreuzungen. Züchter, **28**: 233–237.

HURD, P. D., JR., AND E. GORTON LINSLEY. 1964. The squash and gourd bees—genera *Peponapis* Robertson and *Xenoglossa* Smith—inhabiting America north of Mexico (Hymenoptera: Apoidea). Hilgardia, **35**: 375–477.

WHITAKER, T. W. 1951. A species cross in *Cucurbita*. J. Hered., **42**: 65–69.

——. 1961. Biosystematics of the cultivated *Cucurbita*. Recent Adv. Bot., Univ. Toronto Press, **2**: 858–862 (Sect. 9).

—— AND JUNIUS B. BIRD. 1949. The identification and significance of the cucurbit materials from Huaca Prieta, Peru. Amer. Mus. Nov., No. **1426**: 1–15.

—— AND G. N. DAVIS. 1962. The cucurbits. Leonard Hill [Books] Ltd., London, 250 p.

SECTION III

Reticulate Evolution

ANDERSON, EDGAR. 1948. Hybridization of the habitat. Evolution 2: 1–9.

MANGELSDORF, PAUL C. 1958. Ancestor of corn. Science 128: 1313–1320.

STUTZ, HOWARD C., and L. KAY THOMAS. 1964. Hybridization and introgression in *Cowania* and *Purshia*. Evolution 18: 183–195.

SIBLEY, CHARLES G., and LESTER L. SHORT, JR. 1959. Hybridization in the buntings (*Passerina*) of the Great Plains. Auk 76: 443–463.

OWNBEY, MARION. 1950. Natural hybridization and amphiploidy in the genus *Tragopogon*. Am. Jour. Bot. 37: 487–499.

One of the most important sources of variability in natural populations is genes and gene complexes transferred from other populations. Indeed, it is often the ability that differentiated populations retain for the exchange of genetic material that is of paramount importance in their evolution. In the ongoing process of evolutionary adjustment to a constantly changing environment, it may be precisely those individuals that recombine certain sets of characteristics from the differentiated populations that may prove most successful. When hybridization occurs, evolutionary lines which have been separate reunite genetically, and evolution becomes reticulate.

When differentiated populations come together, a variety of consequences may ensue. The populations may become more distinct, as stressed for example in the paper by Brown and Wilson in the preceding section. Or they may simply not hybridize. Or one or both of the populations may be modified by repeated backcrossing with the relatively rare hybrids (introgressive hybridization), a situation that has long been studied by Edgar Anderson.[*] In the paper chosen here he points out that F_1 hybrids may be expected to be intermediate in habitat requirements between the parental species, and that segregation for relationships to the many factors of the environment will occur in subsequent generations. Heterogeneous habitats in which such segregants can grow are found only rarely in nature, except where man has "hybridized" the habitat. Introgressive hybridization is also of practical importance for some cultivated plants. For example, Mangelsdorf[*] has proposed that the ancestor of modern cultivated corn (maize) was a very much smaller grass with many of the characteristics of present-day corn. In the course of many generations of crossing and backcrossing with the related grass teosinte, introgression from the latter produced the variety of types of corn seen, for example, in Mexico today. In the genera *Cowania* and *Purshia*, shrubs of the arid western United States, fertile hybrids are formed wherever the species come together and introgression occurs. Stutz and Thomas[*] have shown that although the genera are usually separated altitudinally, contacts occur at summits of contrasting north-south slopes and in ravines. Introgression of *Cowania* characters into *Purshia* may have the selective advantage of rendering the latter less palatable. One of the two species of *Purshia* appears to illustrate a second possible consequence of hybridization in nature, as it is apparently a more or less stabilized segregant from the natural hybridization of the other species of *Purshia* and the single species of *Cowania*.

In birds, the well known work of Sibley (1954) provides an excellent example of introgressive hybridization in the Mexican towhees, in which some of the populations occupy disturbed pine woodland and are enormously variable, recombining the features of the parental species. A similar example of

[*] Paper included in this section.

introgression between the indigo and lazuli buntings is provided in the paper by Sibley and Short.* Numerous examples are likewise reported for plants, where introgressive hybridization appears to be more common: for example, the work of Heiser (1949) with the sunflowers *Helianthus annuus* and *H. bolanderi* is an excellent example of the way in which the introgression of genes between species can enhance their morphological and ecological variability. The stabilization of hybrid populations, without changes in chromosome number or special reproductive devices, is likewise demonstrated for many groups, such as *Camissonia*, a genus of mostly annual desert plants (Raven, 1962), *Delphinium*, a genus of perennial herbs (Lewis and Epling, 1959), *Euschistus*, a genus of stinkbugs (Sailer, 1954), and *Thais*, a marine snail (Staiger, 1954). Again, such situations appear to have arisen more frequently in plants than in animals. In some groups of plants, especially those consisting of trees and shrubs, stabilized intermediate populations are readily produced between well differentiated species in all combinations, and the groups have doubtless varied kaleidoscopically through time as the environment has changed. A particularly fine example of this sort of pattern of variation is provided by the work of Nobs (1963) on the mountain lilacs of the genus *Ceanothus* sect. *Cerastes*. Gillett (1966), Rattenbury (1962), and others have stressed the importance of cyclic hybridization of a similar nature in enhancing the potential variability of the often genetically rather homogeneous populations present on isolated islands and archipelagos.

If hybrids between two distinctive lines are able to reproduce asexually, they may come to form large stabilized populations even though they are completely sterile. For example, in the herbaceous plant genus *Circaea*, completely sterile hybrids between two well differentiated species occupy certain areas to the exclusion of either parent (Raven, 1963), their physiological tolerances apparently exceeding those of their parents for these particular conditions. The advantage of asexual reproduction in such a situation is, of course, that a particular, favored genotype can be reproduced rapidly and with a high degree of fidelity in response to a particular environmental challenge. A similar example in animals is that described by Hubbs (1955) for the fish genus *Mollienisia* in some of the rivers of northeastern Mexico, where parthenogenesis allows the reproduction of the all-female species *M. formosa*, presumably a hybrid between two other very distinct species. Additional cases of parthenogenesis are being discovered continually in the vertebrates, while apomictic groups of plants have long been known. In the bluegrasses of the genus *Poa*, for example, most strains set functional seed without fertilization, and the variability of the widespread Kentucky bluegrass, *P. pratensis*, has been greatly enhanced by occasional hybridization with the other species it has contacted in assuming its worldwide distribution.

One of the most common mechanisms available in plants for the elimination of hybrid sterility is that of polyploidy, and it is currently estimated that about half of all species of flowering plants may have had a polyploid origin. Polyploids arise from sterile hybrids by doubling of chromosome number, which occurs occasionally as a mitotic accident. When the chromosome number has doubled, each chromosome has a pairing partner and the fertility of the polyploid derivative may be restored. At the same time, recombination is cut down, since each gene is present in a double dosage, and polyploids are normally expected to vary within somewhat narrower limits than their diploid relatives. Polyploidy appears to be much rarer in animals than in plants, and the reason probably lies in the much more precise control of developmental processes in the former than in the latter, earlier explanations based on sex-determination mechanisms now seeming to be unacceptable. We have included Ownbey's interesting paper* on the spontaneous origin of two polyploids in eastern Washington and adjacent Idaho probably in the present century. The species involved have mutually exclusive ranges where they are native in western Eurasia, and their introduction together into North America has given them the opportunity to form sterile hybrids and eventually polyploid derivates. Another famous example concerns saltmarsh grasses of the genus *Spartina,* in which a native British species hybridized in the 19th century with an introduced American one to provide, first, vigorous diploid hybrids and, eventually, a polyploid derivative that spread rapidly all round the coasts of Britain and to northwestern France, constituting a menace to shipping in Southampton Water during World War II. We have much to learn about polyploidy, involved in the origin of most of our important crop plants and weeds, and theoretical advances in this field will no doubt have a very real economic importance in the decades to come.

BIBLIOGRAPHY

GILLETT, G. W. 1966. Hybridization and its taxonomic implications in the *Scaevola gaudichaudiana* complex of the Hawaiian Islands. Evolution **20:** 506–516.

HEISER, C. B., JR. 1949. Study in the evolution of the sunflower species *Helianthus annuus* and *H. bolanderi.* Univ. Calif. Publ. Bot. **23:** 157–208.

HUBBS, C. L. 1955. Hybridization between fish species in nature. Syst. Zool. **4:** 1–20.

LEWIS, H., and C. EPLING. 1959. *Delphinium gypsophilum,* a diploid species of hybrid origin. Evolution **13:** 511–525.

NOBS, M. A. 1963. Experimental studies on species relationships in *Ceanothus.* Carnegie Inst. Wash. Publ. **623:** i–v, 1–94.

RATTENBURY, J. A. 1962. Cyclic hybridization as a survival mechanism in the New Zealand forest flora. Evolution **16:** 348–363.

RAVEN, P. H. 1962. The systematics of *Oenothera* subgenus *Chylismia.* Univ. Calif. Publ. Bot. **34:** 1–122.

———. 1963. *Circaea* in the British Isles. Watsonia **5:** 262–272.

SAILER, R. I. 1954. Interspecific hybridization among insects with a report on cross-breeding experiments with stink bugs. Jour. Econ. Entom. **47:** 377–383.

SIBLEY, C. G. 1954. Hybridization in the red-eyed towhees of Mexico. Evolution **8:** 252–290.

STAIGER, H. 1954. Der Chromosomendimorphismus beim Prosobranchier *Purpura lapillus* in Bezeihung zur Ökologie der Art. Chromosoma **6:** 419–478.

HYBRIDIZATION OF THE HABITAT

Edgar Anderson

Missouri Botanical Garden, St. Louis 10, Missouri

Received November 7, 1947

It has been the experience of most biologists that hybridization between species is rare in nature. Many biologists encounter interspecific hybrids in the field so rarely as to doubt if they really occur there at all or else find them under special circumstances (Epling, 1947) which raise serious doubts as to the importance of hybridization under natural conditions. After a series of investigations (Anderson, 1936b, 1936d; Anderson and Hubricht, 1938; Anderson and Turrill, 1938) it has been my own experience that clearcut out-and-out hybrids are seldom met with, even when a deliberate search is made for them, and that hybrid swarms of bizarre recombinations are found, if at all, only under peculiar circumstances.

It was once the common opinion (Zirkle, 1935) that this lack of evident hybridization was caused by the sterility of interspecific hybrids. Experimental evidence has not confirmed this judgment and modern advocates of reproductive isolation (Mayr, 1940) as a species criterion have had to phrase their definitions to permit semi-fertility between distinct species. For the higher plants there is an impressive amount of experimental evidence on this point though it is widely scattered. There are the papers of the early hybridizers (Focke, 1881; Roberts, 1929; Zirkle, 1935), much work in genetics (see for instance East, 1913, 1916) and experimental taxonomy (Clausen, Keck, and Hiesey, 1946), and the experience of numerous plant breeders. The latter, by far the largest of these three bodies of evidence, is not too accessible to most scientists since it has to be dug out piecemeal from such compendia as Rehder's Manual of Trees and Shrubs (1940). A critical summary of all this evidence is badly needed. Lacking one, the evidence for the higher plants may be roughly summarized as follows: Well-differentiated species of the same genus may or may not be interfertile when tested experimentally. On the whole it seems to vary with the genus. There are certain genera in which interspecific hybrids are difficult to make and are sterile. There are others, equally exceptional, in which the widest possible crosses within the genus will yield fertile or semi-fertile hybrids (Anderson and Schafer, 1931). The yellow trumpet Narcissi are so completely fertile with the flat, white-flowered Poets' Narcissi that the whole business of supplying new garden hybrids has been founded on it (Calvert, 1929). The Poets' Narcissi (in themselves a whole group of species and sub-species) are so interfertile with the species complex making up the long-crowned yellow daffodils that it has been possible to accomplish

Reprinted by permission of the author and the Society for the Study of Evolution from EVOLUTION, 2, 1–9 (1948).

such recombinations as the transfer of the deep red-orange pigment from the rim of the tiny central eye in a Poets' Narcissus to the brilliant flaring orange trumpet of such modern "red trumpets" as the variety "Fortune" (Anderson and Hornback, 1946). The commonest condition among the higher plants seems to be that in which crosses within a species group are easy to make while intergroup crosses are difficult or impossible.

If, therefore, we base our explanation of the rarity of hybrids under natural conditions on the experimental facts we can make the following summary: 1. In a minority of the cases where related species occur near each other, they are completely intersterile. 2. In certain cases hybrids can be formed but are sterile. 3. In a surprising number of cases the experimental evidence shows that the species can be crossed readily, in the breeding plot, but no hybrids appear under natural conditions. 4. In many cases which have been carefully investigated, hybrids, though usually rare, do occasionally occur but leave no apparent descendants except under unusual conditions.

This experimental evidence, such as it is, justifies the generalization that species maintain themselves as recognizable units even where they are interfertile and even when there is a considerable opportunity for them to hybridize. Why should this be so? Before we can answer the question we must first have clearly in mind the known results of such hybridization under experimental conditions. If we ignore the complications due to polyploidy and other important but more-or-less specialized phenomena, the usual results of hybridization are readily summarized. They were well established by the early hybridizers and have been abundantly confirmed by modern genetic research.

1. The first hybrid generation is intermediate between the parents and is as uniform as they are, or even more so.

It is usually more vigorous than either and more robust in nature.

2. The second hybrid generation, while on the average intermediate, is extremely variable. Usually no two individuals are alike. The variation is usually bewildering, but it can be shown to have a general trend from a few individuals more or less like one of the parental species, to a great bulk more or less like the first generation hybrid, to a very few more or less like the other parental species.

3. The facts with regard to the backcrosses are equally well established but unfortunately have been so little stressed in modern times that they are not as generally familiar to biologists. If the first hybrid generation is crossed back to either parent, the first backcross is made up largely of plants which resemble the species to which they have been backcrossed. If we take one of these and cross it back a second time to the same parent, not only will the seedlings resemble this species very much indeed but some of them may be nearly or quite indistinguishable from it. In all the cases with which I am personally familiar, many, if not most, of the first and second back-crosses, if found in nature, would by taxonomists be accepted as varieties or slightly aberrant individuals of the species to which they were back-crossed (see fig. 1). Few taxonomists, even those specializing in that group of plants, would even suspect that many of these back-crosses were of partially hybrid ancestry. For the genus Apocynum we have a detailed experimental record of back-cross morphology and the taxonomic reaction to it (Anderson, 1936b).

In the genus Tradescantia, by rigidly experimental methods (Anderson, 1936a, 1936d; Anderson and Sax, 1936; Anderson and Woodson, 1935), including the production of experimental backcrosses, it has been possible to demonstrate that the principal result of hybridization, in those cases where it did occur, was a series of such backcrosses to one or to both parents. To this phenomenon I gave the

N. LANGSDORFFII

N. ALATA

FIRST BACK-CROSS

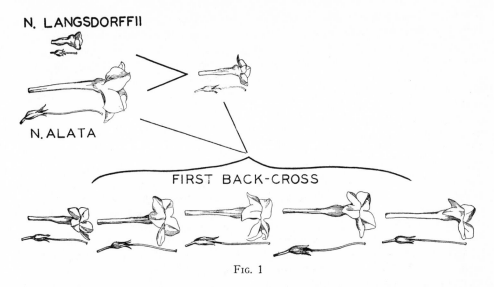

Fig. 1

name *introgressive hybridization* (Anderson and Hubricht, 1938), since it provided a mean by which elements in the germplasm of one species might introgress into the germplasm of the other. The chief result of hybridization under such conditions is the enrichment of variation in the participating species. Such hybridization is cryptic and only by very specialized techniques can we measure its exact importance in any particular case. Since the first publications on the subject, the phenomenon of introgressive hybridization has been confirmed, with experimental verification, in numerous genera. (A comprehensive bibliography on introgression by Dr. Charles Heiser is now under way. The following papers are representative: Goodwin, 1937b; Riley, 1938, 1939a, 1939b; Dansereau, 1941; Marsden, Jones and Turrill, 1946; Epling, 1947; Stebbins, Matzke, and Epling, 1947; and Heiser, in press.) Circumstantial evidence indicates its importance in many more genera. How important is it on the whole in the higher plants and in other groups of organisms? We do not yet have any exact evidence. From those cases where experimenters have gone to the trouble of making experimental backcrosses (Epling, 1947), it is clear that many of the second back-

crosses could not be recognized as of mongrel origin purely by their appearance. It is therefore clearly indicated that gene flow from one species to another may go far beyond any point which could be detected by ordinary morphological techniques. We shall not be able to assess the real importance of introgression until we can study genetically analyzed species in the field and determine the actual spread of certain marker genes. Until such data are available, any generalizations are based on mere opinions.

Introgression therefore gives us a partial answer to our original question as to why hybrids are so seldom met with in nature. It is because when hybrids do occur, they usually perpetuate themselves, if at all, in backcrosses to one or the other parental species and the mongrel nature of their descendants is not apparent to the ordinary biologist. The commonest result of hybridization is introgression, and introgression must be excessive before it will produce results conspicuous enough to impress biologists who are not making a deliberate search for such phenomena. This is only half an answer. Why do interfertile species limit themselves very largely to backcrosses when they meet under natural conditions and most particularly why is the backcrossing

175

largely in areas where natural conditions have been very much disturbed? There are at least two main reasons; one resides in the germ plasm itself, the other in the habitat. As to the internal one, the total effect of all the forces which make for specific cohesion is very great, much greater than one would expect until he made careful calculations (Anderson, 1939a & b). Following the arguments used in these calculations it can furthermore be shown that in well-differentiated species the total effect of linkage is so strong that two well-differentiated but interfertile species, meeting in an idealized environment favorable to hybridization, would remain recognizable units in spite of their interfertility. The details of the argument are largely mathematical and are shortly to appear elsewhere, but the general conclusions can be tersely put. Linkage by itself is a force strong enough to prevent the complete swamping of interfertile species. As a factor in specific cohesion it is proportional to the differentiation of the two hybridizing entities: the greater the differentiation, the stronger the cohesive force of linkage.

The effect of the habitat, however, is also important, and it usually operates in exactly the same direction. The argument is as follows: it is now known that the physiological differences between species segregate in the same way as do the morphological ones. In Neurospora (Beadle, 1945) the mode of inheritance of scores of physiological differences are precisely understood. In yeasts the Lindegrens (1947) have demonstrated with laboratory precision the inheritance of various differences in habitat preference. The higher plants are not so amenable to precise physiological analyses of their nutritional requirements but there is abundant circumstantial evidence that a similar situation prevails and there are precise data for a few characters such as maturity (see for instance Goodwin 1937c, footnote 13, or Marsden Jones and Turrill, 1946), response to day length, etc. Nearly everyone who has grown and

studied the second generation from a species cross has noted the segregation and recombination of such physiological differences as length of blooming season, resistance to diseases, dayblooming habit vs. night blooming, ease of wilting, resistance to cold, light tolerance, etc. If, therefore, we cross two species differing in their ecological requirements we may expect these physiological differences to segregate as follows: The first hybrid generation will be uniform in its requirements and on the whole they will be for conditions intermediate between those required for the two parents. The second generation will be made up of individuals each of which will require its own peculiar habitat.

Let us repeat this last statement; it is the crux of the argument. THE SECOND GENERATION WILL BE MADE UP OF INDIVIDUALS EACH OF WHICH WILL REQUIRE ITS OWN PECULIAR HABITAT FOR OPTIMUM DEVELOPMENT. As a whole the requirements of the second generation will range from a need for something more or less like one parental habitat to something more or less like the intermediate habitat of the F-1 to something more or less like the habitat of the other parent.

In nature therefore we might reasonably expect to find first generation hybrids growing in an intermediate zone between the two parental habitats. The persistence of any considerable variety of the various second generation recombinations would require a habitat such as is seldom or never met with, where various combinations of the two parental habitats are found in close juxtaposition to one another.

As a crude example let us consider the adjacent habitats in which one finds *Tradescantia subaspera* and *Tradescantia canaliculata* at home in the Ozark Plateau (Anderson and Hubricht, 1938). The former grows in deep rich woods at the foot of bluffs while the latter grows up above in full sun at the edge of the cliffs. As an over-simplified example we can list three of the outstanding differences between these two habitats as follows:

```
rich loam............rocky soil
deep shade...........full sun
leaf mould cover......no leaf mould cover
```

Tradescantia canaliculata and *T. subaspera* are well-differentiated species; neither one of them is by any means the closest relative of the other, yet Mr. Hubricht and I have found by actual experiment that not only can they be crossed readily by artificial means but they do cross abundantly when left to themselves in an experimental garden (Hubricht and Anderson, 1941). Even though both he and I were familiar with the appearance of these artificial hybrids and though we searched for them at many points where the species were growing very near one another, we found very few of the first generation hybrids. The habitats of the two species are strikingly different; in the Ozarks one seldom finds the intermediate habitat in which the hybrid is able to germinate and survive. This is a more or less intermediate condition, a gravelly soil, partial shade with some bright sunlight, and a light covering of leaf mould. Imagine, however, the habitat which must be provided if we are to see the second generation recombinations which we obtain in the breeding plot. If we consider only the three contrasting characters of the habitat which have been mentioned above, our recombinations would require the following six new habitats in addition to the parental ones (these six represent only the extreme recombinations; a whole series of intermediates will also be required):

rich loam	rocky soil
full sun	deep shade
no leaf mould	leaf mould
rich loam	rocky soil
full sun	full sun
leaf mould	leaf mould
rich loam	rocky soil
deep shade	deep shade
no leaf mould	no leaf mould

What would have to happen to any natural area before such a set of variedly intermediate habitats could be provided? It has been very generally recognized that if hybrids are to survive we. must have intermediate habitats for them. It has not been emphasized, however, that if anything beyond the first hybrid generation is to pull through, we must have habitats that are not only intermediate but which present recombinations of the contrasting differences of the original habitats. If the two species differ in their response to light, soil, and moisture (and what related species do not?) we must have varied recombinations of light, soil, and moisture to grow their hybrid descendants. Only by a hybridization of the habitat can the hybrid recombinations be preserved in nature.

The actual inherent differences in ecological preference will of course be much more diverse than in the crude example given above. The number of different kinds of habitats required by the hybrids will rise *exponentially* with the number of basic differences between the species. With ten such differences, around a thousand different kinds of habitat would be needed to permit the various recombinations to find a niche somewhere as well suited to them as the original adjacent habitats were to the two parental species. With only twenty such basic differences (and this seems like a conservative figure) over a million different recombined habitats would be needed. Under natural conditions anything like such a situation is close to impossible. Ordinarily it is only through the intervention of man that it is even remotely approached. Even in these cases the new "Recombination Habitats" will largely be limited to habitats pretty much like those required by one of the parental species, but which in a few characteristics approach the requirements of the other parent. We may expect that even in such disturbed habitats there will be back-up recombinations not greatly different from one of the parents which will most readily find an ecological niche suited to them.

One of the best demonstrations yet published of the way in which man can provide strange new niches of hybrid recombinations is that given by H. P. Riley (1938, 1939a) in his analysis of the hybridization between *Iris fulva* and *Iris giganticaerulea,* two species which differ strikingly in their color, morphology, and ecological adaptations (Viosca, 1935). In one of the localities which he studied in detail on the Mississippi delta, a series of long, narrow farms run straight back from the highway side by side, in the fashion set by the French settlers, with almost the precision of experimental plots. The original environment at that point was fairly uniform, but each man has treated his farm a little differently. It was strikingly apparent from Riley's study that the numbers and kinds of hybrids varied from farm to farm. Some had few or none, while others, even when adjacent, had hybrids in great quantities; there were significantly more of them where the meadows had been pastured. In one farm in particular, the little depression which ran parallel to the highway had been subjected to a series of operations. The trees and shrubs had not been entirely removed from this area, but it had been repeatedly cut over and had in addition been heavily pastured. It had a swarm of different hybrid derivatives, almost like an experimental garden, and the hybrid area went right up to the fenceline at the border of the farm and stopped there.

Nor is this an isolated instance. Viosca (1935) and other students of Louisiana irises have worked out in considerable detail the relation between the production of hybrid swarms of these conspicuously different irises and the churning and rechurning of the habitat by ditching, pasturing, lumbering, roadbuilding, etc. It is only where man has hybridized the natural environments of the Mississippi delta that nature can find an appropriate lodging place for the hybrids she has created.

This dependence of interspecific hybridization upon the intervention of man has been described by a number of authors (Darrow and Camp,[1] 1945; Anderson and Hubricht, 1938). It was discussed in some detail by Wiegand (1935) in his paper on "A naturalist's experience with hybrids in the wild." Marie-Victorin has given a vivid description (1922, p. 32; 1935, p. 65) of its operation when the original flora of the St. Lawrence valley was largely replaced by fields and pastures. Epling, Stebbins, Dansereau, and their students have commented upon the connection in a number of different genera. Does this mean that introgression as a phenomenon is limited to the areas disturbed by man and that its results are mere artifacts and not genuine natural phenomena? I think not. Though freely admitting that nearly all the introgression which has been studied experimentally (for one exception see Dansereau, 1941) is of the nature of an artifact, I believe that at particular times, and in particular places, introgression may have been a general evolutionary factor of real importance.

Under the conditions of an experimental garden, natural selection among the progeny of a cross between species is much less severe than it is in nature. Though the optimum environments for the sister hybrids may be quite various, it is possible to raise the majority of them in one plot, providing that they are widely spaced and competition with aggressive weeds is kept at a minimum. The prevalence of iris hybrids on one or two of the farms described by Riley (1938) may have been due in part to the reduction of competition with other plants, particularly grasses, as well as to the variations in shade and moisture brought about by repeated recuttings and overpasturing.

There must have been various times, even without the intervention of man,

---

[1] Darrow and Camp also considered the reaction of hybridizing polyploid complexes with the environment. Polyploidy introduces further complications into hybridization which are beyond the scope of this paper.

when species hybridized under conditions which produced varied new habitats and when competition was not too keen, as for instance when newly colonizable areas emerged from the sea or when various floras spread out onto the northern lands denuded by Pleistocene glaciation. At such times introgression would have been an important evolutionary factor. For one area we are beginning to get actual proof that it did occur. Along the coast of California there are peninsulas which once were isolated islands but which are now united with the main land. In their studies of the California knobcone pines, fossil and living, Mason and his students are demonstrating the actual role of introgression (for a general summary see Cain, 1944, pp. 112–118) in forming these pines as we know them today and to determine in some detail how introgression operated at the time when these islands were joined to the coast.

The Edwards Plateau in central Texas is another area in which introgression may have operated on a grand scale. This comparatively small area is a center of distribution and variation for numerous genera. A mere leafing through of a series of monographs of North American genera (Larsen, 1933; Anderson and Woodson, 1935; Barkley, 1937) will demonstrate that it is one of the outstanding centers east of the Rockies. For many genera the concentration of species is higher there than at any other point and for the genus Tradescantia we know the even more significant fact that it is a center for the diploid strains of polyploid species (Anderson and Sax, 1936; Anderson, 1937). The geological evidence shows that when the Edwards Plateau came into being, it united older land masses in Mexico and in the United States. Certainly at such a time related species in many genera might have met and hybridized under conditions where competition would not have been keen and where associations of plants were in the making instead of already existing as tightly closed corporations. Tradescan-

tias from Mexico would have met species coming down from the Appalachians in an area conducive to the survival of some of the hybrid recombinations.

Woodson has recently (1947) called attention to the importance of peninsular Florida in the speciation patterns of the eastern United States. During parts of the Tertiary it was an island or group of islands which finally became attached to the mainland. Species and varieties which became differentiated during the island period must then have had unusual opportunities to hybridize with their relatives on the mainland. Giles' (1942) studies of Cuthbertia in this area have given cytological proof that such hybridization did actually take place. Careful studies of variation throughout the whole area, for a series of species, should yield data with which we could assess the general overall importance there of introgression.

SUMMARY

1. Experimental evidence shows that sterility will not account for the rarity of hybrids under natural conditions.

2. Careful field analyses have shown that natural hybridization is largely limited to backcrosses which resemble the parental species so closely that special methods are required to detect them readily.

3. One of the factors limiting hybridization to such introgression is imposed by the habitat for the following reason: Two species differing in their habitat requirements will produce a first generation hybrid adjusted to a uniform intermediate environment. The second generation however consists of individuals each of which requires its own peculiar habitat for optimum development. Such heterogeneous habitats are seldom or never met with, the only approach to them being found in places where man has greatly altered natural conditions.

4. It is concluded that hybrid swarms can survive only in "hybridized habitats." While most of the latter result from hu-

man intervention, similar conditions have prevailed in pre-human times when new lands were opened up to colonization by diverse floras. At such times and places introgressive hybridization must have played an important role in evolution.

LITERATURE CITED

ANDERSON, EDGAR. 1936a. A morphological comparison of triploid and tetraploid interspecific hybrids in Tradescantia. Genetics, 21: 61–65.

——. 1936b. An experimental study of hybridization in the genus Apocynum. Ann. Mo. Bot. Gard., 23: 159–168.

——. 1936c. The species problem in Iris. Ann. Mo. Bot. Gard., 23: 457–509.

——. 1936d. Hybridization in American Tradescantias. Ann. Mo. Bot. Gard., 23: 511–525.

——. 1937. Cytology in its relation to taxonomy. Bot. Rev., 3: 335–350.

——. 1939a. The hindrance to gene recombination imposed by linkage: an estimate of its total magnitude. Am. Nat., 73: 185–188.

——. 1939b. Recombination in species crosses. Genetics, 24: 668–698.

—— AND LESLIE HUBRICHT. 1938. The evidence for introgressive hybridization. Am. Jour. Bot., 25: 396–402.

—— AND EARL HORNBACK. 1946. A genetical analysis of pink daffodils: a preliminary attempt. Jour. Cal. Hort. Soc., 7: 334–344.

—— AND RUTH PECK OWNBEY. 1939. The genetic coefficients of specific difference. Ann. Mo. Bot. Gard., 26: 325–348.

—— AND KARL SAX. 1936. A cytological monograph of the American species of Tradescantia. Bot. Gaz., 97: 433–476.

—— AND BRENHILDA SCHAFER. 1931. Species hybrids in Aquilegia. Ann. Bot., 45: 639–646.

——. 1933. Vicinism in Aquilegia vulgaris. Am. Nat., 67: 1–3.

—— AND W. B. TURRILL. 1938. Statistical studies on two populations of Fraxinus. New Phytol., 37: 160–172.

—— AND R. E. WOODSON. 1935. The species of Tradescantia indigenous to the United States. Contrib. Arn. Arb., 9: 1–132.

BARKLEY, F. A. 1937. A monographic study of Rhus. Ann. Mo. Bot. Gard., 24: 265–498.

BEADLE, G. W. 1945. Biochemical genetics. Chem. Rev., 37: 15–96.

CAIN, STANLEY A. 1944. Foundations of plant geography. Harpers. 1–556 pp.

CALVERT, A. E. 1929. Daffodil growing. Dulau. 1–389 pp.

CLAUSEN, JENS, D. D. KECK, AND W. M. HIESEY. 1946. Experimental taxonomy. Carn. Year Book, 45: 111–120.

DANSEREAU, PIERRE. 1941. Etudes sur les hybrides de Cistes. VI. Introgression dans la section Ladanium. Can. Jour. Research, 19: 59–67.

DARROW, GEORGE M., AND W. H. CAMP. 1945. Vaccinium hybrids and the development of new horticultural material. Bull. Torr. Bot. Club, 72: 1–21.

EAST, E. M. 1913. Inheritance of flower size in crosses between species of Nicotiana. Bot. Gaz., 55: 177–188.

——. 1916. Inheritance in crosses between Nicotiana Langsdorffii and Nicotiana alata. Genetics, 1: 311–333.

EPLING, CARL C. 1947. Natural hybridization of Salvia apiana and Salvia mellifera. Evolution, 1: 69–78.

FOCKE, W. O. 1881. Die Pflanzen-mischlinge. 569 pp.

GILES, N. H., JR. 1942. Autopolyploidy and geographical distribution in Cuthbertia graminea Small. Amer. Jour. Bot., 29: 637–645.

GOODWIN, RICHARD H. 1937a. Notes on the distribution and hybrid origin of X Solidago asperula. Rhodora, 38: 22–28.

——. 1937b. The cytogenetics of two species of Solidago and its bearing on their polymorphy in nature. Am. Jour. Bot., 24: 425–432.

——. 1937c. The role of auxin in leaf development in Solidago species. Am. Jour. Bot., 24: 43–51.

HUBRICHT, LESLIE, AND EDGAR ANDERSON. 1941. Vicinism in Tradescantia. Am. Jour. Bot., 28: 957.

LARSEN, ESTHER L. 1933. Astranthium and related genera. Ann. Mo. Bot. Gard., 20: 23–44.

LINDEGREN, CARL C., AND GERTRUDE LINDEGREN. 1947. Mendelian inheritance of genes affecting vitamin-synthesizing in Saccharomyces. Ann. Mo. Bot. Gard., 34: 95–99.

MARIE-VICTORIN, FR. 1935. Flore Laurentienne. Montreal. 917 pp.

——. 1922. Esquisse systematique et ecologique de la flore dendrologique. Contrib. Lab. Bot. de l'Univ. de Montreal, no. 1: 1–33.

MARSDEN JONES, E. M., AND W. B. TURRILL. 1946. Researches on Silene maritima and S. vulgaris. Kew Bull., 1946: 97–107.

MASON, H. L. (see Cain, 1944).

MAYR, ERNST. 1940. Speciation phenomena in birds. Am. Nat., 74: 249–278.

REHDER, ALFRED. 1940. Manual of cultivated trees and shrubs. Second edition. 996 pp. Macmillan.

RILEY, H. P. 1938. A character analysis of colonies of Iris fulva, Iris hexagona var. giganticaerulea, and natural hybrids. Am. Jour. Bot. 25: 727–738.

——. 1939a. The problem of species in the Louisiana irises. Bull. Am. Iris Soc., 3–7.

——. 1939b. Introgressive hybridization in a natural population of Tradescantia. Genetics, 24: 753–769.

ROBERTS, H. F. 1929. Plant hybridization before Mendel. 374 pp. Princeton.

STEBBINS, G. L., E. G. MATZKE, AND C. EPLING. 1947. Hybridization in a population of *Quercus marilandica* and *Quercus ilicifolia*. Evolution, 1: 79–88.

VIOSCA, P. 1935. The irises of southeastern Louisiana. Bull. Am. Iris Soc., 57: 3–56.

WIEGAND, K. 1935. A taxonomist's experience with hybrids in the wild. Science, 81: 161–166.

WOODSON, R. E., JR. 1947. Notes on the historical factor in plant geography. Contrib. Gray Herbarium, 165: 12–25.

ZIRKLE, CONWAY. 1935. The beginnings of plant hybridization. 231 pp. Univ. of Pennsylvania, Phila.

ANCESTOR OF CORN

A genetic reconstruction yields clues to the nature
of the extinct wild ancestor.

PAUL C. MANGELSDORF*

Our purpose in reconstructing the ancestor of corn is to retrace, so far as possible, some of the principal steps which have been involved in its evolution under domestication. We do this in the hope of gaining a better understanding of the corn plant as one of those unique biological systems which man employs on a grand scale to convert the energy of the sun, the carbon dioxide of the air, and the minerals of the soil into food. Corn is one of perhaps not more than a dozen species of cultivated plants of worldwide importance—each one the principal source of food of millions of people—which quite literally stand between mankind and starvation.

But corn is something more than an important food plant; it is also a mystery, a fascinating botanical mystery, as challenging to a scientist as is a mountain to an explorer.

A UNIQUE CEREAL

Modern corn, our starting point in this study (1), is unique among the cereal grasses in the nature of its inflorescences (2, 3). The terminal inflorescence, commonly called the "tassel" (Fig. 1A, C), usually bears only male flowers, each of which contains three pollen sacs or anthers (Fig. 1D) packed tightly with some 2500 pollen grains. These are small, about 1/250 inch in diameter, light in weight, and are easily carried by the wind.

The lateral inflorescences (Fig. 1A, B), which when mature become the familiar ears of corn, have only female flowers which bear the pollen-receptive organs commonly known as the "silks." These are covered with fine hairs and are admirably designed to capture wind-blown pollen (Fig. 1E). Thus corn, in contrast to the majority of cereals, is a naturally cross-pollinated plant. It

* The author is professor of botany at Harvard University. This article, adapted from a paper presented at the annual meeting of the American Philosophical Society in Philadelphia on 25 April 1958, is reprinted, with permission, from the *Proceedings* of the Society.

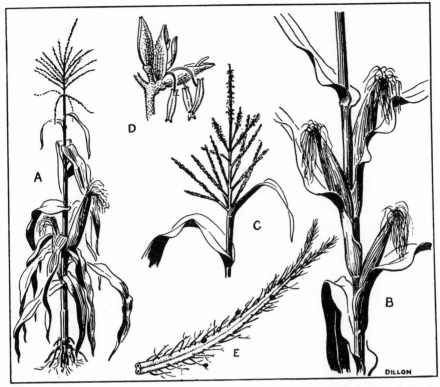

FIGURE 1. Botanical characteristics of the modern corn plant. (A) The entire plant, showing the male inflorescence, the tassel, at the tip of the stalk and the female inflorescences, the ears, in the middle region; (B) young ears enclosed in husks with the pollen-receptive organs (the silks) protruding from the ends; (C) typical tassel; (D) typical male flower with three anthers containing pollen; (E) a single silk magnified to show hairs and adhering pollen grains. [From P. C. Mangelsdorf, "Corn" (3), by permission of *Encyclopaedia Britannica*]

is this feature which makes possible the production of hybrid corn, one of the most spectacular developments in applied biology of this century.

Each silk represents a potential kernel and must be pollinated in order for that kernel to develop. The kernels themselves are firmly attached to a rigid axis, the cob, and are not covered as are those of other cereals by the floral bracts which botanists call "glumes" and which the layman knows as "chaff." Instead the entire ear is enclosed, often quite tightly, by modified leaf sheaths, the husks or shucks (Fig. 1B). Thus, while in other cereals the kernels are protected individually, in corn they are covered en masse. The result is that cultivated corn has no mechanism for the dispersal of its seeds and hence is no longer capable of reproducing itself without man's intervention. The very characteristics which make corn so useful to man render it incapable of existing in nature, and it is probable that corn would quickly become extinct if deprived of man's protection.

How, then, did corn's wild ancestor differ from cultivated corn in ways which enabled it to exist in nature for thousands, if not millions, of years before man appeared on the scene? This is one of the questions which we hoped to answer by reconstructing the ancestral form. Our reconstruction is based in part upon fossil and archeological remains and in part upon genetic recombination of some of the primitive characteristics which still exist in modern corn varieties.

FOSSIL CORN POLLEN

The fossil evidence comprises a number of pollen grains isolated from a drill core taken from a depth of more than 200 feet below the present site of Mexico City. These were recognized as unusually large pollen grains of a grass by Paul Sears of Yale University and Kathryn Clisby of Oberlin College, who, in connection with charting climatic changes, were engaged in pollen studies of the drill core. The pollen was identified by Elso Barghoorn (4) of Harvard University as that of corn, which has the largest pollen of any known grass. Although assigned to the last interglacial period and therefore, on the basis of recent estimates, probably at least 80,000 years old, the fossil pollen is

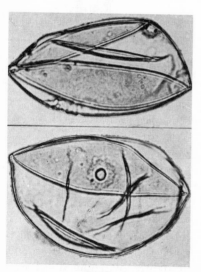

Fig. 2

Fig. 3

FIGURE 2. Fossil pollen of corn (top) from more than 200 feet below the present site of Mexico City compared with a pollen grain of modern corn (bottom) at the same magnification. In spite of some 80,000 years' difference in their ages, these two pollen grains are virtually identical in their characteristics, and they show that the ancestor of corn was corn and not one of its two American relatives, teosinte or *Tripsacum* (× 375). [From Barghoorn *et al.*, "Fossil maize from the Valley of Mexico" (4)]

FIGURE 3. Three cobs of prehistoric corn from Bat Cave compared with a 1-cent piece. Radiocarbon determinations of associated charcoal date these at 5600 years. Actual size.

FIGURE 4. One of the Bat Cave cobs (center) compared with a modern ear of Cornbelt dent (left) and a large-seeded Peruvian flour corn (right). Extremely rapid evolution has been involved in producing such drastic changes even in 5600 years, the estimated difference in age.

scarcely distinguishable in size, shape, and other characteristics from modern corn pollen (Fig. 2). This fact leaves little doubt that the ancestor of corn was corn and not one of its two American relatives, teosinte or *Tripsacum*.

OLDEST CULTIVATED CORN

The oldest known remains of cultivated corn come from a once-inhabited rock shelter in New Mexico known as Bat Cave, which was excavated by

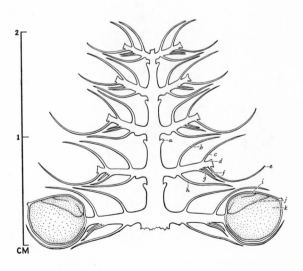

FIGURE 5. Diagrammatic longitudinal section of one of the Bat Cave cobs, based on measurements of dissected parts. The tiny kernels show that this was a popcorn; the long pedicels on which the kernels are borne and the bracts which almost enclose them indicate that it was also a pod corn. [W. C. Galinat]

Herbert Dick, of the Peabody Museum of Harvard University and later of the Colorado University Museum, in two expeditions, in 1948 and 1950 (5, 6). This cave was inhabited for several thousand years by people who practiced a primitive form of agriculture and an even more primitive pattern of sanitation. During the centuries of this occupancy, garbage, excrement, and other debris accumulated in the cave to a depth of six feet, creating exactly the kind of site which archeologists delight to dig into. At the bottom of this accumulation of trash, Dick turned up some tiny cobs of ancient corn which have been dated, on the basis of Willard Libby's radiocarbon determinations of associated charcoal, at about 5600 years.

Three of these ancient cobs are compared in Figure 3 with a one-cent piece whose diameter is about equal to their length. One of the tiny specimens is compared in Figure 4 with ears of two modern races of corn: the dent corn of the United States corn belt and a large-seeded flour corn of Peru. How could a corn like the Bat Cave corn have evolved into these and other modern races even in 5600 years? This is the principal question which we hoped to answer by retracing some of the steps involved in corn's evolution under domestication.

Since there were no living seeds of the Bat Cave corn it was impossible to work forward experimentally from it to modern corn. The alternative was to work backward from present-day corn by combining primitive characteristics still occurring in living varieties. But what characteristics of corn are primitive? My associate, W. C. Galinat, and I sought to determine this by an intensive study of one of the Bat Cave specimens which contained the partial remains of a single kernel. Each part of this cob was carefully dissected out

FIGURE 6. An ear of Argentine popcorn (left) and an ear of present-day pod corn (right). Popcorn is primitive in having small hard seeds. Pod corn is primitive in having its seeds enclosed in pods or chaff, like the other cereals. These two types were crossed in order to combine their primitive characteristics.

and measured. On the basis of the measurements, Galinat prepared the diagrammatical, longitudinal section illustrated in Figure 5. The tiny kernels which this cob must once have borne could only be those of popcorn, a type in which the kernels are small and hard and capable of exploding when exposed to heat. The long stems or pedicels on which the kernels were borne and the long floral bracts which almost completely enclosed them show that the Bat Cave corn was also a form of pod corn, a type in which the individual kernels are enclosed in pods or chaff.

It is interesting to note in this connection that the late E. Lewis Sturtevant, a long-time student of corn, concluded many years ago that both popcorn and pod corn are primitive. My former colleague, R. G. Reeves, and I (7) later reached a similar conclusion. The ancient Bat Cave specimens provide convincing archeological evidence in support of these conclusions.

CROSSING PRIMITIVE CORNS

What we have done, then, is to cross a number of varieties of popcorn from various parts of the world with pod corn (Fig. 6), which still occurs as a "rogue" or "freak" in some South American varieties and which in some localities is preserved by the Indians, who believe it to have magical properties. Pod corn has also sometimes been grown in gardens in the United States as a curiosity. Today it is most likely to be found in the experimental cultures of corn geneticists, who maintain it as one of the "marker" genes on the fourth longest chromosome of corn.

There is no doubt that pod corn is primitive in its characteristic of enclosing the kernel in glumes or chaff, as do all other cereals and virtually all other grasses. Despite this fact, and because it is often monstrous and sometimes sterile, it has been dismissed by a number of botanists from any role in the ancestry of corn (8). We believe that its monstrousness has been misunderstood—that pod corn is monstrous today only because it is a "wild" relict character superimposed upon modern highly domesticated varieties. Today's pod corn is comparable to a 1900 chassis powered by the engine of a 1958 car. The surprising thing is not that pod corn is sometimes monstrous but that it is not more so—that the particular genic locus which governs its expression is capable of functioning at all in a milieu so different from that in which it was undoubtedly well adapted. We have assumed that pod corn would be less monstrous and would exhibit normal grass characteristics when combined with other "wild" genes, and we hoped to find these in varieties of popcorn.

Our hopes have been realized. Popcorns in general tend to reduce the monstrosity of pod corn when crossed with it, and some varieties do so quite drastically. The varieties Lady Finger and Argentine carry complexes of modifying genes which appreciably reduce the monstrosity of pod corn, and a third variety, Baby Golden, carries a major modifying gene which, on the basis of preliminary linkage tests, appears to be on the sixth chromosome and which acts as an inhibitor of pod corn, reducing its expression by approximately half.

Fig. 7

Fig. 8

By combining these modifying and inhibiting genes from several popcorn varieties with the pod-corn gene, we have developed a number of strains of popcorn which, having this gene present on both of their fourth chromosomes, breed true for the pod-corn character. Some of these homozygous strains are much less monstrous than the usual forms of pod corn, are completely fertile, and might under suitable conditions be capable of surviving in the wild.

EFFECTS OF A SINGLE GENE

The majority of these true-breeding pod-popcorns have other characteristics which we may now regard as primitive. The plants, when grown on fertile soils, instead of having one stalk, as do most modern corns, have several (Fig. 7) and in this respect resemble the majority of wild grasses, including all of the known relatives of corn, both American and Asiatic. The plants are shorter than ordinary corn because one of the numerous effects of the pod-corn gene is to shorten and thicken the upper internodes of the stalk. This is well illustrated in Figure 7, which shows three plants of popcorn in one family: one lacking the pod-corn gene, one having the gene on one member of its fourth chromosome pair, and one having the gene on both members of the pair. There is a progressive decrease in height through this series of three genotypes resulting from a shortening of the upper internodes. This shortening causes, or at least is accompanied by, the development of a terminal inflorescence which bears both male and female flowers, the male flowers at the tips and the female flowers at the bases of the same tassel branches (Fig. 8). These branches are quite brittle when mature and break apart easily when disturbed by the wind or by birds. They thus provide one of the most important primitive characteristics which cultivated corn lacks: a mechanism for the dispersal of seeds.

POSITION OF THE EAR

Plants of homozygous pod corn frequently do not have ears—most of their energy is apparently concentrated in the terminal inflorescences—but when

---

FIGURE 7. Three plants of a many-stalked popcorn differing with respect to the pod-corn gene. The first plant (left) lacks this gene; the second (center) has it on one member of the fourth chromosome pair; the third (right) has the gene on both members of the fourth chromosome pair. The progressive decrease in height is associated with the pod-corn gene, which causes, among other effects, a shortening of the internodes of the upper part of the stalk.

FIGURE 8. A tassel and ear of a true-breeding pod corn. The shortening of the internodes of the upper part of the stalk causes or is accompanied by a tassel which bears both male and female flowers. The withered silks immediately below the tassel are from female flowers on the tassel branches which bloomed several weeks before this photograph was taken. Several seeds, resulting from pollination of these flowers, are visible. Such seeds are easily dispersed when mature by the breaking of the fragile tassel branches. The fresh silks to the left of the tassel are from a subtassel ear which is enclosed in husks when young but can emerge from them and disperse its seeds when mature. The silks of this ear can be pollinated by pollen from the anthers in the tassel of the same plant, but the female flowers in the tassel can receive pollen only from another plant. Thus, the reconstructed primitive corn plant has devices for both self- and cross-pollination.

they do have ears these are usually borne high upon the stalk (Fig. 8), often at the joint of the stem immediately below the tassel. This elevation of the position of the ear has profound effects which are illustrated by the diagram in Figure 9. The diagram, which is based on data from several many-eared plants, shows how a number of the characteristics of the ears are determined by their position on the stalk: (i) The higher the position, the smaller the ear, partly for the simple mechanical reason that the stalk at this position is slender and is incapable of bearing a heavy load. It would be mechanically impossible for the large modern ear of corn to be borne near the slender tip of the stalk. (ii) The higher the position, the more likely is the ear to have both male and female flowers. (iii) The higher the position, the shorter the lateral branch or "shank" upon which the ear is borne. The shorter the branch, the fewer the joints from which the husks arise, the fewer the husks and the less completely the ear is enclosed. Thus an ear borne immediately below the tassel is enclosed while the young seeds are developing, but as these mature the husks flare open, allowing the ear to disperse its seeds. In short, a simple change in position determined by a single gene change can provide a mechanism for dispersal of the seeds borne on the ear as well as those borne on the fragile branches of the tassel.

These facts seem to answer several of the most puzzling questions involved in previous attempts to explain corn's evolution: How could wild corn have survived the handicap of an ear incapable of dispersing its seeds? And if wild corn had no ears, how could the ear of modern corn, its most important organ, have come into existence?

The position of the ear has an effect on still another characteristic illustrated in Figure 9, the length of the streamers or leaf blades which in many varieties terminate the outer husks. The higher the ear, the more likely are the leaf blades to be short or absent. This may explain the absence of leaf blades in prehistoric husks found both in Bat Cave (6) and in La Perra Cave (9).

MODERN AND PRIMITIVE CORN COMPARED

The most primitive ear we have so far obtained by combining popcorn and pod corn is shown in Figure 10 in comparison with an ear of modern dent corn and with the most primitive cob, dated at 4445 ± 180 years, from La Perra Cave, which was excavated by Richard MacNeish of the National Museum of Canada.

In weight and number of kernels our reconstruction is much closer to the prehistoric La Perra specimen than to the ear of modern dent corn. The modern ear weighs 317 grams. The ear of pod-popcorn weighs 1.99 grams. However, only 24 of its 38 female flowers developed kernels. Had all done so, it would weigh 2.47 grams, assuming the additional kernels to have the same average weight, 0.034 gram, as those which are present. The La Perra specimen weighs only 0.52 gram, but it lacks both the 48 kernels, which it once bore,

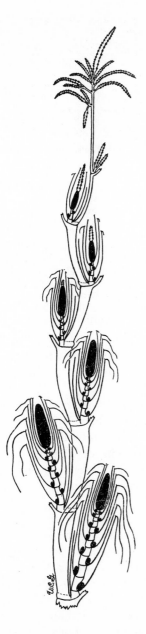

FIGURE 9. Diagrammatic longitudinal section based on data from several plants of a many-eared corn stalk, showing how the position of the ear on the stalk affects its characteristics. The higher the ear, the smaller its size, the fewer its husks, and the more likely it is to bear both male and female flowers. [W. C. Galinat]

FIGURE 10. The reconstructed ancestor of corn, an ear of pod-popcorn (second from left) compared with a modern ear of dent corn (far left) and a prehistoric cob of La Perra Cave corn (second from right). The dent corn weighs 317 grams; the reconstructed ear 1.99 grams. The reconstructed ear has female flowers below and male flowers above and in this respect resembles a spike of *Tripsacum* (far right), a wild relative of corn. The La Perra cob also once had a male portion, which has been lost; only the stump of its stem still remains. Without its kernels and male spike, the reconstructed ear would weigh 0.87 gram—only slightly more than the La Perra cob, which weighs 0.52 gram.

Fig. 12

FIGURE 11. A prehistoric Zapotec funerary urn from Mexico with two representations of primitive corn ears in the headdress and one in the hands of the maize god.
FIGURE 12. Details of one of the ears shown in Figure 11. It is probable that the slender column above the small ear was intended to represent the male spike of a prehistoric ear similar in some of its characteristics to the reconstructed ancestral form illustrated in Figure 10.

Fig. 11

and a male spike. Without its kernels and its male spike, the reconstructed ancestral form weighs 0.87 gram, only slightly more than the prehistoric specimen.

Although we have not yet completely reconstructed wild corn, nor duplicated exactly the most primitive specimens from either Bat Cave or La Perra Cave—the glumes of the pod-popcorns are still too prominent to match those of the prehistoric specimens—we have succeeded in developing what is probably the world's most unproductive corn. This is useful in suggesting that we are on the right track in attempting to retrace corn's evolutionary paths.

The reconstructed ear illustrated in Figure 10 has female flowers on its lower half and male flowers on the remainder. This, as Figure 9 shows, is a characteristic of ears borne in a high position on the stalk. If our reconstruction is valid, should not prehistoric ears also bear male flowers? A reexamination under the microscope shows that at least some of them once did and that these have since been lost in handling. Some of the ancient cobs, including the one illustrated in Figure 10, have stumps, previously unnoticed, of a slender stem on which male flowers were undoubtedly borne. Thus our genetically reconstructed ancestral form has taught us to look for a characteristic in prehistoric ears which we had previously overlooked. It has also shown us the significance of ears bearing terminal male spikes which are still found in certain races of corn in the countries of Latin America: the races Nal-Tel and Chapalote of Mexico (10), Pollo of Colombia (11), and Confite of Peru. Finally it may explain some curious ears, which had previously puzzled us, moulded in bas relief on a prehistoric Zapotec funerary urn from Mexico. The urn is shown in Figure 11, and the details of one of the ears in Figure 12.

In bearing both male and female flowers these ears of pod-popcorn also resemble the lateral inflorescence of *Tripsacum*, a perennial grass and a wild relative of corn (Figure 10). This resemblance has in turn called attention to additional characteristics in which the reconstructed corn resembles *Tripsacum*: (i) the flowering of the female spikelets before the male in both lateral and terminal inflorescences; (ii) the many-stalked condition; (iii) the small, hard, pointed seeds.

Actually this reconstructed corn might easily be classified as an annual form of *Tripsacum*, or conversely, since corn was the first of the two to be given a Latin name, *Tripsacum* could be classified as a perennial form of the genus *Zea*, to which corn belongs and which, until recently, has been represented by the single species *Zea mays*.

These unexpected results of combining popcorn and pod corn—the production of a counterpart of corn's wild relative, *Tripsacum*—we regard as additional evidence that our reconstruction has validity.

EVOLUTION UNDER DOMESTICATION

Figure 13 illustrates some of the principal environmentally induced and genetically controlled changes which are believed to have occurred during domestication. The first three plants illustrate the genetically reconstructed ancestral form as it would be expected to develop in three different environments. The first plant, a short, single-stalked plant with a slender, unbranched tassel bearing both male and female flowers and no ears, is intended to represent the wild corn plant growing in nature in a site of low fertility and in severe competition with other natural vegetation. Such a plant would barely reproduce itself.

The second plant represents this same genotype grown under primitive agricultural conditions. Here it is still single-stalked but under these somewhat better conditions is capable of producing a branched tassel and a single small ear borne high upon the stalk. The third plant (a counterpart of the third plant in Figure 7) represents the genetically reconstructed ancestral form grown under modern agricultural conditions with an abundance of fertilizer and in freedom from competition with weeds. Under these conditions it has several stalks as well as several small ears on each stalk. Plants like these might also have occurred sporadically in the wild under unusually favorable natural conditions.

The ability of the wild corn plant to respond in a spectacular fashion to freedom from competition with weeds and to high levels of fertility is undoubtedly one factor which led to its domestication. This ability to take full advantage of the improved environment usually afforded by an agricultural system is one of the characteristics found in almost all highly successful domesticated species. There are many wild species which do not have this trait; they cannot stand prosperity.

Since the corn plant is genetically plastic as well as responsive to an improved environment, domestication may soon have brought other changes, which are illustrated in the last four plants in Figure 13. One of the most important of these was a mutation at the pod-corn locus on the fourth chromosome. This single genetic change had numerous effects. It reduced the glumes which in wild corn completely surrounded the kernels, and the energy released from chaff production now went into the development of a larger cob, which in turn bore more and larger kernels. The mutation also lowered the position of the lateral inflorescences, and this had profound effects of several

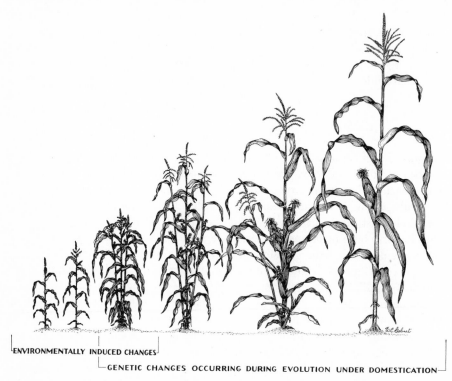

FIGURE 13. Environmentally induced and genetically controlled variation in the corn plant. Plants (from left): (i) a plant of pod-popcorn as it might have grown in nature in a poor site in competition with other natural vegetation; (ii) the same, grown under primitive agricultural conditions; (iii) the same, grown in a fertile site free of competition with weeds (this plant is essentially the same as the plant at right in Fig. 7); (iv) a popcorn plant which has lost the pod-corn gene (this is the counterpart of the plant at left in Fig. 7); (v) New England flint corn, in which human selection for larger ears has tended to eliminate the secondary stalks, reducing them to "suckers"; (vi) Cornbelt dent corn, in which the trend noted for (v) has been carried still further; Cornbelt dent corn is usually single-stalked, commonly bearing a single large ear in the middle region of the stalk. The middle position of the ear has both mechanical and physiological advantages over a terminal position and probably accounts for corn's superiority over other cereals in its capacity to produce grain. [W. C. Galinat]

194

kinds which can be understood by referring again to Figure 9. This shows that: (i) the lower the ear, the stronger the stalk at the position at which the ear is borne and the greater its capacity for supporting large ears. (ii) The lower the ear, the more likely it is to bear only female flowers which develop kernels when pollinated. (iii) The lower the ear, the longer the shank, the branch on which it is borne, and this in turn has a number of important secondary effects: the longer the shank, the more numerous its nodes or joints and the husks which arise from them; the greater the number of husks, the more completely the ear is enclosed and the less capable it is of dispersing its seeds.

In short, a rather simple change but a very important one, the lowering of the position of the ear (comparable, perhaps, to moving the engine of a primitive airplane from a position behind the wings to one in front of them), has separated the sexes, and made for a larger, strictly grain-bearing ear which is completely protected by the husks and is no longer capable of dispersing its seeds. In short, a mutation at a single locus on chromosome 4 has made the corn plant less able to survive in nature but much more useful to man.

The last two plants in Figure 13 show some of the changes which human selection has subsequently effected. Selection for large ears has tended to eliminate the secondary stalks and to reduce the number of ears per stalk. The fifth plant in Figure 13 represents a typical New England flint corn in which the secondary stalks have been reduced to low tillers, known to the farmer as "suckers," which in days of cheaper labor were often removed under the erroneous impression that their removal was a kind of beneficial pruning operation. The last plant represents a typical Cornbelt dent corn which is predominantly single-stalked and often bears only one ear, in approximately the middle region of the stalk.

The corn plant has a distinct advantage over other cereals in bearing its ears in the middle region of the stalk, which, being thicker and stronger than the tip, is capable of supporting a larger ear. This is a simple and obvious mechanical advantage. There may also be a less obvious but even more important physiological advantage. We have evidence (12) that, under otherwise constant conditions with respect to the genotype and the environment, a decrease in the weight of the tassels may be accompanied by an increase five times as great in the weight of the ears. There is at least little doubt that corn, by virtue of its botanical characteristics, is potentially more productive than the other cereals. For example, record yields of wheat seldom exceed 100 bushels per acre; the maximum yields of corn recently reported are more than 300 bushels per acre.

There have, of course, been other factors, not discussed here, in corn's evolution under domestication: mutations at many loci in addition to that governing the characteristics of pod corn; extensive hybridization among distinct races (10, 11); repeated hybridization with teosinte (9, 13) and perhaps also with Tripsacum (7); and human selection for many different characteristics. But it was this one mutation at the pod-corn locus—this single change in a molecule of the hereditary material—which more than any other factor has determined the botanical characteristics of modern corn and which set the plant upon new evolutionary paths that have made it more useful to man and more dependent upon him for survival.

REFERENCES AND NOTES

1. The research reported in this article was supported in part by a grant from the National Science Foundation. I am indebted also to Dr. Walton C. Galinat for his assistance in some aspects of these studies as well as for the drawings reproduced in Figures 5, 9, and 13.
2. O. T. Bonnett, "The inflorescences of maize," *Science* **120**, 77 (1954); P. Weatherwax, "Structure and development of reproductive organs [of corn]," in *Corn and Corn Improvement* (Academic Press, New York, 1955).
3. P. C. Mangelsdorf, "Corn," in *Encyclopaedia Britannica* (1958).
4. E. S. Barghoorn, M. K. Wolfe, K. H. Clisby, "Fossil maize from the Valley of Mexico," in *Botan. Museum Leaflet Harvard Univ. No. 16* (1954), pp. 229–240.
5. P. C. Mangelsdorf, "New evidence on the origin and ancestry of maize," *Am. Antiquity* **19**, 409 (1954).
6. ——— and C. E. Smith, Jr., "New archaeological evidence on evolution in maize," in *Botan. Museum Leaflet Harvard Univ. No. 13* (1949), pp. 213–247.
7. ——— and R. G. Reeves, "The Origin of Indian Corn and its Relatives," *Texas Agr. Expt. Sta. Bull. No. 574* (1939).
8. P. Weatherwax, *Indian Corn in Old America* (Macmillan, New York, 1954); ——— and L. F. Randolph, "History and origin of corn," in *Corn and Corn Improvement* (Academic Press, New York, 1955).
9. P. C. Mangelsdorf, R. S. MacNeish, W. C. Galinat, "Archaeological evidence on the diffusion and evolution of maize in northeastern Mexico," in *Botan. Museum Leaflet Harvard Univ. No. 17* (1956), pp. 125–150.
10. E. J. Wellhausen, L. M. Roberts, E. Hernandez, in collaboration with P. C. Mangelsdorf, *Races of Maize in Mexico* (Bussey Institution, Harvard Univ., Cambridge, Mass., 1952).
11. L. M. Roberts, U. J. Grant, R. Ramirez, W. H. Hatheway, D. L. Smith, in collaboration with P. C. Mangelsdorf, "Races of Maize in Colombia," *Natl. Acad. Sci. Natl. Research Council Publ. No. 510* (1957).
12. A report on this evidence is in preparation.
13. W. C. Galinat, P. C. Mangelsdorf, L. Pierson, "Estimates of teosinte introgression in archaeological maize," in *Botan. Museum Leaflet Harvard Univ. No. 17* (1956), pp. 101–124; P. C. Mangelsdorf and R. H. Lister, "Archaeological evidence on the evolution of maize in northwestern Mexico," in *Botan. Museum Leaflet Harvard Univ. No. 17* (1956), pp. 151–177.

HYBRIDIZATION AND INTROGRESSION IN *COWANIA* AND *PURSHIA*

Howard C. Stutz and L. Kay Thomas[1]

Department of Botany, Brigham Young University, Provo, Utah

Accepted November 15, 1963

Although morphologically quite divergent, *Cowania stansburyana* Torr. (cliffrose) and *Purshia tridentata* (Pursh) D.C. (bitterbrush) frequently form fertile hybrids in nature. Such hybrids often backcross to each of the parental types resulting in genetic introgression in both species.

Cowania stansburyana grows on steep, rocky slopes throughout Utah, Arizona, Nevada, New Mexico, and southern California. *Purshia tridentata* grows in somewhat more mesic sites throughout southern British Columbia, Oregon, Washington, northern California, Montana, Idaho, and Utah. Throughout their range of overlap which includes nearly the entire state of Utah, *Cowania* grows at altitudes of about 5,000 to 8,000 feet and *Purshia* is usually altitudinally immediately below *Cowania* at altitudes of about 3,000 to 6,500 feet. Abundant contacts are provided throughout their range of overlap, at the summits of contrasting north–south slopes and in ravines extending into *Cowania* territory. At these contact sites hybrids and introgressive products are nearly always present.

Purshia glandulosa Curran is common at the southern extension of *P. tridentata* and, as shown below, appears to be a stabilized segregant from the hybridization products of *Cowania stansburyana* and *Purshia tridentata*.

METHODS AND RESULTS

Population samples from a number of sites throughout Utah, Idaho, Montana, and California were scored for various morphological characters which distinguish the two species. Since considerable intraplant and intraspecies variation exists in both taxa, all of the selected characters were

checked for their diagnostic value before scoring the population samples. Those characters having low intraplant and intraspecies variation were given numerical grades which were used in constructing scatter diagrams and hybrid indices for each population (figs. 4–42).

Following Anderson (1949), scatter diagrams of each population were prepared by representing each plant with symbols of the characters scored. *Purshia tridentata* is represented by a plain circle, while *Cowania* characters are shown as darkened sectors of the circle and extended rays from the circle. The values used in recording each of these characters are given in table 1.

The number of leaf lobes and the glandulosity of the upper surface could be measured in a series of grades and, hence, were used as the coordinates in preparation of the scatter diagrams. Hybrid indices were prepared for each plant and plotted as frequencies for each population.

Eleven populations could be scored for all 14 characters, but in others certain parts were scarce so that some characters could not be used. The characters which were scored are indicated on each scatter diagram.

F₁ HYBRIDS

Cowania differs from *Purshia* in so many striking characteristics that hybrids and hybrid derivatives are easily detected in the field. The glandular, glabrous leaves of *Cowania*, with revolute margins and five to seven lobes, are so distinct from the aglandular, pubescent three-lobed leaves of *Purshia* that intermediates for the leaf characteristics alone usually suffice for their detection (fig. 1). In fruit, the hybrids have styles intermediate between the long plumose ones of *Cowania* and short puberulent styles of *Purshia* (fig. 2). As

[1] A portion of this study was supported by a grant from the National Institutes of Health.

TABLE 1. *Symbols and corresponding values for the characters used in preparing the scatter diagrams and hybrid indices of the populations studied*

Character number	Character	Evaluation			
		Purshia	Score	*Cowania*	Score
1	Twig pubescence	Heavy	0	Glabrous	2
2	Dorsal leaf pubescence	Heavy	0	Glabrous	2
3	Hypanthium glands	None	0	3 or more/sq mm	2
4	Stalked glands	None	0	Stalked	2
5	Number of pistils	1 or 2	0	4 or more	2
6	Style length	1.5 cm or less	0	1.6 to 3.4 cm	2
7	Style pubescence	Puberulent	0	Plumose	2
8	L/W ratio of achene	3.1 or less	0	3.3 or more	2
9	Stamen insertion	Hypan. margin	0	Hypan. throat	1
10	Leaf margin revolution	Slight	0	Pronounced	1
11	Hypanthium pubescence	Pubescent	0	Glabrous	1
12	Stamen series	One	0	Two	1
13	Number of lobes per leaf	Three	0	5 or more	2
14	Leaf glandulosity	None	0	3 or more/sq mm	2

shown in table 1, many other characters are also distinctive. Some of these contrasting characters together with a typical intermediate are shown in fig. 3.

Although hybrid derivatives are detectable throughout most populations of Utah, putative F_1 hybrids are usually found only at or near the summits of contrasting slopes. Furthermore, they are usually found only when *Cowania* is occupying the more xeric exposure and *Purshia* is on the less severe east or north slopes. This relationship, together with other indications presented below, suggests that hybridization is enhanced when the flowering period of *Purshia* is retarded, or that of *Cowania* advanced sufficiently to permit a flowering-period overlap. The formation and establishment of hybrids at the summits of such contrasting slopes also enhances the opportunity for subsequent backcrossing to

FIG. 1. Leaves of *Cowania stansburyana* (left), *Purshia tridentata* (right), and a hybrid (center). × ca. 3

FIG. 2. Fruits of *Cowania stansburyana* (left), *Purshia tridentata* (right), and a hybrid (center). × ca. 2

Fig. 3. Twigs of *Cowania stansburyana* (left), *Purshia tridentata* (right), and a hybrid (center). (Separate leaves and fruits of these same three plants are shown in the upper right-hand corner.) × ca. ⅓

each of the parents and hence introgression into both species.

COWANIA AND PURSHIA POPULATIONS IN UTAH

Efforts were made to secure pure *Cowania* populations; the best in this respect were those growing at Escalante (figs. 4, 23) and Kanab (figs. 5, 24), which are near the southern limits of *Purshia tridentata*. But even these show disjunct variation in the direction of *Purshia*. Farther north at Kanosh, *Cowania* shows more variation in the direction of *Purshia* (figs. 6, 25) and still farther north at Edgemont, considerable introgression of *Purshia* into *Cowania* is apparent (figs. 7, 26).

All populations of *Purshia tridentata* in Utah appear to be strongly introgressed with *Cowania*, and it was necessary to use a population from California (figs. 8, 27) as a standard. However, even in this population two plants showed variations in the direction of *Cowania*, suggesting that nonintrogressed populations of *Purshia* may be difficult to find.

MIXED POPULATIONS

Most populations, in which *Cowania* and *Purshia* are sympatric, contain a large variety of morphological variants. Of those

analyzed, only the population at Oak City (figs. 9, 28) consists primarily of distinct *Cowania* and *Purshia*. This is probably because this population is located on a fairly uniform west-facing slope which does not provide the opportunity for overlapping flowering periods and hence little chance for hybridization.

The Edgemont (figs. 10, 29) mixed population is highly variable, consisting of some plants very similar to pure *Purshia*, some plants approaching *Cowania*, and many intermediates. The disjunct distribution of the *Cowania* characters is particularly striking in this population; although they tended to stay together, all but two of the *Cowania* characters measured were variable. The variation in this population is even more striking in the field. All imaginable combinations of habit, pubescence, flowering period, leaf size and shape, etc., are represented. The many recombinant types suggest the presence of F₂ segregants as well as F₁ and backcross derivatives.

In contrast, both the Cove Fort (figs. 11, 30) and Dividend (figs. 12, 31) populations appear to consist of only parentals, F₁ hybrids, and introgressant-type plants. The rather sharp separation of introgressed *Cowania* and introgressed *Purshia* suggests backcrossing but little or no F₂ recombination as at Edgemont.

Related to this is the fact that at Cove Fort and Dividend the populations are located on the sides and summit of a single extensive ridge whereas the Edgemont population is scattered over a series of small multidirectional ravines. The latter situation permits a variety of flowering periods, and thus permits intercrossing of all combinations of hybrid derivatives. With only two slopes available as at Cove Fort and Dividend, hybridization between contrasting types is promoted only at or near the summit and hybrid derivatives are therefore apparently perpetuated only as backcross progeny from one or the other species on each of the two slopes. The terrain occupied is, therefore, apparently of great

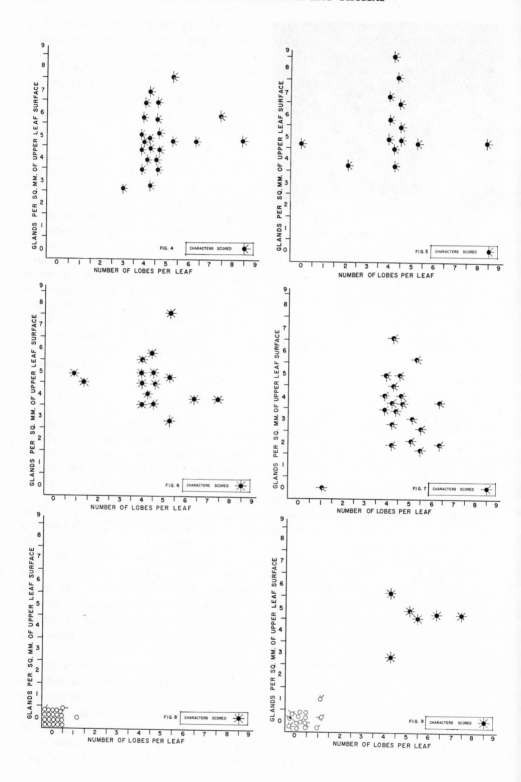

importance not only in providing an opportunity for establishment as described by Anderson (1948), but also in directing the pattern of recombination between these two species. The existence of so-called "hybrid swarms" may thus sometimes be a reflection of opportunity, as much as capacity, for recombination.

PURSHIA POPULATIONS NORTH OF *COWANIA*

Although *Cowania* does not grow north of Utah, *Cowania* characters are present in *Purshia* populations of Idaho and Montana. Immediately north of Utah, at Malad, Idaho, *Purshia* contains, discontinuously, stalked hyphanthium glands, glabrous leaves, and two stamen series on the throat of the hyphanthium (figs. 13, 32). Many plants in these populations, however, have none of these *Cowania*-like characteristics. This disjunct pattern of variation in these populations suggest introgression from *Cowania* even though the nearest *Cowania* plant is 50 miles away. Farther north, just outside Pocatello, Idaho, these same *Cowania* characters are still present sporadically (figs. 14, 33). Still farther north at Dubois (figs. 15, 34) every plant has stalked hyphanthium glands but the other *Cowania* characters are less frequent than in the more southern populations. This trend continues on into Montana where in the Basin populations (figs. 16, 35) every plant examined had stalked hyphanthium glands, many had glabrous leaves and many had glandular leaves. One plant had two series of stamens on the hyphanthium throat and one had revolute margins.

The same constancy for stalked hyphanthium glands and the sporadic occurrence of other *Cowania* characters is also present at Polson, Montana (figs. 17, 36).

PURSHIA GLANDULOSA

Purshia glandulosa has many characters similar to *Purshia tridentata* and several characters similar to *Cowania*. A comparison of the main differences between *Purshia glandulosa*, *Purshia tridentata*, and *Cowania stansburyana* are summarized in table 2.

Populations of *Purshia glandulosa* have been reported from southern Nevada and California, and although not previously reported from Utah, several populations were found throughout the southern part of the state. Each population has a somewhat unique combination of characters, but they have all been considered taxonomically uniform due to the consistent presence of glabrous, glandular leaves, features of *Purshia tridentata* (see fig. 42).

The population from Blanding, Utah (figs. 18, 37) and population no. 1 from White Mountain, California (figs. 19, 38), are more uniformly like *Purshia tridentata* in leaf lobes than are the other populations but are highly variable with respect to some other characters. The Blanding population, for instance, shows discontinuous variations for hyphanthium pubescence and leaf-margin revolution. The hybrid-index scores, based on their similarities to *Purshia tridentata* and *Cowania*, give nearly the same rating to every plant in these two populations. The populations from Mercury, Nevada (figs. 20, 39), Motoqua, California (figs. 21, 40), and population no. 2 from White Mountain, California (figs. 22, 41), show much more interplant variation in hybrid-index scores.

DISCUSSION

Since hybridization and subsequent introgression are common at points of contact

---

←   Scatter diagrams for the characters scored in the following populations:

FIG. 4.   *Cowania stansburyana* from Escalante, Utah
FIG. 5.   *Cowania stansburyana* from Kanab, Utah
FIG. 6.   *Cowania stansburyana* from Kanosh, Utah
FIG. 7.   *Cowania stansburyana* from Edgemont, Utah
FIG. 8.   *Purshia tridentata* from Toiyabe, California
FIG. 9.   Mixed population from Oak City, Utah

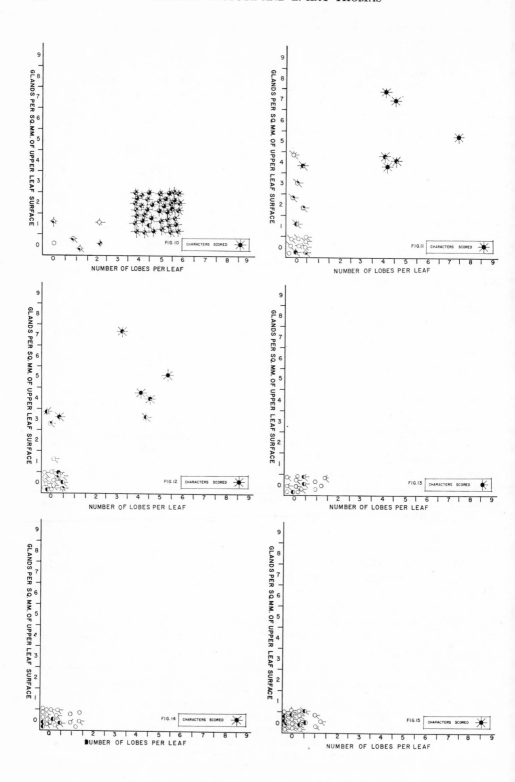

TABLE 2. *A comparison of morphological characters of* Cowania stansburyana, Purshia glandulosa, *and* P. tridentata

Characters	C. stansburyana	P. glandulosa	P. tridentata
Young twig pubescence	glabrous	glabrous	pubescent
Leaf shape	obovate	cuneate	cuneate
Leaf-lobe number	3–5 or more	3 (rarely 5)	3
Leaf-margin revolution	strong	strong	weak
Leaf glandulosity	glandular-punctate	glandular-punctate	none
Dorsal leaf pubescence	glabrous	glabrous	pubescent
Hyphanthium glandulosity	stalked glands	slightly stalked glands	none
Hyphanthium pubescence	glabrous	tomentulose	tomentulose
Pistil number	4–12	1 or 2	1 or 2
Seed shape	linear	obovate	obovate
Style length in fruit	3.9–5.8 cm	1.5 cm or less	1.5 cm or less
Style pubescence	villous	puberulent	puberulent
Stigma position	terminal	decurrent	decurrent
Number of stamen series	2	1	1
Stamen insertion	throat of hypanthium	margin of hypanthium	margin of hypanthium
Achene shape	lanceolate or oblong	fusiform or obovate	fusiform or obovate
Achene pubescence	villous-hirsute	short pubescent	velvety pubescent

between *Cowania* and *Purshia*, reproductive barriers are apparently very weak. In fact, the principal barrier appears to be disjunct flowering periods. *Purshia* usually completes flowering before *Cowania* begins but on contrasting canyon slopes their flowering periods may overlap. This is rather graphically displayed in the populations at Edgemont, Utah. At this site *Purshia* begins flowering in mid-April and is usually finished about the middle of May. *Cowania* begins around the first of June and continues on into August. In this area *Cowania* occupies steep rocky slopes at 5,500 feet to 7,000 feet and extends down some of the ridges to 5,000 feet. *Purshia* is common in ravines at 4,500 feet to 5,000 feet. Occasional *Cowania* plants found on the southern or western slopes of the ravines and occasional *Purshia* plants occupying north-facing or east-facing slopes apparently provide sufficient overlap of flowering in certain years to permit abundant hybridization. On May 20, 1960, at Edgemont, *Purshia* had finished flowering, *Cowania* had not yet started, but near the top of the slopes of each south-facing ravine a cluster of flowering hybrid segregants were strikingly obvious. A careful study of this area revealed at least one plant which was intermediate in most characters, situated near the summit of the west-facing slope of each ridge and early-flowering segregants varying towards both parents in other morphological characters scattered along the slopes. At this site, therefore, *Purshia* growing on east-facing or north-facing slopes are retarded, and *Cowania* growing on west-facing or south-facing slopes are advanced sufficiently to permit an overlap in their flowering periods and hence afford an opportunity for hybridization. The multidirectional ravines in this area provide a wide variety of exposures in close proximity and hybrids and hybrid derivatives are, therefore, given considerable latitude in flowering period. Intercrossing among

←   Scatter diagrams for the characters scored in the following populations:

FIG. 10.   Mixed population from Edgemont, Utah
FIG. 11.   Mixed population from Cove Fort, Utah
FIG. 12.   Mixed population from Dividend, Utah
FIG. 13.   *Purshia tridentata* from Malad, Idaho
FIG. 14.   *Purshia tridentata* from Pocatello, Idaho
FIG. 15.   *Purshia tridentata* from Dubois, Idaho

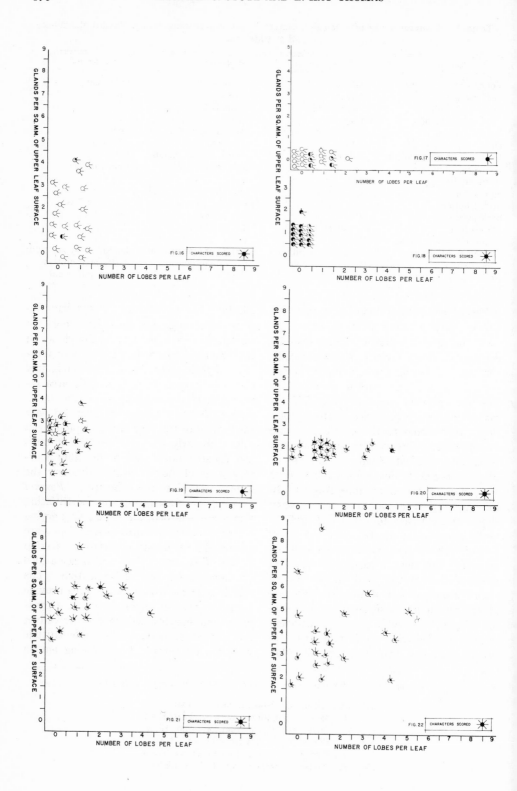

hybrid derivatives as well as backcrossing is permitted, resulting in the large amount of recombination.

Given only two contrasting slopes, such as at Dividend and Cove Fort, hybrids are produced but have little choice of reproductive partners. Because of their comparative scarcity, gametes from the hybrids will nearly always be fertilized by parental gametes. Resulting progeny will be produced and will grow adjacent to the recurrent backcross parent and in turn will have little choice of partner for the following generations. Thus introgression is nearly the only possible outcome when only two contrasting slopes are available. With multidirectional slopes in close proximity, however, derivatives from contrasting backcrosses and other hybrid derivatives have more opportunity to intercross and leave segregating progeny.

Since contact between *Purshia* and *Cowania* at the summit of contrasting slopes is usually near the ecological limits of each species, hybrid products are highly competitive and often form the bulk of the population (e.g., figs. 10, 11, 12). Also at the geographical distributional limits of each species, similar competitive advantages for hybrid derivatives might be expected and indeed appear to be present.

At the southern limits of *Purshia tridentata*, the species *P. glandulosa* appears to be such a successful derivative. The adoption of certain *Cowania* characters appears to have permitted *Purshia* to extend its range southward as a new taxon. As shown in table 2 and fig. 42, *P. glandulosa* has the leaf-lobing and fruit characteristics of *P. tridentata* and the narrow, revolute, glandular, leaf characters of *Cowania*. These features apparently afford the requisite

characteristics for occupation of the more xeric habitat south of the limits of *P. tridentata*.

Each population of *P. glandulosa*, while constant for certain taxonomic characters, is unique for others. Isolated populations might be expected to differ from each other due to mutations and chance fluctuations but the variation shows disjunct associations within each population—a pattern reminiscent of hybridization and introgression. It appears, therefore, that each population has originated from separate hybridizations between *Cowania* and *Purshia*. Natural selection would favor those combinations which permit extension of *Purshia* into the xeric areas and all populations would, therefore, be uniform for these particular characters. But other characters, not having a uniformly similar selective value from population to population, vary from one area to the next, and until fixed by selective forces or by random drift, continue to vary within and between populations.

Because of the marked disjunct associations of non-constant characters which exist within populations of *P. glandulosa*, *P. glandulosa* must either be of fairly recent origins or else hybridization and subsequent introgression is still proceeding. Due to the abundant evidence for contemporary hybridization elsewhere between *Cowania* and *Purshia*, it is likely that introgression into *P. glandulosa* from both *Cowania* and *Purshia tridentata* is still continuing.

The introduction of *Cowania* characters appears to have been advantageous to northern populations of *Purshia* also. As shown in figs. 13 to 17, *Purshia* populations of Idaho and Montana are often character-

---

← Scatter diagrams for the characters scored in the following populations:

FIG. 16. *Purshia tridentata* from Basin, Montana
FIG. 17. *Purshia tridentata* from Polson, Montana
FIG. 18. *Purshia glandulosa* from Blanding, Utah
FIG. 19. *Purshia glandulosa* from White Mountain, California
FIG. 20. *Purshia glandulosa* from Mercury, Nevada
FIG. 21. *Purshia glandulosa* from Motoqua, Utah
FIG. 22. *Purshia glandulosa* from White Mountain, California

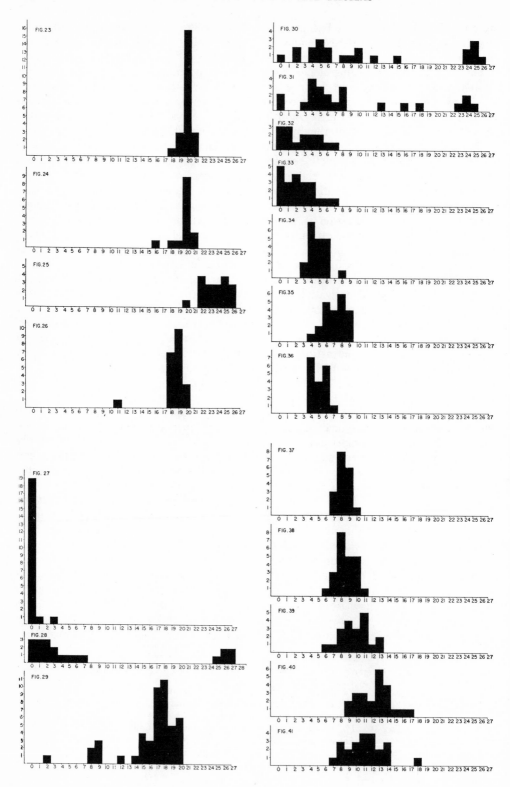

ized by the presence of glands on the leaves and hypanthia. They are distinct from *P. glandulosa*, however, in having broad pubescent leaves, although individual plants with narrow glabrous leaves are found in some populations.

The presence of *Cowania*-like characters in *Purshia* growing more than 200 miles north of *Cowania* suggests that (1) either *Cowania* was formerly growing far north of its present limit and that it left behind hybrid derivatives from its former contacts with *Purshia* or (2) that *Cowania* characters have radiated from hybrids near the current range of *Cowania* and these have extended stepwise into the northern populations of *Purshia*.

Cottam et al. (1961) have presented evidence that the hybrid derivatives between *Quercus gambelli* and *Q. turbinella* found growing throughout the cental valleys of Utah are relics from ancient hybridization which was effected at a time when *Q. turbinella*, which is now restricted to the extreme south of Utah, was growing 200 or 300 miles farther north. If Cottam's analysis is valid, the range of *Cowania* may also have formerly extended several hun-

dred miles north during the same altithermal period. Under such circumstances hybrids and their products might still be perpetuated even though *Cowania* itself is no longer adapted to these areas. However, the variation pattern in these introgressed populations of *Purshia* seem to argue more for distant stepwise introgression from hybrids growing near the current distribution of *Cowania*.

The northern populations of *Purshia* consistently have stalked hypanthium glands and few other *Cowania* features (figs. 26 to 31). The other *Cowania* characters which are present are discontinuous with respect to each other and with respect to the populations. This pattern suggests a strong selective advantage for the glands and since the genetic potential for glands came from *Cowania*, other characters have been brought along also but are dissipating with continued backcrossing onto *Purshia*. If these introgressed populations were produced *in situ* by hybridization with *Cowania*, a random assortment of *Cowania* characters would be expected as in the introgressed populations of Utah and in those in Idaho near the current *Cowania*

Bar graphs of the hybrid-index scores for plants scored in the following populations: (Hybrid-index scores are given on the abscissa and the number of individuals in each class is given on the ordinate axis. A high-index score indicates *Cowania*-like characters; a low hybrid-index score indicates *Purshia*.)

Fig. 23. *Cowania stansburyana* from Escalante, Utah
Fig. 24. *Cowania stansburyana* from Kanab, Utah
Fig. 25. *Cowania stansburyana* from Kanosh, Utah
Fig. 26. *Cowania stansburyana* from Edgemont, Utah
Fig. 27. *Purshia tridentata* from Toiyabe, California
Fig. 28. Mixed population from Oak City, Utah
Fig. 29. Mixed population from Edgemont, Utah
Fig. 30. Mixed population from Cove Port, Utah
Fig. 31. Mixed population from Dividend, Utah
Fig. 32. *Purshia tridentata* from Malad, Idaho
Fig. 33. *Purshia tridentata* from Pocatello, Idaho
Fig. 34. *Purshia tridentata* from Dubois, Idaho
Fig. 35. *Purshia tridentata* from Basin, Montana
Fig. 36. *Purshia tridentata* from Polson, Montana
Fig. 37. *Purshia glandulosa* from Blanding, Utah
Fig. 38. *Purshia glandulosa* from White Mountain, California
Fig. 39. *Purshia glandulosa* from Mercury, Nevada
Fig. 40. *Purshia glandulosa* from Motoqua, Utah
Fig. 41. *Purshia glandulosa* from White Mountain, California

FIG. 42. Fruit and leaves of *Cowania stansburyana* (left), *Purshia glandulosa* (center), and *Purshia tridentata* (right). × ca. 2

source. Hybridization at the current site of *Cowania* could, however, furnish these northern populations with particular characteristics if the selective advantage of these characters were strong enough to perpetuate stepwise backcrossing from population to population.

The strong selective advantage necessary for such screening of *Cowania* characters may be furnished by lowered palatability of introgressed populations. In the western states in which *Purshia tridentata* is native, it is one of the most important browse plants for deer and sheep and in many places its high palatability causes it to be grubbed down to within a few inches from the ground. However, some populations have been reported (e.g., U.S.D.A., 1937) to be less palatable than others and consequently escape such severe grazing. With such a strong selective differential favoring lowered palatability, responsible genes would be expected to spread rapidly from population to population.

It appears likely, therefore, that the *Cowania* characters now present in *Purshia* several hundred miles north of the current distribution of *Cowania* have come from stepwise backcrossing from one population to the next. Those populations near the *Cowania* source (e.g., Malad and Pocatello, Idaho), contain a large amount of discontinuous variation derived from *Cowania*. Farther away from the source, the *Cowania* characters become more and more dilute

and only those having strong selective advantages are represented consistently.

SUMMARY

Hybridization between *Purshia tridentata* (Pursh) D. C. and *Cowania stansburyana* Torr. is common wherever these two species come together in nature. Subsequent introgression is so extensive that non-introgressed populations are rare or absent throughout Utah. The principal reproductive barrier between these two species appears to be disjunct flowering periods. On ridges providing contrasting exposures, the flowering periods are sometimes permitted to overlap and hybridization follows. Terrain having multidirectional exposures promotes abundant recombination that results in "hybrid swarm" types of populations. Where only two contrasting slopes are available, only direct introgression results.

Purshia glandulosa Curran, growing at the southern limits of *P. tridentata,* appears to be a stabilized segregant from the hybrid between *P. tridentata* and *Cowania*. The unique combinations of *Purshia* and *Cowania* characters present in *P. glandulosa* is considered to represent a means for *Purshia* to extend its range southward.

Purshia growing north of the range of *Cowania* also appears to be favored by introgression from *Cowania*. Immediately north of *Cowania's* current distribution, *Purshia* populations contain discontinuous associations of *Cowania* characters. Farther north in Idaho and Montana some of these characters have become stabilized and certain *Cowania* characters are in nearly every plant of many populations. Such widespread migration of *Cowania* characters into *Purshia* must have been promoted by some accompanying strong selective advantage. That this advantage may have been provided by increased unpalatability attending those *Purshia* plants which have been introgressed with *Cowania* characters, is suggested by the recent reports of unpalatable populations of *Purshia* throughout Idaho, Washington, and Montana.

ACKNOWLEDGMENTS

Appreciation is extended to G. L. Stebbins and J. R. Murdock for furnishing some of the specimens.

LITERATURE CITED

ANDERSON, E. 1948. Hybridization of the habitat. EVOLUTION, **2**: 1–9.

——. 1949. Introgressive hybridization. John Wiley and Sons, Inc., New York. 109 p.

COTTAM, W. P., J. M. TUCKER, AND R. DROBNICK. 1959. Some clues to Great Basin postpluvial climates provided by oak distributions. Ecology, **40**: 361–377.

UNITED STATES DEPARTMENT OF AGRICULTURE. 1937. Range plant handbook. Washington, D. C.

HYBRIDIZATION IN THE BUNTINGS (*Passerina*) OF THE GREAT PLAINS

BY CHARLES G. SIBLEY AND LESTER L. SHORT, JR.

INTRODUCTION

The Indigo Bunting (*Passerina cyanea*) breeds over most of eastern North America from southern Canada to the Gulf of Mexico and from the Great Plains to the Atlantic. The Lazuli Bunting (*P. amoena*) occupies the western complement of this range, breeding mainly west of the Great Plains from southern Canada to northern New Mexico and central Arizona and to the Pacific coast (Fig. 1).

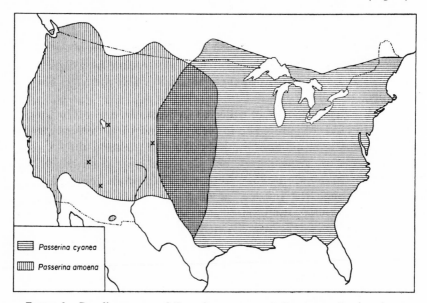

Passerina cyanea

Passerina amoena

FIGURE 1. Breeding ranges of *Passerina cyanea* and *P. amoena* showing the area of overlap. Several western records of *cyanea* mentioned in the text are indicated by an X.

Both forms occur in brushy vegetation and along the edges of woodland. Their songs and calls, general behavior, and nests and eggs are extremely similar or identical. The adult males differ in color but the females are nearly indistinguishable.

The two forms were, until recently, isolated from one another by the unsuitable grassland habitat of the Great Plains. This isolation had endured at least since the Pleistocene when the glaciers divided the ancestral population as they did the populations of many other

Reprinted by permission of Charles G. Sibley and the Editor from THE AUK, **76**, 443–463 (1959).

groups of birds with similar eastern and western representatives today.

With the advent of agriculture in the plains during the past century there have been profound changes in the distribution of vegetation, and hence in the distribution of birds. The planting of trees and shrubs has greatly increased the favorable habitat for woodland and brush-dwelling species (see discussion by Sibley and West, 1959). As a result the two buntings have extended their ranges and the secondary contact between them has become extensive over a broad area in the Great Plains (Fig. 1). Because reproductive isolating mechanisms had not evolved by the time the extrinsic barrier was broken down, the two buntings have interbred. The present paper is a study of the hybridization which is now occurring in the area of overlap in South Dakota, Nebraska, Colorado and Wyoming.

MATERIALS

This study is based mainly upon 95 male specimens of *Passerina* from the states mentioned. Of these 58 are in adult plumage, 37 are subadults.

In 1955, 29 specimens were collected in Nebraska and 31 in South Dakota. In 1956, 10 were taken in Nebraska and 16 in Colorado, and in 1957, three were obtained in Nebraska. In addition three specimens from eastern Wyoming (Crook Co.) and three from the Black Hills region of South Dakota were borrowed from the Pettingill collection through the courtesy of O. S. Pettingill, Jr. Additional comparative material from states east and west of the plains was already available in the Cornell University collection.

PLUMAGE CHARACTERS OF THE MALES

Adult male Indigo Buntings in nuptial plumage are entirely deep blue above and below, the crown somewhat darker and the rump lighter than other areas. Males in their first nuptial plumage are distinguished by having *brown* primary coverts. In adult males the primary coverts are black, edged with blue. Most first year males also have some white on the lower abdomen. This white area is variable in size, sometimes extending beyond the legs but never as far forward as the breast.

The adult male nuptial plumage of the Lazuli Bunting is light turquoise blue above, the crown and rump being nearly concolor with the back. The abdomen and lower breast are white and a band of rusty (cinnamon) brown extends across the breast and down the sides. Two conspicuous white wing bars are present.

THE ANALYSIS OF HYBRIDS

When two forms differing in several characters interbreed it is usually possible to identify the parental source of a given character in the offspring. Variation in backcross products can be analyzed using a "hybrid index". This method has been described and utilized frequently in the past few years (Sibley, 1950; 1954; Sibley and West, 1958; Dixon, 1955) and was originally developed by Anderson (1949) during studies on plant hybrids.

The hybrid index is simply a synoptic description of the observed phenotypes. It is determined as follows. The principal characters by which the two parental forms differ are determined (see Table 1).

TABLE 1

DIFFERING COLOR CHARACTERS OF ADULT MALE INDIGO AND LAZULI BUNTINGS

	P. cyanea	P. amoena
1. Crown color	Deep blue-violet	Turquoise blue
2. Rump color	Azure blue	Turquoise blue
3. Wing bars	Absent	Present
4. Abdomen and lower breast	Blue	White
5. Breast band	Absent	Present

One pure parent is scored "0" on all characters. The hybrid characters are assigned as many values as there are discernible intermediate types and the other pure parent is given the character score at the upper end of the resulting scale. Values for each character of a specimen are determined and the summation of character scores is the hybrid index for the specimen (see Table 2).

For two of the five characters (crown and rump) only one intermediate color type was found in the hybrids. For the other three characters (wing bars, underparts, breast band) three gradations could be easily separated. Characters expressed as in eastern (*e.g.* New York) *P. cyanea* were assigned a score of "0". Those expressed as in western (*e.g.* California) *P. amoena* were scored "2" for crown and rump color and "4" for wing bars, underparts and breast band. The following table provides synoptic descriptions of the hybrid recombination types for each of the five characters in adult males (Table 2).

The subadult males presented a slightly different problem. In the first nuptial plumage males of *cyanea* normally retain some white feathers on the abdomen. However, because they retain the brown

TABLE 2

HYBRID INDEX VALUES OF COLOR CHARACTERS

Crown:	0 = deep blue, as in pure *P. cyanea.*
	1 = intermediate between deep blue and turquoise blue.
	2 = turquoise blue, as in pure *P. amoena.*
Rump:	0 = deep blue, as in pure *P. cyanea.*
	1 = intermediate between azure blue and turquoise blue.
	2 = turquoise blue, as in pure *P. amoena.*
Wing Bars:	0 = absent, as in pure *P. cyanea.*
	1 = slight indication of wing bars.
	2 = intermediate between the two extremes.
	3 = wing bars nearly as complete as in *P. amoena.*
	4 = two white wing bars, as in pure *P. amoena.*
Abdomen and Lower Breast:	0 = blue, as in pure *P. cyanea.*
	1 = approximately one-fourth of the area white.
	2 = approximately half of the area white.
	3 = approximately three-fourths of the area white.
	4 = white, as in pure *P. amoena.*
Breast Band:	0 = absent, as in pure *P. cyanea.*
	1 = a slight tinge of rusty color on the breast.
	2 = intermediate extent of rusty color on breast.
	3 = breast nearly as extensively rusty as in *P. amoena.*
	4 = rusty brown breast band as in pure *P. amoena.*

primary coverts of the juvenile plumage until the first post-nuptial molt, such birds are easy to age. Adults have black primary coverts. We have segregated our specimens into adults and subadults on the basis of the primary coverts. In the adults the color of the abdomen is scored as in Table 2. For subadults this character is omitted because it would not be possible to decide whether white in the abdomen was the result of immaturity or of hybridization with *amoena.* Thus adult males of pure *amoena* have a summated score of "16" ($=2+2+4+4+4$) and the subadult males have a summated score of "12" ($=2+2+4+4$). Hybrid scores range between "0" and "16" for adults and "0" and "12" for subadults.

In the hybrids, *cyanea* and *amoena* characters occur in many recombinations. Many specimens were found to be like one of the parental types except for one or two characters. In otherwise pure *amoena* the wing bars may be basally dark or tinges of violet in the crown or azure in the rump may occur. The breast band may be incomplete and the underparts clouded with blue. In otherwise pure *cyanea* the influence of *amoena* genes is indicated in adults by the presence of white on the underparts, rusty brown feathers in the breast region, traces of wing bars and tinges of lighter blue on the crown and rump.

FEMALES

Only five females were collected during the three summers of field work. This small number was the result of selective collecting of males when given a choice, and the fact that the females are relatively inconspicuous.

These five birds seem to be *P. amoena,* although some may be hybrids. The fact that we cannot distinguish hybrid females helps to emphasize the similarity of the females of *cyanea* and *amoena.* The same situation occurs in two other groups which hybridize widely across the Plains, namely, the Baltimore and Bullock's Orioles (*Icterus g. galbula* and *I. g. bullockii*) and the Rose-breasted and Black-headed Grosbeaks (*Pheucticus ludovicianus* and *P. melanocephalus*). In these two, the males are strikingly different in color, the females extremely similar.

HISTORY OF THE SITUATION

As previously mentioned the modifications of the plant environment by human land-use activities have permitted the two buntings to extend their ranges and to overlap. In 1900, Burnett reported a spring flock of migrant Indigo Buntings in Colorado and expressed the opinion that habitat changes would permit the species to move westward. This prophecy has been amply vindicated by breeding records of the Indigo Bunting in Colorado in 1954 (Baily) and 1955 (Hering). In the Cornell University collection there is an adult male bunting (No. 21594) taken by J. D. Webster in Weber County, Utah, on August 12, 1945 (see map, Fig. 2). The specimen was indexed at "14", appearing like *amoena,* but with traces of *cyanea* in the restriction of the wing bars and the intermediate rump color. Wells (1958) has found Indigo Buntings apparently breeding in Washington County, Utah. Dr. William H. Behle informs us that Indigo Buntings are "exceedingly rare in Utah and are known only from the extreme southwestern part of the state."

A pair of apparently pure Indigo Buntings was found breeding at 4875 feet elevation near Flagstaff, Arizona, by Dearing and Dearing (1946). Lazuli Buntings were found nearby. A male Indigo Bunting was found mated with a female Lazuli Bunting in Soledad Canyon, Los Angeles County, California, by Bleitz (1958) in June, 1956. The nest of this pair contained two bunting eggs and a cowbird egg.

Incubation was apparently normal, but the eggs did not hatch. In June, 1957, a male Indigo Bunting was again observed in the same area (Bleitz, *loc. cit.*). This bird was singing but apparently was unmated when secured as a specimen on June 10. The specimen was examined by us and found to be an adult male which shows possible effects of hybridization in the lightness of the rump color and in the length (69.1 mm. chord) of the wing, which is inter-mediate. The tarsal length (17.2 mm.) is also intermediate, although the difference between the two species in this measurement is so small as to make this intermediacy unimportant. In other measure-ments (bill 7.7 mm., tail 52.2 mm.) and in the other color characters the specimen is similar to eastern *cyanea*. Another recent western record of *cyanea* is that of Boag (1958) who recorded two male Indigo Buntings singing in an area where Lazuli Buntings are noted as "common". This was 20 miles west of Turner Valley at the base of the Rocky Mountains in southwestern Alberta. One male was taken, and the specimen was obtained from Mr. Boag for examination. The specimen proved to be a subadult and showed no indications of hybridization. Measurements of the specimen (Univ. Alberta collection, No. 929) were as follows: wing length 66.1 mm., tail length 50.7 mm., bill length 7.8 mm., and tarsal length 17.8 mm.

Visher (1909) found Indigo Buntings breeding in the Black Hills of South Dakota and our own work indicates that *cyanea* may breed in eastern Wyoming. It should be pointed out that all recent records of "*cyanea*" west of the Plains are likely to be hybrids and that sight records are not satisfactory as the basis for records of "pure" Indigo Buntings in such areas.

The eastward movement of the Lazuli Bunting has also been docu-mented. In 1888, Cooke found Lazuli Buntings in the summer at Vermillion, southeastern South Dakota. The first definite published evidence of *amoena* deep within the normal range of *cyanea* was the first hybrid taken by Breckenridge (1930) along the western border of Minnesota (Marshall Co.) on June 26, 1929. A second hybrid was collected in Cherry County, Nebraska on June 1, 1932 by Young-worth (1932). On July 4, 1933, a pair of *amoena* was found at Yankton, in southeastern South Dakota (Youngworth, 1934), and in June 1935, a male Lazuli was seen in Day County in northeastern South Dakota (Youngworth, 1935). The dates indicate that these birds were probably on their breeding grounds.

The Lazuli Bunting was recorded as a spring migrant at Hastings, Nebraska at least as early as May 7, 1933 (Swenk, 1933). In May,

1938, a "wave" of migrating Lazuli Buntings was recorded at Hastings (Staley, 1938; Jones, 1938). The first record near Omaha was on May 11, 1940 (Nebraska Ornithologists' Union, 1940) and on May 29, 1940, Whelan (1940) found the species near Lincoln. The second record east of Lincoln was at Omaha on May 21, 1944 (Haecker, 1944). The reports of spring migrants at Hastings were regular during the years since approximately 1933, as indicated by the annual reports published in the Nebraska Bird Review. In 1945 a dead Lazuli Bunting was found in Lincoln on May 6 (Jones, 1945) and the editor noted in connection with the record that, "In recent years reports of Lazuli Buntings in eastern Nebraska have become more frequent."

In spite of these numerous records of migrants there have beer no breeding records of *amoena* yet reported in eastern Nebraska although we have found indications of hybridization as far east as Blair on the eastern border and at Crete, near Lincoln. It seems probable that the *amoena* which migrate through eastern Nebraska mostly swing westward before stopping to nest. In North Dakota the easternmost record obtained by Pettingill and Dana (1943) was a pair at Kenmare, Ward County, on June 19. Tordoff (1956) indicates that the Lazuli Bunting is a common transient and probably breeds in extreme western Kansas, but there are no actual nesting records. It is rare in eastern Kansas on migration.

For western Oklahoma there is again evidence of hybridization. Sutton (1938) states that in the same region in which hybrids between the Baltimore and Bullock's Orioles were collected, the Indigo Bunting and the Lazuli Bunting "were actually found to be inter-breeding."

THE ANALYSIS OF COLOR

Each of the 95 male specimens was indexed by the method previously described. Twenty-four were indexed at "0" as phenotypically pure *P. cyanea* and six were indexed as pure *P. amoena*. The remainder, more than two-thirds of the total, showed evidence of hybridization. The maps, Figures 1 and 2, indicate the distribution of hybrids and pure types.

Pure *cyanea* were obtained as far west as Crook, Colorado, on the South Platte River, at Valentine, Nebraska, on the Niobrara River, at Willson, Crook County, Wyoming, and at Rapid City, South Dakota.

Pure *amoena* were found at Rapid City, Mobridge, and Bridger Creek in South Dakota and at Chadron, Nebraska. Previously cited

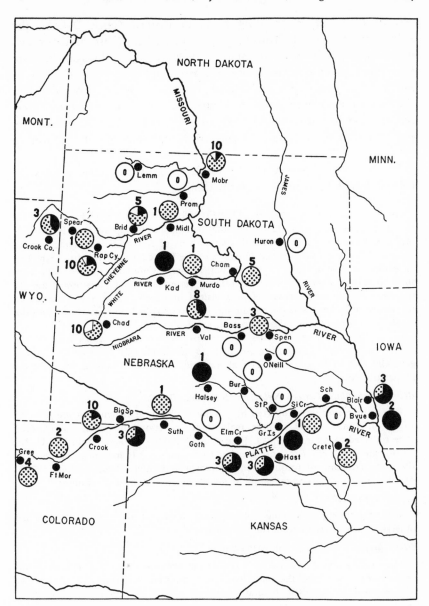

FIGURE 2. Map of the Central Plains showing collecting localities mentioned in the text. Names of the localities are abbreviations and names of nearby towns; exact locations are described in the text. Small black circles indicate the stations. The large circles contain a "0" if no buntings were taken. Numbers beside the large circles indicate the number of specimens. The proportions of pure *cyanea*, *amoena* and hybrid specimens are shown in the larger circles by black, white and dotted areas respectively.

records of probable breeding birds in eastern South Dakota, the hybrid from western Minnesota (Breckenridge, 1930) and our evidence of hybridization at Blair and Hastings, Nebraska, indicate that the zone of overlap between *cyanea* and *amoena* is possibly as much as 400 miles wide in Nebraska. As will be seen from the data the buntings occur in small, discontinuous populations because their habitat occurs in this pattern and, although hybridization is extensive, pure types of both parental forms are found throughout the overlap zone.

In the following section the localities at which specimens were collected will be considered individually.

THE PLATTE RIVER TRANSECT AND SOUTHERN NEBRASKA

During June and July, 1956, ten localities, spaced at approximately 50 mile intervals along the Platte and South Platte rivers of Nebraska and Colorado, were visited. These localities spanned 450 miles of the Platte River system from Schuyler, in eastern Nebraska, to Greeley, in north-central Colorado. Three days were spent in each locality. In order to obtain a better picture of the seasonal aspects, the localities, chosen in advance, were visited in an every-other-one sequence on the westward journey and the remaining ones were visited on the return eastward. The six easternmost localities were again visited in 1957.

In addition five other localities in southern and eastern Nebraska were visited. In the following discussions these first 15 localities will be considered in a generally east to west series. The abbreviations used in Figure 2 are indicated in parentheses.

Bellvue and Blair, Eastern Nebraska (Bvue and Blair).

Two pure *cyanea* were collected by Jerome H. Smith at Bellvue, on the Missouri River, on June 1, 1956. Three male buntings, two adults and one subadult were collected at Blair, Nebraska, June 4-6, 1957. One of these adults (C. U. No. 27610) shows the effects of introgression from *amoena*. It has traces of white on the underparts and of turquoise on the crown and rump (hybrid index = "3"). At Blair the buntings were found in fields among cottonwood saplings.

Schuyler, Nebraska (Sch).

Although favorable bunting habitat was present at this locality we neither observed nor collected one during the two visits.

Silver Creek, Nebraska (3 mi. SSW) (SiCr).

The single adult male is basically *cyanea* but shows the effects of *amoena* in the rump color. This was the only *Passerina* encountered during two visits in an area of seemingly excellent habitat.

Hastings and Crete, Nebraska (Hast and Crete).

One adult, and five subadult males were taken at these two southeastern Nebraska localities (3 mi. SSE Crete and 7 mi. S. Hastings). The adult and one subadult (from Hastings) were phenotypically pure *cyanea*. Three other subadults (2 from Crete, 1 from Hastings) were indexed as "1", showing traces of introgression from *amoena*. One subadult male from Hastings (C.U. No. 25497) was nearly intermediate (hybrid index "5"), showing complete wing bars, indications of the breast band, and intermediate rump and crown color. Frequent reports of *amoena* at Hastings (previously cited) had indicated that hybrids might be found there, and this was verified. All buntings were taken near streams in heavy riparian cover.

Grand Island, Nebraska (7 mi. SSW) (GrIs).

A pure male (subadult) *cyanea* was obtained at this locality, which was visited during all three years for a total of nine days. Only four buntings were seen, two each in 1955 and 1956. All seemed to be pure *cyanea*.

Elm Creek, Nebraska (3 mi. SE) (Elm Cr).

Three males, two adult and one subadult, were taken in 1956. The adult showed traces of *amoena* influence in belly and rump color (C.U. No. 27386), while the others are apparently pure *cyanea*. In the meadows along the Platte five seemingly pure *cyanea* were seen in 1956, none in 1957.

Gothenburg, Nebraska (Goth).

No buntings were collected and none were seen in two visits (1956 and 1957). Seemingly good habitat exists in the riparian meadows and brushy fields near the river.

Sutherland, Nebraska (Suth and Halsey)

A single subadult male was taken one mile southeast of Sutherland, on July 6, 1956. Included with the specimen from this locality is an adult male taken June 13, 1955, two miles west of Halsey, Thomas Co., Nebraska (northeast of Sutherland). The subadult was intermediate in crown and rump color but was otherwise like *cyanea*. The adult was a pure *cyanea* ("0"). During visits to Sutherland in 1956 and 1957 no other buntings were found although numerous brushy fields and riparian meadows seemed to provide favorable habitat. Only one pair of buntings was seen near Halsey, in a clearing in the Nebraska National Forest (Bessey Division).

Big Springs, Nebraska (8 mi. W) (Big Sp).

Three males, two adults and one subadult, were taken in dense cover along the river in 1956. No others were seen. The adults are pure *cyanea* ("0") while the subadult has an intermediate rump color and a hybrid index of "1".

Crook, Colorado (5 mi. ESE) (Crook).

In early July, 1956, buntings were common at this locality and six adult and four subadult males were collected. One adult and one subadult are pure *cyanea* ("0") and one adult (C.U. No. 27400) is nearly pure *amoena* ("15") except for a partly clouded breast band. Of the others four are close to *cyanea* (ad. "1", "1"; subad. "1", "3"), two are close to *amoena* (ad. "13", "14") and one subadult is almost exactly intermediate in all characters ("7").

Large elms and other trees were present with brushy fields in the wide bottom lands along the river. All buntings were taken in the bottom lands and the males, of varying phenotypes, were found on adjacent territories. No differences in habitat preference associated with color type were found.

Fort Morgan, Colorado (8 mi. WNW) (FtMor).

Two male buntings, both showing evidence of hybridization, were collected near Fort Morgan. One, an adult, has an index of "8", the other is a subadult and is close to *cyanea* ("2") but has traces of wing bars and a rump of inter-mediate color. No other buntings were noted in the meadows and woodland edges along the river.

Greeley, Colorado (7 Mi. SW) (Gree).

Four male hybrids (2 ad., 2 subad.) were taken here in 1956. One, a subadult (C.U. No. 27405), is mainly *cyanea* but shows *amoena* influence in the breast band and rump color. It has an index of "2", while the others are closer to *amoena*, the other subadult being indexed at "9", the adults at "13" and "14".

Buntings were common at this locality, especially in brushy fields near the river and both *amoena*-like and *cyanea*-like individuals were seen in addition to the ones collected. All males noted were singing and seemed to be on territories.

THE NIOBRARA RIVER TRANSECT

The Niobrara River flows west to east near the northern border of Nebraska. Three collecting localities were established in its drainage system.

Spencer, Nebraska (5 mi. SSE).

Three adult buntings were taken along the Niobrara River at the edges of oak woodland and fields. All are hybrids and close to *cyanea*, two with indexes of "1", the third has an index of "3".

Valentine, Nebraska (9 mi. ENE) (Val).

This area proved to be of special interest. The eight males collected included five adults and three subadults. Three of the adults are pure *cyanea* ("0") and one adult and two subadults are nearly pure *cyanea* ("1", "1", "2"). These have traces of wing bars and the one indexed at "2" also has turquoise in the rump. The other two specimens index at "9" (subad.) and "14" (ad.). The "9" speci-men has a restricted breast band and wing bars and the crown color is intermediate. The "14" bird is close to *amoena* but the crown color is darker and the breast band smaller.

Most of the buntings were found along the weedy edges of hayfields near the river. In one 300 yard strip of such habitat six males were taken. A pure *cyanea* (C.U. No. 25502) was collected from a singing post on a bush only a few minutes after the nearly pure *amoena* ("14") (C.U. No. 25500), also singing, had been collected from the same bush. The other hybrid ("9") (C.U. No. 25505), which approaches *amoena* in color, was taken while singing in an area between the territories of two pure male *cyanea* (C.U. No. 25506 and 25507).

Chadron, Nebraska (Chad).

Six adults and four subadults were taken near Chadron. One was collected two miles northeast of Chadron, the other nine were taken along Little Bordeaux Creek, six miles southeast of Chadron. Most were found in brushy upland fields near open woodland.

One subadult (C.U. No. 25518) has an index of "6" and is intermediate in the extent of the breast band and in rump color. The crown is as in *amoena* but the wing bars are indicated only by faint traces, thus being more like *cyanea*. Of the other nine, three are pure *amoena*, four are nearly pure *amoena* but show slight traces of *cyanea* in breast band, rump and crown color. The remaining two are intermediate with indexes of "11" (ad.) and "9" (subad.).

SOUTH DAKOTA

The South Dakota localities do not form as complete a pattern, and fewer specimens are available. Eight localities are represented by specimens. Of these, four are represented by small samples, and four by single specimens. Each of the single specimens is included with the specimens from the major locality nearest that where it was taken.

Chamberlain, South Dakota (10 mi. S.) (Cham, Murdo).

Three adults and two subadults were taken in fields along the White River near its junction with the Missouri. One adult was taken west of Chamberlain, 10 mi. SSE Murdo, on the White River. All show evidence of hybridization. One adult (C.U. No. 25546) is nearly pure *cyanea* ("1") but has a lighter rump. The Murdo adult (C.U. No. 25551) is close to *cyanea* ("3") but has wing bar traces, some white on the belly and an intermediate rump. Another (C.U. No. 25547) is almost pure *amoena* ("14") but the crown is intermediate and the breast band is restricted. The other adult indexes at "10" and one of the subadults also at "10". The other subadult is exactly intermediate with an index of "6" (C.U. No. 25548).

Mobridge, South Dakota (9 mi. NNE) (Mobr).

Seven adult and three subadult males were collected on open, brushy hillsides and in meadows near the Missouri River.

One of the subadults (C.U. No. 25544) is a pure *cyanea* ("0") and one adult (C.U. No. 25535) is a pure *amoena* ("16"). The other eight specimens are close to *amoena* but all show evidence of *cyanea* in one or more characters.

Bridger Creek, South Dakota (Brid, Kad and Midl).

Four adults and one subadult were taken at this locality nine miles south-southeast of Howes, Meade County. In addition, one adult was taken six miles south of Kadoka, on the White River, and one subadult was taken on the Cheyenne River, in Haakon County, 45 miles north of Midland. At Bridger Creek a pure *cyanea* and a pure *amoena* were taken in a field, both having sung from the same tree within a few minutes of one another. The other three tend toward *amoena*, the subadult being nearly pure ("11" with the only evidence of *cyanea* influence being slightly restricted wing bars, while the two adults index at "10" and "12" and have indications of *cyanea* genes in the crown, rump, breast band and wing bars. Several other males, all seemingly *amoena*, were observed on song posts. The adult taken near Kadoka is a pure ("0") *cyanea*. The subadult from the Cheyenne River north of Midland has wing bars and crown color intermediate and breast band traces (index "4"), but otherwise is like *cyanea*.

Rapid City, South Dakota (Rap Cy and Spear).

Eight specimens (4 ad., 4 subad.) were taken in 1955 in the vicinity of Rapid City. In addition, two adults collected near Rapid City in 1948, and one adult taken in the Black Hills near Spearfish, South Dakota, were borrowed from the Pettingill collection.

Along Elk Creek, 11 miles north of Rapid City, buntings were quite common in 1955 and six specimens were collected in wooded, grassy areas along the creek. Of these one adult is pure *cyanea* ("0") and one subadult is pure *amoena* ("12"). The other four are hybrids. Two subadult hybrids were collected in brushy fields along Box Elder Creek, six and one-half miles north of Rapid City.

The two Rapid City area specimens in the Pettingill collection are adults, one is a pure *cyanea* from South Canyon and the other a nearly pure *amoena* ("15") from Dark Canyon. Both localities are at the eastern edge of the Black Hills. In 1955 apparently pure *amoena* were seen at the mouth of South Canyon but no *cyanea* were noted. The songs of both forms were heard in this area and seemed identical to all members of the party.

The Spearfish adult in the Pettingill collection is close to *amoena* ("14") but has restricted wing bars and a restricted breast band.

Crook County, Wyoming (Crook Co.)

One adult and two subadult buntings taken in June, 1949, in this eastern Wyoming county were borrowed from the Pettingill collection. Two are from 1 mi. SW Willson, one from 2½ mi. NSundance. The adult is pure *cyanea* and the subadults are hybrids with indexes of "4" and "9". These specimens, in an area where *amoena* would be expected to be the dominant form, indicate that the area of overlap probably extends well into Wyoming.

WEIGHTS AND MEASUREMENTS

The weights and measurements of the plains buntings, and of eastern (New York, Michigan) *cyanea* and western (California, Utah) *amoena* samples, indicate the following:

(1) Mensural differences exist between *cyanea* and *amoena* from eastern and western North America.

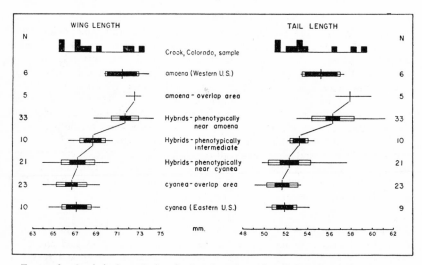

FIGURE 3. Statistical analysis of wing length and tail length of *P. cyanea, P. amoena* and hybrids. Histogram of the sample from one locality shown at the top with each square representing a specimen. Horizontal lines represent the range; rectangles indicate one standard deviation from the mean and the solid black marks twice the standard error of the mean. The means are indicated by vertical lines.

(2) Similar differences exist between pure ("0") *cyanea* and pure ("16" adults and "12" subadults) *amoena* from the plains.

(3) Hybrids are intermediate between the parental forms in weights and measurements.

(4) There is a correlation between the color pattern (i.e., the hybrid index) and the measurements and weights of the hybrids.

These points are illustrated in Figures 3-5 and are discussed below.

Differences Between cyanea and amoena. It is apparent from Figure 4 that *cyanea* is somewhat smaller than *amoena*. While weights were unavailable for far eastern or western buntings, the difference between the two forms in the plains, and the greater wing and tail lengths of *amoena* (see Amadon, 1943, for correlation between wing length and body size) indicate that *amoena* is the larger form. Differences exist in tarsal length and bill length (from nostril), in addition to the wing length (chord) and tail length differences shown in Figure 3. The bill of *cyanea* is slightly larger than that of *amoena* (mean = 7.63 mm. in *cyanea*, 7.27 mm. in *amoena*, for 10 and 8 males respectively). The eastern *cyanea* also has a slightly longer tarsus (mean = 17.39 mm.) than has *amoena* (mean = 16.77 mm., with same N as for bill length). (See Figures 4 and 5 for bill length and tarsal length respectively.)

Differences in Plains Buntings. An average difference in weight of slightly over one gram exists between "pure" ("0") *cyanea* and

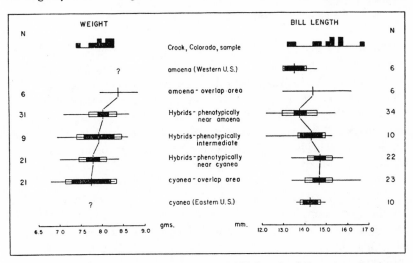

FIGURE 4. Statistical analysis of weight and bill length of *P. cyanea, P. amoena* and hybrids. See Figure 3 for explanation.

"pure" ("16" adults, "12" subadults) *amoena* taken in the plains (Fig. 4). The wing lengths, and tail lengths of the two forms, as shown in Figure 3, differ by more than do the far eastern *cyanea* and western *amoena*. However, the plains buntings approach each other closely in bill length (mean = 7.84 mm. in 23 *cyanea*, mean = 7.70 mm. in 6 *amoena*), and also in tarsal length (mean = 17.27 mm. in 23 *cyanea*, mean = 16.87 mm. in 6 *amoena*).

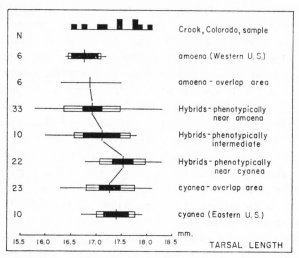

FIGURE 5. Statistical analysis of tarsal length of *P. cyanea, P. amoena* and hybrids. See Figure 3 for explanation.

The significance of these data is twofold. The differences between eastern *cyanea* and western *amoena* have not been lost due to swamping following widespread hybridization and backcrossing. On the other hand, selection against hybridization has not resulted in greatly increased divergence in bill length, tarsal length, wing length or tail length. Some such divergence is to be expected if selection is against the hybrids and isolating mechanisms are being reinforced, for under these conditions competition becomes effective in favoring divergence toward adaptation for different niches (see Sibley, 1957, pp. 169-170, 182-183, for discussion on this point, and Vaurie, 1951, for the fine example in *Sitta neumayer* and *S. tephronota*). In the buntings the time which has elapsed since the breakdown of isolation has apparently been too short to have resulted, as yet, in either reinforcement or swamping.

Intermediacy of Hybrids. This point is shown in Figures 3-5. The three centrally located samples, including all hybrids and backcross individuals, are intermediate between the "pures" in all weights and measurements. This intermediacy is noteworthy (although to be expected), since the hybrids were initially identified as such on the basis of color pattern only.

Correlation Between the Hybrid Index and Weights and Measurements. The three groups of specimens between the "pure" *cyanea* and "pure" *amoena* plains samples in Figures 3–5 are hybrids grouped according to their hybrid index number. Those hybrids phenotypically nearer *cyanea* (index = 1–5 in adults and 1–3 in subadults) were placed in one group; those intermediate in color characters were placed in a second group (index = 6–10 in adults, and 4–8 in subadults; and those nearer *amoena* in color characters (index = 11–15 in adults, and 9–11 in subadults) were placed in the third group. The correlations between wing length and hybrid index is shown in Figure 3. Those individuals indexed closer to *amoena* are nearer *amoena* in wing length also, when compared with the intermediates or with *cyanea*. The phenotypically intermediate individuals are likewise intermediate in wing length between the "pures" of both parental forms from the plains. Those individuals nearer *cyanea* in hybrid index are closer to *cyanea* in wing length, compared with the other hybrids. The same situation is shown by comparing hybrid index with tail length (Figure 3), with weights (Figure 4), with bill length (Figure 4), and with tarsal length (Figure 5). The correlation is clear for weights despite the small difference in mean weights between the two forms in the plains (1.28 gms.). The small differences between *cyanea* and *amoena* in bill length and tarsal length complicate the picture slightly for these measurements. The bill length of plains *cyanea* is greater than that expected on the basis of the bill length of western *amoena*, although the difference is not large. However, the hybrids indexed near *cyanea* are longer billed than those indexed near *amoena*, and the gradient in the three hybrid groups clearly shows the correlation between hybrid index and bill length. In tarsal length, the plains *cyanea* have shorter tarsi than do eastern *cyanea*, although the difference is not large. The gradient exists in the three groups of hybrids for this character also, showing the correlation between tarsal length and hybrid index.

Variation in Linear Measurements and Weights in Locality Samples. Histograms depicting the weights and measurements of the male buntings from Crook, Colorado, (see discussion under that locality concerning the hybrid indexes of the specimens) are included in Figures 3–5. This sample is typical of the larger plains samples in that great variation is shown in all five mensural characters. The variation in wing length, tail length, tarsal length, and bill length approaches that of *all* the phenotypically pure *amoena* and *cyanea* specimens taken in the plains. While the variation in weight is not so great, it is nevertheless quite considerable. As we have shown the linear measurements and weights are closely correlated with color pattern (hybrid index). Statistical treatment of the samples by locality was not carried out because the small size of the samples, and the possibility of non-random mating, cast doubt on the validity of such a treatment. In regard to the latter point, if non-random mating were occurring, samples would represent a non-panmictic population. Hence, statistical treatment of the small samples available was not attempted.

Discussion

The bunting situation in the plains is the result of a recent secondary contact between the two formerly isolated *amoena* and *cyanea* populations. The differences exhibited by the forms could only have arisen under different selective forces acting on allopatric populations. When the barrier between them was broken the forms extended their ranges and came into contact. This contact has resulted in hybridization as described. The changes which have affected bird populations in the plains include the planting of trees and shrubs in shelterbelts, around villages and buildings, and along the rivers. The control of prairie fires, which formerly burned extensive areas periodically, and the control of the rivers, which formerly flooded at intervals washing away vegetation along the banks, have resulted in more continuous riparian vegetation. It is also suggested that removal of the Indians and the buffalo from the plains played a role in increasing the habitats available for woodland birds in that region (see Sauer, 1950, for comments on these effects). Removal of the Indians aided in eliminating the prairie fires they occasionally caused. Periodic trampling of vegetation along rivers, rendering such areas unsuitable for habitation by birds, was an effect of the former huge herds of buffalo.

Natural changes which have increased suitable habitat for buntings and other woodland species of birds include the ameliorating climatic conditions in the plains and the consequent movement of trees and shrubs into the valleys of the plains.

An obvious effect of these changes is the increase in the contact area between the two buntings through the development of suitable habitat for breeding. Furthermore, shelterbelts and tree plantings provide suitable resting places for migratory birds where none previously existed. This has probably aided in the colonization of the plains by the buntings. The discontinuous distribution of the buntings in the plains suggests that stray birds may be aided in colonizing suitable areas by this means. The suggestion of Wells (1958), concerning rapid population expansion in *cyanea* following the last glaciation and opening up of the eastern woodlands, should also be taken into account when considering colonization of the plains by the buntings. Stray birds forced westward by population pressure could exploit favorable areas by such "stepping-stones" as the shelterbelts. The present discontinuous distribution of the buntings in the plains may be influencing the hybridization by limiting gene flow between disjunct populations.

In situations of this nature, the problem of proper taxonomic recognition of the hybridizing forms inevitably arises. As one of us has pointed out (Sibley, 1957), the crucial point is the effect of selection on the apparently fertile hybrids being produced. If selection is operating against the hybrids, reinforcement of isolating mechanisms should occur, resulting in further divergence of the two interbreeding forms. If selection is not operating against the hybrids, then sufficient gene exchange should result in the swamping out of the differences between the two forms as selection fashions a new adaptive combination from the variable gene pool available.

Unfortunately, the determination of the direction of selection acting on the hybrids is difficult in hybrid situations of relatively recent occurrence.

Looking at the situation from one point of view, the number of hybrids taken (66) compared to the number of "pure" individuals of both forms (29) indicates regular gene exchange of sufficient frequency to suggest that all the gene combinations of each form are available to the gene pool of the other. The continuation of such a contact will prevent speciation. On this basis, the forms can be considered conspecific.

Another point of view would stress the fact that "pures" of each form are present with the hybrids at some localities. The great amount of overlap (400+ miles) in which "pures" of both forms, as well as hybrids, are found, would be stressed also. Advocates of this viewpoint would consider the two forms separate species.

The problem in this case can be reduced to a single question, namely: is random mating actually occurring, the large area of overlap being due to the discontinuous distribution of the buntings and their habitat, or is this overlap due to the occurrence of nonrandom mating in which "pure" individuals of one form are tending to mate with individuals of the same form, rather than with hybrids or individuals of the other form? Our data cannot answer this question conclusively. Further study of the populations in the field should give a better basis for a taxonomic decision.

ACKNOWLEDGMENTS

This paper is part of a study of interspecific hybridization in birds supported by a grant to the senior author from The National Science Foundation (N.S.F. G-1842). Additional assistance and equipment have been received from the New York State College of Agriculture at Cornell University. The junior author received grants from the Frank M. Chapman Memorial Fund of the American Museum of Natural History in 1955 and 1956 and a Louis Agassiz Fuertes Research Grant from the

Wilson Ornithological Society in 1956. We also wish to express our thanks to the other members of the field parties, some of whom participated during more than one summer: David A. West (1955, 1956, 1957), Fred C. Sibley (1955, 1956, 1957), David B. Wingate (1956, 1957), William G. Gibson (1955), Jerome H. Smith (1955) and LeRoy Nordby (1955).

The generous and understanding cooperation of the late Mr. Paul Gilbert and of Mr. Lloyd Vance of the Nebraska Game, Parks and Forestation Commission whose help made much of our work possible, is gratefully acknowledged. Dr. William F. Rapp, Jr., Mr. Burton Nelson, Mr. and Mrs. George Blinco, Mr. Carl Smith, Miss Doris Gates, Mr. Harry Behrens and Dr. N. F. Whitney, Jr. helped us in various ways.

SUMMARY

The Indigo Bunting (*Passerina cyanea*) and Lazuli Bunting (*P. amoena*) have formed a secondary contact in the plains as a result of climatic changes and man's activities, which have provided suitable habitat in a formerly unsuitable area. Over a broad area of contact and overlap specimens show that hybridization and backcrossing are occurring, and that both parental forms are present with the hybrids at some localities. The hybrid index technique indicates that 66 out of 95 specimens from 21 localities are hybrids or the result of backcrossing. The hybrids and the situation at each locality are discussed.

Measurements and weights of the specimens show that clear size differences exist between the two forms, that the hybrids are intermediate between the parental forms, and that color pattern is correlated with weights and measurements in the hybrids. No evidence is found for increased divergence of the two forms due to reinforcement of isolating mechanisms and/or the effects of competition. Neither is there clear evidence which indicates that swamping of the existing differences is in progress.

The effects of nature and man in causing the contact between the previously isolated forms are discussed. We postpone a taxonomic decision on the status of the two buntings pending the accumulation of more information, particularly in regard to pairing, mate-selection and habitat preference of the two forms in the area of hybridization and overlap. Data presented in this paper provide bases for arguing for conspecificity, as well as for maintaining the two forms as separate species.

LITERATURE CITED

AMADON, D. 1943. Bird weights as an aid in taxonomy. Wils. Bull., **55**: 164–177.

ANDERSON, E. 1949. Introgressive Hybridization. John Wiley and Sons, New York.

BAILY, A. L. 1954. Indigo bunting nesting in Colorado. Auk, **71**: 330.

BLEITZ, D. 1958. Indigo bunting breeding in Los Angeles County, California. Condor, **60**: 408.

BOAG, D. A. 1958. Parula warbler and indigo bunting in southwestern Alberta. Canad. Field Nat., **72**: 173–174.

BRECKINRIDGE, W. J. 1930. A hybrid *Passerina (Passerina cyanea x Passerina amoena)*. Occ. Pap. Univ. Minn. Mus. Nat. Hist., No. 3: 39–40.

BURNETT, W. L. 1900. The indigo bunting in Colorado. Condor, 2: 90.

COOKE, W. W. 1888. Report on bird migration in the Mississippi Valley in the years 1884 and 1885. U.S. Dept. Agr., Div. of Econ. Ornith., Bull. No. 2, 313 pp.

DEARING, H., and M. DEARING. 1946. Indigo buntings breeding in Arizona. Condor, 48: 139–140.

DIXON, K. L. 1955. An ecological analysis of the interbreeding of crested titmice in Texas. Univ. Calif. Publ. Zool., 54: 125–206.

HAECKER, F. W. 1944. The Lazuli Bunting again seen near Omaha. Nebr. Bird Rev., 12: 10.

HERING, L. 1955. New nesting records from Boulder County, Colorado. Condor, 57: 62.

JONES, MRS. A. H. 1938. Occurrence of the Bewick Wren and other birds in the Hastings vicinity in the spring of 1938. Nebr. Bird Rev., 6: 31.

JONES, K., JR. 1945. The Lazuli Bunting at Lincoln. Nebr. Bird Rev., 13: 52.

NEBRASKA ORNITHOLOGISTS' UNION. 1940. Report on the thirty-eighth annual field day of the Nebraska Ornithologists' Union. Nebr. Bird Rev., 8: 104–105.

PETTINGILL, O. S., JR. and E. F. DANA. 1943. Notes on the birds of western North and South Dakota. Auk, 60: 441–444.

SAUER, C. O. 1950. Grassland climax, fire and man. Jour. Range Management, 3: 16–21.

SIBLEY, C. G. 1950. Species formation in the red-eyed towhees of Mexico. Univ. Calif. Publ. Zool., 50: 109–194.

SIBLEY, C. G. 1954. Hybridization in the red-eyed towhees of Mexico. Evol., 8: 252–290.

SIBLEY, C. G. 1957. The evolutionary and taxonomic significance of sexual dimorphism and hybridization in birds. Condor, 59: 166–191.

SIBLEY, C. G. and D. A. WEST. 1958. Hybridization in the red-eyed towhees of Mexico: the eastern plateau populations. Condor, 60: 85–104.

SIBLEY, C. G. and D. A. WEST. 1959. Hybridization in the Rufous-sided Towhees of the Great Plains. Auk, 76: 326–338.

STALEY, MRS. A. H. 1938. A wave of migrating lazuli buntings at Hastings, Adams County. Nebr. Bird Rev., 6: 32.

SUTTON, G. M. 1938. Oddly plumaged orioles from western Oklahoma. Auk, 55: 1–6.

SWENK, M. H., Editor. 1933. The 1933 migration season. Nebr. Bird Rev., 1: 66–79.

TORDOFF, H. B. 1956. Check-list of the birds of Kansas. Univ. Kans. Publ. Mus. Nat. Hist., 8: 307–359.

VAURIE, C. 1951. Adaptive differences between two sympatric species of nuthatches *(Sitta)*. Proc. 10th Int. Orn. Cong., 163–166.

VISHER, S. S. 1909. A list of birds of western South Dakota. Auk, 26: 144–153.

WELLS, P. V. 1958. Indigo Buntings in Lazuli Bunting habitat in southwestern Utah. Auk, 75: 223–224.

WHELAN, D. B. 1940. Birds of a surviving area of original prairie land in eastern Nebraska. Nebr. Bird Rev., 8: 50–55.

YOUNGWORTH, W. 1932. Another hybrid between the Indigo and Lazuli Buntings. Wilson Bull., 44: 239.

YOUNGWORTH, W. 1934. Field notes from the Sioux City, Iowa, region. Wils. Bull., 46: 62.

YOUNGWORTH, W. 1935. The Lazuli Bunting in northeastern South Dakota. Wils. Bull., 47: 295.

Department of Conservation, Cornell University, Ithaca, New York.

NATURAL HYBRIDIZATION AND AMPHIPLOIDY IN THE GENUS TRAGOPOGON[1]

Marion Ownbey

THE OLD-WORLD GENUS *TRAGOPOGON* (Compositae) is represented in North America by three introduced weedy species, *T. dubius* Scop. (*T. major* Jacq.), *T. porrifolius* L., and *T. pratensis* L. These are coarse herbs from thick biennial taproots which in *T. porrifolius* furnish the familiar salsify or vegetable oyster. The three species are widespread on this continent. In southeastern Washington and adjacent Idaho, all are found. *T. dubius* is the most common here, having successfully invaded waste places, roadsides, fields, and pastures, until its occurrence is practically continuous throughout the region. *T. porrifolius* and *T. pratensis* are more restricted in distribution, being almost wholly confined to towns, and the latter is absent from some towns. It grows abundantly, for instance, in Moscow, Idaho, but has not been found in Pullman, Washington, 10 mi. away. Like *T. dubius,* both *T. porrifolius* and *T. pratensis* can withstand considerable competition, and although their ecological amplitude is not so great, it is strange that they have not become more generally established. According to herbarium records, *T. porrifolius* was established in Pullman prior to 1916 (*Pickett* 314) and *T. dubius* in Pullman prior to 1928 (*Jones* 2066). Local botanists remember the sudden appearance of the latter in great abundance about 1930. *T. pratensis* was collected in Spokane County, Washington, as early as 1916 (*Suksdorf* 8729, 8911).

THE PARENTAL SPECIES.—Each of the three species as it occurs in our area is sharply defined by a combination of qualitative and quantitative characters (table 1) and, with the exceptions to be discussed below, there is never the slightest difficulty in recognizing a given individual as a member of one of the three discrete populations. The genetic hiati are broad, sharp, and absolute, and there simply is no biological intergradation between the entities. The species differ in habit; in the color, shape, crisping, curling, and indument of the leaves; in the color, number, and shape of involucral bracts; in the number of flowers per head; in the relative lengths of involucral bracts and ligules; in the color of ligules; in the shape and relative length of the beak and body of the fruit; in the color of fruit and pappus; and in other ways.

Tragopogon dubius.—This species (fig. 1) is easily recognized by its pale lemon-yellow ligules, all shorter than the involucral bracts. The habit is low

[1] Received for publication November 12, 1949.

This investigation was supported in part by funds provided for biological and medical research by the State of Washington Initiative No. 171.

and bushy, the branches originating from near the base of the stem. The leaves taper uniformly from base to apex, and are neither crisped on the margins nor curled backward at the tip. They are usually conspicuously floccose when young, becoming glabrate and somewhat glaucous with age. The peduncles of well developed heads are strongly inflated and fistulose toward the apex. The flowers of the head are many, ranging in number from 104–180 in the heads counted, with an average of well over 100 flowers per head. The bracts of the involucre are usually thirteen per head—exactly this number in 75 per cent of the first heads of a random sample of forty plants of a pure colony growing under favorable conditions. Occasionally a particularly robust plant may have as many as seventeen bracts in the first head, and frequently the number may be as few as eight on depauperate plants or in late heads. The bracts are long and narrow—always longer than the longest ligules—and are not margined with purple. The expanded mature heads range from 8–12 (av. 10.5) cm. in diameter. The achenes are slender, ranging from 25–36 (av. 33) mm. long, including the beak. The body is gradually narrowed to and not strongly differentiated from the beak. The outer achenes are pale brown, the inner ones straw colored, and the pappus is whitish.

Meiosis was studied in pollen mother cells from two plants, using the aceto-carmine smear technique (employed throughout this study). In both plants, six bivalents regularly were formed at metaphase I (fig. 14). Mature pollen grains, stained with iodine throughout this study, appeared to be 99 per cent good. The mean diameter of mature pollen protoplasts was 29.3 μ. The calculated diameter of mature pollen protoplasts of mean volume was 29.2 μ. These values are identical with those for *T. pratensis*. The species is highly fertile (fig. 5), not more than 2 or 3 per cent of the flowers failing to produce fruits under normal conditions, and even the poorly developed achenes toward the center of the head uniformly contain apparently viable embryos.

Tragopogon porrifolius.—This species is distinguished at once by its pale to dark violet ligules. Lengths of the longest ligules in the wild species are grouped around two means. In the form with long outer ligules, these are nearly as long as the involucral bracts. In the other form, the outer ligules are short, like the inner ones, averaging about half the length of the involucral bracts or less. Both forms are frequent in our populations, the former being more abundant than the latter. The habit is stout but strict, with the branches fewer in number

TABLE 1. *A morphological comparison of the three introduced diploid species of Tragopogon.*

Dubius	Porrifolius	Pratensis
Leaves tapering uniformly from base to apex, neither crisped on margins nor curled backward at tip, usually conspicuously floccose when young, glabrate and somewhat glaucous with age.	*Leaves* tapering uniformly from base to apex, neither crisped on margins nor curled backward at tip, glabrous and glaucous, somewhat broader than in *T. dubius.*	*Leaves* narrowed more abruptly below, the margins concave and crisped, the tips recurved, obscurely floccose when young, later glabrate, pale green, not glaucous.
Peduncles strongly inflated toward apex.	*Peduncles* strongly inflated toward apex.	*Peduncles* scarcely at all inflated, even in fruit.
Heads averaging well over 100 flowers (up to 180 counted), in fruit 8–12 cm. in diameter (av. 10.5).	*Heads* averaging about 90 flowers (up to 117 counted), in fruit 9–11 cm. in diameter (av. 10.0).	*Heads* averaging about 75 flowers (up to 96 counted), in fruit 5–6 cm. in diameter.
Bracts usually 13 (sometimes as many as 17 on the first head of vigorous plants or as few as 8 on the latest heads or on depauperate plants), long and narrow, not margined with purple, longer than the outer ligules.	*Bracts* usually 8 or commonly 9 on the first head, rarely as many as 12, broader than in *T. dubius,* not margined with purple, longer than the outer ligules.	*Bracts* usually 8 or commonly 9 on the first head, rarely as many as 13, broad and short, margined with purple, about equaling the outer ligules in length.
Ligules pale lemon yellow, all shorter than the bracts.	*Ligules* pale to deep violet-purple, all shorter than the bracts, the longest sometimes less than half as long.	*Ligules* chrome yellow, the outer ones about equaling the bracts in length.
Achenes slender, 25–36 mm. long (av. 33), gradually narrowed to the not strongly differentiated beak, outer pale brown, inner straw colored; pappus whitish.	*Achenes* thicker, 29–35 mm. long (av. 32), abruptly tapering to a slender beak longer than the body, outer usually dark brown, inner paler; pappus brownish.	*Achenes* thicker, 20–25 mm. long, abruptly tapering to a slender beak which is often shorter than the body, outer usually dark brown, passing to straw colored inwardly; pappus whitish.

and usually originating higher on the stem than in *T. dubius.* The leaves taper uniformly from base to apex, and are neither crisped on the margins nor curled backward at the tips. They are somewhat broader than in *T. dubius* and glabrous and glaucous from the beginning. The peduncles of well developed heads are strongly inflated and fistulose toward the apex. The number of flowers per head ranged from 84 to 117 (av. 93) in the heads counted. The bracts of the involucre are usually eight per head—exactly this number in 62 per cent of the first heads on a random sample of twenty-nine plants growing under favorable conditions, and in 90 per cent of the second heads of the same plants. Heads with nine bracts are common, this number accounting for 34 per cent more of the first heads and the remaining 10 per cent of the second heads in the population sampled. Heads with as many as twelve bracts, however, are occasionally found. No head with fewer than eight bracts has been noted. The bracts are relatively broader and shorter than in *T. dubius.* They are usually longer than the longest ligules—often twice as long—and are not margined with purple. The expanded mature heads range from 9–11 (av. 10) cm. in diameter. The achenes are stout, ranging from 28–36 (av. 31.7) mm. long including the beak. The thick body is abruptly narrowed to and clearly differentiated from the somewhat longer beak, which is stouter than in *T. dubius.* The outer achenes are dark brown or rarely paler, the inner ones paler, and the pappus is brownish.

Pollen mother cells of three plants were examined. In all three plants, six bivalents regularly were formed at metaphase I of meiosis (fig. 15). Mature pollen grains appeared 97.5 per cent good. The mean diameter of mature pollen protoplasts was 30.8 μ. The calculated diameter of mature pollen protoplasts of mean volume was 31.0 μ. In comparison with those for the other diploid species, and the tetraploid involving *T. porrifolius* and *T. dubius,* these values appear a little high. This species is highly fertile (fig. 6), not more than 2 or 3 per cent of the flowers failing to produce fruits under normal conditions, and even the poorly developed achenes toward the center of the head uniformly contain apparently viable embryos.

Tragopogon pratensis.—This species (fig. 2) is marked by chrome-yellow ligules, the longest about equaling the involucral bracts in length. The *forma minor* with all ligules much shorter than the involucral bracts has not been found in our area. The habit is slender and much branched. The leaves are abruptly narrowed below, resulting in concave margins which are conspicuously crisped. The long acuminate tips are curled backward. The herbage is obscurely floccose when young, later glabrate, and pale green, not glaucous. The slender peduncles are scarcely at all inflated, even in fruit. The number of flowers per head ranged from fifty-one to ninety-six (av. seventy-five) in the heads counted. The number of involucral bracts per head is usually eight (70 ± per cent) or nine (30 ± per cent), rarely as many as thirteen (two observed). The bracts, which about equal the outer ligules in length, are short, broad, and margined with purple. The expanded mature heads average between 5 and 6 cm. in diameter. The achenes are stout, ranging from 20–25 mm. in length, including the beak. The thick body is abruptly narrowed to and clearly differentiated from the usually somewhat shorter beak. The outer achenes are usually dark brown, passing to straw colored inwardly, and the pappus is whitish.

Pollen mother cells of four plants were examined. In three plants, meiosis was regular with six bivalents at metaphase I (fig. 16). In one, a chromatin bridge (but no fragment) was observed in some anaphase I configurations. Since no fragment was found, this may have been a delayed separation of one of the longer chromosome pairs. It was not found in any of the other plants. Mature pollen grains, appeared 98.5 per cent good. The mean diameter of mature pollen protoplasts was 29.3 μ. The calculated diameter of mature pollen protoplasts of mean volume was 29.2 μ. These values are identical with those of *T. dubius.* The species is highly fertile (fig. 7), not more than 2 or 3 per cent of the flowers failing to produce fruits under normal conditions, and even the poorly developed achenes toward the center of the head uniformly contain apparently viable embryos.

INTERSPECIFIC DIPLOID HYBRIDS.—Wherever any two of the three introduced diploid species grow together, natural hybrids can be expected. These hybrids are not found except in patches including both of their parents. All three possible hybrids have been found. They combine certain dominant characteristics derived from the parents involved, and on this basis form three additional classes. In most features, they are not intermediate, but display a re-combination of the characteristics which mark their parents. In two cases, those involving *T. porrifolius* and the two yellow-flowered species, a striking "new" character, bicolored ligules, appears through the interaction of genes for anthocyanin coloration derived from *T. porrifolius* and for yellow plastids derived from the yellow-flowered parent. There is also a gene involved which restricts the anthocyanin to the distal portion of the ligule. As a result, the ligules in these two hybrids are reddish brown to violet brown distally and yellow proximally.

The frequency of the hybrids varies from place to place, presumably depending on the relative opportunities for cross pollination between the parents 2 or more years previously. They usually can be found wherever the two parental species are growing together, and sometimes form a very considerable percentage of the individuals in a patch. The only actual frequency count was made by Dr. Gerald B. Ownbey at Pullman in 1946. He found in one patch, extending for 750 ft. along a roadside, 782 individuals of *T. dubius,* 123 of *T. porrifolius,* and 20 *T. dubius* × *porrifolius* hybrids. His results

by 50-ft. intervals are presented as table 2. This appears to be a relatively typical situation. The total number of individuals of each hybrid combination flowering annually in the Pullman-Moscow area runs into the thousands.

The hybrid individuals as a whole are strikingly uniform for each parental combination. There is some variation in color intensity of the ligules in the hybrids involving *T. porrifolius,* but this is no greater than in this parental species. The factor governing ligule length, also, is passed from *T. porrifolius* to its hybrid offspring, producing long- and short-liguled individuals in about the same proportions as in the parental species.

All three hybrid combinations are extremely sterile. This sterility is usually obvious at a glance (fig. 8, 9, 10). The heads, after flowering, do not continue to develop normally, even though a few fruits with embryos are produced. The bracts of the involucre do not grow as in the species, and the peduncle does not enlarge appreciably. Almost all of the ovaries abort at the flowering stage or shortly thereafter. In all three hybrid combinations, however, individual plants have been observed which appear to develop normal heads of achenes, and at maturity these heads of achenes expand normally. Three such plants were observed in *T. dubius* × *porrifolius,* five in *T. dubius* × *pratensis,* and eleven in *T. porrifolius* × *pratensis.* Each set of these plants was found in only one very limited area, suggesting close genetic relationship between the mem-

TABLE 2. *Frequency of Tragopogon dubius, T. porrifolius, and F₁ hybrids by 50-ft. intervals along roadside, Pullman, Washington, 1946.*

Interval	dubius	porrifolius	hybrids
1	11	18	0
2	56	20	0
3	129	6	0
4	114	1	0
5	44	4	1
6	11	0	0
7	8	2	0
8	19	3	1
9	31	7	0
10	65	14	1
11	99	11	0
12	43	8	8
13	26	5	4
14	51	6	4
15	75	18	1
Totals	782	123	20
Per cent	84.5	13.3	2.2

bers of the set. Paradoxically, these quasi-fertile hybrid individuals were the most sterile of any examined. Although from 15–28 per cent of the flowers produced mature fruits that superficially appeared to be fully developed, direct observation showed that at most only 0.4 per cent produced fruits with embryos.

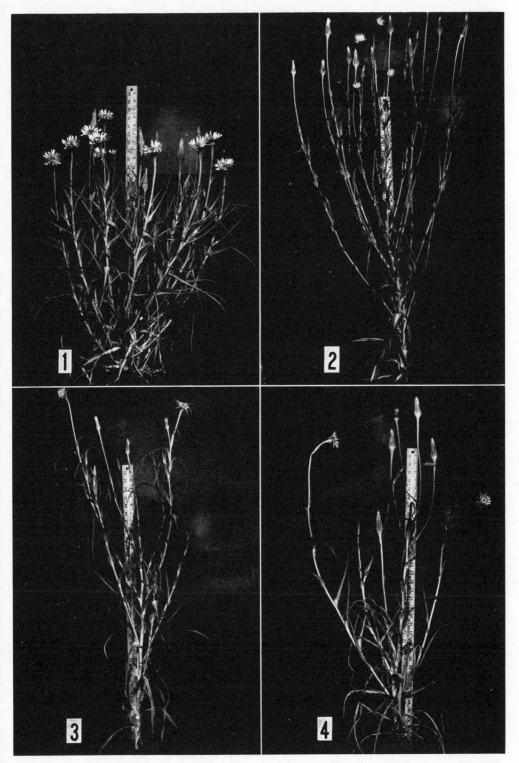

Fig. 1–4. *Tragopogon.*—Fig. 1. *T. dubius.*—Fig. 2. *T. pratensis.*—Fig. 3. Diploid *T. dubius* × *pratensis.*—Fig. 4. mphiploid *T. dubius* × *pratensis* (*T. miscellus*).

The sterile hybrids are often taller, more branched, and more floriferous than the diploid species, particularly with age. They do not, however, possess the marked "gigas" characteristics of the amphiploids to be discussed later.

From the uniformity of the hybrids within each of the three classes, and their sterility, it is inferred that most, of not all, of those observed are F_1 individuals. Evidence for back-cross or F_2 generations is presented in a later section. The characteristics of hybrid individuals of each of the parental combinations follow:

Tragopogon dubius $\times$ *porrifolius* F_1.—Hybrids of this parentage are marked by bicolored ligules, violet brown (or infrequently reddish brown) distally and yellow at the base. They are distinguished from *T. porrifolius* $\times$ *pratensis* hybrids by their uniformly tapering leaves with neither crisped margins nor recurved tips, the number and shape of the involucral bracts which are not margined with purple, and the generally more violet cast of the ligules. The leaves are obscurely floccose when young, but soon become glabrate and glaucous. The habit is generally more strict that in *T. dubius*. The few mature fully developed achenes show a close resemblance to those of *T. porrifolius* in size, shape and color.

The number of bracts per head was determined on the first heads of forty-six plants growing under favorable conditions. Of these, thirty-six (78 per cent) had thirteen bracts, six (13 per cent) had twelve bracts, and the remaining four (9 per cent) had eleven bracts. As in *T. dubius,* late heads and those of depauperate plants were noted commonly to have as few as eight involucral bracts. The bracts resemble those of *T. dubius* in shape as well as number.

These F_1 hybrids are highly sterile (fig. 8). One hundred eighty-seven heads collected at maturity yielded only 161 fruits with embryos. The number of flowers per head was found to average 130 in ten heads. This figure is likely high, since these heads were from particularly robust plants. These same ten heads also produced an average of 1.7 fruits with embryos per head *vs.* the general average of 0.87 for the entire lot. On the basis of 130 flowers per head, the fertility of the hybrid is 0.67 per cent.

Pollen mother cells of two plants were examined. Metaphase I of meiosis was irregular in both plants. In the first, two bivalents and eight univalents were found; in the second a ring of four, two bivalents, and four univalents were observed (fig. 17). Notwithstanding these irregularities, spore-tetrad formation was not conspicuously abnormal. Mature pollen grains, however, were found to be 92 per cent visibly abortive. No mature pollen grains exceeding the diploid size range were observed.

Three quasi-fertile plants, otherwise indistinguishable from the usual F_1 type, were found. Nineteen heads from these plants yielded only seven fruits with embryos. The average number of flowers for 13 heads was 105, and fertility, calculated on this basis, 0.35 per cent. Pollen mother cells were not examined.

Tragopogon dubius $\times$ *pratensis* F_1.—Hybrids of this parentage (fig. 3) are yellow-flowered, the shade being intermediate between those of the parents. They are easily recognized by their recombination of characteristics marking the parents, together with their usually obvious sterility (fig. 9). The relative lengths of involucral bracts and ligules are those of *T. dubius,* as are the number of bracts per head and their shape. The bracts, however, are margined with purple as in *T. pratensis,* and the leaves resemble this parent in their shape, color, crisped margins, and recurved tips. The influence of *T. pratensis* is also evident in the size and shape of the few fully developed achenes matured, although in color these approach those of *T. dubius*.

The number of bracts per head was determined in sixty heads collected for seed. Of these, twenty-three (38 per cent) had thirteen bracts, thirteen (21 per cent) had twelve bracts, eleven (18 per cent) had eleven bracts, five (8 per cent) had ten bracts, five (8 per cent) had nine bracts, and three (5 per cent) had eight bracts. These same 60 heads yielded 101 fully developed fruits, some of which, it was subsequently discovered, lacked embryos. On a basis of an assumed average of 100 flowers per head —no more reliable figure is available—this is a maximum fertility of less than 1.7 per cent. Taking the achenes without embryos into consideration, and the possibility that the assumed number of flowers per head is low, the actual fertility may be as low as 1 per cent.

Five quasi-fertile plants, otherwise indistinguishable from the usual F_1 type, were observed. One of these was studied in considerable detail. As usual in this hybrid (fig. 9), only one or two fruits per head developed beyond anthesis in the earlier heads, but later heads appeared fertile. Twelve later heads from this plant yielded only three fruits with embryos, although many fruits appeared fully developed until they were broken in two. Four heads averaged 114 flowers per head, and on this basis, fertility was 0.22 per cent. It is likely that this plant furnished some of the pollen mother cells studied.

Pollen mother cells of three plants were examined. All three plants were nearly regular with the usual six bivalents at metaphase I of meiosis (fig. 18), occasionally with a pair of univalents, or possibly a ring of four. Evidence of pairing between heteromorphic chromosomes was observed in four cells. A few microspore groups at the tetrad stage contained five and six cells, sometimes of uniform

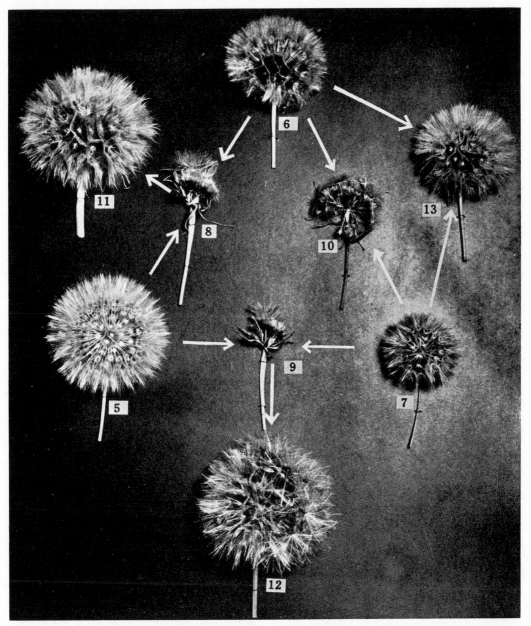

Fig. 5–13. Fruiting heads of *Tragopogon* ($\times \frac{1}{3}$).—Fig. 5. *T. dubius.*—Fig. 6. *T. porrifolius.*—Fig. 7. *T. pratensis.*— Fig. 8. Diploid *T. dubius* $\times$ *porrifolius.*—Fig. 9. Diploid *T. dubius* $\times$ *pratensis.*—Fig. 10. Diploid *T. porrifolius* $\times$ *pratensis.*—Fig. 11. Amphiploid *T. dubius* $\times$ *porrifolius* (*T. mirus*).—Fig. 12. Amphiploid *T. dubius* $\times$ *pratensis* (*T. miscellus*).—Fig. 13. Quasi-fertile diploid *T. porrifolius* $\times$ *pratensis.*

size and sometimes of varying sizes. Mature pollen grains were found to be 93 per cent visibly abortive. No mature pollen grains exceeding the diploid size range were observed.

T. porrifolius $\times$ *pratensis* F_1.—Hybrids of this parentage exhibit bicolored ligules which are red-

dish brown (or infrequently violet brown) distally and yellow at the base. They are distinguished from *T. dubius* $\times$ *porrifolius* hybrids by their abruptly tapering leaves with crisped margins and recurved tips, the number and shape of the involucral bracts, which are margined with purple, and the generally

235

more reddish cast to the ligules. The leaves are glabrous or nearly so from the beginning, and are not very glaucous. The habit is generally strict. Mature, fully developed achenes show a close similarity to those of *T. porrifolius* in size, shape, and color.

The number of involucral bracts per head was counted in sixty-two heads collected for seed. Of these, fifty-two (84 per cent) had eight bracts, eight (13 per cent) had nine bracts, one (1.6 per cent) had ten, and one (1.6 per cent) had seven. Occasionally, a head is found with as many as eleven bracts. These same 62 heads yielded 120 fully developed achenes, a few of which, it was subsequently discovered, lacked embryos. On the basis of an assumed average of ninety flowers per head—no more reliable figure is available—this is a maximum fertility of about 2 per cent.

Eleven quasi-fertile plants (fig. 13), otherwise indistinguishable from the usual F_1 type (fig. 10), were observed. Eight heads from eight of these plants, averaging ninety-five flowers per head, yielded only three fruits with embryos, although 28 per cent of the potential fruits in them appeared fully developed otherwise. This is a fertility of 0.4 per cent.

Pollen mother cells or four plants, including one of the quasi-fertile ones, were examined. Chromosome pairing at metaphase I of meiosis varied greatly. Although six bivalents were found in a number of cells (fig. 19), there were often from two to ten univalents—this last number in the quasi-fertile plant. Microspore groups of three (one much larger than the other two) and six, as well as the usual four were observed. Mature pollen grains from one of the normal hybrids, were found to be only 60 per cent visibly abortive; from one of the quasi-fertile plants, 96 per cent were abortive. No mature pollen grains exceeding the diploid size range were observed in either.

Two AMPHIPLOID SPECIES.—In the season of 1949 four small colonies were detected in which the members differed from the corresponding diploid hybrids in their very evident fertility and in the possession of conspicuous "gigas" features. These four colonies were immediately suspected to represent two newly originated allotetraploid species ($n = 12$), and this chromosomal constitution has since been confirmed. These allotetraploids differ in none of their characters from the corresponding diploid hybrids, but they are much larger in every way. The stems and leaves are thicker, coarser, more massive and succulent. The heads are larger both in flower and in fruit, and the fruits larger and thicker. The mean volume of the spherical pollen grains is almost precisely the sum of the mean volumes of those of the parental species. The fertility averages between 52 and 66 per cent, although there is wide variation in individual plants beyond these limits. In all four colonies, the amphiploids occurred with both the parental species, and the diploid F_1 hybrid. In one patch, three species, three F_1 hybrids and one amphiploid species grew together.

Tragopogon dubius $\times$ *porrifolius Amphiploid* (*T. mirus*).—Two colonies of this amphiploid (fig. 11) were studied, one in Pullman, Washington, and one in Palouse, Washington, 15 mi. away. Extensive search revealed no other individuals. Only *T. dubius* and *T. porrifolius*, with frequent diploid F_1 hybrids between them, are found in either of these two towns. The Pullman colony was studied more intensively. It consisted of fifty-six flowering individuals growing close together in fertile bottom land along a railroad track. The Palouse colony consisted of twenty-five or more individuals growing on a dry hillside. Both these and the associated parental species and diploid F_1 hybrids were considerably smaller than at the Pullman site, which is attributable to the less favorable habitat.

In the Pullman colony, the bract number was thirteen in ten of the twelve heads—one per plant—examined, eleven and nine, respectively, in the remaining two heads. Of five heads (from five plants) from the Palouse population, one had twelve bracts, one had ten, two had nine, and one had eight. The number of flowers was found to average 147 per head in the 12 heads from Pullman, 89 per head in 4 heads from Palouse. The twelve heads from Pullman averaged seventy-six fruits with embryos per head, a fertility of 52 per cent; those from Palouse, fifty-nine fruits with embryos per head, a fertility of 66 per cent.

Pollen mother cells of three plants from the Pullman colony were examined. In all three plants, twelve bivalents were observed at meiotic metaphase I of some cells (fig. 20). Multivalent formation was frequent, however, and many cells could not be analyzed completely. Among the multivalents studied, the maximum number of associated chromosomes discerned was six (fig. 21). It will be recalled that the F_1 hybrid showed a ring of four. Where multivalents were not formed, a strong secondary association between similar bivalents was frequently noted. Spore-tetrad formation appeared normal, with the four microspores notably larger than in the diploid species and hybrids. Mature pollen grains appeared to be 92 per cent good. The mean diameter of mature pollen protoplasts was 37.0 μ. The calculated diameter of protoplasts of mean volume was 36.8 μ. The mean volume of the pollen protoplasts was 8 per cent less than the sum of the mean volumes of those of the parental species. This difference is probably not significant.

Tragopogon dubius $\times$ *pratensis Amphiploid* (*T. miscellus*).—Two colonies of this amphiploid (fig. 4, 12) were studied, both in Moscow, Idaho. Extensive search in Moscow and other towns where the parental species and F_1 hybrids between them occur, revealed no other individuals. All three diploid species and the three diploid hybrids are frequent in Moscow, but only this amphiploid occurs here. Each colony included between thirty and thirty-five individuals, scattered over a few hundred square yards. They were separated by about a mile. At one

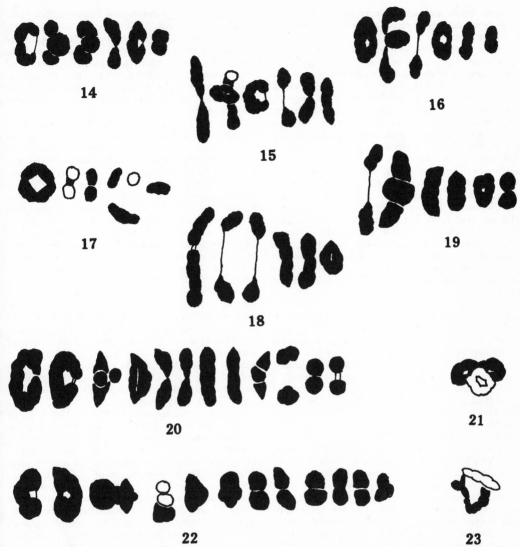

Fig. 14–23. Meiotic chromosomes of *Tragopogon* (×2700).—Fig. 14. *T. dubius.*—Fig. 15. *T. porrifolius.*—Fig. 16. *T. pratensis.*—Fig. 17. *T. dubius* × *porrifolius.*—Fig. 18. *T. dubius* × *pratensis.*—Fig. 19. *T. porrifolius* × *pratensis.*—Fig. 20. Amphiploid *T. dubius* × *porrifolius* (*T. mirus*).—Fig. 21. Multivalent from same interpreted as VI.—Fig. 22. Amphiploid *T. dubius* × *pratensis* (*T. miscellus*).—Fig. 23. Multivalent from same interpreted as heteromorphic IV.

site, in bottom land along a railroad track, conditions were favorable for full development. At the other, along a roadside away from the creek, conditions were not so favorable, and the plants were smaller and less vigorous, as were also those of the parental species and diploid hybrids which occurred there.

In the first colony, the bract number was thirteen in nine of twenty-six heads, twelve in seven heads, eleven in four heads, nine in one head, and eight in one head. Twenty-three heads averaged 115 flowers and 64 fruits with embryos per head, a fertility of 56 per cent.

In the second colony, the bract number was thirteen in two of eighteen heads, twelve in one, eleven in two, ten in seven, nine in five, and eight in one.

Plate 1. Flowering heads of *Tragopogon*. (See frontispiece.) Arranged as in fig. 5–13. *T. dubius* (lower left), *T. porrifolius* (top center), and *T. pratensis* (lower right) form a triangle, along the sides of which are arranged the diploid hybrids, *T. dubius* × *porrifolius* (left center), *T. dubius* × *pratensis* (below center), and *T. porrifolius* × *pratensis* (right center). Adjacent to the diploid hybrids are the corresponding amphiploids, *T. mirus* (upper left), and *T. miscellus* (bottom center). At upper right is the head of the quasi-fertile diploid *T. porrifolius* × *pratensis* hybrid.

Sixteen heads averaged ninety-one flowers and fifty-three fruits with embryos per head, a fertility of 58 per cent.

Pollen mother cells of two plants from the first population were examined. In both, regular or nearly regular plates of twelve bivalents were observed at metaphase I of meiosis (fig. 22). Quadrivalents and some univalents, however, were frequent, and some cells could not be analyzed completely. One configuration interpreted as a quadrivalent involving two heteromorphic chromosome pairs (fig. 23) is of probable significance. It will be recalled that there was evidence also of heteromorphic pairing in the corresponding diploid hybrid. Spore-tetrad formation appeared normal, with the microspores notably larger than in the diploid species and hybrids. Mature pollen grains appeared 91.5 per cent good. The mean diameter of mature pollen protoplasts was 36.3 μ. The calculated diameter of protoplasts of mean volume was 36.4 μ. The mean volume of the pollen protoplasts was only 3 per cent less than the sum of the mean volumes of those of the parental species. This difference is not significant.

F_2 AND BACKCROSS GENERATIONS.—Although the high degree of sterility, both of the pollen and ovules, of the three diploid interspecific hybrids would impose a limitation of major importance on the occurrence of F_2 and backcross individuals, these should nevertheless be expected to appear in small numbers wherever interspecific hybridization is extensive. Furthermore, the well marked dominant characters evident in the F_1 generation should provide "markers" for the study of introgression into the parental species. The absence of such evidence of gene flow across the interspecific barriers, together with the sterility of the individuals showing recombination of characters, was the basis for the earlier statement that most, if not all, of these individuals represent the F_1 generation. Among the thousands of plants examined, however, three individuals appeared to represent a later hybrid generation. Two of these resembled T. pratensis very closely, except for the color of the ligules, which in one were pale orange, and in the other, deep red. That these individuals were of hybrid origin was confirmed by their sterility, which approximated 70 per cent. The other species involved must have been T. porrifolius. The third individual involved T. dubius and T. porrifolius. It was characterized by very pale ligules, and may have represented either a backcross to T. dubius or an F_2 segregate. It was about 99 per cent sterile. In the absence of positive evidence to the contrary, it seems improbable that introgression into any of the three species is taking place.

DISCUSSION.—The genus Tragopogon has furnished a classic example of interspecific hybridization since Linnaeus in the summer of 1759 obtained what is usually considered to be the first interspecific hybrid produced for a scientific purpose,

that between T. pratensis and T. porrifolius (Linnaeus, 1760; Focke, 1881, 1890; Lotsy, 1927; Winge, 1938).[2] This genus now likewise supplies the second and third well documented examples of the origin of a species through amphiploidy in natural populations in historic time. The other example is that of Spartina Townsendii (Huskins, 1931), but both parents of this species are themselves undoubtedly also polyploid.

Linnaeus, after rubbing the pollen from the flowers of Tragopogon pratensis early in the morning, sprinkled the stigmas with pollen T. porrifolius at about eight o'clock. The heads were marked, and the seeds harvested and planted in a separate place. The F_1 hybrids flowered in 1759, producing purple flowers, yellow at the base. Seeds of these F_1 hybrids, along with an essay describing this and other experiments and observations bearing on sex in plants, were submitted in a competition sponsored by the Imperial Academy of Sciences at St. Petersburg. The essay was awarded the prize on September 6, 1760, and the seeds planted in the botanical garden at St. Petersburg, where the F_2 flowered in 1761. These were observed by Kölreuter who recorded (1761) his conclusion that "the hybrid goat's-beard . . . is not a hybrid plant in the real sense, but at most only a half hybrid, and indeed in different degrees" (italics added). This record of segregation in the F_2 of an experimental hybrid, a century before Mendel, has escaped recent notice, even of Roberts (1929), who brought together the pertinent facts. I am indebted to Dr. Jens Clausen for calling it to my attention.

This cross was repeated by Focke (1890), Lotsy (1927), and Winge (1938). Focke's detailed, point by point comparison of the parental species and F_1 hybrids has been overlooked by later workers. Lotsy's contribution is in the form of a color plate illustrating the flowering heads of the parental species, F_1, and F_2 segregates. No attempt at analysis of the spectacular segregation in the F_2 is attempted in the paper. Winge's investigations covered a period of 15 years, and carried the hybrids through the F_7 generation. He was particularly concerned with the genetic bases of specific differences, and gives a detailed account of five independent segregating pairs of genes affecting flower color. It was possible by selection to recover both parental species in apparently pure form from the segregating hybrids. Full fertility was regained in the F_2 and subsequent generations. The chromosomes of the two parental species and hybrids of different generations were thoroughly investigated. Both species and hybrids were diploid, $2n = 12$, with the regular formation of six bivalents at metaphase I of meiosis. No meiotic irregularities were noted which

[2] Zirkle (1935) maintains that the first artificial hybrid was produced by Thomas Fairchild, a London horticulturist, prior to 1717, between the carnation (Dianthus Caryophyllus) and the sweet william (D. barbatus). The evidence that this hybrid resulted from a deliberate experimental cross pollination is conflicting and inconclusive.

would explain the low fertility of the F_1 hybrids. Root-tip mitoses revealed differences in morphology of the somatic chromosomes of the two species, and these differences were found in the reconstituted parental types of hybrid parentage. No tetraploids were found among the 113 plants of Winge's F_2 cultures, although root-tips of 82 were examined. The observation of limited sectors of tetraploid tissue in root-tips of two of these plants, however, is perhaps of significance.

Aside from the work of Winge, chromosome numbers of five species of *Tragopogon* have been reported casually by Poddubnaja-Arnoldi *et al.* (1935) as follows: *T. brevirostris*, $2n = 12$; *T. Cupani*, $2n = 24$; *T. major* (*dubius*), $2n = 12$; *T. marginatus* $2n = 12$; and *T. porrifolius*, $2n = 12$. As the only previously known tetraploid species, *T. Cupani* is of considerable interest. Examination of a single specimen so named, preserved in the Herbarium of the Missouri Botanical Garden, suggests the possibility that this may be the amphiploid involving *T. porrifolius* and *T. pratensis* which has not been found in either Winge's cultures or our wild populations.

In later papers, Focke (1897, 1907) reports additional hybrids including *T. orientalis* $\times$ *porrifolius*, *T. dubius* $\times$ *porrifolius*, and the triple hybrid (*T. pratensis* $\times$ *porrifolius*) $\times$ *orientalis*. The first and last of these were sterile, but the second always matured about a quarter of the usual number of fruits. From it was obtained a fertile, constant line of plants with brownish-purple flowers, which was grown for about eight generations. Focke considered this line to represent a newly originated species, *T. phaeus*, but it does not seem to be our amphiploid of the same parentage. A second constant, fertile form, *T. hortensis*, of uncertain origin, also appeared in his cultures. The first plant of this line was unusually robust, but this characteristic was lost in later generations. It is neither of our amphiploids.

There are numerous brief references to natural hybridization in *Tragopogon*. Linnaeus (1760) records the spontaneous appearance in 1757 of *T. porrifolius* $\times$ *pratensis* in a part of his garden where he had planted its parental species. Schultz-Bipontii (1846) noted this hybrid and also *T. major* $\times$ *pratensis* in his garden. The occurrence of *T. porrifolius* $\times$ *pratensis* in wild populations has been reported in Denmark (Lange, 1864), Germany (Focke, 1887), France (Rouy, 1890), and Sweden (Rouy, 1890). In the United States, it has been found in Illinois (Sherff, 1911) and Michigan (Farwell, 1930). That the hybrid occurred with its parents is definitely stated in most instances. In central Germany, Haussknecht (1884, 1888) found all three possible hybrid combinations of the species occurring there, *T. major* $\times$ *orientalis*, *T. major* $\times$ *pratensis*, and *T. orientalis* $\times$ *pratensis*. The sterility of the first and last was noted. *T. major* $\times$ *orientalis* is also recorded for Austria by Dichtl (1883) and Waisbecker (1897). Chenevard (1899) reports *T. crocifolius* $\times$ *major*? growing with its presumed

parents in France [?] and Cockerell (1912) found sterile *T. dubius* $\times$ *porrifolius* growing with its parents at Boulder, Colorado. Further search of the literature would probably reveal many additional records, but these are sufficient to show that natural hybridization in *Tragopogon* is extensive and involves several species.

The chromosome studies reported in the present paper were directed primarily toward the determination of the ploidy levels of the entities involved and the detection of gross meiotic irregularities which might explain the high degree of sterility in the F_1 together with the success of the amphiploids. The material is suitable for much more detailed analysis, which modify considerably these preliminary observations.

The chromosome complement of all three diploid species consists of three longer and three shorter pairs. The three longer pairs are further generally distinguishable at meiosis by the number and position of chiasmata. At first metaphase, one long pair usually forms a ring with two terminal chiasmata, or through absence of one chiasma, a chain. The second pair is characterized by a submedian localized chiasma, and sometimes by one or two others. The chiasma number in the third long pair is more variable. There are often probably three, but these chromosomes may form a ring with only two, or a chain with only one. The three short pairs are less easily distinguished at metaphase, although one may be a little larger than the other two. Generally in these there is a single terminal chiasma.

The bivalents formed in the F_1 hybrids usually correspond closely to those of the diploid species, indicating a rather high degree of homology between the chromosomes of the different species, at least as far as pairing is concerned. Univalents, when formed, come mostly from the three short pairs. Conclusive evidence as to which two of the long pairs form the ring of four in the *T. dubius* $\times$ *porrifolius* F_1 has not been obtained.

The bivalents of the amphiploids also correspond closely to those of the diploid species, except that there are twice as many. Often this correspondence is obscured by some multivalent formation. Where multivalents are not formed, a strong secondary association between similar bivalents was sometimes noted. Although the chromosomes, at least in *T. dubius* $\times$ *pratensis* F_1 and *T. porrifolius* $\times$ *pratensis* F_1, are able to form normal-appearing allosynaptic bivalents, pairing in the amphiploids, on the whole, seems to be strongly autosynaptic. It should be observed that residual allosynapsis might be expected again to occur in the progeny of such amphiploids as *T. miscellus* when crossed with a third species, and that meiotic pairing in this hypothetical hybrid might not indicate the third species to be an ancestor of the amphiploid.

The high degree of sterility in the F_1 could be caused by evolutionary differentiation of the chromosomes of each species brought about by translocation or interchange of segments between the non-homologous chromosomes of the genome. Ring formation in *T. dubius* × *porrifolius* and evidence of heteromorphic pairing in *T. dubius* × *pratensis* indicate that differences in homology do exist. Around these structural differences, with the resultant interference with random chromosome recombination (because of non-viability of deficient gametes), could be built the association of distinctive genes which mark each species. If all six chromosomes of each parental genome were non-homologous for deficiencies caused by translocation or interchange of essential segments, as compared with the corresponding member of the other parental genome, only those gametes containing a reconstituted parental genome with respect to these structural differences would be viable. Disregarding crossing-over, and given random distribution of the chromosomes of each of the six pairs, one genome of each of the parental species should be reconstituted in each $2^6 =$ sixty-four gametes. In other words, approximately 3.1 per cent of the gametes should contain a parental set of chromosomes. The maximum fertility, if only reconstituted gametes were viable, would be 3.1 per cent, and the F_2 would fall into three classes, reconstituted parental species, 25 per cent for each, and reconstituted F_1 hybrids, 50 per cent. Since any deficient chromosome segments of one parental species might be compensated for by the addition through crossing-over of non-deficient segments of the other parent, the net effect of crossing-over would be an increase in the variability of the F_2, and the genes on the crossover segments would behave in the manner which Winge has described. Some such mechanism might explain the restored fertility in the F_2 and subsequent generations of Winge's hybrids, and the infrequency of detectable later generations in our wild populations.

The mechanism of origin of the amphiploid species, whether by somatic or gametic doubling in the F_1 is obscure. Winge's observation of tetraploid sectors in root-tip tissues would favor the former explanation, as would the absence of pollen grains exceeding the diploid size range in all of the diploid hybrids examined in the present study. Supporting the latter explanation would be the presence of spore triads in some of our hybrids, which suggests that diploid pollen grains might be produced, and the lack of extended vegetative growth. It should be noted that positive evidence favoring either of these mechanisms was observed only in the one of the three hybrid combinations for which no amphiploid is known, that between *T. porrifolius* and *T. pratensis.*

Whatever the mechanism of origin, it is apparent that the amphiploids do not originate with great frequency. The four known colonies probably represent four independent instances of chromosome doubling, and the subsequent establishment of the resultant tetraploid. Considering the frequency of all three F_1 hybrid combinations, however, chromosome doubling must be an exceedingly rare event.

For theoretical reasons, its frequent occurrence in species hybrids with essentially regular meiotic pairing is not to be expected, and amphiploids derived from such should be unsuccessful.

In spite of these theoretical handicaps, the amphiploids of *Tragopogon* have appeared, and have attained a degree of success. Although the populations are still small and precarious, fertility is good, and these species are competing successfully with their parents. Crossing-over has not led to deterioration, presumably because each chromosome usually pairs with its exact homologue, and the consequences of crossing-over, therefore, are not deleterious. Fertility ought to improve with succeeding generations, since any genetic factor which will increase fertility—and there is wide variation in this respect—will enjoy a real selective advantage.

The ecological characteristics of the new amphiploids are not yet apparent. In all instances, they occur within the ecological amplitude of the most restricted parental species. The ecological requirements of natural amphiploids are often such that they have achieved an ecological and geographical distribution somewhat different from the species from which they are presumed to have been derived (Clausen *et al.*, 1945). Since, in both instances, the present amphiploids combine genomes from species with significantly different ecological requirements, it will be interesting to follow their ecological development. At the present time, it is apparent that they have not spread far from their point of origin.

TAXONOMIC CONSIDERATIONS.—The two newly originated amphiploids are to be considered taxonomic species for the following reasons: (1) They are natural groups characterized by a combination of distinctive morphological features. (2) They are reproducing themselves under natural conditions. (3) Gene interchange between the amphiploids and the parental species is prevented by a genetic barrier (ploidy level), and presumably residual sterility factors—evident in the F_1 hybrids—would prevent free interbreeding between the two.

Search of the systematic literature has not revealed the existence of these amphiploid species in Europe, although it would be surprising if they do not occur there. The identification of many obscure species which have been proposed in *Tragopogon* must await a comprehensive taxonomic and cytogenetic study of the genus. Accordingly, these two amphiploids are here described as new species.

Tragopogon mirus Ownbey, sp. nov.—Herbae biennes primum obscure floccosae deinde glabrae glaucaeque. Folia lineari-lanceolata semi-amplexicauliusque ad 5 cm. lata paulatim attenuata, marginibus non crispis, apicibus non cirrosis. Capitula multiflora, pedunculis inflatis fistulosis usque ad 15 mm. crassis. Bracteae involucri lineari-lanceolatae ubique virides, in plantis robustioribus plerumque 13. Ligulae bicoloratae ad apicem lilacinae ad basem flavae bracteis paulum breviores. Achenia rostraque conjuncta 25–35 mm. longa, exteriora fusca, interiora straminea, rostro corpore subaequilongo, pappo cervino.

Type: Washington. Whitman County: in fertile bottom land, Pullman, June 9, 1949, *Ownbey 3195,* in Herbarium of the State College of Washington, Pullman.

Tragopogon **miscellus** Ownbey, sp. nov.—Herbae biennes primum obscure floccosae deinde glabrae viridesque. Folia lineari-lanceolata semi-amplexicaulia usque ad 3 cm. lata abrupte attenuata, marginibus crispis, apicibus cirrosis. Capitula pluriflora, pedunculis inflatis fistulosis usque ad 10 mm. crassis. Bracteae involucri lineari-lanceolatae in plantis robustioribus plerumque 13, marginibus purpureis. Ligulae flavae bractea dimidia subaequilongae. Achenia rostraque conjuncta 25-35 mm. longa, exteriora fusca, interiora straminea, rostro corpore subaequilongo vel longiore, pappo cinereo.

Type: Idaho. Latah County: in fertile bottom land, Moscow, June 10, 1949, *Ownbey 3196,* in Herbarium of the State College of Washington, Pullman.

SUMMARY

Three diploid ($n = 6$) species of the Old World genus *Tragopogon* (Compositae), *T. dubius, T. porrifolius,* and *T. pratensis,* have become widely naturalized in North America. In southeastern Washington and adjacent Idaho, where all three occur, extensive natural hybridization is taking place. Each species crosses readily with both of the others, and wherever two or more grow together, easily detected F₁ hybrids are frequent. These diploid hybrids for all three species combinations are highly sterile, not more than 1–2 per cent of the flowers producing fruits with embryos. They are intermediate only in the sense that they recombine certain dominant characteristics of the parental species involved. F₂ and back-cross individuals are absent or nearly so. Meiosis in the hybrids is fairly regular, although some multivalents and univalents are formed, particularly in *T. dubius* $\times$ *T. porrifolius.* Four small amphiploid populations were discovered in 1949. These represent apparently four recent and independent instances of the doubling of the chromosome sets, two cases each for the *T. dubius* $\times$ *porrifolius* and *T. dubius* $\times$ *pratensis* hybrids. These two tetraploid entities ($n = 12$) are fairly regular meiotically, usually forming bivalents at metaphase I in pollen mother cells. They are moderately fertile, on the average from 52–66 per cent of the flowers producing fruits with embryos. They are established and true-breeding entities, although population size is still precariously small. Morphologically, they are like the corresponding diploid hybrids except for conspicuous "gigas" features and their very evident fertility. Their cell volume, as revealed by measurement of the spherical pollen grains, is almost precisely the summation of the cell volumes of the two parental genomes. They are accorded species rank, described and named *T. mirus* (amphiploid *T. dubius* $\times$ *porrifolius*) and *T. miscellus* (amphiploid *T. dubius* $\times$ *pratensis*).

DEPARTMENT OF BOTANY,
STATE COLLEGE OF WASHINGTON,
PULLMAN, WASHINGTON

LITERATURE CITED

CHENEVARD, P. 1899. Notes floristiques. Bull. Trav. Soc. Bot. Genève 9: 130.

CLAUSEN, J., D. D. KECK, AND W. M. HIESEY. 1945. Experimental studies on the nature of species. II. Plant evolution through amphiploidy and autoploidy, with examples from the Madiinae. Carnegie Inst. of Washington. Publ. No. 564.

COCKERELL, T. D. A. 1912. *Tragopogon* in Colorado. Torreya 12: 244–247.

DICHTL, P. A. 1883. Ergänzungen zu den "Nachträgen zur Flora von Nieder-Österreich." (Fortsetzung). Deutsch. Bot. Monatschrift 1: 187–188.

FARWELL, O. A. 1930. Botanical gleanings in Michigan. VI. Amer. Midl. Nat. 12: 113–134.

FOCKE, W. O. 1881. Die Pflanzen-Mischlinge. Gebrüder Bornträger. Berlin.

———. 1887. *Tragopogon porrifolius* $\times$ *pratensis.* Abhandl. Naturwiss. Ver. Bremen 9: 287–288.

———. 1890. Versuche und Beobachtungen über Kreuzung und Fruchtansatz bei Blütenpflanzen. Abhandl. Naturwiss. Ver. Bremen 11: 413–421.

———. 1897. Neue Beobachtungen über Artenkreuzung und Selbststerilität. Abhandl. Naturwiss. Ver. Bremen 14: 297–304.

———. 1907. Betrachtungen und Erfahrungen über Variation und Artenbildung. Abhandl. Naturwiss. Ver. Bremen 19: 68–87.

HAUSSKNECHT, C. 1884. Botanischer Verein für Gesamtthüringen. I. Sitzungsberichte. Mitteil. Geogr. Ges. (für Thüringen) Jena 2: 211–217.

———. 1888. Kleinere botanische Mitteilungen. Mitteil. Geogr. Ges. (für Thüringen) Jena 6 (Bot. Ver. Gesamtthüringen): 21–32.

HUSKINS, C. L. 1931. The origin of *Spartina Townsendii.* Genetica 12: 531–538.

KÖLREUTER, J. G. 1761. Vorläufige Nachricht von einigen das Geschlecht der Pflanzen betreffenden Versuchen und Beobachtungen. Gleditsch. Leipzig. (Not seen). Reprinted by W. Pfeffer in Ostwald's Klassiker der exakten Wissenschaften 41: 3–37. 1893.

LANGE, J. 1864. Haandbog i den danske Flora. Ed. 3. C. A. Reitzel. Copenhagen.

LINNAEUS, C. 1760. Disquisitio de quaestione ab Academia imperiali scientiarum Petropolitana in annum MDCCLIX pro praemio proposita: "Sexum plantarum argumentis et experimentis novis. . . ." Academy of Sciences, St. Petersburg. (Not seen.) Reprinted as "Disquisitio de sexu plantarum. . . ." in Amoenitates Academicae 10: 100–131. 1790; in English translation as "A dissertation on the sexes of plants," by J. E. Smith. Nichol. London. 1786.

LOTSY, J. P. 1927. What do we know of the descent of man? Genetica 9: 289–328. Plate II.

PODDUBNAJA-ARNOLDI, W., N. STESCHINA, UND A. SOSNOVETZ. 1935. Der Charakter und die Ursachen der Sterilität bei *Scorzonera tausaghys* Lipsch. et Bosse. Beih. Bot. Centralblatt 53A: 309–339.

ROBERTS, H. F. 1929. Plant hybridization before Mendel. Princeton University Press. Princeton, N.J.

ROUY, M. G. 1890. Remarques sur la synonomie de quelques plantes occidentales. Bull. Soc. Bot. France 37: XIV–XX.

SHERFF, E. E. 1911. *Tragopogon pratensis* × *porrifolius*. Torreya 11: 14–15.

SHULTZ-BIPONTII, K. H. 1846. *Tragopogon*. In P. B. Webb and S. Berthelot's Historie Naturelle des Iles Canaries. 32(2): 469.

WAISBECKER, A. 1897. Beiträge zur Flora des Eisenburger Comitates. Österreich. Bot. Zeitschr. 47: 4–9.

WINGE, Ö. 1938. Inheritance of species characters in *Tragopogon*. A cytogenetic investigation. Compt. Rend. Trav. Lab. Carlsberg Série Physiol. 22: 155–193. Plates I and II.

ZIRKLE, C. 1935. The beginnings of plant hybridization. University of Pennsylvania Press. Philadelphia, Pa.

SECTION IV

Major Features of Evolution

MYERS, GEORGE SPRAGUE. 1960. The endemic fish fauna of Lake Lanao, and the evolution of higher taxonomic categories. Evolution **14**: 323–333.

HUTCHINSON, G. E. 1959. Homage to Santa Rosalia; or, why are there so many kinds of animals? Am. Nat. **93**: 145–159.

BROWER, JANE VAN ZANDT. 1958. Experimental studies of mimicry in some North American butterflies. Part I. The monarch, *Danaus plexippus,* and viceroy, *Limenitis archippus archippus.* Evolution **12**: 32–47.

JOHN, BERNARD, and KENNETH R. LEWIS. 1966. Chromosome variability and geographic distribution in insects. Science **152**: 711–721.

COLBERT, EDWIN H. 1948. Evolution of the horned dinosaurs. Evolution **2**: 145–163.

SIMPSON, GAYLORD G. 1950. History of the fauna of Latin America. Am. Scient. **38**: 361–389.

CHANEY, RALPH W. 1948. The bearing of the living *Metasequoia* on problems of Tertiary paleobotany. Proc. Nat. Acad. Sci. U.S. **34**: 503–515.

AXELROD, DANIEL I. 1959. Evolution of the psilophyte paleoflora. Evolution **13**: 264–275.

MICHENER, CHARLES D. 1964. Evolution of the nests of bees. Am. Zool. **4**: 227–239.

LINSLEY, E. G., and J. W. MACSWAIN. 1958. The significance of floral constancy among bees of the genus *Diadasia* (Hymenoptera, Anthophoridae). Evolution **12**: 219–223.

WILSON, EDWARD O., and ROBERT W. TAYLOR. 1964. A fossil ant colony: New evidence of social antiquity. Psyche **71**: 93–103.

THORNE, ROBERT F. 1963. Some problems and guiding principles of angiosperm phylogeny. Am. Nat. **97**: 287–305.

CAMIN, JOSEPH H., and ROBERT R. SOKAL. 1965. A method for deducing branching sequences in phylogeny. Evolution **19**: 311–326.

FITCH, WALTER M., and EMANUEL MARGOLIASH. 1967. Construction of phylogenetic trees. Science **155**: 279–284.

Evolutionists have long been interested in the interpretation of conspicuous patterns in nature. Why do certain lakes contain large numbers of similar species of fishes? Why, indeed, are there several million different kinds of animals? Why do many morphologically dissimilar species of butterflies have similar color patterns on their wings? Partial answers to these questions have been developed, as exemplified in the papers of Myers,* Hutchinson,* and Brower.* Myers shows that a single kind of fish, given the ecological opportunity, can rapidly radiate into a diverse variety of species. Hutchinson takes a broad spectrum approach to biological diversity, ranging over such topics as the splitting of niches, evolution of communities, and differences in the evolutionary processes related to size of organism. Brower, in contrast, examines a single coevolutionary system in detail. She demonstrates that the viceroy butterfly is more palatable than the monarch butterfly which it mimics, and that birds which had tasted the monarch were much less likely to attack a viceroy than were birds which had no experience with the monarchs.

The question of what controls the diversity of organisms in a given place, or in the world as a whole, has received a great deal of attention recently (e.g., see MacArthur and MacArthur, 1961; MacArthur, Recher, and Cody, 1966; and Connell and Orias, 1965). Interestingly, one reason for the great diversity of organisms seems also to be a reason why different kinds of butterflies look alike. Coevolutionary interactions among plants and herbivores may have been a major factor in generating organic diversity (Ehrlich and Raven, 1965); and the chemical weapons used by plants against butterflies have been put to use by the models in mimicry complexes (Brower and Brower, 1964).

Although cytological analyses have been used primarily at infraspecific and specific levels, major patterns of cytological differentiation may also be studied. For example, John and Lewis* provide an overview of geographic variation in karyotype, analogous to that developed by Stebbins (1950) for plants and White (1954) for the entire animal kingdom. Since the majority of animals are invertebrates and the sampling of their diversity is still relatively poor, we may expect important and interesting developments in the future.

When one speaks of major features of evolution, dinosaurs and fossils usually come to mind. Colbert's paper* on the adaptive radiation of the Ceratopsia shows how much may be learned about evolution from a careful analysis of a group with an extensive fossil record. Simpson,* in a different sort of study, uses fossils to interpret the evolution of an entire fauna, showing the migrations and interactions of major vertebrate groups across the connection between North and South America in Cenozoic time.

Often careful study of a particular group may overthrow accepted ideas of biogeography or phylogeny. For example, Chaney* discusses the implications of the recognition that *Metasequoia* rather than *Sequoia* was the dominant conifer of the Arcto-Tertiary Flora. Since *Metasequoia*, first described as a fossil and then later found living in China, is deciduous instead of evergreen

* Paper included in this section.

as *Sequoia* is, reconsideration of the paleoecology and floristics of the Tertiary period for North America is required. Similarly, on the basis of his study of the psilophyte paleoflora, Axelrod* comes to conclusions at variance with the common textbook presentation. Although it is often stated that the psilophytes are ancestral to the major groups of vascular land plants, Axelrod feels they are in fact ancient bradytelic plants of swampy lowlands. The phyla of vascular plants may have had separate origins from various algal groups.

Broad evolutionary patterns in social insects must, in general, be inferred from neontological evidence, as Michener* has done for the evolution of the nests of bees. Linsley and MacSwain* have shown how different patterns of behavior in pollen collecting can lead to different evolutionary patterns. With local changes in availability of pollen plants, less adaptable oligolectic bees may have their range fragmented. If geographic speciation occurs, the result will be closely related allopatric, or possibly sympatric, species with the same pollen plant. On the other hand, adaptable polylectic species can change their pollen sources, and if the flowers are mating sites, isolation can lead to the formation of closely related sympatric or allopatric species with very different pollen plants. Occasionally, fossil evidence may add to our knowledge of the evolution of sociality, as shown by the interesting paper by Wilson and Taylor.*

The final three papers in this section deal with a common problem: how to reconstruct phylogenetic trees in the absence of an adequate fossil record. Thorne* presents a series of principles to be used in making deductions about angiosperm phylogeny, emphasizing the need for broad training of phylogenists. He considers the special problems presented by angiosperms, and postulates the characters of the ancestor of primitive angiosperms. Camin and Sokal* have developed a numerical method for working out cladistic relationships, providing (among other things) that primitive and derived stages of characters can be determined. Fitch and Margoliash* present a scheme based on mutation distances determined by analyses of cytochrome *c* sequences. The potential of this sort of analysis for making statements about past patterns of mutation (especially the distribution of mutations over possible sites) is considerable.

BIBLIOGRAPHY

BROWER, L. P., and J. V. Z. BROWER. 1964. Birds, butterflies, and plant poisons: A study in ecological chemistry. Zoologica **49**: 137–159.

CONNELL, J. H., and E. ORIAS. 1965. The ecological regulation of species diversity. Amer. Nat. **98**: 399–414.

EHRLICH, P. R., and P. H. RAVEN. 1965. Butterflies and plants: A study in coevolution. Evolution **18**: 586–608.

MACARTHUR, R. H., and J. W. MACARTHUR. 1961. On bird species diversity. Ecology **42**: 594–598.

MACARTHUR, R. H., H. F. RECHER, and M. CODY. 1966. On the relation between habitat selection and species diversity. Amer. Nat. **100**: 319–333.

STEBBINS, G. L. 1950. *Variation and Evolution in Plants.* Columbia University Press, New York.

WHITE, M. J. D. 1954. *Animal Cytology and Evolution.* Cambridge University Press, Cambridge, England.

The Endemic Fish Fauna of Lake Lanao, and the Evolution of Higher Taxonomic Categories[1]

George Sprague Myers

Stanford University

INTRODUCTION

The present paper is concerned only incidentally with speciation. Its purpose is to point out some striking but neglected features of lake-fish evolution that illustrate the rapid origin of genera and still higher categories going on at the present time. I have selected the Lanao fishes as an example for several reasons. First, I have examined the fishes myself. Second, the Lanao fishes are in a recognizable stage of what has been called "explosive" evolution. Third, the age of the lake can be determined geologically, and its relative youth cannot be in serious dispute. Fourth, the remarkable zoogeographical situation of Lanao and of Mindanao Island excludes any reasonable possibility that more than one still existing species could have given rise to the 18 endemic species and four endemic genera now inhabiting the lake. The endemic Lanao fish fauna is without parallel, so far as known, in demonstrating explosive specific and generic evolution from a known and still existing ancestral species.

I am deeply indebted to my long-time friend and colleague, Dr. Albert W. Herre, discoverer and describer of the Lanao fish fauna, for many discussions regarding Lake Lanao and its fishes, extending through a period of 30 years. The late

Reprinted by permission of the author and the Society for the Study of Evolution from EVOLUTION, **14**, 323–333 (1960).

Professor Bailey Willis of Stanford, well known for his geological researches on four continents, did me the honor of employing his extensive firsthand knowledge of Philippine geology to prepare the brief geological account of Lake Lanao quoted below. Finally I must present my best thanks to my present graduate student, Mr. Angel Alcala, Instructor in Zoology at Silliman University, Dumaguete, Oriental Negros, for making further collections of Lanao fishes for Stanford. Mr. Alcala was working under National Science Foundation Grant G4381, made to Dr. Walter C. Brown for herpetological research in the Philippines.

THE LAKE

Lake Lanao lies at an altitude of approximately 2,100 feet in the midst of a volcanic area in central Mindanao, the largest island of the southern Philippines. Its exact area is in dispute, Herre giving it 375 square kilometers and others as many as 900. The late Professor Bailey Willis, who had given much attention to Philippine geology, as well as to that of the African Rift Valley and its lakes, investigated what was known of the geological history of Lake Lanao and prepared the following statement for me:

"The island of Mindanao has risen from the ocean gradually and unequally since the Miocene. It now consists of plateaus, hill country, swamps, and volcanoes. The streams were initially small and isolated from each other. The headwaters were, and are, generally swift and the lower courses estuarine.

"A north-central region was built up by basalt flows to a plateau, on which a small system of rivers developed. Some of them flowed southwesterly to Illana Bay, others northwesterly to Iligan Bay. The divide between them ranged from southwest to northeast.

"Volcanoes were built up across the southwesterly flowing streams and they were dammed. Their headwaters gathered in the basin thus formed until they overflowed a low pass in the divide at Camp Keithly and discharged into Iligan Bay on the north coast.

"The impounded waters constitute Lake Lanao. The basin is probably shallow, 200 to 300 feet, perhaps, where deepest. The outlet at Camp Keithly plunges over a fall into a short canyon, indicating an age of 10,000 years, more or less. The principal tributaries to the lake enter from the southeast, from young but dormant volcanoes, and may at times have brought in quantities of ash."

While I have no specific reason to doubt Dr. Willis's estimate of the age of Lake Lanao, 10,000 years seems to be a very short time for the evolution of the Lanao fish fauna. When I brought up this question, Dr. Willis replied that the length of the canyon worn by the Agus River indicated a very brief erosional period. The possibility remains that more than one volcanic damming has been involved in the history of Lake Lanao, but the relative youth of the lake cannot be seriously doubted. The geology of the Lanao Plateau obviously needs more . . . investigation.

THE FISHES

Dr. A. W. Herre collected fourteen species of the Lanao fishes and described them formally in 1924, without mentioning the peculiar evolutionary features concerned. Before the publication of his 1924 paper, he had prepared an account of the zoogeography of Philippine freshwater fishes, in which he implicitly recognized the autochthonous nature of the Lanao fish fauna. However, this distributional paper was not published until considerably later (Herre, 1928). Dr. Herre visited the lake upon later occasions, adding two more species in 1926 and two in 1932.

After Dr. Herre joined the Stanford Museum staff in 1928, I urged upon him the value of preparing an account of the evolutionary features of the Lanao fauna. This resulted in the proposal of a new genus for one remarkable Lanao species (Herre and Myers, 1931) and, finally, in Herre's well-known paper of 1933. Since that time, nothing of importance has been published on these fishes save for Dr. Brooks' review of 1950.

This history is important because of the destruction of Herre's earlier material when the Bureau of Science was dynamited and its collections totally destroyed by Japanese troops in February, 1945, during the battle of Manila. The only sizable collection of Lanao fishes presently available is that in the Natural History Museum of Stanford University. This consists of a few specimens obtained by exchange from the Bureau of Science before World War II; the excellent collection made by Dr. Herre in 1931, including the types of two of his species; and a small collection made at my request in 1959 by Mr. Alcala. Two of the endemic genera (*Mandibularca* and *Spratellicypris*) and the majority of the species are represented. The only other collection of Lanao fishes known to exist in any museum is a small one obtained in 1908 by Dr. Hugh M. Smith and Dr. Paul Bartsch, and now in the U.S. National Museum. This collection was not reported upon *in extenso* until long after Herre's work was completed (Fowler, 1941). I am unable to accept some of Fowler's identifications and have not considered them in the present paper. Two of Herre's endemic genera (*Cephalakompsus* and *Ospatulus*) are known only from the destroyed types.

I have examined the Stanford collection and have had much unpublished information from Dr. Herre. Despite the unavailability of several of the described species, I am convinced that most if not all of the species described by Herre are distinct, some of them remarkably so. Unfortunately, little ecological information is on record. Most of the collections obtained from the lake have been purchased from the native fishermen. The lake is extensively fished, and some of the endemic forms are highly prized as foodfishes by the local Moros.

The endemic forms are all members of the Cyprinidae, the largest family of primary freshwater fishes. The large species flock consists of 13 known species of the genus Dr. Herre called *Barbodes,* better called

Puntius (see Weber and de Beaufort, 1916) but in my opinion not easily distinguished from the widespread genus *Barbus* (Myers, 1960). Five more species are placed in four genera, *Spratellicypris* (1), *Mandibularca* (1), *Ospatulus* (2), and *Cephalakompsus* (1), all of them obviously immediately derived from stocks of *Barbus* within the lake. Other still undescribed species are probably present in the lake. Two non-endemic predators are present, *Channa striata*, perhaps introduced by man, and one diadromus eel (*Anguilla celebesensis*). Eels of this group are known to be able to ascend rapids and waterfalls impassable to other fishes. The North American black bass (*Micropterus salmoides*), a voracious predator, is said to have been introduced in recent years.[2]

DERIVATION OF THE
MINDANAO CYPRINIDAE

Herre (1928 and 1933) has outlined some of the distributional history of the Philippine Cyprinidae, and I have published a general study of the zoogeography of the freshwater fishes of the region (Myers, 1951). The essential facts are as follows:

Central and southern Borneo teems with Cyprinidae, but the cyprinid fauna of North Borneo is relatively depauperate. Cyprinids have entered the Philippines from North Borneo in two widely different directions, through the Palawan-Calamianes chain to Mindoro, and through the Sulu chain to Mindanao. Cyprinids got no farther. The family is absent in the rest of the Philippines, and in Celebes. The Palawan-Mindoro cyprinids do not concern us here.

That Cyprinidae reached Mindanao via a sweepstakes route, across a series of saltwater gaps, is unlikely. My own studies (Myers, 1938, 1949, 1951) indicate that freshwater fishes are less likely to cross such gaps, especially a series of them, than any terrestrial animals, although they must have done so (probably only once, across a very narrow barrier) at Lombok Strait (Myers, 1951). The Lombok crossing, if not by the hand of man, was almost certainly by means of a local cyclone (Darlington, 1938; Myers, 1951), for the saltwater gap at Lombok Strait, although probably broader now than in the Pleistocene, cannot have been bridged very recently (see Bruun and Kiilerich, 1957). Nor is it likely that hurricane (typhoon) winds could have aided the fishes invading Mindanao. The typhoon tracks shown by Dickerson (1928: 40) are all westerly in direction. Finally, freshwater fishes are not well adapted to raft-dispersal across seas!

The obvious conclusion is that freshwater fishes entered Mindanao across a dry-land filter bridge, through the Sulu chain. Just what lowering of sea level occurred there during the Pleistocene, or what elevations or depressions of the Sulu chain may have occurred, is not known. The region is a volcanic, unstable one.

That few or no remains of the cyprinid migration are to be found today on the islands of the Sulu Archipelago is not too surprising. Dr. Herre fished the largest island, Jolo. He found the streams small and without Cyprinidae, but believes that relatively recent volcanic activity has wiped out the freshwater fishes of the island (Herre, 1928).

Quite clearly, then, North Borneo itself, together with the Sulu Archipelago, acted as a filter bridge to limit the access of freshwater fishes to Mindanao. Only three genera of Cyprinidae reached Mindanao (*Barbus, Rasbora,* and *Nematabramis*) and these three are still the dominant cyprinid genera in the streams of North Borneo. Probably only one species of each genus reached Mindanao.

The cyprinid fauna of Mindanao Island outside the Lanao Plateau is very small. There is a single endemic *Rasbora* (*R. philippina*) confined to the western part of the island and closely related to a North Borneo species (Brittan, 1954: 127–131). There are two species of *Nematabramis* (*N. alestes* and *N. verecundus*), very closely allied to each other and to the species of North Borneo (Herre, 1953). Finally, there are four nominal species of *Barbus* (or *Puntius*). *Barbus binotatus* is widespread in Mindanao, and, according to Herre (1953: 123), has been erroneously reported from Lake Lanao by Fowler. *Barbus montanoi* is a doubtful form known only from the type from the Agusan River drainage, eastern Mindanao. *Barbus quinquemaculatus* from the Zamboanga Peninsula is probably a geographical subspecies of *B. binotatus*. *Barbus cataractae* (see Fowler, 1941: 797), also from the Zamboanga Peninsula, is probably a localized variant of *B. binotatus*. After examining the evidence, I suspect that there are really only three well-established cyprinid species in Mindanao outside the Lanao Plateau, one *Rasbora,* one *Nematabramis,* and one *Barbus,* each possibly represented on the island by several subspecies.

NATURE OF THE LANAO FISH FAUNA

Barbus binotatus is the commonest, most widespread, and probably the most variable cyprinid of Sundaland (see Weber and de Beaufort, 1916). It ranges from Siam to Singapore, and throughout Sumatra, Java, and Borneo. It is one of the three cyprinids that have been able to cross Wallace's Line at Lombok Strait; the others are forms of *Rasbora* (Brittan, 1954). *Barbus binotatus* exists in most or all of the lowland streams of Mindanao. It exhibits innumerable local races throughout its range.

With no other large endemic lake fish fauna is it possible with such certainty to identify the ancestral species. Lake Lanao was clearly formed rather rapidly, by volcanic action. The ill defined races of *Barbus binotatus* surrounding the Lanao Plateau form the only local source of invasions. Multiple invasions by dissimilar species of *Barbus* or other cyprinid genera are ruled out, unless one wishes to postulate a series of aerial invasions from Borneo, which dropped fishes only on the Lanao Plateau without colonizing the remainder of Mindanao!

Nor are any cyprinids known from Borneo or elsewhere which parallel or are similar to the strange Lanao genera *Mandibularca* and *Spratellicypris*. The same may be true of the genera *Cephalakompsus* and *Ospatulus,* but the types and only known specimens of these two genera were destroyed in Manila.

We are thus forced to the conclusion that *Barbus binotatus* alone gave rise to at least 18 species on the Lanao Plateau, including four new genera. All of the species that I have examined give evidence of derivation from *Barbus binotatus* or at least a close relative. Two or three of the species are only slightly differentiated from *binotatus* and occur both in the lake and its tributary streams. The most distinctive species are known only from the lake itself. *Mandibularca* occurs only in highly turbulent water at the outlet. One or two of the species are said by local fishermen to inhabit only the deeper waters of the lake, while others are found only in the shallow *Potamogeton* beds. *Barbus binotatus* is not known to occur on the plateau, nor are any of the lake species known from below María Cristina Falls, 65 meters in height, in the Agus River which drains the lake.

THE SUPRALIMITAL SPECIALIZATIONS

In 1936, in connection with a report on fishes from Lake Tanganyika, I briefly pointed out (perhaps for the first time) some of the general features of fish evolution in large lakes throughout the world — the African lakes, Titicaca, Baikal, and Lanao. Brooks (1950) has reviewed the subject of speciation in ancient lakes, including Lanao, but Lanao is not an ancient lake, geologically speaking, and the particular features I wish again to stress are neither limited to ancient lakes nor recognized by Brooks.

In Lake Lanao, the peculiar but quite different lower jaw modifications evolved in the genera *Mandibularca* and *Spratellicypris* (and probably in *Ospatulus* as well) are approached nowhere else in the very large family Cyprinidae, which is generally distributed throughout Eurasia, Africa, and North America, and exhibits many remarkable specializations. In other words, the jaw modifications of some Lanao cyprinids transcend the familial limits of all the 1,500 to 2,000 non-Lanao cyprinid species in the world. For want of a better term I am calling these supralimital specializations.

That peculiar supralimital specializations are not confined to Lanao, but are a common and general feature of the evolution of endemic fish faunas in large lakes, is easily demonstrated. The remarkable scaleless cyprinid *Sawbwa* of the Inlé Lake in Burma (Annandale, 1918), the highly modified species of *Orestias* in Titicaca, the extraordinarily modified cichlid genera of Nyasa and Tanganyika, and many of the cottoids of Lake Baikal, all transcend, in one way or another (often strongly and in many characteristics) the limits of specialization of the large, widespread, and varied families to which they belong.

One illustration will suffice. The Percomorphi form the largest order of bony fishes, containing nine thousand species or more. Within the order, many families are defined by relatively few characteristics, of which dentition is often of considerable importance. The freshwater percomorphs of the family Cichlidae form a large family of perhaps 700 species, distributed throughout Africa, Syria, Madagascar, southern India, and tropical America. Their dental characteristics are generally rather uniform, the modifications usually of small degree. Yet in some of the endemic cichlid genera of Lake Tanganyika, the dental modifications (especially the great, double pointed, heavy-based teeth of *Perissodus* and the utterly strange leaf-like teeth of *Plecodus*) far transcend the limits of dental modification not only of the family Cichlidae, but also of the order Percomorphi and of the entire class of bony fishes. Nothing remotely like them exists. Nor are dental characters the only ones involved. Specializations of the pelvic fins for bottom living (genera *Asprotilapia, Enantiopus*), which elsewhere are considered to be taxonomically of great importance, occur. Indeed, some of the Nyasa and especially the Tanganyika cichlids have come to resemble closely such diverse percomorph families as the Blenniidae (*Telmatochromis*), Girellidae (*Tropheus*), and certain European Percidae (*Asprotilapia*), representing a radiative divergence, and convergence towards different families, entirely unknown elsewhere in the entire gigantic order Percomorphi.

Both *Perissodus* and *Plecodus,* as well as certain other African lake cichlids, might easily be held to represent monotypic families, as has indeed been done with the Comephoridae and (by some) the Cottocomephoridae of Lake Baikal. The late Dr. David Starr Jordan, when shown the jaw of the Lanao genus *Mandibularca*, remarked that a family might well be set up for this genus alone. While I cannot quite agree with this opinion, Jordan's remark is indicative of the situation.

It may be noted that supralimital specializations in fishes are not confined to lake faunas. Any specialization peculiar to one species or genus is, in a sense, a supralimital specialization. However, the general or perhaps the invariable occurrence of extreme and unique specializations in the fishes of lakes that have existed long enough to have produced considerable endemic fish faunas, is notable. Still more notable is the fact that species possessing striking supralimital specializations form a much higher percentage of older lake faunas than they do of stream faunas in general.

The reason for this seems obvious. Most freshwater fishes inhabit streams and are adapted to life in running water. When lakes are formed, only species already adapted to the slow moving, quiet backwaters are able to take immediate and full advantage of an extensive stillwater environment. This extensive new environment usually provides many biotopes not represented in streams, and, in addition, geographical barriers (especially in larger lakes) which may either be present originally or develop with the evolution of the lake itself. The inability of biologists, who are terrestrial animals, to envision these subaquatic facts has greatly hindered studies of fish evolution in lakes.

STAGES OF LAKE FISH EVOLUTION

It is possible to point out sequential steps in the evolution of lake fish faunas, using different existing large lakes as examples; it seems worthwhile to do so. I have specifically refrained from any attempt to evaluate the probably numerous instances in which a relatively small or recent lake has obviously permitted the evolution of one or a few species, sometimes of diverse groups. One such lake is Lake Waccamaw in North Carolina (Hubbs and Raney, 1946). Another is Bear Lake, on the Utah-Idaho boundary, in which three distinct coregonids have evolved (Snyder, 1919). The coregonids have been especially prone to apparent endemism in northern glacial and alpine lakes, but doubt as to the real distinctiveness of many such forms in Postglacial lakes has often been expressed.

In the North American Great Lakes, which have become generally available to fishes only since the geologically recent retreat of glaciation, the coregonids of the "lake herring" (*Leucichthys*) type have experienced a burst of evolution, but many of the endemic species and races are still difficult to separate (Koelz, 1929), if indeed they are really distinct. The fauna is still too young to show anything very definite in the way of supralimital specializations, but the development of species flocks of coregonids is evident. Except for the "lake herrings," no other group of fishes so well preadapted to very cold, still water was present, and this one gained ascendancy.

A similar situation, but probably of greater age because of the greater distinctiveness of the species, is seen in the athernids (*Chirostoma*) of Lake Chapala and other lakes in Mexico (Regan, 1906–1908; Jordan and Hubbs, 1919; Alvarez, 1950) and the cichlids (Meek, 1907; Regan, 1906–1908) of Lakes Nicaragua and Managua. Supralimital specializations among the Cyprinodontidae are clearly foreshadowed in the dwarf, deep-bodied species of *Orestias* in Lake Titicaca (Tchernavin, 1944), which are unlike any of the non-Titicaca *Orestias*.

A clearly more advanced stage is represented by Lake Lanao, in which a single ancestral species of cyprinid has given rise to a species flock, five members of which have become so distinct as to be referable to four endemic genera. Their supralimital specializations have been mentioned above. The excellent work of Mr. Greenwood on the Cichlidae of Lake Victoria shows that the Victoria cichlids are in a state more or less comparable to that of the Lanao cyprinids, although evolution is proceeding on a far grander scale. The species flocks are much larger and there are four distinctive endemic genera (Greenwood, 1956, 1959), but the ancestral types are either lost or unidentifiable. However, as in Lanao, endemics of families other than the dominant one are absent.

A much older stage is represented by the fishes of Lake Nyasa, which Brooks (1950: 135) estimates to be approximately 500,000 years old. Fryer (1959: 264) gives evidence pointing to greater age. As in all other large Central African lakes, the cichlids (Trewavas, 1935; Fryer, 1959) are dominant. They present the greatest of all known species flocks among lake fishes — over 100 species of the widespread genus *Haplochromis*. In addition, there are over 70 cichlid species belonging to 20 endemic genera, several of which exhibit remarkable supralimital specializations. However, fishes of other families have entered the lake and established endemic species, but only one endemic genus (Worthington, 1933; Jackson, 1959). Most large lakes are drained by physiographic evolution before they attain any age such as that of Nyasa, and it alone remains to represent the evolutionary stage of its fish fauna. The same is true of the two still older lake fish faunas, those of Tanganyika and Baikal.

Lake Tanganyika is at least 1,500,000 years old and may be even older (Brooks, 1950: 148). Its fish fauna (Poll, 1946; 1953) indicates a much later evolutionary stage than that of Nyasa, this being especially notable because of the comparable size and geographical proximity of these two immense Rift Valley lakes. The cichlids are still dominant; they are fewer in number of species than in Nyasa, but the vast majority belong to endemic Tanganyika genera. The only group that could be called a "species flock" is formed by the 19 species of *Lamprologus,* a genus also represented in the Congo.[3] Several of the endemic genera, as has already been noted, are morphologically worthy of familial or subfamilial groupings, and several have come to resemble quite different families of Percomorphi. In non-cichlid fishes, Tanganyika has had time to develop, in addition to a number of endemic species belonging to non-endemic genera, two endemic genera of Clupeidae, two of Bagridae, two of Clariidae, one of Cyprinodontidae (representing a distinctive subfamily; Myers, 1936) and one (*Luciolates*) of Centropomidae (Worthington and Ricardo, 1937; Poll, 1953). Evolution of some of these must have been accomplished in the face of strong competition by the entrenched Cichlidae.

Lake Baikal is the oldest of all, perhaps as much as 75,000,000 years old; its southern basin is Paleocene or possibly even late Cretaceous in age. However, the present lake basin was enlarged and deepened as late as the Pleistocene (Brooks, 1950: 33), and it is doubtful that even the most distinctive Baikal fishes arose prior to the Mid-tertiary. The Cottidae and their derivatives are dominant in Baikal; species of no other fish families are endemic to the lake (Taliev, 1955). The absence of non-cottoid endemics is notable; it is probably due to the poverty of the Siberian fish fauna. The 26 endemic cottoid species belong to nine endemic genera, eight referred by Taliev to two endemic subfamilies of the Cottidae and one genus with two species to the endemic family Comephoridae.

Other lake fish faunas might be fitted into the sequence, but this seems unnecessary.[4]

In all the larger endemic lake-fish faunas, from the youngest to the very oldest, a single family group, preadapted over other stream fishes for lake life, has gained dominance over all others and has retained it. This accounts for my former belief (Myers, 1936) that access to lakes dominated by a single fish family must have been restricted. Access was restricted in Lake Lanao, but probably this has only rarely been true in other lakes. Moreover, in all except the youngest lake fish faunas, supra-limitally specialized forms are evident and continue to become more striking until some of them, in the older lakes, could be or are accepted by taxonomists as distinct families.

One other important point should be made. The greater richness in genera and species of the older lake fish faunas, insofar as the dominant family is concerned, compared to the fluviatile fauna of the same family in the same region, is always striking. The Lanao cyprinid fauna dwarfs the cyprinid fauna of Mindanao outside the lake. More than half the African species and far more than half the African genera of the large family Cichlidae are endemics in the lakes of East Central Africa. The greater part of the North American forms of *Leucichthys* are lake en-demics. Probably the same is true of Mexican atherinids of the genus *Chirostoma*. The forms of *Orestias* in Lake Titicaca are more numerous than those in the rest of the Andean Altiplano. The cottoid genera of Baikal comprise over three-fourths of the known genera of freshwater cottoids in the world.

ISOLATED ENDEMICS

Whether the strange little mastacembelid-like *Chaudhuria caudata* (Annandale, 1918) of the Inlé Lake, sole representative of the family Chaudhuriidae, and the possibly even stranger *Indostomus paradoxus* (Prashad and Mukerji, 1929) of the Indawgyi Lake, sole representative of the family Indostomidae, are to be considered as vastly modified relicts of autochthonous lake-fish families, is unknown. If so, they would be the ultimate examples of lake-fish specialization, but neither species has any known close relatives, and both may be mere survivors of once widely distributed families. The two genera and three known species of the strange family Adrianichthyidae, from Lake Posso and Lake Lindu in Celebes (see Weber and de Beaufort, 1922), which are undoubtedly derivatives of the family Cyprinodontidae, likewise have no known close relatives by which to judge their exact origin. I would suspect them to be derivatives of the subfamily Oryziatinae, members of which are still widely distributed in fresh waters from India and Japan to Timor, and which have given rise, in India, to the remarkable fish *Horaichthys*. Isolated lake-fish endemics are not too rare, often in lakes in which fishes of another family have become dominant, but the endemic nature of the genus or higher category represented by them is sometimes in doubt.... Perhaps some of these isolated endemics are relicts of previous cycles of lake-fish evolution in the same basins, cycles which were terminated by great changes in the basin itself.

NEW AREAS,
NEW GROUPS

What has happened, in the normal course of evolution, when one or more representative of an animal group not hitherto represented in the fauna has suddenly gained access to a large area replete with numerous available and unoccupied biotopes, seems to be clear. If the invaders are unable to withstand the competition of the older fauna, they disappear. If they can overcome competition, or especially if there is little or none, rapid or tachytelic evolution occurs, evolution that was impossible in their old home, where better balanced ecological conditions and a balanced fauna held evolutionary divergence more tightly in check. New genera, often utterly unlike their ancestors in one or more striking characteristics, appear with great rapidity. The rapid proliferation of proboscideans, and their development of supralimital specializations after their invasion of America, is a case in point.

The same sort of evolution has happened time and again when island groups were colonized. The supralimital bill specializations of the Galápagos finches, and (whatever their ancestors may have been) especially those of the drepanidid birds in Hawaii, are well known instances. Island evolution of this kind, like lake-fish evolution, is often striking, because the original colonizers found abundant biotopes totally unoccupied when they arrived.

However, the situation differs somewhat in lakes. The colonizers and founders of evolutionary dynasties in lakes must contend not only with the same types of problems that confront island or continent colonizers. In addition, they must face the change from a flowing to a still-water environment, and, in many instances, problems of depth, pressure, and salinity, perhaps new or inimical to them. In fact, it seems possible that gradually increasing salinity in a closed lake basin might eventually check the evolution of some freshwater fish groups very severely (Myers, 1938; 1949).

The tachytelic evolution of lake fishes, in part at least representing quantum evolution in Simpson's sense, seems to point out in a really striking way how genera, families, or even higher categories of different animal groups have evolved. If they could get out of their lakes and use their supralimital specializations in other lakes or in streams, as some undoubtedly have done in the past, many existing lake fishes could easily become the founders of large and flourishing new groups at new adaptive levels. Terrestrial groups are not usually as limited in their ability to escape their ranges as are lake animals. As Simpson has so ably pointed out, the tachytelic evolution of new superior groups has seldom left a fossil record because of the speed with which events progressed, and, we may add, because of the probable localization of those events.

It seems probable that events of the sort I have been discussing account for the almost unbelievably rich fauna of characid fishes of the greatest of all rivers, the Amazon. In its present form the Amazon is not an old river. In its lower course it is probably a reversed river; its old structural basin plunges westward. Its Peruvian reaches formed a great lake in relatively recent geological times, and the immense but fluctuating lakes that now line its lower course comprise one of the largest areas of ponded fresh water now existing on earth.

Finally, we cannot forbear to mention the largest of all bodies of still, quiet water, the deep seas. The supralimital specializations exhibited by the highly modified deep-sea descendants of invaders from more turbulent shallow waters have long been the wonder of all zoologists.

It follows that opportunity — the absence of well-adapted competing groups — is extremely important as a factor in the evolution of higher categories. The importance of such a conclusion in relation to the early, rapid evolution of the main animal phyla is obvious.

SUMMARY

1. The endemic fish fauna of Lake Lanao, all belonging to the family Cyprinidae, consisting of a species flock of 13 species and five species referred to four endemic genera, has evolved in a relatively short time, possibly as little as 10,000 years.

2. The distributional facts permit the identification, beyond reasonable doubt, of the single, still-existing, ancestral species that gave rise to the entire endemic fish fauna.

3. Certain specializations of the endemic Lanao genera are paralleled or approached by no others in the large, widespread family Cyprinidae; because they transcend the morphological limits of all non-Lanao cyprinids, these are termed supralimital specializations.

4. Supralimital specializations are shown to be very characteristic if not invariable features of all large, older, endemic lake-fish faunas; some are so distinctive as to provide characters worthy of family rank.

5. The stages of endemic lake-fish evolution are illustrated by examples, the youngest being the American Great Lakes, the oldest Lake Baikal.

6. A single preadapted fish family represented in the surrounding fluviatile fish fauna assumes dominance in the evolution of large endemic lake-fish faunas.

7. The evolution of lake-fish faunas is compared to that of island faunas, and to the evolution of any groups newly admitted to extensive areas where competition is light or absent, and shown to be essentially similar in the relatively rapid production of supralimitally specialized forms.

8. The latter are often capable of becoming the founders of new genera, families, or perhaps even higher categories, at new adaptive levels. They have unquestionably already done so in the older lake-fish faunas, where certain endemic Tanganyika and Baikal genera are worthy of subfamilial or familial rank.

9. It is suggested that the origin of the excessively rich characid fauna of the Amazon River, and of the striking forms and groups of deep-sea fishes, has been due to similar tachytelic or quantum evolution.

10. It follows that opportunity for rapid radiative evolution is of very great importance in the evolution of higher categories, and that such opportunity still may occur from time to time through geological changes.

Received January 25, 1960

REFERENCES AND NOTES

[1] Abstract published in *Proc. XVth Internat. Congr. Zool.* 151–52 (1959).

[2] It is difficult to see why such an introduction should have been considered. Ecologically, and as a measure for increasing food production, it is clearly unsound. Scientifically, in view of the unique nature of the endemic Lanao fish fauna, it becomes a crime!

[3] The interesting possibility presents itself that Lamprologus is an autochthonous Tanganyika genus which has colonized the Congo basin.

[4] Some other lakes, with the families to which the dominant endemics belong, are: Lake Biwa, Japan (Cyprinidae); the Celebes lakes (Atherinidae, usually); various Mexican lakes (Atherinidae); the African lakes George, Albert, etc. (Cichlidae); various Central Asiatic lakes, such as Lop Nor, Koko Nor, etc. (Cyprinidae or Cobitidae); Utah Lake (Catostomidae).

J. Alvarez, Claves para la determinacion de especies en los peces de las aguas continentales Mexicanas, Secretaria de Marina, Dirreción General de Pesca e Industrias Conexas (Mexico, 1950), 136 pp.

N. Annandale, Fauna of the Inle Lake. Rec. Ind. Mus. 14, (1918), 214 pp., 26 pls.

M. L. Brittan, A revision of the Indo-Malayan fresh-water fish genus *Rasbora*, *Inst. Sci. Tech. (Manila), Monograph* 3 (1954), 224 pp., 3 maps.

J. L. Brooks, Speciation in ancient lakes, *Quart. Rev. Biol.* 25, 30–60, 131–76 (1950).

A. Bruun and A. Kiilerich, Bathymetrical features of the Bali-Lombok Strait, *Marine Research in Indonesia* 3, 1–6 (1957).

P. J. Darlington, The origin of the fauna of the Greater Antilles, with discussion of dispersal of animals over water and through the air, *Quart. Rev. Biol.* 13, 274–300 (1938).

R. E. Dickerson and others, Distribution of life in the Philippines, *Bureau Sci. (Manila), Monograph* 21 (1928), 322 pp., 42 pls.

H. W. Fowler, Fishes of the groups Elasmobranchi . . . Ostariophysi obtained by the . . . Albatross . . . chiefly in the Philippine Islands, *U.S. Nat. Mus. Bull.* 100 (13) (1941), 879 pp.

G. Fryer, The trophic interrelationships and ecology of some littoral communities of Lake Nyasa with especial reference to the fishes, and a discussion of the evolution of a group of rock-frequenting Cichlidae, *Proc. Zool. Soc. London* 132, 153–281 (1959), 2 pls.

P. H. Greenwood, The monotypic genera of cichlid fishes in Lake Victoria, *Bull. Brit. Mus. (Nat. Hist.)* 3, 295–333 (1956).

_____, Evolution and speciation in the *Haplochromis* (Pisces, Cichlidae) of Lake Victoria, *Proc. XVth Int. Congr. Zool. London* (1959), pp. 147–50.

A. W. Herre, The Philippine Cyprinidae, *Philippine J. Sci.* 24, 249–307 (1924), 2 pls.

_____, Two fishes from Lake Lanao, *Philippine J. Sci.* 29, 499–502 (1926), 2 pls.

_____, True fresh-water fishes of the Philippines, in Dickerson, 1928 (which see), 242–47. [This paper was written previous to the publication of Herre's 1924 paper, and some of the fish names do not agree with those of the 1924 paper.]

_____, Five new Philippine fishes, *Copeia* 1932, 139–42 (1932).

_____, The fishes of Lake Lanao: A problem in evolution, *Amer. Nat.* 68, 154–62 (1933).

_____, Check list of Philippine fishes, *U.S. Fish and Wildlife Service, Research Report* 20 (1953), 977 pp.

_____ and G. S. Myers, Fishes from southeastern China and Hainan, *Lingnan Sci. J.* 10, 233–54 (1931).

C. L. Hubbs and E. C. Raney, The endemic fish fauna of Lake Waccamaw, North Carolina, *Misc. Publ. Mus. Zool. Univ. Michigan* 65 (1946), 30 pp.

P. N. B. Jackson, Revision of the clarid catfishes of Nyasaland, with a description of a new genus and seven new species, *Proc. Zool. Soc. London* 132, 109–28 (1959).

D. S. Jordan and C. L. Hubbs, Studies in ichthyology: A monographic review of the family of Atherinidae or silversides, *Leland Stanford Jr. Univ. Publ. Univ. Ser.* (1919), 87 pp., 12 pls.

W. Koelz, Coregonid fishes of the Great Lakes, *Bull. U.S. Bur. Fisher.* 27 (2), 297–643 (1929).

S. E. Meek, Synopsis of the fishes of the Great Lakes of Nicaragua, *Field Columbian Museum, Zool. Ser.* 7 (4), 97–132 (1907).

G. S. Myers, Report on the fishes collected by H. C. Raven in Lake Tanganyika in 1920, *Proc. U.S. Nat. Mus.* 84, 1–15 (1936), 1 pl.

_____, Fresh-water fishes and West Indian zoogeography, *Ann. Rep. Smithsonian Inst.* 1937, 339–64 (1938), 3 pls.

_____, Salt-tolerance of fresh-water fish groups in relation to zoogeographical problems, *Bijdr. Dierk.* 28, 315–22 (1949).

_____, Fresh-water fishes and East Indian zoogeography, *Stanford Ichth. Bull.* 4, 11–21 (1951).

_____, Preface to any future classification of the fishes of the genus Barbus, *Stanford Ichth. Bull.* 7 (4) (1960), in press.

M. Poll, Revision de la faune ichthyologique de Lac Tanganika, *Ann. Musée du Congo Belge, zool.* 4 (1), 145–364 (1946), 3 pls., map.

_____, Poissons non Cichlidae, *Explor. Hydrobiol. Lac Tanganika (1946–1947), Result. Scientif.* 3 (5A) (1953), 251 pp., 11 pls.

B. Prashad and D. D. Mukerji, The fish of the Indawygi Lake and the streams of the Myitkyina District (Upper Burma), *Rec. Ind. Mus.* 31, 161–223 (1929), pls. 7–10.

C. T. Regan, *Biologia Centrali-Americana. Pisces* (London, 1906–1908), xxxiv + 203 pp., 26 pls.

G. G. Simpson, *The Major Features of Evolution* (New York, 1953), xx + 434 pp.

J. O. Snyder, Three new whitefishes from Bear Lake, Idaho and Utah, *Bull. Bur. Fisher.* 36, 1–9 (1919).

D. E. Taliev, Bitschki-podkamenschtschiki Baikala (*Cottoidei*) (Akademiia Nauk U.S.S.R., Moskva, 1955), 603 pp.

V. Tchernavin, A revision of the subfamily Orestiinae, *Proc. Zool. Soc. London* 114, 140–233 (1944).

E. Trewavas, A synopsis of the cichlid fishes of Lake Nyasa, *Ann. Mag. Nat. Hist.* 16 (10), 65–118 (1935).

M. Weber and L. F. de Beaufort, *The Fishes of the Indo-Australian Archipelago,* Vol. 3 (Leiden, 1916), xiv + 455 pp.

_____, *ibid.* (Leiden, 1922), 4, xiv + 410 pp.

E. B. Worthington, The fishes of Lake Nyasa (other than Cichlidae), *Proc. Zool. Soc. London* 1933, 285–316 (1933).

_____ and C. K. Ricardo, The fish of Lake Tanganyika (other than Cichlidae), *Proc. Zool. Soc. London* 1936, 1061–1112 (1937).

HOMAGE TO SANTA ROSALIA

OR

WHY ARE THERE SO MANY KINDS OF ANIMALS?[*]

G. E. HUTCHINSON

Department of Zoology, Yale University, New Haven, Connecticut

When you did me the honor of asking me to fill your presidential chair, I accepted perhaps without duly considering the duties of the president of a society, founded largely to further the study of evolution, at the close of the year that marks the centenary of Darwin and Wallace's initial presentation of the theory of natural selection. It seemed to me that most of the significant aspects of modern evolutionary theory have come either from geneticists, or from those heroic museum workers who, suffering through years of neglect, were able to establish about 20 years ago what has come to be called the "new systematics." You had, however, chosen an ecologist as your president and one of that school at times supposed to study the environment without any relation to the organism.

A few months later I happened to be in Sicily. An early interest in zoogeography and in aquatic insects led me to attempt to collect near Palermo, certain species of water-bugs, of the genus Corixa, described a century ago by Fieber and supposed to occur in the region, but never fully reinvestigated. It is hard to find suitable localities in so highly cultivated a landscape as the Concha d'Oro. Fortunately, I was driven up Monte Pellegrino, the hill that rises to the west of the city, to admire the view. A little below the summit, a church with a simple baroque facade stands in front of a cave in the limestone of the hill. Here in the 16th century a stalactite encrusted skeleton associated with a cross and twelve beads was discovered. Of this skeleton nothing is certainly known save that it is that of Santa Rosalia, a saint of whom little is reliably reported save that she seems to have lived in the 12th century, that her skeleton was found in this cave, and that she has been the chief patroness of Palermo ever since. Other limestone caverns on Monte Pellegrino had yielded bones of extinct pleistocene Equus, and on the walls of one of the rock shelters at the bottom of the hill there are beautiful Gravettian engravings. Moreover, a small relic of the saint that I saw in the treasury of the Cathedral of Monreale has a venerable and petrified appearance, as might be expected. Nothing in her his-

[*] Address of the President, American Society of Naturalists, delivered at the annual meeting, Washington, D.C., December 30, 1958.

Reprinted by permission of the author and publisher from THE AMERICAN NATURALIST, 93, 145–159 (1959). A version of this article appears in ENCHANTED VOYAGE, published by Yale University Press, 1962.

tory being known to the contrary, perhaps for the moment we may take Santa Rosalia as the patroness of evolutionary studies, for just below the sanctuary, fed no doubt by the water that percolates through the limestone cracks of the mountain, and which formed the sacred cave, lies a small artificial pond, and when I could get to the pond a few weeks later, I got from it a hint of what I was looking for.

Vast numbers of Corixidae were living in the water. At first I was rather disappointed because every specimen of the larger of the two species present was a female, and so lacking in most critical diagnostic features, while both sexes of the second slightly smaller species were present in about equal number. Examination of the material at leisure, and of the relevant literature, has convinced me that the two species are the common European *C. punctata* and *C. affinis*, and that the peculiar Mediterranean species are illusionary. The larger *C. punctata* was clearly at the end of its breeding season, the smaller *C. affinis* was probably just beginning to breed. This is the sort of observation that any naturalist can and does make all the time. It was not until I asked myself why the larger species should breed first, and then the more general question as to why there should be two and not 20 to 200 species of the genus in the pond, that ideas suitable to present to you began to emerge. These ideas finally prompted the very general question as to why there are such an enormous number of animal species.

There are at the present time supposed to be (Muller and Campbell, 1954; Hyman, 1955) about one million described species of animals. Of these about three-quarters are insects, of which a quite disproportionately large number are members of a single order, the Coleoptera.[1] The marine fauna, although it has at its disposal a much greater area than has the terrestrial, lacks this astonishing diversity (Thorson, 1958). If the insects are excluded, it would seem to be more diverse. The proper answer to my initial question would be to develop a theory at least predicting an order of magnitude for the number of species of 10^6 rather than 10^8 or 10^4. This I certainly cannot do. At most it is merely possible to point out some of the factors which would have to be considered if such a theory was ever to be constructed.

Before developing my ideas I should like to say that I subscribe to the view that the process of natural selection, coupled with isolation and later mutual invasion of ranges leads to the evolution of sympatric species, which at equilibrium occupy distinct niches, according to the Volterra-Gause principle. The empirical reasons for adopting this view and the correlative view that the boundaries of realized niches are set by competition are mainly indirect. So far as niches may be defined in terms of food, the subject has been carefully considered by Lack (1954). In general all the indirect evidence is in accord with the view, which has the advantage of confirming theoretical expectation.

---

[1] There is a story, possibly apocryphal, of the distinguished British biologist, J. B. S. Haldane, who found himself in the company of a group of theologians. On being asked what one could conclude as to the nature of the Creator from a study of his creation, Haldane is said to have answered, "An inordinate fondness for beetles."

Most of the opinions that have been held to the contrary appear to be due to misunderstandings and to loose formulation of the problem (Hutchinson, 1958).

In any study of evolutionary ecology, food relations appear as one of the most important aspects of the system of animate nature. There is quite obviously much more to living communities than the raw dictim "eat or be eaten," but in order to understand the higher intricacies of any ecological system, it is most easy to start from this crudely simple point of view.

FOOD CHAINS

Animal ecologists frequently think in terms of food chains, of the form *individuals of species S_1 are eaten by those of S_2, of S_2 by S_3, of S_3 by S_4*, etc. In such a food chain S_1 will ordinarily be some holophylic organism or material derived from such organisms. The simplest case is that in which we have a true *predator chain* in Odum's (1953) convenient terminology, in which the lowest link is a green plant, the next a herbivorous animal, the next a primary carnivore, the next a secondary carnivore, etc. A specially important type of predator chain may be designated Eltonian, because in recent years C. S. Elton (1927) has emphasized its widespread significance, in which the predator at each level is larger and rarer than its prey. This phenomenon was recognized much earlier, notably by A. R. Wallace in his contribution to the 1858 communication to the Linnean Society of London.

In such a system we can make a theoretical guess of the order of magnitude of the diversity that a single food chain can introduce into a community. If we assume that in general 20 percent of the energy passing through one link can enter the next link in the chain, which is overgenerous (cf. Lindeman, 1942; Slobodkin in an unpublished study finds 13 percent as a reasonable upper limit) and if we suppose that each predator has twice the mass (or 1.26 the linear dimensions) of its prey, which is a very low estimate of the size difference between links, the fifth animal link will have a population of one ten thousandth (10^{-4}) of the first, and the fiftieth animal link, if there was one, a population of 10^{-49} the size of the first. Five animal links are certainly possible, a few fairly clear-cut cases having been in fact recorded. If, however, we wanted 50 links, starting with a protozoan or rotifer feeding on algae with a density of 10^6 cells per ml, we should need a volume of 10^{26} cubic kilometers to accommodate on an average one specimen of the ultimate predator, and this is vastly greater than the volume of the world ocean. Clearly the Eltonian food chain of itself cannot give any great diversity, and the same is almost certainly true of the other types of food chain, based on detritus feeding or on parasitism.

Natural Selection. Before proceeding to a further consideration of diversity, it is, however, desirable to consider the kinds of selective force that may operate on a food chain, for this may limit the possible diversity.

It is reasonably certain that natural selection will tend to maintain the efficiency of transfer from one level to another at a maximum. Any increase in the predatory efficiency of the nth link of a simple food chain will however always increase the possibility of the extermination of the $(n-1)^{th}$ link. If this occurs either the species constituting the nth link must adapt itself to eating the $(n-2)^{th}$ link or itself become extinct. This process will in fact tend to shortening of food chains. A lengthening can presumably occur most simply by the development of a new terminal carnivore link, as its niche is by definition previously empty. In most cases this is not likely to be easy. The evolution of the whale-bone whales, which at least in the case of *Balaenoptera borealis*, can feed largely on copepods and so rank on occasions as primary carnivores (Bigelow, 1926), presumably constitutes the most dramatic example of the shortening of a food chain. Mechanical considerations would have prevented the evolution of a larger rarer predator, until man developed essentially non-Eltonian methods of hunting whales.

Effect of Size. A second important limitation of the length of a food chain is due to the fact that ordinarily animals change their size during free life. If the terminal member of a chain were a fish that grew from say one cm to 150 cms in the course of an ordinary life, this size change would set a limit by competition to the possible number of otherwise conceivable links in the 1–150 cm range. At least in fishes this type of process (metaphoetesis) may involve the smaller specimens belonging to links below the larger and the chain length is thus lengthened, though under strong limitations, by cannibalism.

We may next enquire into what determines the number of food chains in a community. In part the answer is clear, though if we cease to be zoologists and become biologists, the answer begs the question. Within certain limits, the number of kinds of primary producers is certainly involved, because many herbivorous animals are somewhat eclectic in their tastes and many more limited by their size or by such structural adaptations for feeding that they have been able to develop.

Effects of Terrestrial Plants. The extraordinary diversity of the terrestrial fauna, which is much greater than that of the marine fauna, is clearly due largely to the diversity provided by terrestrial plants. This diversity is actually two-fold. Firstly, since terrestrial plants compete for light, they have tended to evolve into structures growing into a gaseous medium of negligible buoyancy. This has led to the formation of specialized supporting, photosynthetic, and reproductive structures which inevitably differ in chemical and physical properties. The ancient Danes and Irish are supposed to have eaten elm-bark, and sometimes sawdust, in periods of stress, has been hydrolyzed to produce edible carbohydrate; but usually man, the most omnivorous of all animals, has avoided almost all parts of trees except fruits as sources of food, though various individual species of animals can deal with practically every tissue of many arboreal species. A major source of terrestrial diversity was thus introduced by the evolution of almost 200,000 species of flowering plants, and the three quarters of a million insects supposedly known today are in part a product of that diversity. But of itself merely providing five or ten kinds of food of different consistencies and compositions does not get us much further than the five or ten links of an Eltonian pyramid. On the whole the problem still remains, but in the new form: why are there so many kinds of plants? As a zoologist I do not want to attack that question directly, I want to stick with animals, but also to get the answer. Since, however, the plants are part of the general system of communities, any sufficiently abstract properties of such communities are likely to be relevant to plants as well as to herbivores and carnivores. It is, therefore, by being somewhat abstract, though with concrete zoological details as examples, that I intend to proceed.

INTERRELATIONS OF FOOD CHAINS

Biological communities do not consist of independent food chains, but of food webs, of such a kind that an individual at any level (corresponding to a link in a single chain) can use some but not all of the food provided by species in the levels below it.

It has long been realized that the presence of two species at any level, either of which can be eaten by a predator at a level above, but which may differ in palatability, ease of capture or seasonal and local abundance, may provide alternative foods for the predator. The predator, therefore, will neither become extinct itself nor exterminate its usual prey, when for any reason, not dependent on prey-predator relationships, the usual prey happens to be abnormally scarce. This aspect of complicated food webs has been stressed by many ecologists, of whom the Chicago school as represented by Allee, Emerson, Park, Park and Schmidt (1949), Odum (1953) and Elton (1958), may in particular be mentioned. Recently MacArthur (1955) using an ingenious but simple application of information theory has generalized the points of view of earlier workers by providing a formal proof of the increase in stability of a community as the number of links in its food web increases.

MacArthur concludes that in the evolution of a natural community two partly antagonistic processes are occurring. More efficient species will replace less efficient species, but more stable communities will outlast less stable communities. In the process of community formation, the entry of a new species may involve one of three possibilities. It may completely displace an old species. This of itself does not necessarily change the stability, though it may do so if the new species inherently has a more stable population (cf. Slobodkin, 1956) than the old. Secondly, it may occupy an unfilled niche, which may, by providing new partially independent links, increase stability. Thirdly, it may partition a niche with a pre-existing species. Elton (1958) in a fascinating work largely devoted to the fate of species accidentally or purposefully introduced by man, concludes that in very diverse communities such introductions are difficult. Early in the history of a community we may suppose many niches will be empty and invasion will proceed easily; as the community becomes more diversified, the process will be progressively more difficult. Sometimes an extremely successful invader may oust a species but add little or nothing to stability, at other times the invader by some specialization will be able to compete successfully for the marginal parts of a niche. In all cases it is probable that invasion is most likely when one or more species happen to be fluctuating and are underrepresented at a given moment. As the communities build up, these opportunities will get progressively rarer. In this way a complex community containing some highly specialized species is constructed asymptotically.

Modern ecological theory therefore appears to answer our initial question at least partially by saying that there is a great diversity of organisms because communities of many diversified organisms are better able to persist than are communities of fewer less diversified organisms. Even though the entry of an invader which takes over part of a niche will lead to the reduction in the *average* population of the species originally present, it will also lead to an increase in stability reducing the risk of the original population being at times underrepresented to a dangerous degree. In this way loss of some niche space may be compensated by reduction in the amplitude of fluctuations in a way that can be advantageous to both species. The process however appears likely to be asymptotic and we have now to consider what sets the asymptote, or in simpler words why are there not more different kinds of animals?

LIMITATION OF DIVERSITY

It is first obvious that the processes of evolution of communities must be under various sorts of external control, and that in some cases such control limits the possible diversity. Several investigators, notably Odum (1953) and MacArthur (1955), have pointed out that the more or less cyclical oscillations observed in arctic and boreal fauna may be due in part to the communities not being sufficiently complex to damp out oscillations. It is certain that the fauna of any such region is qualitatively poorer than that of warm temperate and tropical areas of comparable effective precipitation. It is probably considered to be intuitively obvious that this should be so, but on analysis the obviousness tends to disappear. If we can have one or two species of a large family adapted to the rigors of arctic existence, why can we not have more? It is reasonable to suppose that the total biomass may be involved. If the fundamental productivity of an area is limited by a short growing season to such a degree that the total biomass is less than under more favorable conditions, then the rarer species in a community may be so rare that they do not exist. It is also probable that certain absolute limitations on growth-forms of plants, such as those that make the development of forest impossible above a certain latitude, may in so acting, severely limit the number of niches. Dr. Robert MacArthur points out that the development of high tropical rain forest increases the bird fauna more than that of mammals, and Thorson (1957) likewise has shown that the so-called infauna show no increase of species toward the tropics while the marine epifauna becomes more diversified. The importance of this aspect of the plant or animal substratum, which depends largely on the length of the growing season and other aspects of productivity is related to that of the environmental mosaic discussed later.

We may also inquire, but at present cannot obtain any likely answer, whether the arctic fauna is not itself too young to have achieved its maximum diversity. Finally, the continual occurrence of catastrophes, as Wynne-Edwards (1952) has emphasized, may keep the arctic terrestrial community in a state of perennial though stunted youth.

Closely related to the problems of environmental rigor and stability, is the question of the absolute size of the habitat that can be colonized. Over much of western Europe there are three common species of small voles, namely *Microtus arvalis*, *M. agrestis* and *Clethrionomys glareolus*. These are sympatric but with somewhat different ecological preferences.

In the smaller islands off Britain and in the English channel, there is only one case of two species co-occurring on an island, namely *M. agrestis* and Clethrionomys on the island of Mull in the Inner Hebrides (Barrett-Hamilton and Hinton, 1911–1921). On the Orkneys the single species is *M. orcadensis*, which in morphology and cytology is a well-differentiated ally of *M. arvalis;* a comparable animal (*M. sarnius*) occurs on Guernsey. On most of the Scottish Islands only subspecies of *M. agrestis* occur, but on Mull and Raasay, on the Welsh island of Skomer, as well as on Jersey, races of Clethrionomys of somewhat uncertain status are found. No voles have reached Ireland, presumably for paleogeographic reasons, but they are also absent from a number of small islands, notably Alderney and Sark. The last named island must have been as well placed as Guernsey to receive *Microtus arvalis*. Still stranger is the fact that although it could not have got to the Orkneys without entering the mainland of Britain, no vole of the *arvalis* type now occurs in the latter country. Cases of this sort may be perhaps explained by the lack of favorable refuges in randomly distributed very unfavorable seasons or under special kinds of competition. This explanation is very reasonable as an explanation of the lack of Microtus on Sark, where it may have had difficulty in competing with *Rattus rattus* in a small area. It would be stretching one's credulity to suppose that the area of Great Britain is too small to permit the existence of two sympatric species of Microtus, but no other explanation seems to have been proposed.

It is a matter of considerable interest that Lack (1942) studying the populations of birds on some of these small British islands concluded that such populations are often unstable, and that the few species present often occupied larger niches than on the mainland in the presence of competitors. Such faunas provide examples of communities held at an early stage in development because there is not enough space for the evolution of a fuller and more stable community.

NICHE REQUIREMENTS

The various evolutionary tendencies, notably metaphoetesis, which operate on single food chains must operate equally on the food-web, but we also have a new, if comparable, problem as to how much difference between two species at the same level is needed to prevent them from occupying the same niche. Where metric characters are involved we can gain some insight into this extremely important problem by the study of what Brown and Wilson (1956) have called *character displacement* or the divergence shown when two partly allopatric species of comparable niche requirements become sympatric in part of their range.

I have collected together a number of cases of mammals and birds which appear to exhibit the phenomenon (Table 1). These cases involve metric characters related to the trophic apparatus, the length of the culmen in birds and of the skull in mammals appearing to provide appropriate measures. Where the species co-occur, the ratio of the larger to the small form varies from 1.1 to 1.4, the mean ratio being 1.28 or roughly 1.3. This latter figure may tentatively be used as an indication of the kind of difference necessary to permit two species to co-occur in different niches but at the same level of a food-web. In the case of the aquatic insects with which I began my address, we have over most of Europe three very closely allied species of Corixa, the largest *punctata*, being about 116 percent longer than the middle sized species *macrocephala*, and 146 percent longer than the small species *affinis*. In northwestern Europe there is a fourth species, *C. dentipes*, as large as *C. punctata* and very similar in appearance. A single observation (Brown, 1948) suggests that this is what I have elsewhere (Hutchinson, 1951) termed a fugitive species, maintaining itself in the face of competition mainly on account of greater mobility. According to Macan (1954) while both *affinis* and *macrocephala* may occur with *punctata* they never are found with each other, so that all three species never occur together. In the eastern part of the range, *macrocephala* drops out, and *punctata* appears to have a discontinuous distribution, being recorded as far east as Simla, but not in southern Persia or Kashmir, where *affinis* occurs. In these eastern localities, where it occurs by itself, *affinis* is larger and darker than in the west, and superficially looks like *macrocephala* (Hutchinson, 1940).

This case is very interesting because it looks as though character displacement is occurring, but that the size differences between the three species are just not great enough to allow them all to co-occur. Other characters than size are in fact clearly involved in the separation, *macrocephala* preferring deeper water than *affinis* and the latter being more tolerant of brackish conditions. It is also interesting because it calls attention to a marked difference that must occur between hemimetabolous insects with annual life cycles involving relatively long growth periods, and birds or mammals in which the period of growth in length is short and of a very special nature compared with the total life span. In the latter, niche separation may be possible merely through genetic size differences, while in a pair of animals like *C. punctata* and *C. affinis* we need not only a size difference but a seasonal one in reproduction; this is likely to be a rather complicated matter. For the larger of two species always to be larger, it must never breed later than the smaller one. I do not doubt that this is what was happening in the pond on Monte Pellegrino, but have no idea how the difference is achieved.

TABLE 1

Mean character displacement in measurable trophic structures in mammals (skull) and birds (culmen); data for Mustela from Miller (1912); Apodemus from Cranbrook (1957); Sitta from Brown and Wilson (1956) after Vaurie; Galapagos finches from Lack (1947).

	Locality and measurement when sympatric	Locality and measurement when allopatric	Ratio when sympatric
Mustela nivalis	Britain; skull ♂ 39.3 ♀ 33.6 mm.	(*boccamela*) S. France, Italy ♂ 42.9 ♀ 34.7 mm. (*iberica*) Spain, Portugal ♂ 40.4 ♀ 36.0	♂ 100:128 ♀ 100:134
M. erminea	Britain; " ♂ 50.4 ♀ 45.0	(*hibernica*) Ireland ♂ 46.0 ♀ 41.9	
Apodemus sylvaticus	Britain; " 24.8	unnamed races on Channel Islands 25.6–26.7	100:109
A. flavicollis	Britain; " 27.0		
Sitta tephronota	Iran; culmen 29.0	races east of overlap 25.5	100:124
S. neumayer	Iran; " 23.5	races west of overlap 26.0	
Geospiza fortis	Indefatigable Isl.; culmen 12.0	Daphne Isl. 10.5	100:143
G. fuliginosa	Indefatigable Isl.; " 8.4	Crossman Isl. 9.3	
Camarhynchus parvulus	James Isl.; " 7.0 Indefatigable Isl.; " 7.5 S. Albemarle Isl.; " 7.3	N. Albemarle Isl. 7.0 Chatham Isl. 8.0	James 100:140:180 100:129
C. psittacula	James Isl.; " 9.8 Indefatigable Isl.; " 9.6 S. Albemarle Isl.; " 8.5	Abington Isl. 10.1 Bindloe Isl. 10.5	Indefatigable 100:128:162 100:127
C. pallidus	James Isl.; " 12.6 Indefatigable Isl.; " 12.1 S. Albemarle Isl.; " 11.2	N. Albemarle Isl. 11.7 Chatham Isl. 10.8	S. Albemarle 100:116:153 100:132

Mean ratio 100:128

I want to emphasize the complexity of the adaptation necessary on the part of two species inhabiting adjacent niches in a given biotope, as it probably underlies a phenomenon which to some has appeared rather puzzling. Mac-Arthur (1957) has shown that in a sufficiently large bird fauna, in a uniform undisturbed habitat, areas occupied by the different species appear to correspond to the random non-overlapping fractionation of a plane or volume. Kohn (1959) has found the same thing for the cone-shells (Conus) on the Hawaiian reefs. This type of arrangement almost certainly implies such individual and unpredictable complexities in the determination of the niche boundaries, and so of the actual areas colonized, that in any overall view, the process would appear random. It is fairly obvious that in different types of community the divisibility of niches will differ and so the degree of diversity that can be achieved. The fine details of the process have not been adequately investigated, though many data must already exist that could be organized to throw light on the problem.

MOSAIC NATURE OF THE ENVIRONMENT

A final aspect of the limitation of possible diversity, and one that perhaps is of greatest importance, concerns what may be called the mosaic nature of the environment. Except perhaps in open water when only uniform quasi-horizontal surfaces are considered, every area colonized by organisms has some local diversity. The significance of such local diversity depends very largely on the size of the organisms under consideration. In another paper MacArthur and I (Hutchinson and MacArthur, 1959) have attempted a theoretical formulation of this property of living communities and have pointed out that even if we consider only the herbivorous level or only one of the carnivorous levels, there are likely, above a certain lower limit of size, to be more species of small or medium sized organisms than of large organisms. It is difficult to go much beyond crude qualitative impressions in testing this hypothesis, but we find that for mammal faunas, which contain such diverse organisms that they may well be regarded as models of whole faunas, there is a definite hint of the kind of theoretical distribution that we deduce. In qualitative terms the phenomenon can be exemplified by any of the larger species of ungulates which may require a number of different kinds of terrain within their home ranges, any one of which types of terrain might be the habitat of some small species. Most of the genera or even subfamilies of very large terrestrial animals contain only one or two sympatric species. In this connection I cannot refrain from pointing out the immense scientific importance of obtaining a really full insight into the ecology of the large mammals of Africa while they can still be studied under natural conditions. It is indeed quite possible that the results of studies on these wonderful animals would in long-range though purely practical terms pay for the establishment of greater reservations and National Parks than at present exist.

In the passerine birds the occurrence of five or six closely related sympatric species is a commonplace. In the mammal fauna of western Europe no genus appears to contain more than four strictly sympatric species. In Britain this number is not reached even by Mustela with three species, on the adjacent parts of the continent there may be three sympatric shrews of the genus Crocidura and in parts of Holland three of Microtus. In the same general region there are genera of insects containing hundreds of species, as in Athela in the Coleoptera and Dasyhelea in the Diptera Nematocera. The same phenomenon will be encountered whenever any well-studied fauna is considered. Irrespective of their position in a food chain, small size, by permitting animals to become specialized to the conditions offered by small diversified elements of the environmental mosaic, clearly makes possible a degree of diversity quite unknown among groups of larger organisms.

We may, therefore, conclude that the reason why there are so many species of animals is at least partly because a complex trophic organization of a community is more stable than a simple one, but that limits are set by the tendency of food chains to shorten or become blurred, by unfavorable physical factors, by space, by the fineness of possible subdivision of niches, and by those characters of the environmental mosaic which permit a greater diversity of small than of large allied species.

CONCLUDING DISCUSSION

In conclusion I should like to point out three very general aspects of the sort of process I have described. One speculative approach to evolutionary theory arises from some of these conclusions. Just as adaptive evolution by natural selection is less easy in a small population of a species than in a larger one, because the total pool of genetic variability is inevitably less, so it is probable that a group containing many diversified species will be able to seize new evolutionary opportunities more easily than an undiversified group. There will be some limits to this process. Where large size permits the development of a brain capable of much new learnt behavior, the greater plasticity acquired by the individual species will offset the disadvantage of the small number of allied species characteristic of groups of large animals. Early during evolution the main process from the standpoint of community structure was the filling of all the niche space potentially available for producer and decomposer organisms and for herbivorous animals. As the latter, and still more as carnivorous animals began to appear, the persistence of more stable communities would imply splitting of niches previously occupied by single species as the communities became more diverse. As this process continued one would expect the overall rate of evolution to have increased, as the increasing diversity increased the probability of the existence of species preadapted to new and unusual niches. It is reasonable to suppose that strong predation among macroscopic metazoa did not begin until the late Precambrian, and that the appearance of powerful predators led to the appearance of fossilizable skeletons. This seems the only reasonable hypothesis, of those so far advanced, to account for the relatively sudden appearance of several fossilizable groups in the Lower Cambrian. The process of diversification would, according to this argument, be somewhat autocatakinetic even without the increased stability that it would produce; with the increase in stability it would be still more a self inducing process, but one, as we have seen, with an upper limit. Part of this upper limit is set by the impossibility of having many sympatric allied species of large animals. These however are the animals that can pass from primarily innate to highly modifiable behavior. From an evolutionary point of view, once they have appeared, there is perhaps less need for diversity, though from other points of view, as Elton (1958) has stressed in dealing with human activities, the stability provided by diversity can be valuable even to the most adaptable of all large animals. We may perhaps therefore see in the process of evolution an increase in diversity at an increasing rate till the early Paleozoic, by which time the familiar types of community structure were established. There followed then a long period in which various large and finally large-brained species became dominant, and then a period in which man has been reducing diversity by a rapidly increasing tendency to cause extinction of supposedly unwanted species, often in an indiscriminate manner. Finally we may hope for a limited reversal of this process when man becomes aware of the value of diversity no less in an economic than in an esthetic and scientific sense.

A second and much more metaphysical general point is perhaps worth a moment's discussion. The evolution of biological communities, though each species appears to fend for itself alone, produces integrated aggregates which increase in stability. There is nothing mysterious about this; it follows from mathematical theory and appears to be confirmed to some extent empirically. It is however a phenomenon which also finds analogies in other fields in which a more complex type of behavior, that we intuitively regard as higher, emerges as the result of the interaction of less complex types of behavior, that we call lower. The emergence of love as an antidote to aggression, as Lorenz pictures the process, or the development of cooperation from various forms of more or less inevitable group behavior that Allee (1931) has stressed are examples of this from the more complex types of biological systems.

In the ordinary sense of explanation in science, such phenomena are explicable. The types of holistic philosophy which import *ad hoc* mysteries into science whenever such a situation is met are obviously unnecessary. Yet perhaps we may wonder whether the empirical fact that it is the nature of things for this type of explicable emergence to occur is not something that itself requires an explanation. Many objections can be raised to such a view; a friendly organization of biologists could not occur in a universe in which cooperative behavior was impossible and without your cooperation I could not raise the problem. The question may in fact appear to certain types of philosophers not to be a real one, though I suspect such philosophers in their desire to demonstrate how often people talk nonsense, may sometimes show less ingenuity than would be desirable in finding some sense in such questions.

273

Even if the answer to such a question were positive, it might not get us very far; to an existentialist, life would have merely provided yet one more problem; students of Whitehead might be made happier, though on the whole the obscurities of that great writer do not seem to generate unhappiness; the religious philosophers would welcome a positive answer but note that it told them nothing that they did not know before; Marxists might merely say, "I told you so." In spite of this I suspect that the question is worth raising, and that it could be phrased so as to provide some sort of real dichotomy between alternatives; I therefore raise it knowing that I cannot, and suspecting that at present others cannot, provide an intellectually satisfying answer.

My third general point is less metaphysical, but not without interest. If I am right that it is easier to have a greater diversity of small than of large organisms, then the evolutionary process in small organisms will differ somewhat from that of large ones. Wherever we have a great array of allied sympatric species there must be an emphasis on very accurate interspecific mating barriers which is unnecessary where virtually no sympatric allies occur. We ourselves are large animals in this sense; it would seem very unlikely that the peculiar lability that seems to exist in man, in which even the direction of normal sexual behavior must be learnt, could have developed to quite the existing extent if species recognition, involving closely related sympatric congeners, had been necessary. Elsewhere (Hutchinson, 1959) I have attempted to show that the difficulties that *Homo sapiens* has to face in this regard may imply various unsuspected processes in human evolutionary selection. But perhaps Santa Rosalia would find at this point that we are speculating too freely, so for the moment, while under her patronage, I will say no more.

ACKNOWLEDGMENTS

Dr. A. Minganti of the University of Palermo enabled me to collect on Monte Pellegrino. Professor B. M. Knox of the Department of Classics of Yale University gave me a rare and elegant word from the Greek to express the blurring of a food chain. Dr. L. B. Slobodkin of the University of Michigan and Dr. R. H. MacArthur of the University of Pennsylvania provided me with their customary kinds of intellectual stimulation. To all these friends I am most grateful.

LITERATURE CITED

ALLEE, W. C., 1931, Animal aggregations: a study in general sociology. vii, 431 pp. University of Chicago Press, Chicago, Illinois.

ALLEE, W. C., A. E. EMERSON, O. PARK, T. PARK and K. P. SCHMIDT, 1949, Principles of animal ecology, xii, 837 pp. W. B. Saunders Co., Philadelphia, Pennsylvania.

BARRETT-HAMILTON, G. E. H., and M. A. C. HINTON, 1911–1921, A history of British mammals. Vol. 2. 748 pp. Gurney and Jackson, London, England.

BIGELOW, H. B., 1926, Plankton of the offshore waters of the Gulf of Maine. Bull. U.S. Bur. Fisheries **40**: 1–509.

BROWN, E. S., 1958, A contribution towards an ecological survey of the aquatic and semi-aquatic Hemiptera-Heteroptera (water-bugs) of the British Isles etc. Trans. Soc. British Entom. **9**: 151–195.

BROWN, W. L., and E. O. WILSON, 1956, Character displacement. Systematic Zoology **5**: 49–64.

CRANBROOK, LORD, 1957, Long-tailed field mice (Apodemus) from the Channel Islands. Proc. Zool. Soc. London **128**: 597–600.

ELTON, C. S., 1958, The ecology of invasions by animals and plants. 159 pp. Methuen Ltd., London, England.

HUTCHINSON, G. E., 1951, Copepodology for the ornithologist. Ecology **32**: 571–577.

———, 1958, Concluding remarks. Cold Spring Harbor Symp. Quant. Biol. **22**: 415–427.

———, 1959, A speculative consideration of certain possible forms of sexual selection in man. Amer. Nat. **93**: 81–92.

HUTCHINSON, G. E., and R. MACARTHUR, 1959, A theoretical ecological model of size distributions among species of animals. Amer. Nat. **93**: 117–126.

HYMAN, L. H., 1955, How many species? Systematic Zoology **4**: 142–143.

KOHN, A. J., 1959, The ecology of Conus in Hawaii. Ecol. Monogr. (in press).

LACK, D., 1942, Ecological features of the bird faunas of British small islands. J. Animal Ecol. London **11**: 9–36.

———, 1947, Darwin's Finches. x, 208 pp. Cambridge University Press, Cambridge, England.

———, 1954, The natural regulation of animal numbers. viii, 347 pp. Clarendon Press, Oxford, England.

LINDEMAN, R. L., 1942, The trophic-dynamic aspect of ecology. Ecology **23**: 399–408.

MACAN, T. T., 1954, A contribution to the study of the ecology of Corixidae (Hemipt). J. Animal Ecol. **23**: 115–141.

MACARTHUR, R. H., 1955, Fluctuations of animal populations and a measure of community stability. Ecology **35**: 533–536.

———, 1957, On the relative abundance of bird species. Proc. Nat. Acad. Sci. Wash. **43**: 293–295.

MILLER, G. S., Catalogue of the mammals of Western Europe. xv, 1019 pp. British Museum, London, England.

MULLER, S. W., and A. Campbell, 1954, The relative number of living and fossil species of animals. Systematic Zoology **3**: 168–170.

ODUM, E. P., 1953, Fundamentals of ecology. xii, 387 pp. W. B. Saunders Co., Philadelphia, Pennsylvania, and London, England.

SLOBODKIN, L. B., 1955, Condition for population equilibrium. Ecology **35**: 530–533.

THORSON, G., 1957, Bottom communities. Chap. 17 in Treatise on marine ecology and paleoecology. Vol. 1. Geol. Soc. Amer. Memoir **67**: 461–534.

WALLACE, A. R., 1858, On the tendency of varieties to depart indefinitely from the original type. In C. Darwin and A. R. Wallace, On the tendency of species to form varieties; and on the perpetuation of varieties and species by natural means of selection. J. Linn. Soc. (Zool.) **3**: 45–62.

WYNNE-EDWARDS, V. C., 1952, Zoology of the Baird Expedition (1950). I. The birds observed in central and southeast Baffin Island. Auk **69**: 353–391.

EXPERIMENTAL STUDIES OF MIMICRY IN SOME NORTH AMERICAN BUTTERFLIES

PART I. THE MONARCH, *DANAUS PLEXIPPUS,* AND VICEROY, *LIMENITIS ARCHIPPUS ARCHIPPUS* [1]

Jane Van Zandt Brower

Department of Zoology, Yale University

Received May 25, 1957

INTRODUCTION

When the vast literature on mimicry is considered, the striking lack of experimental evidence for its existence is remarkable. Morgan (1896, 1900), while studying learning in chicks, designed mimicry experiments which showed that they can associate an unpleasant feeding experience with a particular color and pattern. Thereafter, the chicks would also reject modifications ("mimics") of the same color pattern. More recently, Mühlmann (1934) used dyed and treated mealworms as "models," and partially dyed ones as "mimics" in experiments with several species of passerine birds in an attempt to show how similar a model and mimic must be to deceive the birds. The work of Mostler (1935) on wasp-mimicry showed that birds could learn to reject wasps, and then also would mistake like-colored insects for wasps and reject them. Working on the problem of beetle mimicry, Darlington (1938) carried out experiments with captive *Anolis* lizards, which showed that they rejected the model beetle, and also mimic beetles. The laborious efforts of Finn (1895, 1896, 1897a, 1897b), Marshall (1902), Pocock (1911), Swynnerton (1919), Carpenter (1921, 1942), and Jones (1932) are paramount among the many attempts to determine the relative edibility of mimetic butterflies to various vertebrate predators. Both Marshall and

[1] Submitted to the Department of Zoology, Yale University, in partial fulfillment of the requirements for the degree of Doctor of Philosophy, June 1957.

Swynnerton reported some evidence for the existence of mimicry in the complex African butterfly fauna, on the basis of feeding experiments with captive Baboons and captive Rollers (*Coracias garrulus* Linné) respectively, but the major parts of both works were devoted to the more general problem of cryptic *versus* warning coloration in butterflies.

As Poulton (1909) pointed out, in North America there are three relatively simple examples of supposed mimicry in butterflies. The purpose of the present study is to describe an experimental investigation of mimicry in these North American butterflies, and it will be presented as three papers which deal separately with each of these three mimicry complexes. The same methods were employed for each complex, and the three parts were carried out as a continuous investigation over a period of 60 days. The first series of experiments was carried out with *Danaus plexippus* (Linné) and *Limenitis archippus archippus* (Cramer), presumed model and mimic, respectively. *D. Plexippus* is known respectively as the Monarch and *L. a. archippus* is known as the Viceroy; they will hereafter be referred to by their common names. The second series of experiments was a study of the model, *Battus philenor* Linné, and its mimics, *Papilio troilus* Linné, *P. polyxenes* (Fabricius), and the black female form of *P. glaucus* Linné. The third series was a study of the model, *Danaus gilippus berenice* (Cramer), and its mimic, *Limenitis archippus floridensis* (Strecker). The experiments were designed to investigate the following relationships between models and mimics and a selected bird species, to be used as a caged predator:

1—the reaction to models by individually caged experimental birds;
2—the reaction to mimics by the same experimental birds, after they had had initial laboratory experience with the models;
3—the reaction to mimics by individually caged control birds, which had had no prior laboratory experience with the models.

An experimental study demonstrating these three points could be expected to show the effectiveness of mimicry, within the limitations of the experimental conditions.

MATERIALS AND METHODS

The technical difficulties inherent in these experiments were minimized by the choice of an especially favorable situation in which to undertake the investigation. The Archbold Biological Station, near Lake Placid, Florida, provided excellent laboratory facilities, without which the work would have been impossible. In addition the required butterflies are relatively abundant in this area of Florida.

The Florida Scrub Jay, *Cyanocitta coerulescens coerulescens* (Bosc), was selected as the predator in the mimicry experiments. It is non-migratory and is found in areas in which Sand Pine (*Pinus clausa* (Engelm.) Vasey), scrubby oaks (*Quercus myrtifolia* Willd., *Q. geminata* Small, and *Q. catesbaei* Michx.), Saw Palmetto (*Serenoa repens* (Bartr.) Small), and Dwarf Wax Myrtle (*Myrica pumila* Michx.) predominate (Bent, 1946, and Amadon, 1944). The diet of the Scrub Jay is said to be about 60% animal matter, on the basis of analyses of stomach contents of sixteen birds (Bent, 1946), and includes beetles, butterflies, moths, caterpillars, and grasshoppers. Sprunt (1954) stated that the animal matter is 50% and did not note the presence of Lepidoptera in the stomach contents. Amadon (1944) observed Scrub Jays feeding in nature at the Archbold Biological Station, primarily on acorns and insects. The male and female Scrub Jays have similar plumage and size, though the males may be slightly brighter in color and larger than the females. Amadon also observed that in his experience a hiccup sound is peculiar to the female Scrub Jay. These birds are particularly easy to trap, and readily adapt to life in a cage (Amadon, 1944, and Bent, 1946).

Eight Florida Scrub Jays were trapped on the Archbold Biological Station property between 14 April and 17 April 1956. Since the young are known to hatch in early to mid April, it may be assumed that these Scrub Jays were all at least one year old. As noted above, the sex of these jays is difficult to determine from plumage, and even from size. However, in an attempt to ascertain the sex of the nine individuals used in the experiments, all but one were weighed prior to release. The following weights were recorded on 17 June 1956:

No. of bird	Weight in gms.	Tentative sex determination
C-1	84.0	male
C-2	66.5	female
C-3	83.0	male
C-4	77.0	female (hiccup)
E-1	88.0	male
E-2	74.0	female (hiccup)
E-3	71.0	female
E-4	—	mate of E-3
E-4A	77.5	female

From a generalization based on weight alone, C–2, E–3, and E–4A (a replacement for E–4, captured 1 June 1956) seemed to be females. E–4, the probable wild mate of E–3, was not weighed prior to release. On the basis of the hiccup sound mentioned by Amadon (1944), C–4 and E–2 could be considered females. C–1, C–3, and E–1 could have been males.

Each bird was confined in a cubic cage thirty inches on a side, with sides and top covered with aluminum-painted wire of one-half inch square mesh. The cages were arranged in the laboratory in two racks of four each, within two adjacent enclosures 6′ wide × 13′ 5″ deep × 7′ 8″ high. Each enclosure had a door (3′ 6″ wide × 7′ high) at one end, and both the door and the top of each enclosure were made of one-half inch square mesh. The eight bird cages were identical in every possible respect, as were the two enclosures. The individual bird cages were separated from one another by opaque cardboard, so that at no time could one bird see another. In each enclosure there was a pair of white porcelanized reflectors, each with a 100 watt incandescent bulb, fastened on the wall opposite the rack bearing the cages. These lights were on during all the experiments, and off when experiments were not in progress. Daylight entered the laboratory through a large skylight of northern exposure. The aluminum-painted steel tray floor of each of the eight bird cages was covered with sifted white sand obtained from the area where the birds were caught. Two perches at heights of 8″ and 16″ were provided in each cage, and each had a water bottle accessible at all times.

The eight birds were given a regular feeding at 5:30 P.M. daily. The standard laboratory diet consisted of approximately: 5 cc scratch (cracked corn and wheat), 1 cc pebbles, 2 cc Purina chow (for hens), 2 pecan meats, 1 peanut, 2 sunflower seeds, and 4 Scarabaeid beetles (*Phyllophaga prununculina* Burmeister). Occasionally, one or more additional items were given simultaneously to all birds. These included hard boiled egg, egg shell, lettuce, chopped meat, bread, and insects of various orders.

EXPERIMENTAL INSECTS

Insects of the orders Coleoptera, Hemiptera, Orthoptera, and Lepidoptera were attracted by a 15 watt G-E black light stationed on an outside platform of the laboratory. These were collected each night and stored in a cold room (about 3° C.) for use in the feeding experiments with the Scrub Jays. It is of interest that wild birds, including the Florida Scrub Jay, fed regularly at dawn on the remaining insects that had been attracted to the light the night before. The butterflies used in the experiments were obtained by collecting in the field, or by rearing the adults from eggs laid by confined female butterflies, or from larvae found in the field and reared in the laboratory. Supplies of butterflies were also stored in glassine envelopes in the cold room for use as needed. The particular source of each species will be noted as the experiments are described. No effort was devoted at this time to a study of the proportions of models and mimics in given localities.

PRELIMINARY EXPERIMENTS

To determine whether or not any erratic behavior existed among the eight Scrub Jays, all of the birds were given identical preliminary tests with several orders of insects. All birds responded similarly to representative Coleoptera (e.g., *Phyllophaga prununculina* and *Dyscinetus morator* Fabricius, Scarabaeidae, *Epicauta tenuis* (Leconte), Meloidae); Orthoptera (e.g., Acrididae, and *Gryllotalpa hexadactyla* Perty, Gryllidae); Hemiptera (e.g., *Lethocerus uhleri* (Montandon), Belostomatidae); and Lepidoptera (e.g., *Pholus fasciatus* (Sulzer) and *Xylophanes tersa* (Linné), Sphingidae; *Phoebis sennae eubule* (Linné), Pieridae; *Papilio glaucus* Linné (yellow female and male), *P. palamedes* (Drury), and *P. marcellus* (Cramer), Papilionidae). In each trial for each bird, a stopwatch was used to record the time in seconds for the bird to seize an insect, and if the bird then ate the insect, this time was also recorded. Similarity among all the birds in their reaction times in seizing the insects, and also in their responses to the insects after seizure, indicated that they were a reasonably uniform group with which to conduct experiments on mimicry. The set of mean reaction times, based on twelve trials for each of the eight birds, gave an observed standard deviation of 1.34 seconds, with a mean value of 3.31 seconds and a range of from 1.5 to 5.0. A table in David, Hartley, and Pearson (1954) showed that for eight observations the ratio of range to standard deviation must be 3.399 at the 5% significance level; the ratio of range to standard deviation here is 2.61 so that there is no significant difference among the eight observations, i.e., the birds' mean reaction times in seizing insects.

During the preliminary trials, two readily available butterflies, *Papilio glaucus* (yellow female and male) and *P. palamedes* which are not known to be involved in mimicry either as models or as mimics, were eaten in every case by all eight birds. It was therefore decided that these two species, obtained as living adults by local field collecting, would be used as the edible control butterflies throughout the course of the experiments. Hereafter they will be referred to as "non-mimetic butterflies." In all of the experiments the butterflies were immobilized by pinching the thorax before they were placed with a pair of forceps on the floor of a bird cage. For uniformity and stability all butterflies were presented lying on their sides, with wings together dorsally. Therefore in the experiments with models and mimics only mimicry in the characters of the underside of the wings was being tested. The immobilization of the butterflies and their sideways placement in the cages were arbitrarily decided upon to eliminate the following variables: (1) a mobile butterfly might be more or less difficult for a bird to catch depending on its amount of activity and its location in a cage; (2) mimicry might be more or less effective depending on whether a bird saw the upper or lower wing surfaces of a temporarily resting butterfly, or both surfaces of a flapping butterfly. The role of behavior of models

and mimics in increasing or diminishing the effectiveness of mimicry would be interesting in itself (e.g., it is known that two forms of the African butterfly, *Hypolimnas dubius* de Beauvais, which mimick two closely allied *Amauris* models, differ from one another in behavior as well as color and pattern, as discussed by Ford, 1953), but the present experiments do not attempt to investigate this aspect of the problem. Every bird was allowed two minutes to react to each butterfly presented. At two minutes an uneaten butterfly was removed. Whenever possible, living butterflies were used, but the data indicated that the reaction to any given species of butterfly was the same whether live or dead specimens were presented to the birds. In a few trials, dead and rather dried specimens, of non-mimetic butterflies only, had to be used, and rarely a slightly moldy non-mimetic butterfly was used in the absence of fresh material. Even these butterflies were quite acceptable as food to the jays. If a living model or mimic remained untouched throughout a trial, it was used again in successive trials. If a model or mimic was in any way torn or injured by a bird, however, it was not used again.

THE MIMICRY EXPERIMENTS

Of the eight Scrub Jays, four were randomly selected as experimental birds; the other four were control birds. The mimicry experiments were designed so that each trial consisted of giving a bird a pair of butterflies in succession, one non-mimetic butterfly and one model or one mimic. In each trial, the order of presentation of the non-mimetic butterfly and the model or mimic was determined by a random number table, with the use of consecutive digits in a different vertical column for each bird. If a digit read 0–4, a non-mimetic butterfly was given first, followed by a model (or mimic), but if a digit read 5–9, a model (or mimic) was given first, followed by a non-mimetic butterfly. By this method

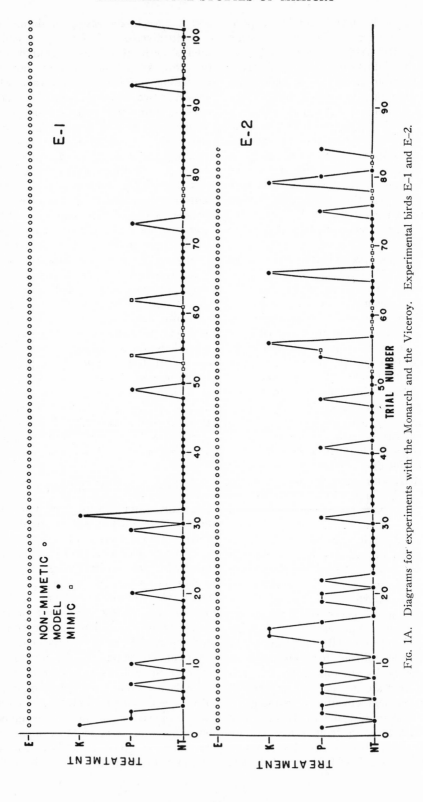

Fig. 1A. Diagrams for experiments with the Monarch and the Viceroy. Experimental birds E-1 and E-2.

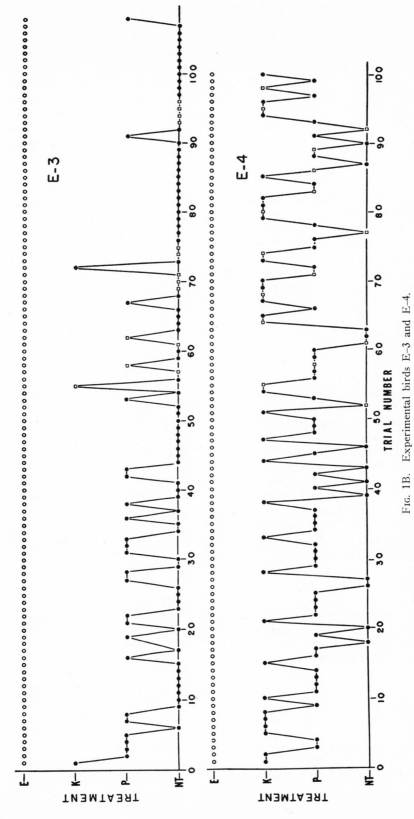

Fig. 1B. Experimental birds E-3 and E-4.

281

runs of more than two of each kind of butterfly were eliminated, and the following consecutive trials were possible (model or mimic = M; non-mimetic butterfly = N): (1a) M,N; (1b) M,N. (2a) N,M; (2b) N,M. (3a) M,N; (3b) N,M. (4a) N,M; (4b) M,N. Use of these randomized pairs avoided subjective repetition of any sequence in the presentation of the butterflies to the birds, and prevented the birds from reacting to the butterflies on the basis of an expected order of sequences. After each bird was given the first butterfly in a trial, it did not receive the second until each of the other birds had received its first butterfly. Thus for each bird the time interval between trial 1a and 1b was about the same as it was between trial 1b and 2a. The design of the experiments did not eliminate the possibility that the birds might predict the second butterfly given in each trial on the basis of the first one given, but the data suggested that this was not the case.

The experimental birds were given models and non-mimetic butterflies, randomly in pairs as described, until the birds had developed a relatively reliable pattern of behavior toward the model species. At this time, the mimic was substituted for the model in one trial. Subsequent substitutions of the mimic for the model depended on the particular pattern of behavior of the individual bird, and will be discussed when the data are considered.

The control birds were given mimics and non-mimetic butterflies randomly in pairs, by the same procedure used for the experimental birds. The difference between the two sets of birds was that only the experimental birds were given experience with models.

EXPERIMENTS WITH THE MONARCH AND VICEROY

The classic example of mimicry among North American butterflies is the Monarch-Viceroy situation, cited by Walsh and Riley (1869). In spite of a small amount of evidence to the contrary, the Monarch generally has been considered relatively unpalatable to vertebrate predators. Poulton (1909) commented upon the relative edibility of the Viceroy. He was of the opinion that the Viceroy is a Müllerian mimic, unpalatable like its model, basing his views on the supposed origin of the Viceroy from a warningly colored ancestor, like *Limenitis arthemis* (Drury), and on the assumption that warningly colored butterflies are unpalatable to predators. Walsh and Riley (1869) assumed that the Viceroy is a Batesian mimic, edible to vertebrate predators. It seemed fitting to begin the mimicry experiments with this long-debated problem of the Monarch and the Viceroy.

GEOGRAPHIC DISTRIBUTION AND SOURCES OF BUTTERFLIES

The range of the Monarch covers North America, northeastward to central Ontario (Klots, 1951). The Viceroy is more limited in its distribution, ranging from central Canada south to South Carolina, Georgia, and Louisiana. The species possibly forms a north-south cline with *Limenitis archippus floridensis,* the mimic of the southern danaid, *Danaus gilippus berenice.* The latter mimic and model both occur in Florida. The Viceroy (*L. archippus archippus*) does not reach central Florida, which makes it certain that the Florida Scrub Jays used in these experiments had never had experience with the Viceroy in nature. However, the birds may have attempted to eat Monarchs, which are present at the Station in winter and spring.

The source of Viceroys for the feeding experiments was over-wintering hibernacula collected in Litchfield Co., Conn., in February 1956. The larvae from these were reared to the adult stage at the Archbold Biological Station. The Monarchs were obtained locally in Florida by collecting living adults and by rearing adults from eggs obtained from females in outdoor insect cages, and also from larvae collected in the field. Both male and female butterflies were used in the experiments, but because female Viceroys resembled Monarchs more closely in size, females of this species were used in most trials. It should be noted that the relative size of models and mimics in nature is probably of little significance compared to their similarities of color and pattern, and that the effect of size on mimicry could assume a disproportionate importance under experimental conditions. The sex of a butterfly *per se* did not affect the reaction of any bird. A total of approximately 1,000 butterflies was used.

RESULTS

The basic data for the feeding experiments with Monarchs and Viceroys are presented in figures 1A. and 1B., diagrams E–1, E–2, E–3, and E–4, and in figure 2, diagrams C–1, C–2, C–3, and C–4. The four categories of reaction to the butterflies by the birds were selected on the basis of observed behavior of the birds. "NT" means that the butterfly was not touched by the bird during the two minute test period. The NT category sometimes was accompanied by characteristic behavior on the part of a bird which will be discussed below. The "P" category means that the bird pecked the butterfly but not to the point of any injury which in nature would impair the insect's ability to reproduce. Pecking could imply tasting, but the contact of the beak of the bird with the external surface of the butterfly is what is meant here. The "K" (killed) category is used when a bird had torn the body of the butterfly so that in the wild it would have died, or could not have reproduced, but the bird left the torn specimen uneaten. "E" refers to the fact that the bird had eaten the butterfly, leaving only the wings and legs, which were picked off and discarded.

From an examination of the diagrams of the experiments (see figs. 1A and 1B;

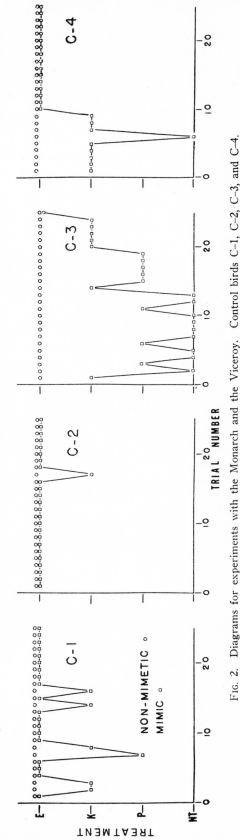

FIG. 2. Diagrams for experiments with the Monarch and the Viceroy. Control birds C–1, C–2, C–3, and C–4.

283

fig. 2), it will be evident that in all trials for both experimental and control birds, the non-mimetic butterfly (white circle) of each pair of butterflies in any given trial was eaten. In only four trials in this entire investigation, a bird was reluctant to eat a non-mimetic butterfly. When such hesitation occurred, the trials were stopped for a few minutes, and were not continued again until the bird readily accepted and ate the non-mimetic butterfly. Therefore every recorded trial indicates that a non-mimetic butterfly was eaten by a bird. The model, the Monarch, (black circle) was given in couplet with a non-mimetic butterfly to the four experimental birds for at least 51 trials prior to the substitution of the mimic, Viceroy, (white square) for the Monarch. The Monarch was not eaten by the four experimental birds in any trial. The diagrams for E–1, E–2, and E–3 show that during the initial trials, the Monarchs were pecked, killed, and not touched, and that the "not touched" category became more frequent as the birds learned that the Monarch was not palatable. All four birds reacted in their initial trial with the Monarch by killing or pecking the butterfly. This suggests either that the four experimental birds had not had experience with Monarchs in the field prior to capture, or, if they had experienced Monarchs in the wild, they had not remembered the unpalatability of Monarchs on sight alone under the cage conditions. That the lesson of unpalatability was never finally learned in the course of the experiments is seen in the repeated lapses of E–1, E–2, and E–3 into pecking or killing a Monarch after several trials during which the Monarch was not touched. On the basis of sight alone, E–4 was outstanding in its failure to remember for more than two successive trials that the Monarch was unpalatable.

The question of when to substitute Viceroys for Monarchs was complicated by the fact that the birds showed these periodic lapses when a model was again pecked or killed. In order to minimize the chance that a Viceroy would fall on the observed "error" pattern, i.e., the killing or pecking of the model, the presentation of each mimic was determined by the individual error pattern of each bird. A Viceroy was substituted for a Monarch soon after a bird had made an error on a Monarch. This meant that a bird had just been exposed to the unpleasant qualities of a Monarch before being offered a Viceroy. Because experience with each bird was the only guide, the technique of substitution of the mimic necessarily improved with time. For E–1, from trial 63 on, for E–2, from trial 57 on, and for E–3, from trial 63 on, no Viceroy was given unless it followed (1) a trial in which a Monarch was pecked or killed, and (2) a trial in which a Monarch was not touched, in that order. With the design of the experiments adjusted so that any pattern of natural pecking and/or killing lapses would be likely to fall on the model, as can be seen on the diagrams, the mimic was not touched.

Although E–4 did not learn to refuse the Monarch on sight, its treatment of the Viceroy shows no discrimination of the latter from the Monarch. The Viceroy was not eaten by any of the four experimental birds, and was not even killed by E–1 and E–2.

The four control birds, C–1, C–2, C–3, and C–4, were given trials with the Viceroy (mimic) and non-mimetic butterflies. Because the number of Viceroys available was limited, each control bird could be offered only 25. After these 25 Viceroys had been used, each control bird was given only the non-mimetic butterfly in each trial for the total number of trials shown in the "no. seize" column for each control bird on table 2. Each of the control birds ate every non-mimetic butterfly offered, although only the 25 which correspond to the Viceroy trials are shown in fig. 2, diagrams C–1, C–2, C–3, and C–4. The reaction to the Viceroy by C–1 indicates that it was palatable to that

TABLE 1. *Reactions of the experimental and control birds to Viceroys*

A. Comparison of no. "not touched" *vs.* no. "pecked—killed—eaten"

| | Control birds | | | | | Experimental birds | | | |
	C-1	C-2	C-3	C-4		E-1	E-2	E-3	E-4
NT	0	0	9	1		14	12	12	4
P—K—E	25	25	16	24		2	1	3	12

B. Comparison of no. "not touched—pecked—killed" *vs.* no. "eaten"

| | Control birds | | | | | Experimental birds | | | |
	C-1	C-2	C-3	C-4		E-1	E-2	E-3	E-4
NT—P—K	6	1	24	9		16	13	15	16
E	19	24	1	16		0	0	0	0

bird in most of the trials (diagram for C–1). C–2 ate the Viceroy in all but one trial as the diagram shows. In the case of C–3, most of the Viceroys were not touched, or were pecked or killed, and in only one trial, the last, was a Viceroy eaten. In the first nine trials, C–4 killed Viceroys, and once did not touch a Viceroy, but from trial 10 on, it ate all Viceroys.

STATISTICAL ANALYSIS OF THE DATA

Table 1,A shows a comparison of the treatment of the Viceroy for the category "NT" compared with the lumped categories "P-K-E" for all eight birds. On the hypothesis that the experimental birds and the control birds reacted to the Viceroy in the same way, a chi-squared test gave a value of 80.81, d.f. = 7, with the Yates correction factor, which was used in all chi-squared tests (table 1,A). The probability of obtaining these results, or worse ones, given this hypothesis, is less than .001. It may therefore be said that the two groups of birds did not react to the Viceroy in the same way, and that the control birds pecked, killed, and ate Viceroys significantly more than the experimental birds did. Similarly, when the data were analyzed to compare the categories "NT-P-K" with "E," the chi-squared value was 116.81, d.f. =7, P less than .001 (table 1,B). The control birds ate significantly more Viceroys than the experimental birds did; in fact, no Viceroys were eaten by the latter group.

In addition to an analysis of the response to the Viceroys by the experimental and control bird groups, con-

TABLE 2. *Reaction times of jays in seizing butterflies (in seconds to the nearest whole second)*

| Birds | Monarch | | | | | Viceroy | | | | | Non-mimetic butterflies | | | | |
	Mean time seize	Min. time	Max. time	No. seize	No. NT	Mean time seize	Min. time	Max. time	No. seize	No. NT	Mean time seize	Min. time	Max. time	No. seize	No. NT
C-1	—	—	—	—	—	8	1	100	25	0	3	1	14	92	0
C-2	—	—	—	—	—	5	2	11	25	0	5	2	25	95	0
C-3	—	—	—	—	—	10	1	36	16	9	1	1	3	101	0
C-4	—	—	—	—	—	11	2	46	24	1	6	1	76	94	0
E-1	9	1	31	12	76	14	6	22	2	14	1	1	3	102	0
E-2	27	1	102	25	48	20	20	20	1	12	1	1	2	84	0
E-3	36	1	119	24	69	22	4	41	3	12	2	1	16	108	0
E-4	12	1	88	72	12	30	2	112	12	4	3	1	10	100	0

sideration was also given to the reaction times of the birds in seizing the butterflies. The measure of time which has particular application for mimicry is the interval between the time a bird first saw a butterfly placed in its cage to the time when the bird first pecked or seized the butterfly. The mean time in seconds that each bird took to seize the Monarch, the Viceroy, and the non-mimetic butterflies used in the present experiments was calculated, and is shown on table 2. To indicate the range of seconds for each bird in seizing the butterflies of each group, the minimum and maximum times in seconds are also given. Since the experimental birds did not touch many Monarchs and Viceroys, the number of butterflies seized (from which the means were calculated) and also the number that were not touched are given in separate columns.

As table 2 shows, the time which the experimental birds took to seize Monarchs and Viceroys was considerably greater than that for non-mimetic butterflies, which suggests that the birds did not discriminate the Viceroy from the Monarch. If a similar hesitation in seizing a Monarch and its mimic were shown by an experienced bird in nature, escape of the butterfly from predation would be likely because of the time factor alone.

These data also suggest a correlation with the relative palatability of the various butterflies. The mean-times-seize of all the birds for the palatable non-mimetic butterflies are less than those of the control birds for the Viceroy.

Behavior of the Scrub Jays

In the description of the categories of reaction to the butterflies by the birds, it was noted that the "NT" category was sometimes accompanied by characteristic behavior on the part of a bird. This consisted of the bird ruffling its feathers and shaking its body, and/or by what I termed a "hop routine." The hop routine was a repetition of a series of hop movements by a bird, from perch, to side of cage, to floor, to perch, which often persisted for the full two minutes of a test, if an unpalatable model or its mimic had been presented.

A detailed examination of the occurrence of the feather-ruffling reaction in the individual birds shows a definite correlation between the reaction and the unacceptability of a given butterfly species to a bird. For the experimental birds, the feather-ruffling often occurred when either a Monarch or a Viceroy was presented. Thus E–1 gave this reaction in 77 out of 88 trials (88%) with the Monarch, and in 13 out of 16 trials (81%) with the Viceroy. The reaction was given by E–2 in 43 out of 73 trials (59%) with the Monarch, and in 9 out of 13 trials (69%) with the Viceroy. E–3 gave the reaction in 42 out of 94 trials (45%) with the Monarch, and in 5 out of 15 trials (33%) with the Viceroy. E–4 showed this reaction in 6 out of 84 trials (7%) with the Monarch, and in 2 out of 16 trials (13%) with the Viceroy. The reaction was never given by any of the birds when a non-mimetic butterfly (palatable) was presented.

The control birds also gave this same reaction when the Viceroy was presented, although on the whole less frequently than the experimental birds did. C–1 gave the reaction for 3 out of 25 Viceroys (12%); C–2 for 0 out of 25 Viceroys (0%); C–3 for 19 out of 25 Viceroys (76%); C–4 for 3 out of 25 Viceroys (12%). As might have been expected on the basis of the experimental birds, C–3, the bird that reacted to the Viceroy as an unpalatable butterfly during all but the last trial, also gave a high proportion of feather-ruffling reactions to the Viceroy.

Learning and Memory in the Scrub Jays

Although a study of learning in the Florida Scrub Jays was not the primary purpose of this inquiry, a few words should be devoted to this aspect of the experiments. De Ruiter (1952) described, in his work with Jays (*Garrulus glandarius* Linné) and Chaffinches (*Fringilla coelebs* Linné), how the birds became used to the inedibility of small sticks, and refused to peck at them. After experience with the twigs, the birds also refused to peck at caterpillars bearing close similarity to the twigs. Only if a caterpillar were pecked by accident would the birds, thus rewarded, continue to hunt for caterpillars. If they found only sticks again, they soon ceased pecking. This behavior has been termed an example of habituation by Thorpe (1956). In so far as the Scrub Jays found the Monarch butterfly inedible in a series of 50 trials, one might have expected habituation to develop in the course of the experiments. Indeed, the theory of mimicry suggested by Müller (1879, 1881) assumes that young birds learn by experience which butterflies are inedible and remember what they have learned. However, the repeated lapses of the Scrub Jays into pecking the Monarch show a persistent trial-and-error learning pattern. Swynnerton (1915) in referring to the mistaken attacks of his caged birds on unpalatable insects noted: ". . . no bird could be too old or too experienced to make continual mistakes of this kind." Similar "forgetfulness" is reported by Sadovnikova (1923). She found that in maze learning in passerine birds, individual birds would occasionally show periods of "forgetting" when they entered blind alleys which they had previously learned to avoid. The pattern of apparent forgetfulness shown by the Scrub Jays thus may be of a general nature, or may be associated with cage experiments. The experimental behavior can not be extended to imply that such short-term forgetfulness (day to day) exists among Scrub Jays in the wild; this is not known.

In spite of the short-term lapses of memory seen in the Scrub Jays, the data did show that the birds could remember to reject a Monarch and a Viceroy on sight alone after a period of about two weeks. E-1 rejected a Monarch and a Viceroy after 16 days of 82 trials with unrelated butterflies of the *Battus* mimicry complex; E-2, after 19 days of 84 such interim trials; E-3, after 15 days of 82 such interim trials. Tests of memory in the Scrub Jays after longer periods had elapsed were not possible in these experiments.

DISCUSSION

The first point to be considered is that of the reaction to the model, the Monarch, by the four experimental birds. As the data showed, the Monarch was unacceptable on sight alone at some time to all the experimental birds. The theory that models are unpalatable, and that their color pattern is a sign of unpalatability, is thus supported. Following a period of learning during which the experimental birds were given the Monarch, these birds did not even touch the Viceroy in many trials, and in no case did the birds eat a Viceroy. That the Viceroy is not as inherently unpalatable as the Monarch was shown by the control birds, and this will be discussed below. The highly significant difference in the treatment of the Viceroy by the two sets of birds is attributed to the experience of the experimental birds with the unpalatable Monarch, and to the subsequent association by these birds of the color pattern of the Viceroy with that of the Monarch. Under the conditions of the experiment, it has been shown that mimicry in the case of the Monarch and Viceroy is effective.

The status of the edibility of the Viceroy demands further consideration. According to Bates's idea (1862), the mimic was presumed to be a butterfly edible to vertebrate predators, especially to birds. Müller (1879), in dealing with a particular complex of closely related species of mimetic butterflies in South America (Heliconiidae) which had puzzled Bates, resolved the problem by suggesting that the entire complex of "models" and "mimics" was unpalatable to predators. The pooling of their numbers thus reduced the number of losses per species to the learning of inexperienced birds. In the present experiments, the status of the Viceroy as a Batesian or Müllerian mimic is not entirely evident, and it brings to mind Swynnerton's repeated emphasis on the range of edibility of butterflies to birds (1919). That the experimental birds in no instance regarded the Viceroys as edible is clear. The reaction to the Viceroy by E–1 and E–2 (fig. 1A) shows that those birds never killed that butterfly, although E–2 killed three Monarchs after the commencement of Viceroy trials. E–1 and E–2 were not discriminating the Viceroy from the Monarch as something different and edible. E–3 (fig. 1B) in trial 55 apparently did discriminate between its first Viceroy and Monarchs. Subsequent trials indicate either that the bird failed to maintain its discriminative ability, perhaps in part due to the design of the trials plus the adjustment for natural error, or that the bird found the Viceroy unpalatable, and established a general reaction to both Monarch and Viceroy as inedible. The fluctuating responses of E–4 (fig. 1B) to the Monarch and Viceroy show that the bird failed to remember on sight alone that the Monarch was inedible. The treatment of the Monarch and Viceroy was so consistent that it seems likely that this bird was not discriminating between the two, and perhaps found them both unpalatable. At any rate the Viceroy was not eaten in preference to the Monarch by E–4.

All four experimental birds showed identical, characteristic behavior, discussed above, to both the Monarch and Viceroy, which supports the idea that there was no discrimination of one from another. However, although the Monarch and Viceroy were treated in this generalized manner, a trial can be cited in which a bird clearly distinguished one Viceroy from Monarchs on the basis of a slight difference in color. For E–3, trial 62, there is reason to believe that the pecking of this Viceroy was due to its coloration which was somewhat more brown than previous or succeeding ones. The butterfly had been presented inadvertently, and the instant curiosity and pecking reaction of the bird to the slight color discrepancy was noted. The problem of discrimination *vs.* generalization of models and mimics by the Scrub Jays will be discussed in more detail in Part III of this series of papers. For the present, it can be said that although the data for the experimental birds show that the Viceroy was rejected by them, they do not clearly show why. For E–1 and E–2, the rejection of the Viceroy seems to be based on the fact that the birds learned that the Monarch was unpalatable, and could not discriminate the Viceroy from the Monarch. The data for E–3 and E–4 could be interpreted in the same way as for E–1 and E–2, or alternatively, that the Monarch and Viceroy were both found by experience to be unpalatable and were recognized as one or as separate color patterns, but in either case rejected.

The control birds gave further indication of the inherent edibility of the Viceroy. As the diagrams showed (fig. 2), the Viceroy was not as edible as the non-mimetic butterflies for C–3, and in part this was true for C–1 and C–4. C–2 regarded the Viceroy as an edible species. C–4 appears to have learned to eat the Viceroy. The reaction of C–3 to the Viceroy is comparable to the initial learning pattern of E–1 for the Monarch, but the Viceroy was more acceptable to C–3 toward the end of the experiment. It is possible that the control birds, particularly C–3, had some pre-capture experience with the Monarch, and associated the Viceroy with the Monarch, although no bird refused to peck its first Viceroy. The geographic distribution of the Viceroy precludes any experience with that exact color pattern in nature by these jays.

The learning patterns of E–3 and E–4 and of C–1, C–3, and C–4 could be interpreted to lend support to the hypothesis that the Viceroy is a classical Müllerian mimic. Additional evidence for this view is suggested by the reaction times of the control birds in seizing Viceroys, which were longer than those for seizing non-mimetic butterflies. However, rather than try to place the Viceroy in a rigid, all-or-none category which implies more than the data show, the Viceroy is here considered more edible than its model, the Monarch, but initially less edible (except to C–2) than the non-mimetic butterflies used in these experiments.

SUMMARY

1) This paper is the first in a series of three which present experimental studies of mimicry in some North American butterflies.

2) The experiments were designed to study the effectiveness of mimicry in these butterflies with the use of eight Florida Scrub Jays (*Cyanocitta coerulescens coerulescens*) as caged predators. The butterflies were immobilized and their wings were folded together dorsally, so that only mimicry in the characters of the underside of the wings was being tested in these experiments.

3) The present experiments tested mimicry in the classic example of the Monarch (*Danaus plexippus*) and Viceroy (*Limenitis archippus archippus*).

4) The results of these experiments show that the non-mimetic butterflies, used in couplet with each model or mimic, were eaten in every trial by all birds.

5) The four experimental birds were given numerous trials with the model, the Monarch. The Monarch was not eaten by these birds in any trial, and in many trials was not touched, after initial learning had taken place.

6) After the experimental birds had been given more than 50 trials with the Monarch, the Viceroy was substituted for the Monarch at intervals. The Viceroy was never eaten by the four experimental birds, and in many trials was not even touched.

7) Characteristic behavior shown by the four experimental birds after the presentation of both Monarchs and Viceroys indicated no discrimination between the two species of butterflies.

8) The four control birds had no prior laboratory experience with the Monarch, and these birds ate the Viceroy in many trials.

9) A statistical analysis of the reaction to the Viceroy by the experimental and control birds indicated that the two groups did not react to the Viceroy in the same way. The difference in response is attributed to the prior laboratory experience of the experimental birds with the Monarch. The color pattern of the Viceroy was apparently associated with the complete inedibility and similar color pattern of the Monarch. Under the conditions of the experiment, mimicry has been shown to be effective.

10) The data indicate that the Viceroy is more edible than the Monarch, but less edible than the non-mimetic butterflies used in the experiments. In addition, the control birds took longer to seize Viceroys, on the average, than they took to seize the non-mimetic butterflies. Therefore the Viceroy is not termed either a Batesian or a Müllerian mimic in the classical sense.

11) Learning behavior and memory in the Scrub Jays were considered briefly. The records showed that three of the four experimental birds remembered to reject a Monarch and a Viceroy on sight alone, after a period of over two weeks had elapsed since their last experience with these butterflies.

ACKNOWLEDGMENTS

I want to express my appreciation to Dr. C. L. Remington, under whom this work was carried out, for suggesting the problem of mimicry to me and for arranging my facilities at the Archbold Biological Station. I am indebted to Mr. Richard Archbold, Director of the Archbold Biological Station, where the experiments were conducted, for his generous cooperation and material assistance, and I wish to extend my thanks to the members of his staff for their help.

The suggestions of several persons were offered concerning the design and analysis of these experiments, and thanks are given to: Drs. C. I. Bliss, L. P. Brower, E. S. Deevey, Prof. G. E. Hutchinson, Drs. R. MacArthur, C. L. Remington, M. T. M. Rizki, and H. Seal. I am grateful to Drs. P. F. Bellinger, J. L. Brooks, E. B. Ford, F. R. S., Prof. G. E. Hutchinson, and Drs. C. L. Remington and P. M. Sheppard for reading and criticising the manuscript.

Dr. S. D. Ripley offered useful advice on the capture and care of the birds, and Drs. M. W. Sanderson and F. G. Werner identified the beetles.

Mr. S. A. Hessel very kindly helped with locating and collecting the *Viceroy hibernacula*.

The inestimable assistance of my husband, Lincoln P. Brower, in many phases of this work is gratefully acknowledged.

The experiments were conducted with the support of the Fanny Bullock Workman Scholarship offered by Wellesley College, and of a terminal, pre-doctoral National Science Foundation Fellowship. Summer field work in the preliminary stages of this investigation was supported by a Sigma Xi RESA Grant, and by a grant from the Higgins Fund of Yale University.

LITERATURE CITED

AMADON, DEAN. 1944. A preliminary life history study of the Florida Jay, *Cyanocitta c. coerulescens*. Amer. Mus. Nov. No. 1252.

BATES, H. W. 1862. Contributions to an insect fauna of the Amazon Valley. Lepidoptera: Heliconidae. Trans. Linn. Soc. Lond., **23**: 495–566, 2 pls.

BENT, A. C. 1946. Life Histories of North American Jays, Crows, and Titmice. U. S. Nat. Mus. Bull. **191**: 77–88.

CARPENTER, G. D. H. 1921. Experiments on the relative edibility of insects, with special reference to their coloration. Trans. Ent. Soc. Lond., **1921**: 1–105.

——. 1942. Observations and experiments in Africa by the late C. M. F. Swynnerton on wild birds eating butterflies and the preferences shown. Proc. Linn. Soc. Lond., **154**: 10–46.

DARLINGTON, P. J., JR. 1938. Experiments on mimicry in Cuba, with suggestions for further study. Trans. Roy. Ent. Soc. Lond., **87**: 681–695, 1 pl.

DAVID, H. A., H. O. HARTLEY, AND E. S. PEARSON. 1954. The distribution of the ratio, in a single normal sample, of range to standard deviation. Biometrika, **41**: 482–493.

DE RUITER, L. 1952. Some experiments on the camouflage of stick caterpillars. Behaviour, **4**: 222–232.

FINN, FRANK. 1895. Contributions to the theory of warning colours and mimicry. I. Experiments with a Babbler (*Crateropus canorus*). Journ. Asiatic Soc. Bengal, **64**: 344–356.

——. 1896. II. Experiments with a lizard *Calotes versicolor*). Journ. Asiatic Soc. Bengal, **65**: 42–48.

——. 1897a. III. Experiments with a tupaia and a frog. Journ. Asiatic Soc. Bengal, **66**: 528–533.

——. 1897b. IV. Experiments with various birds. Journ. Asiatic Soc. Bengal, **66**: 613–668.

FORD, E. B. 1953. The genetics of polymorphism in the Lepidoptera. Advances in Genetics, **5**: 43–87.

JONES, F. M. 1932. Insect coloration and the relative acceptability of insects to birds. Trans. Ent. Soc. Lond., **80**: 345–386, 11 pls.

KLOTS, A. B. 1951. A Field Guide to the Butterflies. Houghton Mifflin Co., Boston.

LINDLEY, D. V., AND J. C. P. MILLER. 1953. Cambridge Elementary Statistical Tables. Cambridge Press.

MARSHALL, G. A. K. 1902. Five years' observations and experiments (1896–1901) on the bionomics of South African insects, chiefly . . . mimicry and warning colours. Trans. Ent. Soc. Lond., **1902**: 287–584, 15 pls.

MORGAN, L. P. 1896. Habit and Instinct. Edward Arnold, London.

——. 1900. Animal Behavior. Edward Arnold, London.

MOSTLER, G. 1935. Beobachtungen zur Frage der Wespen-Mimikry. Zs. Morph. Oekol. Tiere, **29**: 381–455.

MÜHLMANN, H. 1934. In Modellversuch künstlich erzeugte Mimikry und ihre Bedeutung für den "Nachahmer." Zs. Morph. Oekol. Tiere, **28**: 259–296.

MÜLLER, FRITZ. 1879. (Trans. by R. Meldola.) *Ituna* and *Thyridia;* a remarkable case of mimicry in butterflies. Proc. Ent. Soc. Lond., **1879**: xx–xxix.

——. 1881. Bemerkenswerthe Fälle erworbener Aehnlichkeit bei Schmetterlingen. Kosmos. (Reviewed by A. R. Wallace, 1882. Nature, **26**: 86.)

POCOCK, R. I. 1911. On the palatability of some British insects, with notes on the significance of mimetic resemblances. Notes by E. B. Poulton. Proc. Zool. Soc. Lond., **1911**: 809–868.

POULTON, E. B. 1909. Mimicry in butterflies of North America. Ann. Ent. Soc. Amer., **2**: 203–242.

SADOVNIKOVA, MARY P. 1923. The study of the behavior of birds in the maze. Journ. Comp. Psych., **3**: 123–139.

SPRUNT, ALEXANDER, JR. 1954. Florida Bird Life. Coward-McCann Inc., New York, and Nat. Audubon Soc.

SWYNNERTON, C. M. F. 1915. A brief preliminary statement of a few of the results of 5 years' special testing of the theories of mimicry. Proc. Ent. Soc. Lond. **1915**: 32–44 (quote p. 42).

——. 1919. Experiments and observations bearing on the explanation of form and colouring, 1908–1913, Africa. Journ. Linn. Soc. Zool., **33**: 203–385.

THORPE, W. H. 1956. Learning and Instinct in Animals. Methuen and Co. Ltd., London.

WALSH, B. D., AND C. V. RILEY. 1869. Imitative butterflies. Amer. Entomologist, **1**: 189–193, 3 figs.

CHROMOSOME VARIABILITY AND
GEOGRAPHIC DISTRIBUTION IN INSECTS

Chromosome rather than gene variations provide
the key to differences among populations.

BERNARD JOHN AND KENNETH R. LEWIS*

There is no group of organisms in which the analysis of chromosome variation in relation to geographical distribution has been carried farther than in the Insecta. This kind of variation has tended to be neglected by many and ignored by some. Yet, in reality, it is more spectacular and, though less understood, at least as important as either the external variation or indeed the remaining genetic variation that exists in natural populations.

The chromosome complement is not just another character. To regard it as such is to misunderstand the nature of phylogenetic change and thus the whole basis of biological evolution. The material of the genotype itself forms part of the structure of the chromosomes. For this reason the chromosome phenotype is far less influenced by external factors than is the morphological or the physiological phenotype. Moreover, the chromosome phenotype is often a much more sensitive indicator of biological change and biological distinctiveness.

Chromosome variation of different kinds has been described within or between many natural insect populations (Table 1). In most cases, however, no analysis of this variation has been undertaken. The detailed study of chromosome variation in different geographical areas was initiated in the United States by the pioneer investigation of Dobzhansky and Sturtevant (1). They studied the polymorphism obtaining in the banding sequence of the giant polytene chromosomes of *Drosophila*. Their approach, that of comparing patterns of polymorphism within and between populations, has since been used by many workers in many lands and with many species. The *Drosophila* studies, however, still represent the most comprehensive and formidable body of data available on chromosome variation in geographically defined areas, for they have been in progress now for almost 30 years. Let us begin, then, by considering the extent, the validity, and the applicability of the conclusions reached from these studies.

* Dr. John is reader in cytology in the department of genetics at the University of Birmingham, England. Dr. Lewis is university lecturer in botany and Fellow of Exeter College at the University of Oxford, England.

TABLE 1

Patterns of chromosome polymorphism within and between natural populations of insects. The preponderance of polymorphisms in the Coleoptera (beetles), the Diptera (flies), and the Orthoptera (cockroaches, grasshoppers, crickets, and mantids) undoubtedly reflects a lack of adequate study in other insect groups.

	Type of polymorphism		Organism		Reference
			Order	Species	
STRUCTURAL	Paracentric inversion		Diptera	Many species of *Drosophila* but especially *melanica, melanogaster, pseudoobscura, persimilis, robusta,* and *willistoni*	(49)
				Chironomus dorsalis and *tentans* *Glyptotendipes barbipes*	(50) (51)
				Anopheles punctipennis and *quadrimaculatus*	(52)
				Cnephia mutata *Eusimulium aureum* *Simulium tuberosum* *Tenipes decorus*	(53) (54) (55) (56)
	Pericentric inversion		Coleoptera	*Pissoides approximatus, canadensis* and *terminalis*	(32)
			Diptera	*Drosophila algonquin* *D. robusta*	(57) (58)
			Orthoptera	*Circotettix undulatus* *Moraba scurra* *M. viatica* *M. virgo* *Scapsipedus aspersus* *Trimerotropis sparsa*	(59) (60) (61) (62) (63) (64)
	Interchange		Orthoptera	*Periplaneta americana* and *Blaberus discoidalis*	(27, 29)
	Centric fusion		Coleoptera	*Chilocorus stigma* *Pissoides spp.*	(35) (32)
			Diptera	*Drosophila americana*	(65)
			Orthoptera	*Ameles heldreichi* *Anaxipha pallidula* *Moraba viatica* *M. virgo*	(36) (66) (61) (62)
	Dissociation		Coleoptera	*Chilocorus spp.* *Pissoides spp.*	(35) (32)
			Orthoptera	*Moraba scurra*	(60)
	Supernumerary chromosome segments		Orthoptera	*Calliptamus palaestinensis* *Chorthippus parallelus*	(67) (39)
NUMERICAL / Aneuploidy		Supernumerary or B chromosomes	Coleoptera	*Diabrotica undecimpunctata*	(68)
			Hemiptera	*Cimex lectularius* *Pseudococcus citri*	(69) (22)
			Orthoptera	*Acrida lata* *Calliptamus palaestinensis* *Myrmeleotettix maculatus* *Trimerotropis sparsa*	(70) (71) (38) (72)
		Sex chromosome variation	Dermaptera	*Forficula auricularia* $XY,XX/X_1X_2Y,X_1X_1X_2X_2$	(73)
			Diptera	*Phryne cincta* $XY,XX+(1—7)$ extra Y's	(74)
			Hemiptera	*Dicranotropis hamata* $XY,XX/XO,XX$	(75)
			Lepidoptera	*Solenobia triquetrella*	(76)
	Polyploidy		Coleoptera	*Scepticus griseus* diploid ♂ and ♀ / pentaploid parthenogenetic ♀	(77)
			Diptera	*Cnephia mutata* diploid ♂ and ♀ / triploid parthenogenetic ♀	(53)
	Undefined		Orthoptera	*Gryllotalpa gryllotalpa* $2x$ ∝ 12, 14, 15, 17, 19 and 23	(78)

293

THE DROSOPHILA AFFAIR

Populations of many, though by no means all, species of *Drosophila* are mixtures of individuals with differently constructed chromosomes. In particular, a large number of distinct paracentric inversions (Fig. 1) of the band sequences in the giant polytene chromosomes have been found in the heterozygous state, and each inversion tends to have its own definite range.

A few of these inversions occur throughout most of the species area, but most are restricted to varying degrees and some are quite local. The frequencies of some of the more abundant types vary along regular geographical clines and, since the clines do not coincide, each region is characterized by different frequencies of its principal chromosome types.

Different geographical populations of the same species may vary considerably with regard to their degree of polymorphism. Some are structurally monomorphic, some are moderately polymorphic, and others highly so. Moreover, in *D. subobscura* the inversions show a pronounced tendency to overlap, so forming complex heterozygotes, whereas in *D. willistoni* many of the inversions are small and independent.

Four main correlations have been established in relation to these varying patterns of polymorphism:

1) In species such as *D. willistoni*, whose geographical races differ in the extent of their polymorphism, the chromosome variability of natural populations is highly correlated with environmental conditions. Populations in heterogeneous environments are more variable than those living in more homogeneous habitats (2). This suggests that chromosome polymorphism allows for a more efficient exploitation of the environment.

2) In a number of cases, inversion polymorphism is richest in the center of distribution and falls off toward the margins. This holds, for example, in *D. willistoni* when the average number of inversions per individual is used as an index of the structural diversity in a given population (3, 4). It holds also in *D. robusta* (3, 4), where the average length of euchromatin devoid of inversions increases from 65 percent in the center of the distribution to 85 percent in the marginal areas (Fig. 2). Similarly, by using an index of structural diversity similar to that of Carson, Stumm-Zollinger and Goldschmidt reported, contrary to earlier accounts (5), a higher index in the marginal populations of *D. subobscura* from Israel than in populations from central and western Europe. All three cases point to the same conclusion—geographically or ecologically marginal populations tend, on the average, to be less polymorphic than central populations.

The polymorphism of numerous populations of *D. willistoni* in the West Indies and in Central America follows the same rule. Not only does structural heterozygosity decrease with distance from the South American continent but, within the Archipelago, its extent is also clearly connected with the size of the islands (6). Thus island populations and those of distributional pockets are less polymorphic than continental populations. Likewise, when closely related

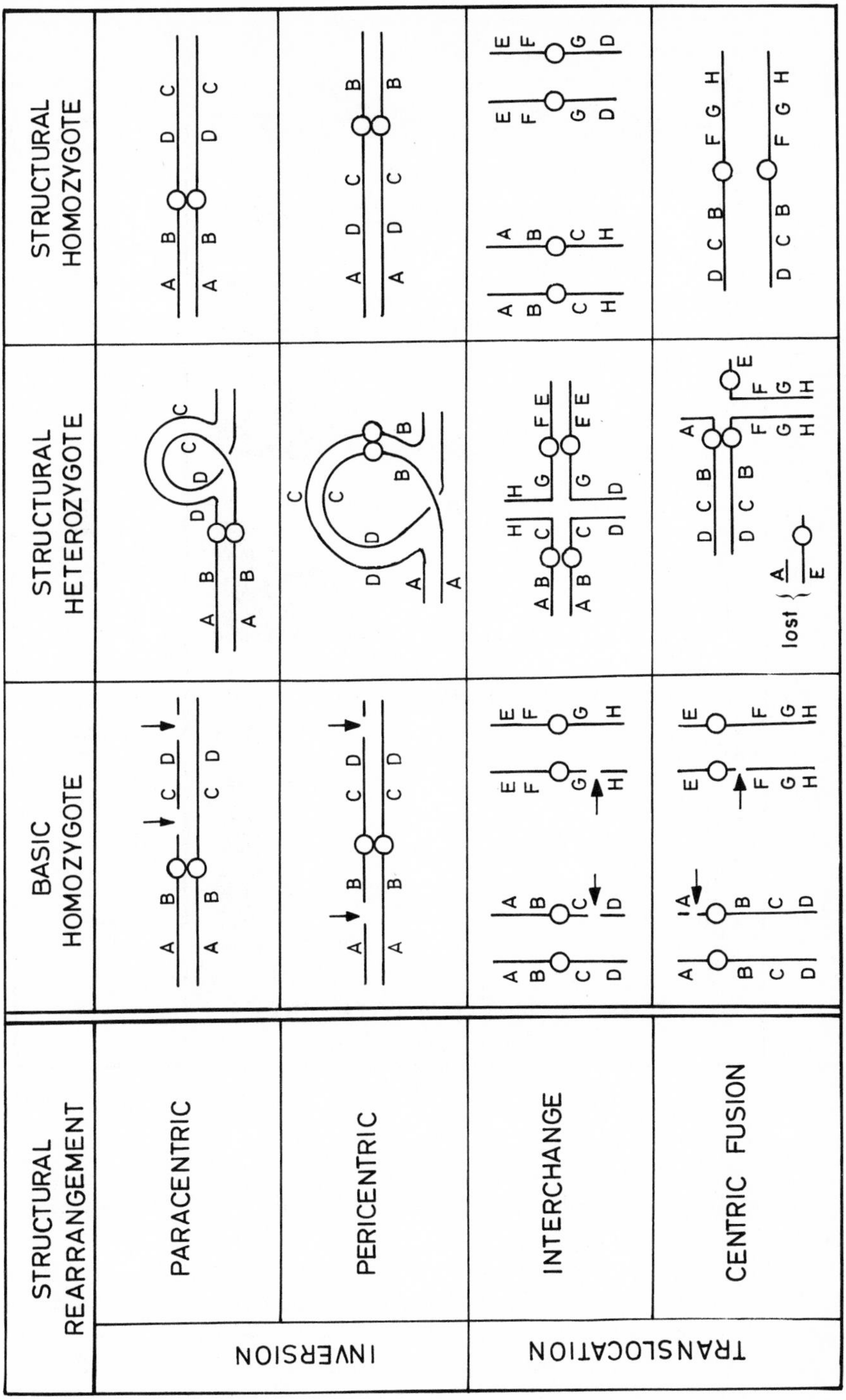

FIGURE 1. The four principal types of structural chromosome mutation found in insect populations (compare with Table 1).

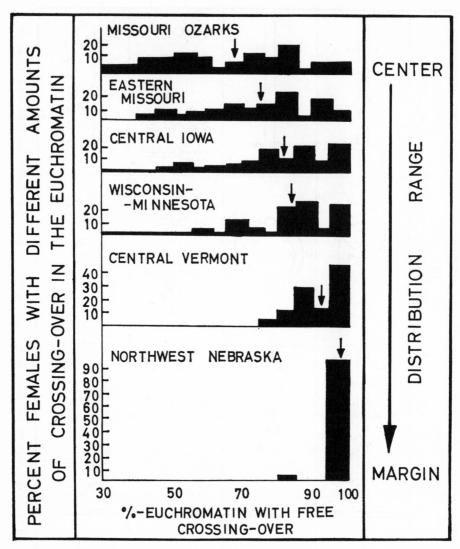

FIGURE 2. Differential patterns of recombination in natural populations of *Drosophila robusta* as determined by Carson (19).

species are analyzed, the ecologically more versatile prove to be more variable chromosomally (7).

Occasionally the interaction between such situations leads to what may appear to be paradoxical situations. Thus in *D. pseudoobscura* the chromosomal polymorphism is low in the populations of the Colorado plateau and the Great Basin, which are ecologically marginal though geographically central, and high in California and the Rocky Mountains, which are geographically marginal but ecologically hospitable (8). This implies that a species may evolve a specially adapted population in any ecologically "marginal" area, whether this is in the center of the species range or at its periphery.

Notice, however, that these conditions do not obtain in all cases. Brncic (9), for instance, finds that the chromosomally polymorphic species D. pavani, which lives in the ecologically diversified parts of Chile and Argentina, shows no geographical differences in the frequencies of its chromosomal types. Likewise Kunze-Mühl, Müller, and Sperlich (10) found no reduction of the extent of polymorphism in island populations of D. subobscura, a situation which contrasts markedly with that discovered in D. willistoni on the islands of the Caribbean.

3) In some populations the chromosomal composition is known to undergo secular change. Thus cyclical, seasonal changes have been reported in the relative frequencies of the karyotypes of D. pseudoobscura on Mount San Jacinto and the Yosemite regions of California (11). On the other hand, in D. willistoni, which is the most widespread species in the genus and whose chromosome variability is the largest known, the inversions do not show seasonal fluctuations in frequency. It may be significant, however, that the inversions here are short and recombination between them is frequent (12).

4) Finally, the genetic composition of a population may change directionally with time. For example, between 1940 and 1957, populations of D. pseudoobscura from ten localities in different parts of California have all undergone a decrease in the frequency of the inverted gene arrangement CH in chromosome III with a corresponding appearance and increase in the frequency of the PP arrangement in the same chromosome (13). Sometimes the changes have affected populations over a very large territory, but attempts to correlate such changes with environmental variables have met with little success, and the causation of these changes remains an enigma.

CHARACTERS, CORRELATIONS, AND CAUSATIONS

Interesting as these findings are, the key question is—what confers adaptive significance on these different polymorphisms? There have been two main views on this subject. According to Dobzhansky, chromosomal polymorphism is maintained in natural populations of Drosophila chiefly by superior fitness of the structural heterozygotes for various combinations of the gene arrangements in a given population. This conclusion is based predominantly on the fact that in chromosomally polymorphic and monomorphic experimental populations, the polymorphic ones are fitter than the monomorphic if fitness is measured in terms of ability to convert nutrient medium into biological material. Polymorphic populations also appear to be superior in homeostatic properties (14). Rather surprisingly, however, no serious attempt has been made to elucidate the precise polygenic architecture of the inverted segments although techniques are available for doing this (15).

Epling and his colleagues (16), on the other hand, have repeatedly argued that the importance of these inversion systems depends on the restrictions and extensions to recombination which they effect. Of course, since crossing-over does not occur in the male of *Drosophila,* these restrictions and extensions will be immediately effective only in females. Thus genes within an inverted segment form a tightly linked constellation since even if recombination occurs between them the majority of the recombinants, being genetically unbalanced, will be inviable. Inversions in *Drosophila* also lead to interchromosomal influences on recombination, and different inversions differ in the intensity of their effect (*17*). Indeed, Epling and his co-workers suggest that the seasonal changes of arrangement in chromosome III can be explained in terms of an increased recombination in genes other than those present in this chromosome. Moreover they believe that recombinants produced by crossing-over in the inversion-free chromosomes have effects on the adaptive values of the inversions themselves and that this influences their frequencies.

Likewise, two explanations have been advanced to account for the reduction of structural heterozygosity in peripheral populations. According to da Cunha and Dobzhansky (*3*) and da Cunha *et al.* (*18*) the gene arrangement has an ecotypic function. Carson (*19*), however, argues that the difference is due to selection for increased or decreased amounts of recombination. From his studies on *D. robusta* he has shown that the response to selection tends to be greater in strains originating from the marginal populations than in those from central populations. This undoubtedly reflects the occurrence of more recombination in the marginal populations.

Much of the difficulty in resolving the *Drosophila* affair undoubtedly stems from the fact that there is not one problem to solve but several. A second difficulty stems from the fact that it is not easy to distinguish effects due to genic heterozygosity from those due to recombination (*20*). A third arises from the fact that correlations need not be causations. Although it may be possible to demonstrate a clear correlation between a polymorphism and an environmental variable, such a correlation by no means proves that the variable is, or has been, instrumental in the establishment and maintenance of the polymorphism. Finally, there has been a tendency to confuse the properties of different levels of genetic organization. Thus conclusions relevant to simple gene heterozygotes—many of which in themselves are suspect—have been applied, without qualification, to chromosome heterozygotes. To take one example, inversions and interchanges, when heterozygous, produce tight linkage which leads to the development of what have been called "supergenes." And, provided this supergene combination shows heterotic properties, it may produce a system which simulates a simple gene heterosis. There are, however, very real differences between these two states. In essence we are dealing here with the question of the distinction between gene and chromosome mutation. It is true that this distinction is not absolute, but a comparison of these two kinds of mutation shows that it is not merely one of convenience. There are quite fundamental differences between them, differences we can conveniently summarize under four headings:

1) The magnitude of the change produced at the chromosome level bears no relation to the magnitude of its effect on the external phenotype, or

exophenotype. Thus, in general, chromosome mutations, especially structural ones, cannot be detected in the exophenotype. There is, however, a second component to the phenotype, a component which includes, among other things, the behavior of the chromosomes themselves. And all chromosome mutations affect this aspect of the endophenotype, for they all interfere to some extent with the course, and hence the consequences, of meiosis. Where meiosis is abnormal, recombination and segregation are also likely to be abnormal.

Gene mutations as such, on the other hand, do not affect the course of meiosis, which is the same in genic homozygotes and genic heterozygotes. Chromosome mutations thus commonly modify meiosis in a way that gene mutations rarely do.

2) Most gene mutations are roughly recessive at their inception. Therefore, except in organisms whose principal vegetative phase is haploid and mono-karyotic, they can persist, masked in the heterozygous state, even when their effects are harmful or indeed lethal. This means that they can be injected into new genotypes and dispersed *before* they are tested on phenotypic grounds.

Chromosome mutations, on the other hand, have their most pronounced endophenotypic effects in the condition in which they originate. A decision regarding the future of a chromosome mutation must therefore be made at the meiosis, or even at the mitosis, immediately following its origin. And the mutant must pass these mechanical tests before any of its other properties can be considered.

3) In general, as we have seen, chromosome mutations cannot be detected in the exophenotype. Even where they can, as in the case of position effects and polyploidy, the changes they determine are not usually different in kind from those that can be produced—and without the accompanying decrease in fertility—by gene mutations. This means that if selection takes the line of greatest fecundity it should, wherever possible, favor gene mutation as a basis for evolutionary change. Or, reversing the argument, we can conclude that where selection has favored chromosome mutation it has done so either because the innovation could not have been effected in any other way or else because it represents the only means of conserving an existing genetic regime in the face of changing circumstances.

4) Chromosome mutations may be maintained in populations by virtue of inherent mechanisms of accumulation at mitosis or at meiosis which establish systems of meiotic drive (21). Such systems need not be immediately useful, as Nur (22) has shown from his studies on the supernumerary chromosomes of the mealy bug. These chromosomes lower the "fitness" of the individuals possessing them under a variety of experimental regimes. Nevertheless, accumulation by mitotic nondisjunction appears to maintain them within natural populations. However, if these B chromosomes have an effect on variance, as Moss (23) has found in rye, they may confer longer-term advantages on the population.

These four principles have rarely been adequately recognized, let alone practiced. Thus many who have studied chromosome mutations have looked

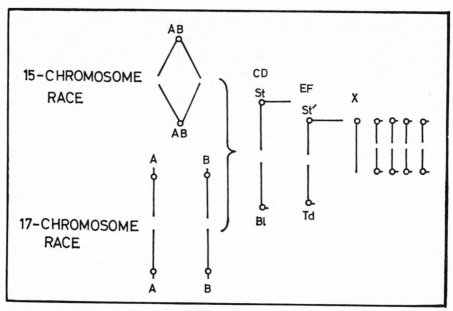

FIGURE 3. Karyotypic variation in the eumastacid grasshopper *Moraba scurra*. This species exists in two geographically distinct races both of which carry identical polymorphisms with respect to the CD and EF chromosomes. White (37) believes these two races to be related by a process of dissociation rather than by centric fusion or centric fission (misdivision).

exclusively for exophenotypic effects and have ignored the endophenotype. Some few have even demonstrated an apparent exophenotypic influence and have then argued for a positive role for this influence in the evolution of the polymorphism in question.

THE MORABA AFFAIR

The small, wingless, Australian eumastacid grasshopper, *Moraba scurra*, exists as two geographically defined chromosome races with either 15 or 17 chromosomes in the male. This difference in number depends on the presence in the 15-chromosome race of a metacentric AB pair, both members of which are replaced in the 17-chromosome race by two acrocentrics A and B (Fig. 3). *Moraba scurra* is a species of the southern tableland of New South Wales and of Northern Victoria, and the two races differ in distribution. The one $(2n\ \delta\ = 15)$ is eastern, whereas the other $(2n\ \delta\ = 17)$ is western and much more restricted (24).

In both races the CD and EF chromosomes may exist in a number of forms, the commonest of which are shown in Figure 3. And different populations may be polymorphic for different combinations of them.

White and Andrew (25) and White, Lewontin, and Andrew (26) find that at Wombat and Walendbeen (17-chromosome-race populations) and at Murrumbateman, Royalle, and Tarago swamp (15-chromosome-race populations) the Blundell (Bl) and Tidbinbilla (Td) chromosomes are size-decreasing while the corresponding standard (St and St') elements increase the size of the individual (Table 2). White and his colleagues are of the opinion that this effect has a very definite role in the "genetic ecology" of the species, the origin and spread of the Bl and Td sequences having been coincident with the invasion of previously unexploited ecological niches. This conclusion is maintained although the two sequences show no apparent weight-reducing effect at Michelago.

Even accepting the correlation between chromosome constitution and size as a fairly general one, we may still legitimately question whether this correlation has anything to do with the maintenance of the sequences in the natural populations in question. Correlations are notoriously dangerous things

TABLE 2

The mean net weight (W) in milligrams of (N) adult male individuals with various combinations of CD and EF chromosomes from five populations of *Moraba scurra*. Data from (25) and (26).

		CD-CHROMOSOME						
		St/St	St/BL	BL/BL	St/St	St/BL	BL/BL	
		Wombat 1958–59			Wallendbeen 1959			
	St'/St'	23	246	729	27	138	220	N
		34.28	33.18	32.75	37.06	35.37	34.51	W
Td/Td	St'/Td	3	65	271	6	39	57	N
		35.00	32.53	31.75	34.58	35.74	33.56	W
	Td/Td	0	4	12	1	2	4	N
			32.63	29.25	38.00	39.25	35.25	W
		Murrumbateman 1959			Murrumbateman 1961			
	St'/St'	107	359	262	39	194	132	N
		41.34	40.52	39.90	40.17	38.99	39.72	W
Td/Td	St'/Td	34	89	84	10	47	54	N
		39.91	39.03	37.56	40.60	39.07	37.91	W
	Td/Td	0	3	5	0	1	3	N
			37.67	37.90		39.50	35.00	W
		Royalla 1958			Tarago swamp 1960			
	St'/St'	22	95	75				N
		36.57	35.90	35.91	40.25	35.41	34.91	W
Td/Td	St'/Td	8	57	64	0			N
		35.69	35.65	35.34		35.00	35.08	W
	Td/Td	0	6	6	0			N
			37.00	36.25		34.60	33.85	W

EF—CHROMOSOME

with which to work. Consider, for instance, the situation in the plant *Oeno-thera*, where large sections of the genus are permanent interchange heterozy-gotes. These also contain a balanced system of recessive lethal mutations. But it is not the recessive lethals which determine the structural heterozygosity since, clearly, a balanced lethal system could not evolve in a structurally monomorphic situation. Rather, the development of a system of permanent structural hybridity has created a situation which allows for the accumulation of recessive lethals within the limits of the genetically differential segments that have been generated in the process (27).

In *Oenothera* we have an organism which uses the processes and the struc-tures designed for sexual reproduction in order to effect an essentially clonal reproduction. For meiosis and gamete development have been so modified that only two gametic types are produced, and these are identical with the gametes from which the parent itself arose. This is because, under the cir-cumstances, truly sexual reproduction is prohibited by the unsuitable nature of its products, and we have here one of the classical examples of the conser-vation of heterozygosity (28).

THE PERIPLANETA AFFAIR

During our own work we have encountered a similar though less extreme situation in the American cockroach, *Periplaneta americana*. Here we have an approach to the system of permanent hybridity seen in *Oenothera*, for all pop-ulations of this orthopteran species contain a proportion of interchange hetero-zygotes (29, 30). That the situation is simpler here than in *Oenothera* can be explained by the fact that dioecious animals, unlike self-compatible monoecious plants, cannot inbreed so completely.

White and Andrew (25) have complained that no serious attempt has been made in this—or, indeed, other instances—to "go beyond the descriptive stage and analyze the adaptive role played by the rearrangement, although on gen-eral principles and by analogy with what is known in *Drosophila* we may suspect that heterosis (selective superiority of heterozygotes) or frequency-dependent selective values are involved."

That the structural heterozygotes are selectively superior in many cases of chromosomal polymorphism is evident. It is a question of where their superior-ity lies. By analogy with the situation in *Campanula* (31), we have argued that the interchange system of *Periplaneta* helps to conserve genic heterozygosity in the face of inbreeding. For interchanges decrease the frequency of produc-tion of the nonparental types which are expected to be subject to negative selection. In support of this thesis we have shown that the extent of structural heterozygosity is highest under conditions where inbreeding is also expected to be most marked (29, 30).

In this case, then, we are arguing that the principal role of the structural polymorphism is related to its effects on the distribution of genic hybridity between individuals in the population. Indeed, it could be argued that much of

TABLE 3

Karyotype polymorphism in bark weevils of the genus *Pissoides*. Note a, b, and c represent acrocentric and A, B, and C equivalent—(aa), (bb), and (cc)—metacentric elements, respectively. Data from (32) and (33).

Species	2x	Chromosome constitution (2x = 22+)		
strobi engelmanni sitchensis	34	2(aa)	2(bb)	2(cc)
affinis fasciatus radiatae dubius notatus	30	AA	BB	2(cc)
yosemite	28	AA	BB	CC
approximatus matus canadensis	30–34	2(aa) A(aa) AA	2(bb) B(bb) BB	2(cc)
terminalis	28–32	2(aa) A(aa) AA	B(bb) BB	C(cc), ♂ only CC, ♀ only

the chromosome variation which occurs in insect populations is related to the recombination process. This applies not only to structural mutations but to numerical ones too. And it applies also to cases which, though structural in character, are numerical in outcome.

THE PISSOIDES AND CHILOCORUS AFFAIRS

A Robertsonian variation in chromosome number exists in the coleopteran genus *Pissoides* (32, 33). Here five species have a diploid complement of 30, three have 34, and one has 28 chromosomes (Table 3). In the 34-chromosome species all the members of the complement are acrocentric. Species with lower numbers have varying and proportionate numbers of metacentric elements. Thus two metacentric pairs (AA and BB) replace four acrocentrics [2(aa) and 2(bb)] in the 30-chromosome species, whereas the 28-chromosome forms have three metacentric pairs (AA, BB, and CC). In addition, three species, *P. approximatus, P. canadensis, and P. terminalis,* are chromosomally polymorphic, exhibiting a variety of karyotypes bridging the gap between the 28- and the 34-numbered species. And in different populations the frequencies of A and B metacentrics is subject to considerable variation.

303

In *P. terminalis* the polymorphism with regard to the C chromosome is complicated by its association with an incompatability system which is unique among animals (*34*). The males of this species are hybrid for the centric fusion [C(cc)] and for the sex-chromosomes (XY), so that four types of sperm are produced in equal numbers. The females, on the other hand, are homozygous for the fusion (CC) and for the X chromosomes (XX), so that all the eggs are of one kind. The system can perpetuate only if fertilization is confined to gametes which either (i) differ with regard to both the "autosomal" fusion and the sex chromosomes or (ii) are similar in both these respects (Table 4). The *Drosophila* polymorphisms which we discussed earlier were investigated from salivary gland preparations, which means, of course, that males and females could be equally investigated. However, for technical reasons, most studies on insect polymorphism have been confined to the analysis of meiosis in males. But the *Pissoides* affair shows that one polymorphism can react with another, so that males and females may differ with regard to "autosomal" polymorphism.

Centric fusion is also found in the beetle *Chilocorus stigma* (*35*), where there is a sequential increase in the frequency of fusion chromosomes in populations running east to west on the North American continent (Table 5). Three distinct fusions are involved in this sequential polymorphism. One, the Kentville, is found in Nova Scotia and Maine. A second, morphologically distinct fusion occurs at Vineland, Ontario, while at Morden, Manitoba, a third fusion, again morphologically distinct, is found together with the more easterly pair. From their point of initial occurrence the frequencies of all three fusions increase steadily as populations progress north and west, so that this species is, in reality, a complex of cytologically differentiated forms.

In cases such as *Pissoides* and *Chilocorus*, chromosomal polymorphism exerts its control over recombination by virtue of the fact that it reduces the number of linkage groups and hence the extent of interchromosomal recombination at meiosis. Wahrman (*36*) has encountered a similar polymorphism for centric fusion in the mantid *Ameles heldreichi* in Jerusalem. Indeed here, as in *Drosophila*, there is a seasonal shift in the frequency of the structural types. That this is a genuine centric fusion and not a fission or dissociation process, as White (*37*) has suggested, is clear from Wahrman's observation (*36*) of a fusion *in statu nascendi*. The fusion had evidently arisen in the individual in which it was observed for this male was mosaic and the small chromosome (Fig. 1) was still present at meiosis.

Centric fusion, then, is actually an unequal interchange which is followed by the loss of the small product. It has an effect on recombination comparable to that of the more usual type of interchange hybridity. The latter, however, can be successful only when approximately isobrachial chromosomes are involved, whereas acrocentric or telocentric chromosomes are more amenable to fusion. What is more, fusion is equally effective in both the homozygous and the heterozygous condition because, although the centromeres are not joined in the latter, they are linked by the first-anaphase movement to a common pole which balance demands.

TABLE 4

The incompatability system of *Pissoides terminalis*. Data from (34).

Egg	Sperm			
	X-type		Y-type	
	C	(cc)	C	(cc)
X, C	♀ ♀ XX, CC	Inviable combinations	♂ ♂ XY, C(cc)	

THE TRUXALINE AFFAIRS

In the grasshopper *Myrmeleotettix maculatus*, British populations are polymorphic with respect to the presence of supernumerary or B chromosomes. These are completely absent from populations in Scotland and in northern England, but most of the southern populations contain a percentage of individuals with various combinations of from one to three supernumerary elements of two distinct morphological types. Where these extra chromosomes are present in a population they tend to raise the chiasma frequency of individuals which possess them above that found in normal representatives of that population (38). The same is true of supernumerary chromosome segments which are present in some British populations of a second member of the subfamily Truxalinae, *Chorthippus parallelus* (39).

In both these cases the presence of supernumerary, heterochromatic material leads to an increase in the range of recombinant types within a popula-

TABLE 5

Sequential chromosome polymorphism in populations of the North American ladybird beetle, *Chilocorus stigma*. Data of Smith 1959 (31).

Region	Locality	Autosomal fusions per population (%)			
		1. Kentville	2. Vineland	3. Morden	Fusions
Florida	Moss Bluff and Minneola	Monomorphic populations—no fusions present $2x = 25 ♂ (X_1X_2Y); 26 ♀ (X_1X_1X_2X_2)$			
Atlantic seaboard	Kentville, Nova Scotia	8	0	0	Polymorphic populations $2x = 25-19 ♂$ $26-20 ♀$
Southern Ontario	Vineland, near Niagara Falls	14	6	0	
Central Ontario	Agawa River	27	36	0	
Manitoba	Morden	68	23	20	
Saskatchewan	Conquest	100 (fixation)	29	44	

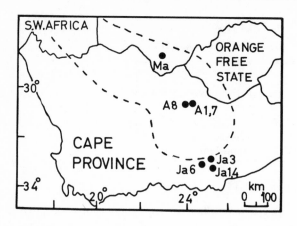

FIGURE 4. The location of Nolte's (*41*) collecting stations for populations of *Locustana pardulina* taken from the outbreak region in the Karoo plateau (dotted line).

TABLE 6

Mean chiasma frequencies among males in strains of the brown locust, *Locustana pardalina*, at various levels of gregarization in populations taken from the Karoo plateau. The population density is given as low when 3 to 40 individuals were counted in 400-meter transects. High-density populations have several hundred to 1000 individuals in equivalent transects. P indicates adults collected in the field and X indicates generations reared in cages under conditions of crowding from either egg pods or from offspring of field adults. Twenty diplotene cells were scored per male individual for each of 10+ males per strain. The male complement ($2x \, \delta = 23 = 22+X$) consists of three long (L), five medium (M), and three short (S) autosomal pairs. The three S bivalents are not included in the scores since each invariably forms only a single chiasma. A difference in chiasma frequency of 0.3 to 0.4 indicates a probability of .001. Data from (*41*), and see Figure 4.

Strain and symbol		Field collection		Generation scored	Chiasma frequency	
		Date	Population density		$3L_{II}$	$5M_{II}$
Matsup	Ma1	Nov. 1960	low	X_1 Mar. 1961	5.68	5.21
	Ma2	Feb. 1962	medium	P Feb. 1962	6.63	5.56
	Ma3	Dec. 1963	swarm	P Dec. 1963	7.44	6.97
				X_1 Apr. 1964	7.36	6.60
De Aar	A1	Nov. 1960	low	X_1 Mar. 1961	5.40	5.07
	A7	Mar. 1963	swarm	X_1 Aug. 1963	6.99	6.37
				X_2 Feb. 1964	7.37	6.61
	A8	Aug. 1963	swarm	X_1 Sep. 1963	7.11	6.43
				X_2 Mar. 1964	7.33	6.68
Jansenville	Ja1	Oct. 1961	congregating	P Oct. 1961	6.47	5.82
	Ja3	Nov. 1961	high	P Oct. 1961	6.34	5.37
	Ja4	Jan. 1962	low	P Jan. 1962	5.91	5.14
	Ja6	Aug. 1963	low swarm	X_1 Oct. 1963	6.01	5.46
				X_2 Mar. 1964	7.10	6.44

tion. Indeed, variation in chiasma frequency itself probably represents one of the most common types of chromosome variability which exists in geographically distinct insect populations. And, since chiasma variation offers one of the most direct means of modifying the extent of recombination in an organism, one presumes that these variations are adaptational. Thus British populations of the grasshoppers *Chorthippus brunneus*, *Chorthippus parallelus*, *Myrmeleotettix maculatus*, and *Omocestus viridulus* all show significant differences in chiasma frequency, differences which are maintained from year to year, at least on a short-term basis (*40*).

THE LOCUSTANA AFFAIR

A few of the many species of the Acrididae possess a capacity for phase transformation which leads to the development of migratory swarms from solitary individuals. This transformation is reversible, so that a particular population of locusts may exist in the solitaria phase or the gregaria phase or in an intermediary transiens phase. The brown locust, *Locusta pardalina*, of South Africa is currently in a cycle of intensive gregarization after a period of some 7 years of predominantly solitary life. Gregarization began during the summer of 1962–1963 in a number of areas of the Karoo plateau, a region of some 260,000 square kilometers. Nolte (*41*) has compared the chiasma frequencies of different phases in populations from this region. He studied field samples of solitaria forms, congregating populations, and swarms with a history of one, two, or three generations of gregarization (Fig. 4 and Table 6). There has been no great mixing of populations during the present swarming cycle, at least up to the end of 1963, and most of the collecting stations were at least 80 kilometers apart. Nolte found that in every case gregarization in the field led to an increased chiasma frequency and that this increase involved both long- and medium-type chromosomes. This increased frequency is carried over into laboratory offspring of field congregations and swarms. Moreover the phase status of X_1 individuals in cages does not seem to affect the increase.

There are, as Nolte in part points out, a number of internal discrepancies in the data which require more intensive study. However, if we accept his results at face value they indicate that in *Locustana* there is a progressive increase in chiasma frequency during the periods of gregarization which precede the outbreak of migrating swarms. Notice that this variation differs in three respects from that obtaining in most of the cases described earlier. First, it reflects genotypic and not structural control. Second, it is correlated with marked exophenotypic changes both in appearance and behavior. Third, although it is not directly related to existing spatial variation, it is followed by a process of migration.

THE ISOLATION AFFAIR

It is relatively simple to show that the members of an outbreeding group are not genetically identical. With the exception of the chromosomes concerned with sex determination, the typical members of a mating group are far less often distinguishable chromosomally. Most of the heritable variation within a breeding group is thus unquestionably due to gene rather than to chromosome variation. When members of different species are compared, however, one often finds that the genetic differences between them are large enough to be detected by looking at the chromosomes. This is especially obvious when the chromosomes of their hybrids can be examined at the stages when maternally and paternally derived chromosomes pair. That is at meiosis in most organisms or in the polytene tissues of dipteran flies.

Now close adaptation to a given environment is possible only if the type favored in that environment breeds true to its own kind. In practice, the plant and animal breeder keeps his breeds apart, and it is this isolation that preserves their integrity. Nature is faced with the same problem of preventing gene flow between different groups, for evolutionary divergence is possible only when this flow is prohibited or at least curtailed. Chromosome heterozygotes frequently have one thing in common—an abnormal meiosis. Where meiosis is abnormal, semisterility can follow, and this semisterility is a potential barrier to gene flow. Indeed, in all those cases which show stable chromosomal polymorphism, the structural heterozygotes must be able to pass through meiosis without producing an appreciable number of unbalanced gametes.

Chromosome changes of the kind that distinguish species must arise within species from chromosomally atypical individuals which are maintained in the heterozygous state by the pressure of mutation. And these floating variants, in turn, must arise from atypical cells in an otherwise normal individual. Grasshoppers illustrate this sequence nicely. Interchanges, for example, have been found in some cells within a testis, in some individuals in a population, and in hybrids between some geographically distinct groups (42). Indeed, any adequate survey of chromosome variation both within and between populations of insects leaves no doubt that there has been no shortage of either structural or numerical variation for selection to act on (43, 44). It is true that speciation involves discontinuity between populations, but the development of discontinuity between populations depends, in the first instance, on that discontinuity arising within an individual.

It has long been argued, largely on mathematical grounds, that owing to the sterility of heterozygotes, there must be very strong selection against the establishment of structural changes in the homozygous state. Yet there are numerous cases which show quite clearly that such changes have occurred (42). Evidently here, as indeed elsewhere too, mathematical probability fails to accord with biological reality. Part of the problem in resolving this paradox is in deciding the precise role of the structural change relative to the production of the structural homozygote. As we have seen, structural changes are a common device for conserving the gene combinations of heterozygotes by protecting them from the ravages of recombination. They also offer one means of producing hybrid sterility. Many have assumed that it is the latter role which they perform in speciation. However, structural changes which behave regularly at their inception—and hence might be expected to reach fixation as structural homozygotes—are not likely to serve as effective isolating mechanisms. For their efficiency as isolating agents depends upon the meiotic inefficiency of their heterozygotes. It may be, therefore, that their importance in maintaining genic dissimilarity on crossing structurally differentiated chromosome homozygotes depends more upon the efficiency with which they maintain supergene blocks than on their capacity for producing hybrid sterility (42).

The difficulty of resolving whether a polymorphism can or cannot be supplanted by a monomorphism stems also from the problem of recognizing the correct role of structural change in natural populations. Despite earlier statements to the contrary, White, one of the foremost students in this field, has recently concluded that "not all the chromosomal rearrangements that establish themselves in evolution pass through a stage in which they are in a state of balanced polymorphism based on heterosis" (43). Instead, he believes that those which have not passed through such a polymorphic state must have arisen by chance drift in small local colonies probably situated on or close to the geographic periphery of the species range.

We have discussed the problem in detail elsewhere (42) and will say only this. The requirements for a successful polymorphic existence are usually quite distinct from those favoring the replacement of one monomorphic state by another. In time circumstances will, of course, change. But it does not follow that stable polymorphisms are necessarily sources of new, specific monomorphisms. Indeed, it is very clear that, in many cases, stable polymorphism is not, and cannot be, speciation in transit. And the kind of variation observed as a stable polymorphism within a species frequently differs strikingly from that seen between species related to it (contra 45). Of course, species may arise from a previously polymorphic group, and they may differ from each other in the same way as the original morphic types. But "new differences would be superimposed on the polymorphism and would not spring essentially from it" (46).

THE END OF THE AFFAIR

Most of the new genes or chromosomes which arise by mutation are eliminated (stabilizing selection). They have, therefore, little effect on the species as a whole, and they pass undetected by the observer. Those that are favored may serve as focal points in the splitting of the mating group in which they arise (speciation), or they may persist within that group. In the latter event they can increase the variation potential of the breeding unit. At some time or place the new element may replace the old (directional selection), or disruptive selection within the breeding unit may produce two (or more) mutually dependent forms and so create a condition common to all stable polymorphisms. But, paradoxically, while retention of the new element can increase variation potential, it may decrease the rate at which the existing potential is converted into free variation. This paradox goes a long way toward resolving the issue of whether a species is more variable at the margin or at the center of distribution.

An awareness of the distinction symbolized by the terms exo- and endo-phenotype adds a further dimension to the standard Darwinian argument, though even Darwin was aware of the difference. The endophenotype, by definition, does not affect the competitive efficiency or, therefore, the adaptedness of the individual; it affects the number and nature of the offspring and is, in consequence, the subject of retrospective selection. As an aspect of endo-phenotype what goes on at meiosis (or fertilization; compare *Pissoides*) has no meaning for the individual in which it occurs. This must hold for the various chromosome conditions which affect this division. And it is in this light that chromosome polymorphism must be viewed.

The essence of the argument is, again, seen most clearly in the ring-forming species of *Oenothera,* where the chromosome polymorphism within the breeding unit does not extend effectively into the zygotic phase. The ring-formers are clearly at an advantage. And, because their hybridity is at two levels, so also is their advantage. First, they are developmentally better: they alone survive (adaptedness). This must depend on the relational balance of the genotype. In this connection hybridity at the level of the karyotype does not matter as such: adaptation is a job for genes. But the ring-formers owe their genic hybridity to the fact that they are the structurally hybrid offspring of structurally hybrid parents and the parental genotype is transmitted more faithfully than it would be in the absence of a hybrid karyotype. Thus, genotypes make for good (or bad) individuals, karyotypes for good (or bad) parents. In the inbreeding, ring-forming species of *Oenothera,* genic heterozygosity and structural hybridity are absolutely correlated. Consequently the adapted individuals are also the best parents from the short-term point of view. *Drosophila tropicalis* approaches *Oenothera,* for there up to 90 percent of the adult population are hybrid (47).

Where, as in all the cases described earlier, structural homozygotes of various kinds survive and breed, the above correlation cannot be as close, because both homozygotes and heterozygotes, genic and chromosomal, can be derived from parental homozygotes or heterozygotes or both. But, clearly, selection will favor the restriction of recombination only if it favors the genotypes where restriction is practiced. Thus, in short-term evolution, under conditions of stabilizing selection the adapted (present fitness) genotype and the restricting karyotype will tend to go together. The nonrestricting karyotype, on the other hand, will go with the adaptational (future flexibility) genotype. And in these terms the "opposing" views on the *Drosophila* affair, for example, are reconcilable. We see, therefore, that while the genotype matters to the individual, the karyotype does not—so long as it is mitotically competent. But the karyotype matters to the unborn and thus to the population.

In those cases where it has proved possible to analyze the situation in some detail, there are good grounds for arguing that the chromosome variability shown within and between insect population is concerned with the regulation of recombination. Clearly, recombination has a meaning only in hybrids. It is not easy, therefore, to distinguish the effects of heterozygosity from those of recombination. And, whereas recombination can be concerned only with adaptability, heterozygosity must be concerned in both adaptation and adaptability. We can be warned, however, that it is not the sequence of genes which linkage protects that matters but the relations between these genes and those on the partner chromosome. Where, as for example with inversions, alternative sequences are internally balanced but in different ways, a restriction of recombination is important. But, under these same circumstances, structural homozygotes are similar with regard to nonallelic interaction of a polygenic kind. Perhaps this situation is approached in those *Drosophila* polymorphisms which do not show spatial or temporal variation.

Where, on the other hand, alternative sequences are balanced only in relation to each other, structural homozygotes will show less balance. They may, however, increase under directional or disruptive selection. Perhaps this situation is approached in those cases where the chromosome polymorphism does change either cyclically or directionally with time and place.

CONCLUSION

Mayr has recently claimed (45) that "no substantial work dealing with the better known groups of animals fails to include information on the geographical variation of the species treated." Unfortunately, most such works regularly fail to include information on chromosome variation. It is our hope that this review will serve to show that, as far as the study of geographical distribution in insects is concerned, it is clearly time to examine more fully not the exophenotype but the endophenotype, not the obvious and external but the microscopic and internal, not the genic but the chromosomal. For as Darlington (48) has so aptly put it, "While marker genes, the chief legacy of classical genetics, with their pedigrees and their mutation rates, are of great importance for the study of evolution, they are of little importance in carrying it out."

REFERENCES

1. Th. Dobzhansky and A. H. Sturtevant, *Genetics* **23**, 28 (1938).
2. A. B. da Cunha, H. Burla, Th. Dobzhansky, *Evolution* **4**, 212 (1950); J. I. Townsend, *ibid.* **6**, 428 (1952).
3. A. B. da Cunha and Th. Dobzhansky, *ibid.* **8**, 119 (1954).
4. H. L. Carson, *J. Comp. Cellular Physiol.* **45**, Suppl. 2, 221 (1955); *Cold Spring Harbor Symp. Quant. Biol.* **20**, 276 (1955).
5. E. Goldschmidt, *J. Genet.* **54**, 474 (1956); E. Stumm-Zollinger and E. Goldschmidt, *Evolution* **13**, 89 (1959).
6. Th. Dobzhansky, *Evolution* **11**, 280 (1957).

7. A. B. da Cunha, *Ann. Rev. Entomol.* **5**, 85 (1960).
8. Th. Dobzhansky, *Carnegie Inst. Wash. Pub.* **554**, 47 (1944).
9. D. Brncic, *Chromosoma* **8**, 699 (1957); *Genetics* **42**, 798 (1957).
10. E. Kunze-Mühl, E. Muller, D. Sperlich, *Z. Induktive Abstammungs-Verebungslehre* **89**, 638 (1958).
11. Th. Dobzhansky, *Genetics* **33**, 158 (1948); *Evolution* **10**, 82 (1956).
12. B. Battaglia and L. C. Birch, *Nature* **178**, 1005 (1956).
13. Th. Dobzhansky, W. W. Anderson, O. Pavlovsky, B. Spassky, C. J. Willis, *Evolution* **18**, 164 (1964).
14. Th. Dobzhansky, in *Insect Polymorphism*, J. S. Kennedy, Ed. (Royal Entomological Society, London, 1961), p. 30.
15. E. L. Breeze and K. Mather, *Heredity* **11**, 373 (1957); J. M. Thoday, *Nature* **191**, 368 (1961).
16. C. Epling, D. F. Mitchell, R. H. T. Mattoni, *Evolution* **7**, 342 (1953); *Proc. Nat. Acad. Sci. U.S.* **41**, 915 (1955); *Evolution* **11**, 225 (1957).
17. T. Komai and T. Takaku, *Cytologia* **12**, 357 (1949); J. Schultz and H. Redfield, *Cold Spring Harbor Symp. Quant. Biol.* **16**, 175 (1951); D. Suzuki, *Genetics* **48**, 1605 (1963).
18. A. B. da Cunha, Th. Dobzhansky, O. Pavlovsky, B. Spassky, *Evolution* **13**, 389 (1959).
19. H. L. Carson, *Cold Spring Harbor Symp. Quant. Biol.* **23**, 291 (1958).
20. D. F. Mitchell, *ibid.*, p. 279.
21. L. Sandler and E. Novitski, *Amer. Naturalist* **91**, 105 (1957).
22. U. Nur, *Genetics* **47**, 1679 (1962), and unpublished communication.
23. P. Moss, D. Phil. thesis, University of Oxford (1965).
24. M. J. D. White, *Evolution* **10**, 298 (1956); ——— and L. J. Chinnick, *Australian J. Zool.* **5**, 338 (1957).
25. M. J. D. White and L. E. Andrew, in *The Evolution of Living Organisms* (Symposium, Royal Society of Victoria, 1959), p. 94; *Evolution* **14**, 284 (1960).
26. M. J. D. White, R. C. Lewontin, L. E. Andrew, *Evolution* **17**, 147 (1963).
27. B. John and K. R. Lewis, *Genetics* **44**, 251 (1959).
28. K. R. Lewis and B. John, *Chromosome Marker* (Churchill, London, 1963).
29. B. John and K. R. Lewis, *Heredity* **12**, 185 (1958).
30. K. R. Lewis and B. John, *ibid.* **11**, 11 (1957); B. John and H. B. Quraishi, *ibid.* **19**, 147 (1964).
31. C. D. Darlington and L. F. LaCour, *ibid.* **4**, 217 (1950).
32. G. K. Manna and S. G. Smith, *Nucleus* **2**, 179 (1959).
33. S. G. Smith, *ibid.* **5**, 65 (1962).
34. ——— and Y. Takenouchi, *Science* **138**, 36 (1962).
35. S. G. Smith, *Nature* **193**, 1210 (1962); *Can. Entomol.* **94**, 941 (1962).
36. J. Wahrman, *Proc. Intern. Congr. Genet. 9th Bellagio, Italy, 1953, Caryologia* (1954), p. 683, and unpublished communication.
37. M. J. D. White, *Australian J. Zool.* **5**, 258 (1957).
38. B. John and G. M. Hewitt, *Chromosoma* **16**, 548 (1965); **17**, 121 (1965).
39. ———, *ibid.*, in press.
40. G. M. Hewitt, *ibid.* **15**, 212 (1964); **16**, 579 (1965).
41. D. J. Nolte, *ibid.* **15**, 367 (1964).
42. K. R. Lewis and B. John, *ibid.* **14**, 618 (1963); B. John and G. M. Hewitt, *ibid.*, p. 638; B. John and K. R. Lewis, *ibid.* **16**, 308 (1965).
43. M. J. D. White, *Proc. Intern. Congr. Genet., 11th* **2**, 391 (1964).
44. G. M. Hewitt and B. John, *Heredity* **20**, 123 (1965).
45. E. Mayr, *Animal Species and Evolution* (Harvard Univ. Press, Cambridge, Mass., 1963).

46. K. Mather, *Evolution* **9**, 52 (1955).
47. Th. Dobzhansky and O. Pavlovsky, *Proc. Nat. Acad. Sci. U.S.* **41**, 289 (1955).
48. C. D. Darlington, *Proc. Roy. Soc. London Ser. B* **145**, 350 (1956).
49. See text and, for a summary, M. J. D. White, *Animal Cytology and Evolution* (Cambridge Univ. Press, Cambridge, 1954).
50. A. B. Acton, *J. Genet.* **55**, 61 (1957); *Proc. Roy. Soc. London Ser. B* **151**, 277 (1959).
51. V. R. Basrur, *Chromosoma* **8**, 597 (1957).
52. G. Frizzi and J. B. Kitzmiller, *Entomol. News* **70**, 33 (1959); J. B. Kitzmiller and W. L. French, *Amer. Zool.* **1**, 366 (1961).
53. V. R. Basrur and K. H. Rothfels, *Can. J. Zool.* **37**, 571 (1959).
54. R. W. Dunbar, *ibid.*, p. 495.
55. R. Landau, *ibid.* **40**, 92 (1962).
56. K. H. Rothfels and T. W. Fairlie, *ibid.* **35**, 221 (1957).
57. D. D. Miller, *Genetics* **24**, 699 (1939).
58. H. L. Carson, *Advan. Genet.* **9**, 1 (1958).
59. W. L. Evans, *Amer. Naturalist* **88**, 21 (1954).
60. M. J. D. White, *Australian J. Zool.* **5**, 285 (1957).
61. ———, H. L. Carson, J. Cheney, *Evolution* **18**, 417 (1964).
62. M. J. D. White, J. Cheney, K. H. L. Key, *Australian J. Zool.* **11**, 1 (1963).
63. F. Ohmachi and N. Ueshima, *Mie Diagaku Nogakubu Gakujutsu Hokoku* **14**, 43 (1957).
64. M. J. D. White, *Evolution* **5**, 376 (1951).
65. J. T. Patterson and W. S. Stone, *Evolution in the Genus* Drosophila (Macmillan, New York, 1952).
66. N. Ueshima, *J. Nagoya Jogakain Coll.* No. 4, 78 (1957).
67. U. Nur, *Chromosoma* **12**, 272 (1961).
68. S. G. Smith, *J. Heredity* **47**, 157 (1956).
69. C. D. Darlington, *J. Genet.* **34**, 101 (1939).
70. H. Kayano, M. Sannomiya, K. Nakamura, *Nippon Idengaku Zasshi* **35**, 95 (1960).
71. U. Nur, *Chromosoma* **14**, 407 (1963).
72. M. J. White, *Genetics* **36**, 31 (1951).
73. W. P. Morgan, *J. Morphol.* **46**, 241 (1928).
74. B. E. Wolf, *Verhandl. Deut. Zool. Ges.* **1961**, 110 (1961).·
75. O. Halkka, *Ann. Acad. Sci. Fennical Ser. AIV* **43**, 1 (1959).
76. J. Seiler, *Chromosoma* **10**, 73 (1959).
77. Y. Takenouchi, *Can. J. Genet. Cytol.* **3**, 237 (1961).
78. M. Tosi, *Caryologia* **12**, 189 (1959).

EVOLUTION OF THE HORNED DINOSAURS

Edwin H. Colbert

The American Museum of Natural History, New York 24, N. Y.

Received February 13, 1948

INTRODUCTION

The horned dinosaurs or ceratopsians are of particular interest to the student of evolution for various reasons. In the first place these dinosaurs are restricted geologically. They were the last of the dinosaurs, appearing at a late stage in the Mesozoic Era and going through the entire range of their phylogenetic history in a relatively short space of geologic time. It is therefore obvious that evolution in the horned dinosaurs was comparatively rapid. Secondly, these dinosaurs are restricted geographically. Except for the ancestral forms which occur in Mongolia, the horned dinosaurs are, practically speaking, limited to the continent of North America. Therefore at the present time the horned dinosaurs may be considered as a group of north Asiatic origin and of North American development. In the third place, the horned dinosaurs show a consistent and rather limited pattern of morphological evolution, as might be expected in a group of such restricted geologic limits and geographic distribution. In the light of these facts, how is the evolution of the horned dinosaurs to be interpreted? What conclusions can be drawn from the evidence of the fossils and of their occurrence?

Before becoming involved in a detailed consideration and discussion of the problem before us it may be useful to review briefly at this place the classification of the ceratopsians, and in addition our knowledge of their geographic distribution and geologic occurrences.

Classification

The Ceratopsia constitute a suborder of the order Ornithischia. Other sub-orders of this order of dinosaurs are the Ornithopoda, or duckbilled dinosaurs, the Stegosauria, or plated dinosaurs, and the Ankylosauria, or armored dinosaurs. All of the dinosaurs contained within the four suborders of the order Ornithischia are herbivorous types, and rather specialized in their morphology.

The suborder Ceratopsia can be divided into two families, the Protoceratopsidae, or the primitive horned dinosaurs, and the Ceratopsidae, the large, specialized horned dinosaurs. The genera contained within the two families of ceratopsian dinosaurs are as follows.

Protoceratopsidae
  Protoceratops, Leptoceratops
Ceratopsidae
  *Anchiceratops,   Arrhinoceratops,
  Brachyceratops,   Chasmosaurus,
  Ceratops, Eoceratops, Monoclonius, ?Notoceratops, Pentaceratops, Styracosaurus, Torosaurus,
  Triceratops*

Of the above-listed genera, *Brachyceratops* possibly is synonymous with *Monoclonius*, the type species being based upon an immature individual that may be a growth stage of this last-named genus. (Whether or not *Brachyceratops* is a distinct genus, the fact that it is now known only from immature material makes it rather unsuitable for the present study, which is concerned with a comparison of adult animals.) *Ceratops, Eoceratops* and *Notoceratops* are known from such insufficient materials as perforce to be excluded from a discussion of ceratopsian evolution. Therefore, for these reasons the genera *Brachyceratops, Ceratops, Eoceratops* and *Notoceratops* will not be in-

Reprinted by permission of the author and the Society for the Study of Evolution from EVOLUTION, 2, 145–163 (1948).

cluded in the present treatment of the Ceratopsia.

Geographic distribution

As mentioned above, the ceratopsians are essentially a group of North American development. *Protoceratops,* the structural ancestral type for the Ceratopsia, is known from abundant materials found in Mongolia. *Pentaceratops* has also been recorded from Mongolia, but upon the basis of a single small element from the frill of the skull—the epoccipital. The genus *Notoceratops,* described by von Huene from South America, is, as already mentioned, founded upon such insufficient materials as to be of little value.

The remaining genera of ceratopsians, including the well defined type species of *Pentaceratops,* are found in the western portion of North America, in Cretaceous sediments of the Rocky Mountain region. Thus, these fossil reptiles are found in a long north and south belt, extending from

that the Djadochta is no later in age than the Belly River formation of North America, and it is possibly slightly older than the Belly River.

In North America the Ceratopsia are distributed in three successive stratigraphic horizons of Upper Cretaceous age. The lowest of these levels comprises sediments of the Belly River series in Alberta, and the Two Medicine and Judith River formations in Montana. In the middle level are the Edmonton formation of Alberta and the Kirtland and Fruitland formations of New Mexico. Finally, the upper level, the last phase of Cretaceous sedimentation in North America, consists of the Lance and Hell Creek formations of Montana and Wyoming, the Denver and Arapahoe beds of Colorado and the Ojo Alamo and McDermott formations of New Mexico.

The relationships of these ceratopsianbearing formations can be indicated as shown on the following correlation chart.

	Mongolia	Alberta	Montana	Wyoming	Colorado	New Mexico
			Lance	Lance Hell Creek	Denver Arapahoe	Ojo Alamo McDermott
Upper Cretaceous		Edmonton				Kirtland Fruitland
		Belly River	Two Medicine Judith River			
	Djadochta					

northern Coahuila and southern Texas and New Mexico on the south well into Alberta on the north.

Geologic range

The ceratopsian dinosaurs are confined to the upper part of the Cretaceous period, even in their most primitive manifestations. In Mongolia, *Protoceratops* occurs in the Djadochta formation, a Cretaceous horizon that upon the basis of present knowledge is difficult to correlate with possible equivalents in North America and Europe. It is probable, however,

ADAPTIVE RADIATION IN THE HORNED DINOSAURS

It was said in the introduction to this paper that the ceratopsian dinosaurs show a consistent and limited pattern of morphological evolution during their geologic history, and this fact must be kept in mind in a review of the group. It is probably correct to say that in the post-cranial evolution the ceratopsians are on the whole fairly conservative; the skeletons of the last and largest of the horned dinosaurs are essentially large editions of the skeleton of *Protoceratops,* the ancestral type, with of course the consequent changes in proportions that take place as a result of growth in size, changes made necessary because of weight problems. It is in the skull that adaptive radiation in the Ceratopsia becomes most apparent, and even here it is not a phylogeny involving great and profound changes. Rather, the pattern of evolution in the ceratopsian skull is a consistent one; or to use a musical comparison, it is composed of variations on a theme.

Before going into the problem of adaptive radiation in the Ceratopsia as demonstrated by the skull it may be well to review briefly the evolutionary trends in the skeleton as a whole. The structural design for the ceratopsian dinosaurs, established in the genus *Protoceratops,* is that of a quadrupedal ornithischian, with an extremely large skull, of which the posterior dorsal bones are extended to form a frill over the neck and shoulder region. In following this structural type from *Protoceratops* to the ceratopsians of Lance times there is a considerable increase in size, an evolutionary trend that is general among all of the dinosaurs, and various developments in skull morphology, devel-

opments that will be discussed in some detail below. Moreover, there are certain changes in proportions in the post-cranial skeleton; for instance in the evolution of the ceratopsians there is a definite proportional shortening of the tail and of the limbs. Nevertheless, the basic design holds from the beginning of this evolutionary line to the end, and the changes that take place affect the details of the design without changing its fundamental characters.

The points mentioned above are illustrated by figure 1, based upon measurements of skeletons in the genera *Protoceratops, Monoclonius* and *Triceratops.* It can be seen from this figure that the skull in the ceratopsians was large from the beginning—indeed, it is interesting to note how the proportional size of the skull held to an approximate constant during the adaptive radiation of these dinosaurs. The proportional shortening of the tail and of the limbs are trends that would be expected to accompany increase in size; they are part of a picture of correlated changes in body proportions from light animals capable of fairly rapid movements, to heavy, ponderous beasts. It is known that the ancestral dinosaurs were

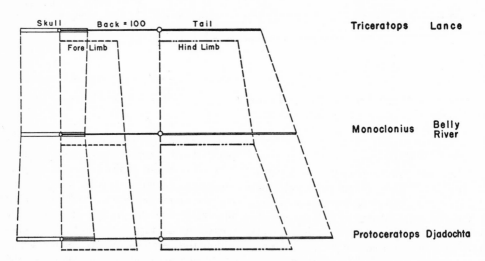

Fig. 1. Skeletal proportions in three genera of Ceratopsia. The length of the back, from the occipital condyle of the skull to the acetabulum of the pelvis, is taken as the unit basis for comparison.

thoroughly bipedal, and that there was a secondary reversion to quadrupedalism in most of the forms that showed definite size increases. Such an evolutionary trend was inevitable as an adaptation to the need for more powerful support in the front quarters for an ever-increasing body weight. Figure 1 shows that this trend to quadrupedalism in the ceratopsians was brought about, not by a relative increase in the size of the forelimbs, as has often been stated, but rather by a relatively great decrease in the size of the hindlimbs. As can be seen from this figure, both fore and hindlimbs suffered a reduction in relative size in the evolutionary sequence from *Protoceratops* to *Triceratops,* but whereas the relative decrease of the forelimbs was slight, that of the hindlimbs was very marked. The net effect, of course, was that of enlargement of the forelimbs as compared with the hindlimbs.

Such were the general trends in the postcranial evolution of the ceratopsians. Let us turn now to a consideration of the evolution of the skull.

In *Protoceratops* the skull is thoroughly ceratopsian. It is extremely large in comparison with the skeleton as a whole. It is deep, and anteriorly the front of the skull and of the lower jaws is compressed into a sort of parrot-like beak. In all of the ceratopsians except *Protoceratops* and *Leptoceratops* this beak is thoroughly edentulous and bird-like, but in these two comparatively primitive genera small premaxillary teeth are retained. Moreover, the maxillary and dentary teeth on the sides of the jaws in *Protoceratops* and *Leptoceratops* are simpler than in the more advanced genera. But these are details of no great significance in this present study. Of more importance is the fact that in *Protoceratops* there is a well developed fenestrated frill on the back of skull, which in life served primarily for the insertion of powerful neck muscles, and secondarily as protection for the cervical region. In the fully adult *Protoceratops* this frill is proportionately almost

as large as it is in some of the later ceratopsians. The ontogeny of the frill is known in *Protoceratops,* and this shows that the frill underwent a great proportional increase during development from the newly hatched individual to the mature adult. Finally, there are no horns on the skull in *Protoceratops,* a distinct contrast to the condition in all other ceratopsians.

In tracing the adaptive radiation of the ceratopsian skull beyond *Protoceratops,* we can follow several evolutionary trends developing simultaneously. These are:

1. Reduction and final supression of the premaxillary teeth.
2. Changes in the proportion of the frill.
3. Changes in the fenestration of the frill.
4. Development of nodes and spikes on the edges of the frill.
5. Development of the nasal horn.
6. Development of the supraorbital horns.

From *Protoceratops,* taken as the central ancestral type, the ceratopsians would seem to show a dichotomy so far as the evolution of the skull is concerned, and this dichotomy of the ceratopsians had taken place by Belly River times. On the one hand, there was an evolutionary line characterized by a rather short frill, a line typified by the genera *Brachyceratops, Monoclonius, Styracosaurus* and *Triceratops.* The other line of evolution was that in which the frill became relatively long, and this line is typified by the genera *Chasmosaurus, Anchiceratops, Arrhinoceratops, Pentaceratops* and *Torosaurus.*

The differences in proportional frill length in these two evolutionary lines are not great, but they are none the less well defined when analyzed. In the first group, those genera with the short frill, the frill, or more properly that portion of the skull behind the orbit, has a length less than or at the most, equal to the length of the skull in front of the orbit. In the long-frilled line, on the other hand, the postorbital length of the skull is considerably greater than the preorbital length.

In both short-frilled and long-frilled lines the frills are fenestrated, except in the genus *Triceratops,* which has a solid frill. There is every reason to think, however, that the solid frill of *Triceratops* evolved from a fenestrated frill. Lull has suggested that the fenestrae in the two lines of ceratopsians were independently derived. In the short-frilled phylum the fenestrae, according to Lull, probably were formed by a perforation of the parietal bones, because in the genera belonging to this group the fenestrae are contained entirely within the parietals, a condition established in *Protocceratops* and continuing to *Triceratops,* in which form the fenestrae are secondarily closed. In the long-frilled phylum, according to Lull's suggestion, the fenestrae were formed by the manner in which the parietal bone grew back and laterally to join the squamosal. "Ancestrally, therefore, the outer limit of the fenestra must have been the squamosal. At the anterior end of the fenestra, behind the supratemporal openings, a plate of bone extends laterally to join the squamosal near its anterior end, and from these transverse portions of the parietal, branches developed forward and backward, as the case may be, extending along the squamosal until they met in an overlapping suture which, at any rate in *Chasmosaurus,* failed to fuse and in one case failed to meet. This now excludes the fenestra from contact with the squamosal and the aperture thus formed is persistent throughout the recorded history of the phylum." (Lull, 1933, p. 24.) Whether or not one accepts Lull's idea of an independent origin for the parietal fenestrae in the two lines of ceratopsians, there is no doubting the fact that these fenestrae were persistent through ceratopsian history.

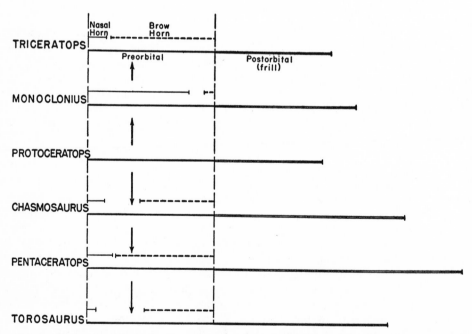

FIG. 2. Proportions of certain parts and elements of the skull in various genera of Ceratopsia. The short frilled genera, *Monoclonius* and *Triceratops,* and the long-frilled genera, *Chasmosaurus, Pentaceratops* and *Torosaurus,* are arranged in geologic sequence as they diverge from the earliest and most primitive genus, *Protoceratops.* The preorbital length is taken as the unit basis for comparison.

Except for *Protoceratops,* the ceratopsian dinosaurs are characterized particularly by the development of horns and spikes on the skull. There is always a nasal horn and it may be large or small. Generally there is a pair of supraorbital horns, one above each eye, although in some genera these may be so small as to be almost nonexistent. Occasionally there are spikes or nodes around the edges of the frill.

To consider first the spikes and nodes on the frill, these are plainly separate dermal ossifications that during individual growth became fused to the edge of the frill. As such they have been given a distinctive osteological name and are called the epoccipital bones. They appear early in ceratopsian evolution, being characteristic of the Belly River genera *Chasmosaurus, Monoclonius* and *Styracosaurus;* indeed, in this last genus they reach the culmination of their development and form long spikes, radiating laterally and posteriorly from the frill. Subsequent to Belly River times the epoccipitals seem to have suffered on the whole a retrogressive trend in evolution, and in most of the later genera they became much reduced or even disappeared, during which process the edge of the frill either remained crenulated, or in the later forms became smooth and straight. In *Triceratops* of Lance times, the epoccipitals were retained.

The development of the nasal and brow horns is more difficult to interpret than that of the epoccipitals. Brown and Schlaikjer have shown that in *Protoceratops,* even though there are no horns, there is a very distinct uparching of the nasals in old individuals, a morphologic development that might subsequently lead to the formation of a nasal horn. In *Leptoceratops* the nasals grow and become conjoined to form a well-developed horn core, and this process is continued in the genus *Brachyceratops.* Both of these genera show that the horn core is formed by the upgrowth and union of

the nasal bones into a single, solid structure. Moreover, in *Brachyceratops* there is on each side a terminal ossicle at the end of the nasal horn, indicative of a dermal element with a separate center of ossification.

In *Monoclonius* and *Styracosaurus,* characterized by large nasal horns, these horns seem to be formed by an upgrowth of the nasal bones, as in *Brachyceratops,* and the same would appear to be true of the small nasal horns in the various "long-frilled" genera of Ceratopsia. In *Triceratops* the nasal horn is small or of medium size. Brown and Schlaikjer have maintained that the nasal horn is suturally distinct from the nasal bones, and this has led them to think that in this genus there was a regression of the expanded nasal bones and the development of a new nasal horn from dermal ossicles, similar to those seen in *Brachyceratops.* According to this interpretation, then, the nasal horn of *Triceratops* is not strictly homologous with the small nasal horn of the various long-frilled genera of ceratopsians. As against this, however, is recent evidence obtained from some material of *Triceratops* collected by Mr. Charles M. Sternberg of the National Museum of Canada. The new material, which fortunately includes the nasal horn of a young *Triceratops,* shows that the horn in this genus is formed, just as in the case of other ceratopsian genera, by an upgrowth of the conjoined nasal bones. Upon the basis of this new evidence, therefore, it is reasonable to suppose that the nasal horn can be homologized throughout the known genera of ceratopsians, and that in all cases it is formed by an upgrowth of the conjoined nasal bones. Consequently, it is necessary to assume that in the sequence from *Monoclonius* to *Triceratops* there was a considerable regression in size of the nasal horn.

The evolution of the nasal horn in these dinosaurs can be outlined as follows.

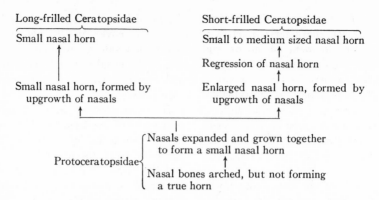

Long-frilled Ceratopsidae	Short-frilled Ceratopsidae
Small nasal horn	Small to medium sized nasal horn
↑	↑
	Regression of nasal horn
	↑
Small nasal horn, formed by upgrowth of nasals	Enlarged nasal horn, formed by upgrowth of nasals
↑	↑

Protoceratopsidae {
Nasals expanded and grown together to form a small nasal horn
↑
Nasal bones arched, but not forming a true horn
}

The brow horns, according to Brown and Schlaikjer, are in each case formed by an upgrowth of the postorbital bone above the eye. In *Leptoceratops* and *Brachyceratops* the brow horns are quite small, and they remain small in the Belly River genera having very large nasal horns, namely *Monoclonius* and *Styracosaurus*. In the other genera of ceratopsians, however, the brow horns show a progressive increase in size, while there is a regression of the nasal horn, as in *Triceratops,* or a lack of growth in the nasal horn, as in the long-frilled ceratopsian genera. In this connection it is interesting to see that among the earlier long-frilled forms, such as *Chasmosaurus,* with rather small brown horns, the nasal horn is moderately large, whereas, in the late genera such as *Torosaurus,* with very large brow horns, the nasal horn is relatively very small. A suggestive parallel to this is to be seen within the genus *Triceratops*. Those species having the smallest brow horns have the largest nasal horn, while those forms having the largest brow horns have the smallest nasal horns. It would appear that there was a correlation in horn development throughout ceratopsian evolution, whereby an increase in the

TABLE 1. *Diagram of horn and frill evolution in ceratopsians*

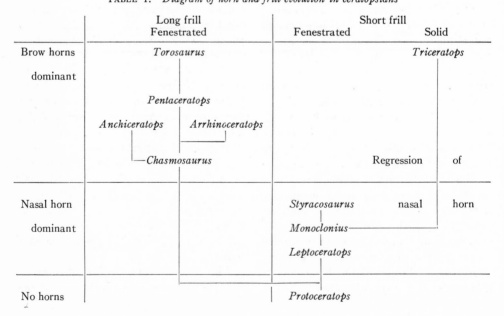

	Long frill Fenestrated	Short frill Fenestrated	Solid
Brow horns dominant	*Torosaurus*		*Triceratops*
	Pentaceratops		
	Anchiceratops *Arrhinoceratops*		
	—*Chasmosaurus*	Regression	of
Nasal horn dominant		*Styracosaurus* nasal	horn
		Monoclonius———	
		Leptoceratops	
No horns		*Protoceratops*	

nasal horn retarded development of the brow horns, while an increase in the brow horns retarded the nasal horn.

From the foregoing discussion we see that the ceratopsian skull followed two simultaneous lines of adaption during upper Cretaceous times and within each of these lines there were adaptational trends. Perhaps the discussion can be outlined in a diagrammatic way as follows (table 1).

Evolutionary Rates of the Ceratopsia

Among the dinosaurian suborders the Ceratopsia were the most limited in their time range, being restricted to the upper part of the Cretaceous period. The ankylosaurs were almost as restricted, but their evolutionary history did extend throughout the full extent of Cretaceous times, while the other suborders persisted through at least parts of two Mesozoic periods, and in some cases, through the entire range of the Mesozoic era. A comparison of the time ranges in the six recognized dinosaurian suborders can be shown in tabular form.

other restricted groups, the restriction is more apparent than real, generally being due to the inadequacy of the fossil record rather than to the brevity of the phylogenetic history. Such, for instance, is true with regard to the eunotosaurs from the Permian of South Africa, known from a single genus, or to the mesosaurs from the Lower Permian of South Africa and South America, known from three genera. Our knowledge of ceratopsian evolution, on the other hand, is fairly complete, and while future discoveries may fill in many details it can safely be said that they will not extend the geologic range of the group to any appreciable extent.

As a matter of comparison, among the persisting reptiles, pleurodire and cryptodire turtles date back to Cretaceous and Jurassic times respectively, the eusuchian crocodiles to the Jurassic, the rhynchocephalians to the Triassic, and the lizards and snakes to the Cretaceous. There is reason to think that the history of the lizards and snakes extends back into Jurassic times.

This means that evolutionary rates in the ceratopsian dinosaurs were rapid, even

	Triassic	Jurassic	Cretaceous
Order Saurischia			
Suborder Theropoda			
Suborder Sauropoda			
Order Ornithischia			
Suborder Ornithopoda			
Suborder Stegosauria			
Suborder Ankylosauria			
Suborder Ceratopsia			

A broader comparison will show that the ceratopsians were not only a short-lived suborder of dinosaurs, but also a short-lived group of reptiles. In the entire history of reptilian evolution there are few groups of subordinal rank with so restricted a time range. Moreover in

allowing for the fact that this is a group in which the amount of evolutionary development was rather limited. Perhaps this fact can best be illustrated by comparing the evolution of size, as measured by total length in the ceratopsian dinosaurs and in the other lines of dinosaur evolu-

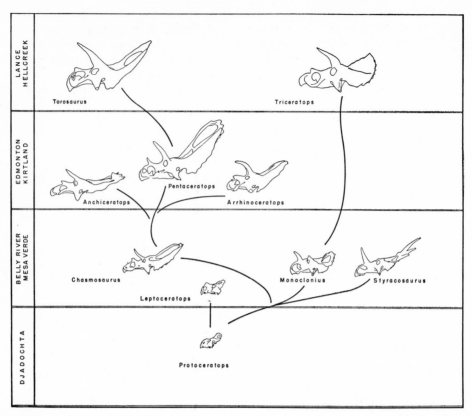

Fig. 3. Adaptive radiation of the Ceratopsia, as shown by evolution in the skull. The evolutionary line to the left is that of the long-frilled ceratopsians, the one to the right, that of the short-frilled ceratopsians. Modified from Lull, 1933. All figures approximately to the same scale.

tion, with duration of geologic time. This is shown by the graph, figure 4.

In this chart it can be seen that the Ceratopsia progressed from adult animals having lengths of about two meters to adult animals having lengths of about seven meters, and this size increment took place within the 15 or 20 million years that is here assigned to the upper part of the Cretaceous period.

In contrast with this, the ornithopod dinosaurs showed a similar size increment that extended over a period of time about three times the length of that required for the entire evolution of the ceratopsians. The armored dinosaurs, being relatively slowly evolving types at least so far as increase in size is concerned, showed a very small increment in a period of time that was roughly twice the length of ceratopsian evolutionary history, while the stegosaurs or plated dinosaurs also showed a smaller size increment occupying a greater time lapse than is seen in the ceratopsians. The theropod dinosaurs showed a length increment of from two to 14 meters in the time interval between the upper Triassic and the end of the Cretaceous, a large size increase but at a rather moderate rate, since a greater part of the Mesozoic period was involved in its completion. The sauropod dinosaurs showed a size increment of from about six meters in the upper Triassic to 18 meters or more in the upper Jurassic, an evolutionary rate that is, interestingly enough, closely parallel to that for the ceratopsians.

This comparison of evolutionary rates in the six suborders of dinosaurs is concerned with total length only. It would be desirable to have other quantitative comparisons, but such comparisons would be difficult to obtain. For instance, a comparison of body masses would be enlightening, and if it could be made with any degree of certainty would be more indicative of evolutionary rates in the dino-

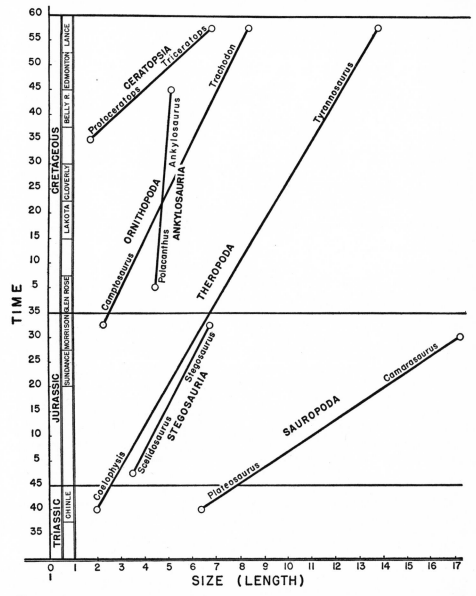

FIG. 4. A comparison of evolutionary rates, as based upon total lengths, in the suborders of dinosaurs. In each suborder a straight line connects an early, primitive genus and a late, specialized genus, thus giving an approximate indication of the average evolutionary rate for the suborder. The more nearly horizontal the line, the higher the rate of evolution as regards size increase. Time is in millions of years, size in meters. Characteristic formations in the North American Mesozoic sequence are shown.

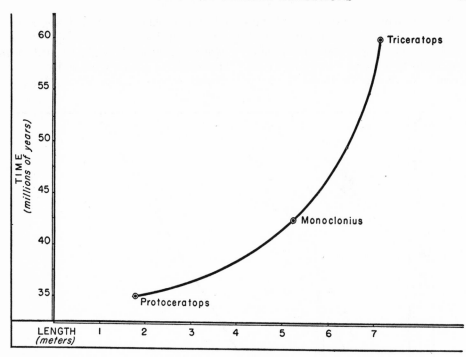

Fig. 5. The evolutionary rate, as based upon total lengths, in the phylogenetic line from *Protoceratops* (Djadochta) through *Monoclonius* (Belly River) to *Triceratops* (Lance).

saurs than the comparison of length. But such a comparison would involve estimates of body weights in each case, and would thus be subject to a large degree of error. To carry the comparisons down to individual parts of the body, such as the skull, or the legs, is virtually impossible, because of the highly varied and different adaptations in the dinosaurs that make direct comparisons like these almost useless. Even this simple comparison of lengths must not be taken too literally. For instance, the assignment of time durations within the Mesozoic periods are rather arbitrary, and this fact must be kept in mind. Moreover, the representation of evolutionary rates as straight lines connecting in each case a small early representative of each suborder with a large late form is not strictly correct. Where we have the evidence of intermediate forms, such as in the ceratopsians or the theropods, we know that evolution in size was comparatively rapid during the first part of the sequence, and relatively slow during the later phases of phylogenetic history. But since intermediate forms are not known in all of the phylogenetic lines under consideration, this method of showing merely early and late representatives connected by a straight line is used to indicate the average rate of evolution.

In this connection it may be interesting to attempt an analysis of the evolutionary rate of length increment within the phylogenetic sequence running from *Protoceratops* through *Monoclonius* to *Triceratops*. This sequence, as pointed out above, probably represents a valid evolutionary line, and it is a sequence in which complete skeletons of the genera concerned are well known.

If skeletal lengths of typical examples of the three genera named above are plotted against their approximate positions in Cretaceous time, a curve—not a straight line—is obtained. This curve represents the rate of increase in total length in the short-frilled group of ceratopsians through geologic time, and it shows that in the earlier phases of the phylogenetic history of these animals there was a rapid increase in length, while in the later phases of the history the rate became appreciably slowed down. Thus, *Monoclonius* which probably was not far removed from *Protoceratops* in time, was many times larger than the Mongolian genus, whereas *Triceratops,* probably separated from *Monoclonius* by a considerable time lapse, was not a great deal larger than this latter genus.

The shape of the curve is, of course, governed by the assumptions made as to relative lengths for the various segments of geologic time involved in the comparison, namely those time lapses during which the Djadochta, Belly River, Edmonton and Lance formations were deposited. But upon the basis of any reasonable assumption as to the duration of upper Cretaceous time, founded upon our knowledge of stratigraphic relationships in the several continental areas, it seems logical to suppose that some sort of a differential rate of increase in this phylogenetic line will be the result.

There is nothing surprising in this; indeed, the picture of a rapid increase in size during the earlier phases of evolutionary history in the *Protoceratops— Triceratops* line followed by a distinct slowing down of size increase during the later portions of the sequence, is in line with what we know about many other examples of phylogenetic history. While a more or less constant rate of evolution is frequently found in the study of phylogenies as based upon fossil materials, it is not at all uncommon to find lines in which evolutionary rates show profound differences at different stages of geologic time. We often see a phylogenetic line evolving very rapidly during the early phases of its history, only to slow down, and at times to become almost static, once it has become well established.

The ceratopsians as a group provide an example of this phenomenon. We do not know ceratopsian history with any degree of certainty prior to the appearance of *Protoceratops.* It would seem probable, however, that the basic transitions from a generalized ornithischian dinosaur to the primitive ceratopsian stage as represented by *Protoceratops* were made with great geologic rapidity; in other words, there was a period during which quantum evolution established the ceratopsian adaptational pattern. From *Protoceratops* the development of specialized ceratopsian adaptations was also rapid; not much time was involved in the transition from a small, hornless ceratopsian to a giant, horned ceratopsian. After this last stage was attained, however, evolution was comparatively slow, and, as pointed out above, it involved mainly a limited increase in size and various adaptational changes in the structure of the skull.

Geographic Limitations of the Ceratopsia

Why should the Ceratopsia, with the exception of *Protoceratops,* be confined to the continent of North America? Does this represent a condition that prevailed during the upper part of the Cretaceous period, or is the limitation of the ceratopsians to North America, as based upon our present information, more apparent than real, being the result of accidents in preservation with a resultant imperfect knowledge of the fossil record? Let us turn first to the problem of absences of ceratopsians in the fossil record, and their significance.

The remains of *Protoceratops* in the Djadochta formation of Mongolia constitute abundant evidence as to the presence of ceratopsians in Asia during the opening phases of upper Cretaceous times. But beyond *Protoceratops* our published information as to the presence of the Ceratopsia in Asia is limited to a single fragment, identified by Gilmore some 15 years ago as the epoccipital from the frill of a *Pentaceratops*—like dinosaur. This is indeed slender evidence, but slight as it is, it appears to be valid. The bone was found at Baiying Bologai, Mongolia, a locality of which the geologic horizon has never been accurately determined. It may be later than the Djadochta in time, but if so it represents our first inkling as to Cretaceous sediments that were laid down in Mongolia subsequent to the deposition of the Djadochta formation. All of the other Cretaceous horizons described are as old as or older than the Djadochta.

Thus we find ourselves against a blank wall in an effort to follow the later history and distribution of the Ceratopsia in Asia. To date, the Djadochta formation is the latest Cretaceous formation in Mongolia containing an identifiable fauna, and this yields the most primitive of the ceratopsians. It is quite possible that ceratopsians were present in northeastern Asia in the later phases of the Cretaceous period, but this is a question that will have to wait on future discoveries for its solution.

While the future discovery of later Cretaceous ceratopsians in Asia is here considered as probable, the discovery of these animals in the upper Cretaceous sediments of Europe is here considered as unlikely. Upper Cretaceous dinosaur-bearing beds are now known in various parts of Europe, and although these sediments carry remains of various other suborders of dinosaurs, there are no evidences in them of ceratopsians. Similarly, the upper Cretaceous dinosaur-bearing sediments of Africa, so far as they are known, do not reveal the presence of ceratopsians in their contained faunas. Therefore, the absence of ceratopsians in the upper Cretaceous of Europe and of Africa is regarded as representing a probable real absence of these animals at that time, rather than an imperfection of the fossil record, as is very likely the case in northeastern Asia.

Turning now to South America we find one ceratopsian, described by von Huene upon the basis of a fragment of a mandible. But this specimen is so poorly preseved that its assignment to the Ceratopsia cannot be considered as beyond question. Consequently the presence of ceratopsians in the upper Cretaceous of South America must at the present time be regarded as a debatable point. It may be the result of imperfections in the fossil record, or it may be a real absence.

So we see that the Ceratopsia were, in the light of our extant knowledge, essentially a North American group of reptiles. They very possibly were present in northeastern Asia in uppermost Cretaceous times, but this is at the present time mere speculation. They very probably were not present in Europe or Africa, and probably not in South America, either. Granting, then, for the sake of the present consideration, that the ceratopsians above the evolutionary level of *Protoceratops* were confined to North America, what can we deduce from their geographic distribution in this region?

In North America the ceratopsians are known at the present time from the western Great Plains and Rocky Mountain regions, the localities at which these reptiles have been collected being contained within an area including Alberta, Saskatchewan, Montana, the Dakotas, Wyoming, Colorado, New Mexico, western Texas and Coahuila. Within this area are most of the continental upper Cretaceous exposure in North America. Therefore, it seems evident that discoveries of ceratopsian dinosaurs in North America have been limited to the regions listed above primarily because of the limitations of the areas of exposures in which such dinosaurs might well be expected. Now it is an interesting fact that other upper Cretaceous dinosaurs have been found in scattered localities outside of the Great Plains–Rocky Mountain region. For instance, hadrosaurs have long been known from the Cretaceous of New Jersey, and recently hadrosaurian remains have been excavated in California. It must be remembered, however, that the hadrosaurs were semiaquatic dinosaurs and their fossils are to be expected in beds of marine origin where the fossils of upland ceratopsians would not be preserved. It is certain that the hadrosaurs found in New Jersey come from a marine facies, probably an off-shore deposit, and the same may be assumed for the material from California.

Therefore it might be assumed that the absence of ceratopsians from the Cretaceous of New Jersey, for instance, is the result of the imperfection of the record—that these off-shore marine sediments have yielded hadrosaurs because the hadrosaurs were water-loving dinosaurs, and have not yielded the remains of ceratopsians because the horned dinosaurs were upland forms. But as against this assumption is the fact that certain carnivorous theropods have been found in the Cretaceous of New Jersey and these were upland dinosaurs, as were the ceratopsians. Is it possible, then, that the absence of ceratopsians from the Cretaceous of eastern North America represents a real absence of these animals from this region during upper Cretaceous times? Is it possible that the

confinement of the ceratopsians to the western Great Plains—Rocky Mountain area represents more or less the actual distribution of these dinosaurs during the geologic ages in which they were living?

According to paleogeographic evidence it would seem that an arm of the sea extended from the gulf region northward through the western Great Plains area during upper Cretaceous times. During the later phases of the upper Cretaceous period, at a time about equivalent to that of Belly River sedimentation, this sea arm or embayment was rather large, extending far north into Canada and to the east over the northern Great Plains states. By the end of Cretaceous times, however, during the period of Lance sedimentation, this sea arm had diminished to a narrow trough extending northwardly through eastern New Mexico and Colorado and western Nebraska and the Dakotas. It

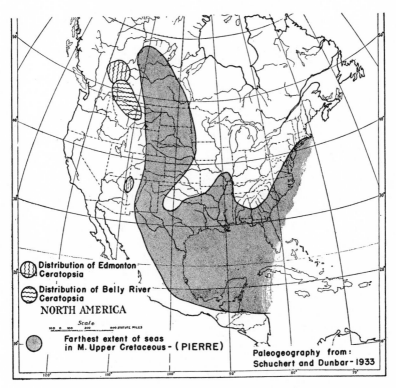

Fig. 6. The known distribution of Belly River and Edmonton ceratopsians and the extent of the Pierre Sea, in middle Upper Cretaceous times.

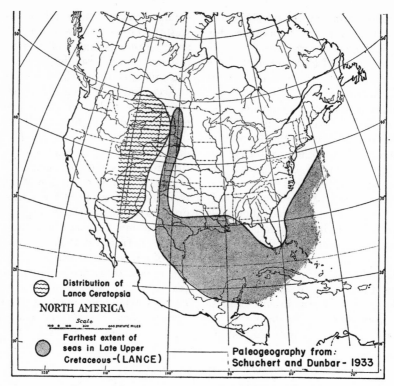

Distribution of
Lance Ceratopsia

NORTH AMERICA

Scale

Farthest extent of
seas in Late Upper
Cretaceous-(LANCE)

Paleogeography from:
Schuchert and Dunbar - 1933

FIG. 7.   The known distribution of Lance ceratopsians and the extent of the Lance
(Cannonball) Sea, in late Upper Cretaceous times.

barely crossed the Dakota border into Saskatchewan and Manitoba.

Now it is interesting to see that the sediments in which ceratopsians have been discovered lie along the western border of this epeiric seaway, in regions that during upper Cretaceous times were continental areas. None of the ceratopsian-bearing sediments are to be found to the east of the marine incursion.

Is it not possible, therefore, that the upper Cretaceous sea formed a barrier to the eastward spread of the ceratopsians? If it is assumed that the presence of *Protoceratops* in Mongolia indicates a northern Asiatic center of origin for the ceratopsians, then it can further be assumed that during upper Cretaceous times these dinosaurs migrated or spread from their Asiatic point of origin to the east, across the Bering region and down into western North America, from whence they were

prevented from extending their range directly eastward by the sea barrier, and to the northeast, around the upper end of the seaway, by adverse climatic conditions. On the basis of the known facts, such as a conclusion appears to be logical.

In this connection it is interesting to note the known distribution of the ceratopsians in North America in Belly River, Edmonton and Lance times, respectively (table 2). In the Belly River, the horned dinosaurs are confined to an area in southern Alberta and northwestern Montana. In the Edmonton, these animals are found in Alberta, generally to the north of their Belly River distribution, and also in rocks of comparable age in New Mexico. In the Lance the ceratopsians are widely spread, from the Canadian border and Montana in the north, southwardly through the Dakotas, Wyoming, Colorado and New Mexico. Does this sequence

TABLE 2. *Geographic and geologic distribution of the Ceratopsia*

Genera contained within a square are believed to have existed simultaneously in the same area.

	Mongolia	Alberta Saskatchewan	Montana N. Dakota	Wyoming S. Dakota	Colorado	N. Mexico	Texas Mexico
Lance Hell Creek Ojo Alamo		*Triceratops*	*Triceratops*	*Triceratops* *Torosaurus*	*Triceratops*	*Triceratops* *Monoclonius*	(Ceratopsian)
Edmonton Kirtland		*Anchiceratops* *Arrhinoceratops* *Monoclonius* *Leptoceratops*				*Pentaceratops* *Monoclonius*	
Belly River		*Chasmosaurus* *Styracosaurus* *Monoclonius* *Eoceratops**	*Styracosaurus* *Monoclonius* *Brachyceratops** *Leptoceratops* *Ceratops**				
Djadochta	*Protoceratops*						

* Not discussed in this paper.

indicate the spread during geologic time from a northern center to a wide north and south range in western North America? Probably not. For instance, the presence of ceratopsians in the Edmonton sediments to the far north and in the contemporaneous Kirtland deposits in New Mexico would seem to indicate that the apparent restriction of horned dinosaurs to these two areas is the result of geologic processes which have resulted in the elimination of fossiliferous rocks of this age in the intervening regions. In other words, it is reasonable to think that the distribution of Edmonton ceratopsians, and of Belly River ceratopsians before them, was continuous along the western border of the upper Cretaceous seaway, as from the evidence we know it was during Lance times.

It is realized, of course, that in this discussion different conclusions are being drawn from negative evidence. On the one hand, it is postulated that the lack of ceratopsians in the eastern Cretaceous is probably the result of a real absence of these animals from this region during Cretaceous times. On the other hand, it is suggested that the small areas in which Belly River and Edmonton ceratopsians are now found are the result of geologic processes, and that these animals were once present in a continuous range running north and south through the western Plains and Rocky Mountain region, as is true of the Lance ceratopsians. But it is felt that the facts justify these arguments. The presence of the upper Cretaceous seaway offers good evidence for a barrier to the eastward spread of the ceratopsians. The continuous range of the Lance ceratopsians along the western border of the sea suggest that similar relationships held during the preceding ages, when the Edmonton, and before them, the Belly River ceratopsians were living.

AN INTERPRETATION OF CERATOPSIAN EVOLUTION

We have so far reviewed the evolution of the ceratopsian dinosaurs in several of its aspects. Thus we have considered the problem of adaptive radiation or the evolutionary pattern within this suborder of reptiles, the problem of evolutionary rates as seen in these long-extinct animals and the problem of the geographic limitations of the ceratopsians during the course of their evolution. Interpretations of these several problems have been set forth in connection with each of them. At this place it may be useful to attempt a broader interpretation of ceratopsian evolution, based upon the varied facts and their interpretations offered in the preceding discussion.

In the first place, it must be realized that, by and large, size increase is a constant throughout the evolutionary history of the ceratopsians. With the exception of the genus *Leptoceratops*, all of the horned dinosaurs after *Protoceratops* were large animals, and they were large to about the same degree of largeness. We know that there were certain size differences in the adults of the various ceratopsian genera, but generally speaking they all were animals on the order of about 20 feet in length, with their other proportions corresponding; consequently, it is proper to say that the ceratopsians all showed a size increase during evolution of about the same degree of magnitude.

Moreover, as pointed out on a preceding page of this discussion, the ceratopsian dinosaurs were all pretty much alike as regards the post-cranial skeleton. Indeed, a study of the osteology of these forms will show that the differences between the various genera, so far as the skeleton behind the skull is concerned, were differences in details of morphology. They were all adapted along the same structural pattern that was first established by *Protoceratops*.

Therefore, in studying the adaptive radiation of the ceratopsians, we see that lines of phylogenetic differentiation are to be recognized mainly on the basis of horn and frill patterns. All of the ceratopsians had frills, but the frills differed from genus to genus. All of the ceratopsians above the level of *Protoceratops* had horns, but here again, the horns differed from genus to genus. What is more, genera differing from each other by reason of their horn and frill structures were contemporaneous. Therefore, we are led to the conclusion that selection pressures during ceratopsian evolution did not favor one pattern of horns and frill to the exclusion of others, but rather that once the survival value of horns and frill had been established, these could develop in a variety of ways. A ceratopsian with large brow horns, a small nasal horn and a fenestrated frill could live side by side with a genus characterized by similar horns, but with a solid frill, and both of these could be contemporaneous with a type having a fenestrated frill, but differing from the others by virtue of a very large nasal horn and reduced brow horns. It would seem as though horns and frill as such had a high adaptive value, the horns serving for defense, the frill as an attachment for large muscles that gave great power to the thrust of the horns. But, as we have seen, the pattern or combination of horns and frill might vary from genus to genus.

Is it not reasonable to suppose, therefore, that the various forms of horns and frill in the ceratopsians were the result of random mutations, not suppressed by selection? And if this be so, is it not possible that these mutations became established as a result of comparative isolation in small populations?

We have seen that the large, specialized ceratopsians seemingly were limited to North America, and how, in this continent, there is reason to think that they were confined to the western regions, west of the upper Cretaceous seaway. Of course, a range that stretches from New Mexico into Alberta is not particularly limited, but on the other hand this is not an extensive range for large terrestrial vertebrates such as the ceratopsians. Therefore, it is logical to suppose that in the early stages of ceratopsian evolution, perhaps after these animals had migrated into the North American continent from Asia, there were established several geographic centers more or less isolated from each other. The ceratopsians developed in these centers, and since populations were relatively small, mutations could be established and spread with comparative speed by a process of evolutionary drift through these limited populations. It may be supposed that subsequently these isolated and differing populations expanded, with a resultant coexistence of differing genera, mutually tolerant to each other. Such is the hypothetical picture as here suggested upon the basis of our knowledge of ceratopsian evolution and distribution.

It may be that we can see a modern parallel to the ceratopsian dinosaurs in the African antelopes. Like the Ceratopsia, the antelopes of Africa have evolved very rapidly, geologically speaking. Like what is here presumed for the Ceratopsia, these antelopes are for the most part limited to a single continental area. And like the Ceratopsia, the African antelopes show a variety of adaptations in certain characters (particularly the horns) that seem to be of equal selective value. Thus, in the antelopes the ability to run fast and the possession of horns are of primary importance for survival. But the form of the horns seems to be of secondary importance, so we find various genera, characterized by widely differing horn structures, living together successfully in the same environment.

An example of the variety of horn structure to be found in a single subfamily of African Bovidae is to be seen in the Hippotraginae. In this assemblage are included the sable antelope, *Hippotragus,* with the horns recurved posteriorly; the oryx, *Oryx,* with long, straight horns; the addax, *Addax* with the horns openly spiral; the water buck, *Kobus,* the puku, *Adenota* and the lechwe, *Onotragus,* with recurved horns, laterally divergent; the reedbuck, *Redunca,* with the tips of the horns curved forwardly; the blesbok, *Damaliscus,* with short, simple horns; the rhebok, *Pelea,* with slightly recurved, spike-like horns; the gnus, *Connochaetes* and *Gorgon,* with the horns curved down and out and then up; and the hartebeest, *Alcelaphus,* with horns something like those of the gnu, but more complexly curved in their distal regions. Here is a variety of horn development much greater than that to be found in the ceratopsians, having evolved in genera many of which now have contiguous or overlapping distributions.

It must be admitted that, even though limited to one continent, the populations of many genera of African antelopes are now very large. We know from the fossil evidence, however, that the present African antelope fauna had its origins during Pliocene times to the north, in the Mediterranean region. And it is possible that, during the relatively brief geologic time when the various phylogenetic lines of antelopes were becoming established, there were comparative isolated centers of development in which the determining mutations were taking place.

Whether these suppositions are valid or not, we do know the end results in the modern antelope fauna of Africa, an assemblage of closely related genera that show certain parallels in their evolution to what we see in the ceratopsian dinosaurs.

SUMMARY

In this discusion of Ceratopsian evolution certain factors in the phylogenetic development of the horned dinosaurs have been stressed. The adaptive radiation of the Ceratopsia has been outlined, particularly as it is concerned with the phylogenetic development of the skull; and problems of evolutionary rates in these dinosaurs, as compared with other dinosaurs have been considered. Moreover, the probable geographic distribution of the Ceratopsia during upper Cretaceous times has ben elucidated, and reasons to explain this distribution have been suggested.

Upon the basis of what we know as to the phylogeny and distribution of the ceratopsian dinosaurs, it is suggested that these animals probably went through the early stages of their evolutionary development as small populations, limited to the western part of North America. Random mutations affecting the form and development of the horn cores and the frill took place in these small populations, with the result that several phylogenetic lines, characterized by different skull patterns, were quickly established. Since the skull patterns so evolved had equal survival values, the phylogenetic lines of which they were respectively characteristic continued through the upper part of the Cretaceous period. Moreover, since the original limited populations probably expanded, it would appear that the genera typical of the various lines of ceratopsian evolution became established side by side in ranges that were contiguous or probably to a large degree overlapping. They were mutually tolerant, and it is likely that there was no great amount of competition between them. So established and so living together, the various ceratopsians continued through the last and the final phases of the Cretaceous period, to become extinct, along with all of the other dinosaurs, during the transition from Mesozoic to Cenozoic times.

LITERATURE CITED

BROWN, B. 1914a. *Anchiceratops,* a new genus of horned dinosaurs from the Edmonton Cretaceous of Alberta. Bull. Amer. Mus. Nat. Hist., 33: 539–548.

——. 1914b. A complete skull of *Monoclonius,* from the Belly River Cretaceous of Alberta. Bull. Amer. Mus. Nat. Hist., 33: 549–558.

——. 1914c. *Leptoceratops,* a new genus of Ceratopsia from the Edmonton Cretaceous of Alberta. Bull. Amer. Mus. Nat. Hist., 33: 567–580.

BROWN, B., AND E. M. SCHLAIKJER. 1937. The skeleton of *Styracosaurus* with the description of a new species. Amer. Mus. Novitates, no. 955: 1–12.

——. 1940a. The origin of ceratopsian horncores. Amer. Mus. Novitates, no. 1065: 1–7.

——. 1940b. A new element in the ceratopsian jaw with additional notes on the mandible. Amer. Mus. Novitates, no. 1092: 1–13.

——. 1940c. The structure and relationships of *Protoceratops.* Ann. N. Y. Acad. Sci., 40: 133–265, pls. 1–12.

——. 1942. The skeleton of *Leptoceratops* with the description of a new species. Amer. Mus. Novitates, no. 1173: 1–15.

COLBERT, E. H., AND J. D. BUMP. 1947. A skull of *Torosaurus* from South Dakota and a revision of the genus. Proc. Acad. Nat. Sci. Phila., 99: 93–106.

GILMORE, C. W. 1917. *Brachyceratops,* a ceratopsian dinosaur from the Two Medicine formation of Montana, with notes on associated fossil reptiles. U. S. Geol. Surv. Prof. Paper, 103: i–v, 1–44, pls. 1–4.

——. 1919. A new restoration of *Triceratops,* with notes on the osteology of the genus. Proc. U. S. Nat. Mus., 55: 97–112.

GRAY, STEPHEN W. 1946. Relative growth in a phylogenetic series and in an ontogenetic series of one of its members. Amer. Jour. Sci., 244: 792–807.

HATCHER, J. B., O. C. MARSH AND R. S. LULL. 1907. The Ceratopsia. Monogr. U. S. Geol. Surv., 49: i–xxx, 1–198.

LAMBE, L. M. 1904. On the squamoso-parietal crest of two species of horned dinosaurs from the Cretaceous of Alberta. Ottawa Nat., 18: 81–84.

LULL, R. S. 1908. The cranial musculature and the origin of the frill in the ceratopsian dinosaurs. Amer. Jour. Sci., 25: 387–399, pls. 1–3.

——. 1915. The mammals and horned dinosaurs of the Lance formation of Niobrara County, Wyoming. Amer. Jour. Sci., (4) 40: 319–348.

——. 1933. A revision of the Ceratopsia or horned dinosaurs. Mem. Peabody Mus. Nat. Hist., 3: pt. 3: i–xii, 1–175, pls. 1–17.

MARSH, O. C. 1896. The dinosaurs of North America. 16th Ann. Rept. U. S. Geol. Surv., 133–244.

PARKS, W. A. 1925. *Arrhinoceratops brachyops,* a new genus and species of Ceratopsia from the Edmonton formation of Alberta. Univ. Toronto Studies, Geol. Ser., no. 19: 5–15.

RUSSELL, L. S. 1930. Upper Cretaceous dinosaur faunas of North America. Proc. Amer. Philos. Soc., 69: 133–159.

——. 1935. Musculature and functions in the Ceratopsia. Bull. Nat. Mus. Canada, 77: 39–48.

SCHLAIKJER, E. M. 1935. The Torrington member of the Lance formation and a study of a new *Triceratops.* Bull. Mus. Comp. Zoöl., 76: 31–68, pls. 1–6.

SCHUCHERT, E., AND C. O. DUNBAR. 1933. Text book of geology, part II, Historical geology, 3d ed. New York, John Wiley and Sons.

SIMPSON, G. G. 1945. The principles of classification and a classification of mammals. Bull. Amer. Mus. Nat. Hist., 85: i–xvi, 1–350.

STERNBERG, C. M. 1927. Homologies of certain bones of the ceratopsian skull. Trans. Roy. Soc. Canada, 3rd ser., 21: 135–143.

——. 1940. Ceratopsidae from Alberta. Jour. Paleontology, 14: 468–480.

TAIT, J., AND B. BROWN. 1928. How the Ceratopsia carried and used their head. Trans. Roy. Soc. Canada, (3) 22: 13–23.

HISTORY OF THE FAUNA OF LATIN AMERICA

By GEORGE GAYLORD SIMPSON

American Museum of Natural History and Columbia University, New York City

IT IS odd that there should be *a* Latin American fauna, a broad unit that can be roughly designated by such a term as "Latin American," defined by human linguistics and culture. The animals inhabiting this area can hardly have foreseen that the dominant languages of the twentieth century would here be Spanish and Portuguese or that the European cultural elements imported here would come mainly from Latin Europe—from Spain and Portugal and also, in considerable measure, from France and Italy. Nevertheless, there is a characteristic fauna that coincides approximately with Latin America and that differs in some major traits from the fauna of English-speaking America. The coincidence is not precise. The fauna of northern Mexico, although transitional in some respects, is more nearly allied to that of the United States than to that of most of Latin America. Exact correspondence of native fauna and imported culture would be a miracle, and it is still a wonder that the equivalence is as close as it really is. There is, indeed, a common factor that removes the correspondence from the realm of pure coincidence. The demarcation both of faunas and of cultures has been influenced by climatic factors.

Radical differences in the two major faunal realms of the Americas were noticed by the early explorers and are still obvious enough to the modern traveler. A New Englander traveling in Brazil does not need to be a zoologist to observe that the animals of that country are at least as exotic as are the speech and customs of its human inhabitants. He will see some animals which, although subtly different, look reasonably familiar to him: deer, foxes, field mice, squirrels, rabbits, and a few others. More will be completely new to him outside of zoos: peccaries, tapirs, jaguars, kinkajous, guinea pigs, agoutis, capybaras, armadillos, tree sloths, monkeys, and a host of others.

The distinction is not confined to mammals, a few of which have been named, but extends to all sorts of animals. The river rays, the lungfish, the piranhas, and many other freshwater fish are strange to northern eyes. The frogs and toads may look familiar at first sight, but on closer inspection such forms as the Surinam toad, incubating the young in its back, and, indeed, almost all others will be found distinctive. Among turtles, the matamata and other side-necked forms are obviously exotic, and so are the boa constrictors and numerous other snakes. The ostrich-like rheas and the wing-clawed hoatzins are only two among the numerous purely Latin American birds. Additions to the long roster could be provided among earthworms, insects, and innumerable others.

The fauna is by no means uniform all over Latin America, but it is evident, first, that broadly similar faunal characteristics do appear throughout most of this great area and, second, that these characteristics distinguish the region sharply from non-Latin North America or any other continent. These facts led the students of animal distribution in the latter half of the nineteenth century (the Sclaters, Wallace, Beddard, and Lydekker, to name some of the more eminent) to set Latin America aside as the Neotropical Region or Neogaea. In the classical arrangement, this region includes all of South America (even those parts decidedly nontropical), Central America, tropical Mexico (but not the temperate central plateau and northern Mexico), and the West Indies. Although the boundaries are sharp and definite on the map, it was of course recognized that the line in Mexico is not awesomely respected by the animals and that it really lies within a broad transition zone. Some mainly neotropical animals, such as the peccaries or jaguars, range into the United States, far north of the map line. Some mainly nearctic (non-Latin North American) mammals, such as shrews, similarly range well south of the line. It has also long been recognized that the West Indian fauna is not typically or fully Latin American or neotropical. It is impoverished relative to the mainland, has its own peculiar forms, and has a few special resemblances to the North American fauna.

In spite of some ambiguities, the Neotropical Region does have a well-established clarity and validity in the zoogeography of the world as it exists today. This static picture is, however, the result of a long and dynamic historical process. The nature of the fauna in what is now designated as the Neotropical Region has changed radically during geological history. Different parts of that region have not had the same history. Faunal resemblances and distinctions have sometimes been greater, sometimes less than they are today. Boundaries of faunal assemblages have not remained in the same place. Recent neotropical elements may be old in that region or may be latecomers with their historical faunal associations elsewhere.

Until relatively recently, geologically speaking (well into the Pliocene), Central America had faunal affinities almost exclusively with North America and hardly at all with South America. There was then no Neotropical Region in the present sense. American camels, tapirs, and other animals now exclusively neotropical were pan-American in the Pleistocene and exclusively (in this hemisphere) North American before that. They are surely not neotropical in the historical sense, or in the same sense as, say, armadillos, which arose in South America and were until the late Tertiary confined to part of the Neotropical Region as now delimited.

In a historical view, then, the Neotropical Region ceases to be clear and consistent. Its fauna is not a coherent unit from this point of view, and its boundaries are not even approximately constant. In the historical study the static concept must be abandoned. The region and its fauna cannot be taken as either definite or invariable, but must be analyzed through a long series of shifts and fluxes.

Faunal Strata

In any given region, the various groups of animals will be found to have occupied that territory for different lengths of time. In general, the longer the group has been there, the more peculiar it will be to the local scene and the more strongly differentiated from relatives living elsewhere. The results of this process are particularly striking in South America. Armadillos and sloths belong to an order (Edentata) known nowhere else (aside from marginal spread into North America). Differentiation has proceeded so far in that region that there is now no clear trace of special relationship to animals of other regions, aside from the broadest fact that these edentates are placental mammals. The monkeys of South America are quite distinct, as a group, from those of the Old World and yet clearly related, belonging to the same order, Primates. They show an intermediate degree of regional differentiation. The field mice of South America, although distinctive as to species and, usually, genera, are closely related to those of North America, belonging not only to the same order (Rodentia) but also to the same family (Cricetidae) and even to the same subfamily and tribe. They have a low degree of regional differentiation.

The fossil record clearly confirms the fact that these varying degrees of differentiation are correlated with the time when the ancestors of these animals were emplaced in South America: edentates, high differentiation, in the earliest Cenozoic; primates, medium differentiation, in the mid-Cenozoic; cricetids, low differentiation, in the late Cenozoic. The three groups represent three readily distinguished faunal strata. The faunal history of South America has clearly been episodic.

The faunas of all regions are apparently stratified and their histories episodic in much this same way. On most continents, however, episodes of emplacement of new groups have been so frequent and so scattered in time, and their isolation from allied groups of other regions has been so imperfect, that the stratification is highly complex and the distinction of various strata is blurred. Only in South America and in the present island continent, Australia, are the strata relatively few in number and, as a rule, sharply and clearly separable. This clarity is a result of the physical history of the continent. Stratigraphic and paleontological evidence agree in clearly demonstrating that South America was isolated by sea barriers from all other continents from about the beginning of the Tertiary until near its end (probably early Paleocene to late Pliocene). During this long span, on the order of 70 million years, its animals were genetically isolated from all other continental faunas, and introduction of new stocks was, although not completely prevented, extremely restricted.

Some complications exist in each case, but in broad lines the South American mammalian fauna can be analyzed into three strata. The oldest stratum, which may be called that of the "ancient immigrants,"

TABLE I—MAMMALIAN FAUNAL STRATIFICATION IN SOUTH AMERICA

Time of Emplacement	Faunal Stratum	Groups Introduced		Differentiation in South America
Late Miocene to Recent	III LATE (ISLAND-HOPPERS AND) IMMIGRANTS	Deer Camels Peccaries Tapirs Horses Mastodons Cats Weasels Raccoons Bears Dogs Mice Squirrels Rabbits Shrew		Already differentiated before emplacement in South America. Local differentiation of many genera, species, subspecies, no families or higher groups.
Late Eocene to Oligocene	II OLD ISLAND-HOPPERS	Protrogomorph rodents		Caviomorph rodents (many groups)
		Advanced lemuroids		New World monkeys
Around earliest Paleocene	I ANCIENT IMMIGRANTS	Ferungulates (Condylarth-like complex)	Litopterns Notoungulates (many groups) Astrapotheres Pyrotheres	
		Palaeanodonts	Xenarthrans Ground sloths Tree sloths Anteaters Armadillos Glyptodonts	
		Didelphoids —	(Didelphoids continued) Borhyaenoids Caenolestoids	

includes groups that reached South America before its complete isolation from the rest of the world, in latest Cretaceous or earliest Tertiary times, and the numerous and varied descendants of these ancient stocks. The second stratum, that of the "old island-hoppers," includes only two groups, old native rodents and monkeys, which reached South America while it was isolated. The third major stratum, of "late island-hoppers" and "late immigrants," with considerable complexity of detail, includes a great variety of animals that reached the continent in the late Tertiary and the Quaternary, shortly before and during its re-connection with North America. The three mammalian strata are shown in more detail in Table I, and their correlation with geographic events is diagrammatically suggested in Figure 1.

For animals other than mammals, the fossil evidence is relatively poor. Most of the vertebrates have more or less clear indications of the same threefold stratification, with some probable blurring of the picture for groups less rigidly restricted by a sea barrier (such as some birds and probably some fishes). Among freshwater and terrestrial invertebrates, the fossil record of which is almost nil, there may be an added complication in the form of faunal strata still older than the oldest for mammals and most other vertebrates. On the whole, however, the

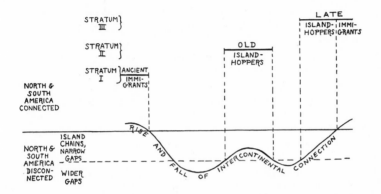

FIG. 1. Relationships between faunal strata in South America and the rise and fall of intercontinental land connections. The graph is diagrammatic only, as the history of the connection was not so simple as shown, and the sea barriers shifted in position.

three designated strata are pervasive in historical interpretation of the entire fauna.

These faunal strata can be designated as such and thus dated only with respect to the geographic unit of South America and by virtue of its Tertiary isolation. In Central America, for instance, much the same groups of animals occur, but their time relationships and their associations in strata are quite different *with respect to the region occupied.* The oldest mammalian faunal strata in Central America include what are in South America the old island-hoppers and various of the late island-hoppers and immigrants. The old immigrants of South America, forming the *oldest* stratum there, belong to what is generally speaking the *youngest* stratum in Central America. There are profound differences in regional history in parts of what now is the broadly unified single Neotropical Region.

The Problem of Basic Mammalian Faunal Types

A fundamental problem regarding the Latin American mammalian fauna arises at the very beginning of its history. When the Age of Mammals began, with extinction of many groups of Mesozoic reptiles and the beginning of the rise of mammals to dominance in land faunas, the mammals were already, in fact, an old group. Although still small, obscure, and relatively unvaried, the major lines of mammals had then already split into two basically distinct, primitive groups: marsupials and placentals or, technically, Metatheria and Eutheria.

Africa, Europe, Asia, and North America then formed an essentially continuous land mass, a World Continent. The continuity has been interrupted at various points from time to time and there have been innumerable faunal changes and marked regional differentiation in various groups, but the mammalian faunal type was then and remains today fundamentally the same throughout all parts of the World Continent. Marsupials were present at the start (at least in North America and Europe, and probably throughout), but they were of minor importance. The major ecological roles, and specifically those of carnivorous and herbivorous types, were played, as they still are, by placentals.

In Australia, probably then already an island continent (Notogaea), and in South America, then or shortly thereafter becoming an island continent (Neogaea), the basic faunal types with which the Age of Mammals began were radically different from the World Continent type. In Australia all the mammalian ecological roles were played by marsupials. (Such early faunas have not, in fact, been found in Australia, but this is a probable and generally accepted inference from the evidence of later faunas.) In South America, the herbivores were mainly placentals, but the insectivorous, gnawing, and carnivorous types were marsupials.

Early attempts to explain this extraordinary anomaly between the South American island continent mammalian faunal type and the World Continent type usually involved the theory that South American marsupial carnivores were derived from Australia. (Why the carnivores of Australia were marsupials rather than placentals is another fundamental problem not here under consideration.) Among several serious objections to this idea is the extreme improbability that marsupial carnivores would spread from Australia to South America unaccompanied by their ecological associates and prey, the Australian marsupial herbivores. Other possible sources of mammalian faunas all had placental carnivores and placental herbivores, and equal difficulty is encountered in explaining the spread to South America of these herbivores without their associates, the placental carnivores. That the carnivorous and herbivorous elements in the first, balanced, basic South American mammalian fauna should have come each separately and from a totally distinct source is simply incredible.

An alternative view is that the basic South American fauna did have an essentially unified geographic origin, all coming from (or at any rate being connected with) the World Continent fauna. In that case, however, it would appear that placental carnivores must have been included but must almost immediately have become extinct in South America. Such extinction would seem inherently improbable, because in the established cases of competition between marsupial and placental carnivores, the placentals have survived and the marsupials have become extinct. The placental dingo survived in Australia and its marsupial analogue, the thylacine, became extinct (except on the separate island of Tasmania which was not reached by the dingo). The last South American marsupial carnivores disappeared as placental carnivores (of the latest major faunal stratum) arrived. It is an additional difficulty that specialized marsupial carnivores are quite unknown from any age on the World Continent and probably never occurred there. Similarly, placental carnivores are totally unknown in the early South American faunas, and extinction so rapid and complete as to eliminate all traces in the now rather abundant early Tertiary fossil collections seems improbable, although not impossible.

These objections largely disappear, and a reasonable solution of this long-disputed problem can be suggested, if one gives consideration to the relatively undifferentiated and primitive mammals of the earliest Tertiary, rather than thinking in terms of the more familiar, sharply distinct and specialized later forms. The basic World Continent fauna, at its very beginning, did not include radically differentiated placental carnivores and herbivores. These two later ecological types were then ancestrally represented by one basic stock, to which I have elsewhere applied the name "ferungulate." This stock was rapidly becoming considerably varied and apparently included some rather more herbivorous and some rather more carnivorous forms, but as a whole it was omnivorous and all its members were still closely similar. Among the fossils of this group, some are classified as Carnivora and some as Condylarthra (primitive ungulates), because of our knowledge of the *subsequent* sharp ordinal distinctions of their descendants. If we did not know their later history, the early forms would certainly be placed in the same order and very likely in the same family or even smaller group. For instance, *Protogonodon*, an early Paleocene form classified as a carnivore, and *Desmatoclaenus*, also early Paleocene, classified as an ungulate, are far more alike than numerous pairs of recent genera referred to one family or subfamily, say *Mustela*, the weasel, and *Gulo*, the wolverine, both commonly placed in the subfamily Mustelinae.

It was this more generalized ferungulate stock, and not any later and then truly distinctive placental carnivores and herbivores, that figured in the beginnings of the oldest faunal stratum of South America. On the World Continent, this stock was associated with likewise primitive marsupials, which also lacked as yet any distinctive specializations as carnivores but were equally capable (as the event proved) of such a development. In the World Continent, *after* it was cut off from South America, specialized carnivores arose among the ferungulate lines, and their occupation of this ecological specialty impeded the rise there of marsupial carnivores. In South America, likewise after separation from the World Continent, marsupials more rapidly developed carnivorous types. This in itself would tend sufficiently to inhibit the rise there of placental carnivores among the ferungulates, which rapidly developed a great variety of types all more or less herbivorous.

Thus there was no competition between marsupial carnivores and placental carnivores, as such, and probably only marginal competition between marsupials and placentals as a whole, but only a parceling out of the various ecological zones, which happened to receive different occupants in the World Continent and in South America. Why the ferungulates evolved more rapidly into specialized carnivores on the World Continent and the marsupials (didelphoids) in South America is not evident. It is, nevertheless, plausible that this could occur, and the hypothesis that it did occur seems to be the only one that reasonably accounts for these differences in basic faunal type.

There may be some remaining objection that placentals in general are superior to marsupials and would tend, in South America or elsewhere, to occupy any and all ecological niches, including those of carnivores, at the expense of the marsupials. This possible objection really has little or no force. Present evidence is that the placentals are not more advanced derivatives from backward or older marsupials, as was commonly believed in the nineteenth century and is still occasionally stated in textbooks. Placentals and marsupials seem rather to represent a basic dichotomy of the main mammalian stock and to have been about equally progressive and adaptively efficient when they arose. Primitive forms of the two major branches apparently lived together in ecological equilibrium, and even today the opossums of North and South America remain abundant and are eminently successful in holding their own in the midst of the dominant placental faunas. Ecological incompatibility between marsupials and placentals seems to arise only when late and narrowly specialized forms come in contact within essentially the same ecological niche, a situation in which *any* two groups, and not only marsupials and placentals, become ecologically incompatible. Even on this score, the extinction of South American and Australian marsupial carnivores in competition with placental carnivores gives evidence not particularly that placentals are superior to marsupials but that the late World Continent groups had become competitively superior to those of the island continents. In South America, the old native placental groups were also decimated when they came into contact with placentals from the World Continent. They fared no better than the marsupials of similar geographic history.

Origins of the Oldest Faunal Elements

Probably the most disputed single question of Latin American zoogeography has been the geographic origin or, at least, connections of the older faunal elements. The principal question raised has concerned possible direct relationships among the southern continents, between South America and Australia, on one side, or Africa, on the other. The various postulates include transoceanic land bridges or continents, land connections by way of Antarctica, or early continental union followed by fracturing and drift (Wegenerian) to the present widely separated positions of the three continents. A summary of the truly voluminous and polemic literature of this subject is outside the scope of

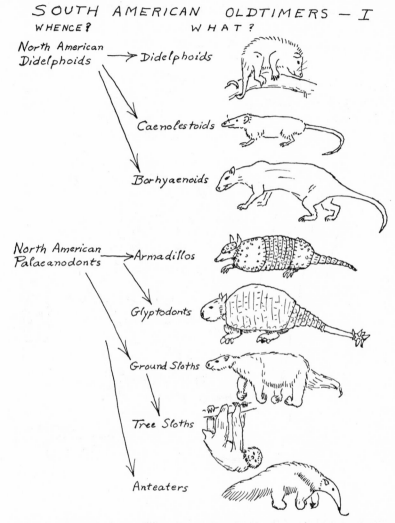

FIG. 2. Marsupials and edentates, evolved in the oldest mammalian faunal stratum of South America, and their possible origins. (Not drawn to scale.)

the present study, but the nature of the older mammalian faunas and the evidence these give as to their origin will be briefly reviewed.

The major elements among the mammalian old immigrants and their possible origins are as follows (see also Figs. 2 and 3).

MARSUPIALS. These were already quite varied in the older Tertiary, with primitive, more or less insectivorous types, rodent-like types, and marsupial carnivores. A possible common origin of all would be in a varied assemblage of relatively unspecialized marsupials, didelphoid or

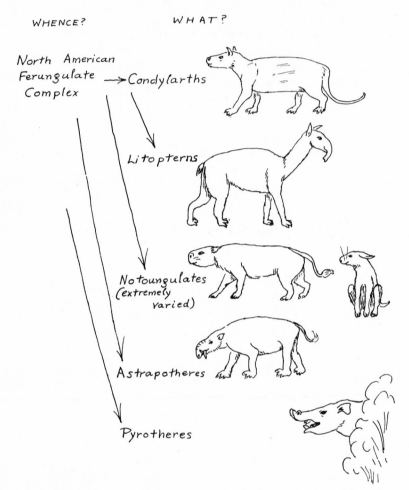

SOUTH AMERICAN OLDTIMERS - II

WHENCE?   WHAT?

North American
Ferungulate   →Condylarths
Complex

            Litopterns

            Notoungulates
            (extremely
                varied)

A strapotheres

            Pyrotheres

FIG. 3. Ungulates of the oldest mammalian faunal stratum of South America, and their possible origins. (Not drawn to scale.)

extremely primitive dasyuroid in general character. Such an assemblage is known from the late Cretaceous of North America, where primitive marsupials (opossums) also occurred through the Paleocene and later. Similar forms occur doubtfully in the Paleocene and surely in the Eocene of Europe. Elsewhere the evidence is purely negative.

EDENTATES. The oldest South American faunas include only armadillos, of primitive type, among edentates. The other groups appear, evidently by evolution within the continent, during the early and middle Tertiary: glyptodonts and ground sloths by late Eocene, anteaters in the Miocene, tree sloths (with practically no established fossil record) by rather minor differentiation from the less specialized ground sloths sometime around the mid-Tertiary. The only firmly established special relationships with any non-South American mammals are with the Palaeanodonta, a group more primitive in general character than any of the South American edentates and known only from North America (late Paleocene to middle Eocene, with a probable more specialized offshoot in the early Oligocene).

CONDYLARTHS. These most primitive of ungulate herbivores were fairly common in the Paleocene-Eocene faunas of South America and some lingered on into the Oligocene (or possibly the Miocene). The same order was important in the basic World Continent fauna. It occurs abundantly throughout the Paleocene and Eocene of North America and some North and South American genera are suggestive of special relationship.

LITOPTERNS. This order, known only from South America, was common and varied in early faunas and persisted, in decreasing variety, into the Pleistocene. Early forms are near the condylarths, to such an extent that the litopterns might be considered merely as surviving and diversely specialized condylarths. They seem to have originated in South America from the South American condylarths, and therefore to have the same source as the latter.

NOTOUNGULATES. This great order of hoofed herbivores constitutes the bulk of all the earlier South American faunas and continues, with radically decreasing variety, into the Pleistocene. It suggests a group similar in origin and parallel in history to the litopterns. An odd anomaly arises from the discovery of a notoungulate in the late Paleocene of Asia and a related form in the early Eocene of North America, the only occurrences of the order outside of South America. Origin in Asia and migration to South America by way of North America are suggested by the face of these facts, and this remains a possibility but is rendered rather improbable by various considerations. Early Eocene is too late a time for entry into South America. The most primitive South American forms are slightly but definitely less specialized than those known from Asia and North America. Another possibility is that the latter were strays *from* South America. The question cannot now be resolved, but a faunal connection of one sort or another is indicated with the northern continents.

ASTRAPOTHERES. Although never highly varied, these aberrant hoofed herbivores appeared early in South America and persisted into the Miocene. They probably arose in that continent and have no evident close or special relationships with other known groups, except that they probably originated ultimately from condylarths or most primitive ferungulates in a broader sense. They could have some collateral relationship or, at least, functional parallelism with archaic World Continent forms like the pantodonts and uintatheres, known in particular abundance from North America but also spreading to Eurasia.

PYROTHERES. These odd, superficially mastodon-like ungulates were never much varied or particularly common, as far as known, but they appear in early Eocene faunas and persist into the Oligocene. They are known only from South America and probably arose in that continent. Special relationships are not known, but in broad terms differentiation from the basic ferungulate complex is indicated, more or less as for the astrapotheres. True relationship to the Proboscidea has been suggested but now seems untenable except as the Proboscidea may also represent a separate branch from a part (paenungulate) of the ferungulate complex.

The data on the very earliest Tertiary mammals of South America and of the world as a whole are so scanty that tracing of exact lineages cannot be expected and is not, in fact, possible at present. In broad terms, this assemblage certainly suggests derivation from the World Continent fauna and *could not* be derived from Australia unless it is assumed, quite gratuitously and contrary to such evidence (all indirect) as exists, that Australia did once have a basic fauna of World Continent type and later eliminated almost the whole of this fauna. Within the World Continent, there is absolutely no evidence of any special relationship of Africa with South America. This is partly a negative conclusion, because Paleocene mammals are unknown from Africa, but it would, again, be wholly gratuitous to assume that relationships existed and left no trace in the late Eocene and subsequent African faunas.

Such definite evidence of relationships as exists all points most nearly to North America. Every South American stock is related at least as closely to one known from North America as to any other known group outside of South America, and the edentates have no established relationships except with an exclusively North American group. In view of these relationships and of the fact that South America is now geographically closest to North America (and nothing impels the belief that this was untrue at the end of the Cretaceous), the tendency of so many students to look elsewhere for the main geographic relationships of the old South American fauna almost smacks of a preference for the unlikely over the obvious.

The question remains whether the World Continent fauna might not have been derived from South America, as the great Argentine student, Ameghino, insisted, rather than the other way around. In the exact sense of Ameghino, who believed that later specialized orders and families originated in South America and spread hence over the rest of the world, this certainly is not true. In the sense that some elements of the most basic World Continent fauna might have become differentiated in South America while that continent was united to North America and hence in a sense part of the World Continent, the possibility remains but it seems quite improbable. The old South American faunas seem to represent diversification on that continent from a sampling of the World Continent fauna that was partial only (no insectivores, no early primates, no early rodents, no differentiated creodonts, only highly aberrant paenungulates). No forms conceivably near the ancestry of any World Continent lineages have ever actually been found in the old South American faunas.

Clearly inconclusive, the evidence does suggest North America as the probable source of the old South American fauna. It does not exclude, but definitely does not support, other possibilities. This conclusion finds further, indirect but strong substantiation from the evidence that South America was connected with North America toward the end of the Age of Reptiles. Although opposite statements may still be found in the literature, it is at present recognized by the most competent specialists on these faunas that the late Cretaceous reptiles of South America are, as a group, more like those of North America than like any known faunas elsewhere in the world.

The Old Island-Hoppers

The origin of the second faunal stratum of South America, although less discussed as a separate problem, has been in many ways even more puzzling. This stratum comprises the old native rodents, which are the so-called South American hystricomorphs, and the neotropical primates (see Fig. 4). These rodents first appear in the record in beds somewhat uncertainly correlated as early Oligocene, and primates are first known from later beds, considered with similar uncertainty as late Oligocene. Both occurrences are marginal on the continent (in Patagonia) and do not exclude the possibility that the groups had been for some time in more central or northern parts of the continent, where adequate faunas of appropriate age have not been discovered. It is, however, improbable that emplacement of these groups in South America was long prior to the Oligocene and it seems almost certain that their ancestors were not among the early immigrants. There is no evidence that entry of the two groups was absolutely simultaneous, and, indeed, it probably was not. Both, however, entered South America at about the same time, roughly midway between the two major immigrations; the two have become comparably differentiated there, and it is justified to consider them broadly as of the same faunal stratum.

Both these groups have repeatedly been cited as indicating faunal relationships with Africa. The neotropical monkeys, although distinctly definable as a group, resemble the Old World (including African) monkeys and are on a similar evolutionary level. The old South American rodents also show resemblances to some Old World rodents (porcupines figure in both regions, for instance), and among them are some, in the general group of the hutias, degus, tucutucus, and spiny "rats" (not true rats), that particularly resemble some African rodents, the cane and rock "rats" (also not true rats).

Recent studies seem rather conclusively to controvert these apparent African affinities. The South American primates, including the earliest forms, are in some respects more primitive than the Old World forms of similar or later age and in some respects differently specialized. The former characters seem to prohibit derivation of the New from the Old World forms, and the latter seem to exclude filiation in the other direction. There is a strong suggestion that the New and Old World monkeys

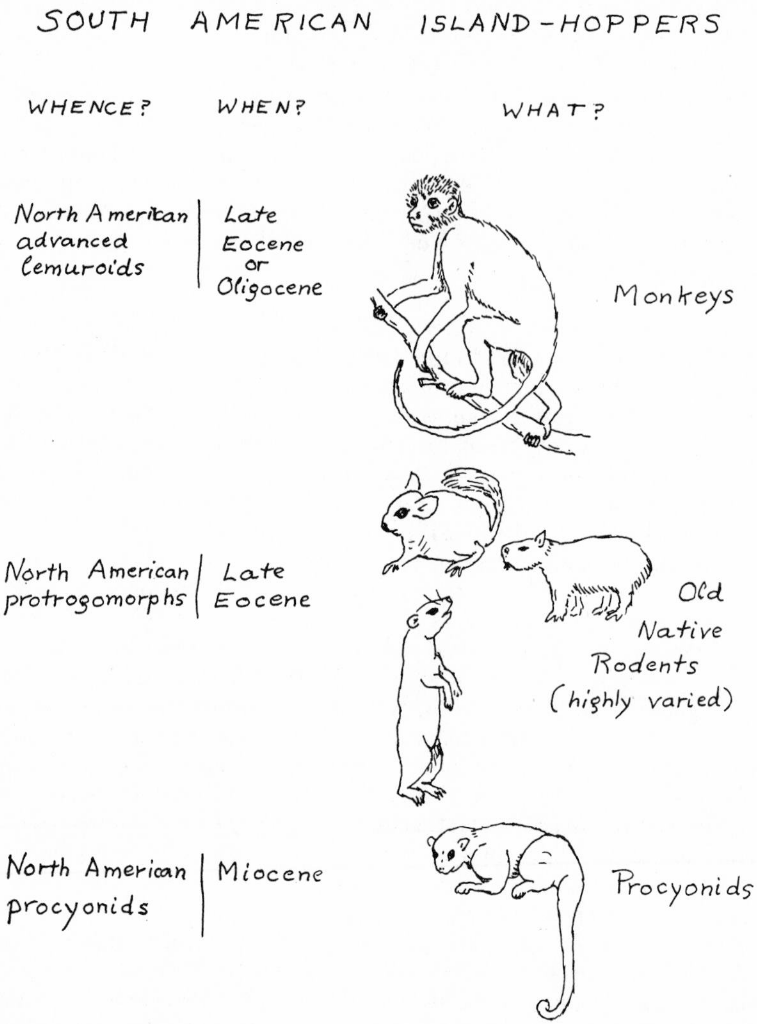

SOUTH   AMERICAN   ISLAND-HOPPERS

WHENCE?   WHEN?   WHAT?

| North American advanced lemuroids | Late Eocene or Oligocene | | Monkeys |

| North American protrogomorphs | Late Eocene | | Old Native Rodents (highly varied) |

| North American procyonids | Miocene | | Procyonids |

FIG. 4.   Derivatives of island-hopping immigrants into South America, and their probable origins. The monkeys and old native rodents form the second or intermediate mammalian faunal stratum. The procyonids (allies of the raccoon) may be considered rather as forerunners of the last, relatively complex faunal stratum. (Not drawn to scale.)

represent geographically separated parallel developments from a more remote and primitive (technically prosimian) ancestry. About twenty-five years ago, the late J. W. Gidley suggested that neotropical monkeys might be derived from a group of prosimians (Notharctinae) relatively abundant in the Eocene of North America, and the Old World monkeys from Old World allies of this group. Too little attention has been given to this suggestion, but recent study is adding some evidence in its favor and it is now the best working hypothesis as regards the New World forms, at least.

It has been suspected from time to time that the history of the New and Old World "hystricomorph" rodents might be a similar case of independent, parallel development from allied New and Old World groups of primitive Eocene rodents, but concrete evidence has been scanty. Quite recently (in 1949), in describing relatively complete material of the oldest and most primitive known South American rodent, A. E. Wood has found positive evidence for their derivation not from a distinct hystricomorph stock but from a widespread World Continent group of most primitive rodents (Ischyromyidae, *sensu lato*). Among these, he finds particular resemblance to some North American forms (especially the mid-Eocene *Reithroparamys*).

There is, then, good reason to believe that the idea of special African relationships for these groups, old South American rodents and monkeys, is incorrect and that both are of North American origin. The evidence is, indeed, better than for the older immigrants, for in each case a possible North American ancestry can be rather closely designated among well-known groups.

It seems quite clear that these groups did not follow a land bridge from North America. When they entered South America, North America was swarming with rapidly progressive mammals of other types, notably many placental carnivores and a variety of perissodactyl and artiodactyl ungulates. It is incredible that an open migration route existed without any effect other than spread southward of just two stocks, possibly only a single introduction in each case. Entry was almost certainly by waif dispersal over what I have called a "sweepstakes route." Both groups, initially small and probably arboreal animals, are ecological types especially apt for such dispersal. Geological evidence in Central America and northwestern South America perfectly fits this picture. During late Eocene and Oligocene, the pertinent times in this connection, there was clearly a series of seaways between North and South America, interrupted by a series of islands. The seaways would bar any extensive faunal interchange. The islands would facilitate overseas spread of a few special groups, literally island-hoppers. Although it would, of course, be possible to postulate a similar island chain elsewhere, to Africa, for instance, no evidence known to me really suggests this and the postulate is unnecessary and unsupported.

The immediate source of the immigrants would, of course, be Middle America or what is now tropical North America, and not the region from New Mexico to Montana where early Tertiary faunas are now known. Transition from the archaic ancestral groups (prosimians for the monkeys and protrogomorphs [of Wood] for the rodents) to the characteristic Latin American groups (ceboids and "hystricomorphs" or, perhaps

better, caviomorphs, respectively) doubtless occurred in the paleontological *terra incognita* of early Middle America.   Some basic diversification of these groups may also have occurred in Middle America and
have been under way even before they island-hopped to the southern
continent.

Development of the Native Fauna

The oldest reasonably well-known South American mammalian faunas
(Eocene of Patagonia) are dominated by the typical and highly varied
native ungulate herbivores of the Order Notoungulata, which includes
nearly half of the known genera of that time.   The rest of the known
fauna is divided about equally among condylarths, litopterns, edentates,
and marsupials (groups characterized on previous pages).   Pyrotheres
and astrapotheres were present and are striking animals, but were quite
minor elements in the total fauna.

Until the late Pliocene, the faunal composition changed rather steadily
but with few really profound modifications.   The condylarths dwindled
and finally became extinct, with ecological replacement by their collateral descendants, the litopterns.   The notoungulates, exuberantly
varied in the Eocene, continued in force but show a steady decrease in
variety as primitive and intermediate lines were weeded out and a
smaller number of more sharply distinct and specialized lines continued.
On the other hand, the edentates, relatively little varied in the Eocene,
expanded steadily into the Miocene when, in variety of genera, they
constituted about a third of the known faunas.   Pyrotheres and astrapotheres died out, the former in the Oligocene and the latter by the end
of the Miocene.

The most noteworthy change before late Pliocene followed the appearance of the second faunal stratum, that of the old island-hoppers.
The old native rodents expanded steadily and greatly into the Pliocene,
where they include about a third of the known mammalian genera.
Similar, but less intense, expansion of the primates may be postulated,
although they are absent in most of the known fossil deposits, which
generally represent facies unsuitable for this predominantly tropical
and arboreal group.   The broader lines of this long faunal development
are seen in Figure 5.

The greatest interest of the phase of South American faunal history
while the continent was an island lies in the fact that it is a sort of large-
scale natural experiment in evolution.   The old immigrants rapidly occupied the large and varied continent, and the faunas then evolved
there in dynamic equilibrium, undisturbed by wider genetic interchange
or by irruptions from without other than those of the old island-hoppers—and this exception is itself so relatively simple and analyzable
that it almost ideally exemplifies the process and consequences of single
major additions to an evolving fauna.

The first striking evolutionary phenomena illustrated are those of "explosive" or "eruptive" evolution and adaptive radiation.   The poorly
known Paleocene faunas and, particularly, the better known early

Eocene faunas are at a most active stage of this process. Everything here indicates the culmination of an exceptionally rapid and burgeoning expansion of the mammalian fauna into a great variety of ecological niches which were, before this episode, empty or nearly so. The number of separate groups, from generic to family levels, at least, is exceptionally large. Intergradation between lines later widely distinct is still common. There seems to be considerable overlapping and even duplication in ecological types within the same or adjacent local faunas. Variation within specific populations is often exceptionally great, a basis for rapid diversification speciational in pattern, and an indication that marked segregation of characters and specialization of adaptive type are under way but still incomplete.

Disappearance of intermediate types and fixation of a smaller number of well-defined groups each with a characteristic, separate, and progres-

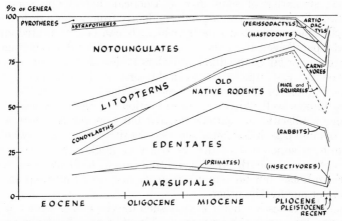

Fig. 5. Development of the land mammals of South America. For each epoch, the composition of the fauna is shown in terms of percentage of known genera belonging to the various orders of mammals.

sively specialized adaptive and ecological status were processes evident through the later Eocene and Oligocene. This process was essentially completed in the Miocene as far as the descendants of most of the ancient immigrants are concerned, although the old native rodents and some of the edentates were then still in an expanding phase. The result of the process is a sort of parceling out of the available ways of life among the various stocks of mammals, an adaptive radiation.

In the meantime, on the World Continent even more varied ways of life were being occupied by adaptive radiation, or a more complex, interlocking series of over-all and local adaptive radiations, going on without contact with the South American fauna. When World Continent and South American lines became specialized for similar ecological roles, they also came to resemble each other functionally and morphologically.

Parallel and convergent evolution was thus illustrated on a large scale. Another independent radiation in Australia produced another set of parallel and convergent types. Sometimes the separate lines departed from the same more or less remote common ancestry and evolved in close parallel, as in the case of the carnivorous marsupials of South America and of Australia. This process produces closest resemblance, a fact responsible for long debate on the affinities of these marsupial carnivores and for former insistence on the part of some students that South America and Australia must somehow have shared advanced and specialized marsupials and not merely the remote and primitive ancestors of these.

In other cases quite different groups have evolved toward similar adaptive types, a process producing less complete, convergent resemblance, as between the marsupial carnivores and the World Continent's placental carnivores. The two processes of parallelism and convergence intergrade and cannot be sharply defined in given cases. The striking similarity of some North American horses and some South American litopterns, evolving independently from a more or less remote condylarth ancestry, is a case in point. It can be interpreted either as straight parallelism from the common ancestral condylarth stage or as divergence, origin of the different orders Perissodactyla and Litopterna, followed by convergence between lineages in two families of these orders, Equidae in the first and Proterotheriidae in the second.

The faunas well illustrate the limitations of these processes, which produce similarities of various degrees but apparently never, even in cases of close parallelism, produce real identity, in part or in whole. In the flesh, a superficial or distant observer might well have confused *Diadiaphorus*, a South American litoptern, with *Miohippus*, a North American horse, but no competent anatomist would mistake any tooth or bone of one for the other.

Another interesting point is that such developments were not necessarily synchronous in the two cases. *Thoatherium*, a litoptern, was completely one-toed in the early Miocene. Horses did not become one-toed until the Pliocene, and even today *Equus* is less advanced than *Thoatherium* was in this respect (see Fig. 6). Some lines of notoungulates in South America had very high-crowned, complexly crested, cement-covered grazing teeth in the early Oligocene; horses did not reach a comparable stage until the late Miocene. These examples illustrate, by the way, that South American animals were not altogether less progressive or more slowly evolving than those of the World Continent, as has sometimes been supposed.

In many cases convergence was quite incomplete or would involve only a particular functional resemblance and not a close equivalence of total ecological status. Glyptodonts, for instance, the rigidly bulky cousins of the armadillo, seem to have been grazing forms and so have this functional resemblance with various ungulate grazers, but even their teeth are built on a plan wholly different from that of any ungulate. The glyptodonts as a whole can hardly be compared with any ungulate, or indeed with any World Continent animals. Such forms as some litopterns and some horses may be considered ecological vicars in their respective areas, but others, like the glyptodonts, are ecological uniques.

Late Faunal Mixture and Its Outcome

In the World Continent, there was a radical turnover in faunal type rather early in the Tertiary, mainly during the Eocene. In terms, for instance, of percentage composition of the mammalian faunas by orders or suborders, the difference between a Paleocene and an Oligocene fauna in North America is striking and almost absolute. Changes in this respect, of broad lines of faunal composition, have been relatively slight since the Oligocene. The modern faunal type was beginning to appear and to replace the oldest type even in the Eocene, thus here aptly called "Dawn of the Recent." Not so, however, in South America. There, as we have already seen in passing, change was gradual and involved no really fundamental upset of faunal type into the Pliocene. The mid-Pliocene fauna, in most of its broadest features, was not radically unlike a Paleocene fauna in spite of very pronounced advancing specialization in most of the orders and the Oligocene insertion into the fauna of two new orders (Primates, Rodentia).

A change like that going on in the Eocene on the World Continent also occurred in South America, but at a greatly later date, in the late Pliocene and Pleistocene (Fig. 5). Its cause was the rise of the Central American bridge and the consequent irruption into South America of many derivatives from the fauna of the World Continent. This third

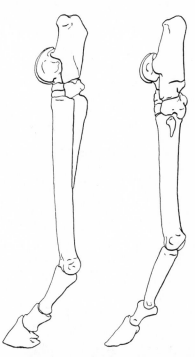

Fig. 6. Side views of hind feet of the modern horse, *Equus* (*left*), and of an extinct South American pseudo-horse, the litoptern *Thoatherium* (*right*), to show convergence in foot structure of these two one-toed mammals. Note vestiges of side-toes, larger in the true horse than in this pseudo-horse. (Not drawn to scale; *Equus* is larger than *Thoatherium*.) Redrawn after W. D. Matthew.

broad faunal stratum did not come in all at once, in a single wave. Already in the late Miocene a few northern forms appeared, small arboreal placental carnivores more or less related to the raccoon. Not long thereafter, apparently in early Pliocene times, some South American animals, ground sloths, reached North America. These forerunners do not seem to indicate a continuous land connection but probably utilized the island chain, gaps in which were closing progressively as the Central American and northwestern South American regions rose relative to sea level. The exact moment when the bridge became complete is not es-

SOUTH AMERICAN NEWCOMERS
(All from North America in late Tertiary to Recent)

Shrews

Rabbits

Squirrels

Mice

Dogs

Bears

Raccoons

Weasels

Cats

Mastodons

Horses

Tapirs

Peccaries

Camels

Deer

FIG. 7. Representatives of the principal families of previously North American mammals that invaded South America late in the Cenozoic, and which form the youngest mammalian faunal stratum there. (Not drawn to scale.)

tablished, but this probably occurred during the age called Chapad-malalan in South America and Blancan in North America, placed by some authorities as latest Pliocene and by others as earliest Pleistocene. Even then the exchange was at first rather limited in scope and the full surge of intermigration did not occur until somewhat later, in unequivocally Pleistocene times. Soon or late, at least fifteen (possibly sixteen) families invaded South America in this great episode (see Fig. 7).

Invasion occurred in both directions. By a moderate tabulation, fifteen families of North American mammals then spread into South America and seven families spread in the reverse direction. The main migrants to the south were rabbits, squirrels, field mice, dogs, bears, raccoons, weasels, cats, mastodons, horses, tapirs, peccaries, camels, and deer, including in most of these cases some variety of related forms.

The immediate effect was to produce in both continents, but particularly in South America, a greatly enriched fauna. To a fauna already large and essentially complete or closed ecologically were added a large number of new forms from the other continent. The enrichment inevitably involved some duplication. No two forms of different origin can have been precisely and fully equal in their needs and capacities, but many were sufficiently similar to be in competition for food and, in general, living space. Some native groups held their own and some invading groups became extinct, but some native groups disappeared and (as a rule) were replaced by invaders.

In the end, that is, at the present time, South America has returned to

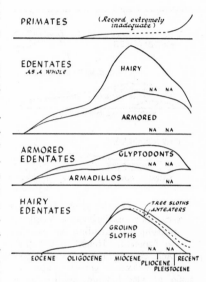

FIG. 8. Development of some South American groups that were ecologically unique with respect to late invaders from North America. Height of the graph in each case represents the relative number of known genera. The time scale at the bottom applies to all graphs. NA = migration to North America. (Some of the old native rodents were also ecologically unique; see Fig. 9.)

about the same basic richness of fauna as before the invasion. Recent families of mammals there number the same (more or less, depending on the classification used) as in the Pliocene before invasion, but the faunal composition is radically different. The notoungulates, litopterns, and marsupial carnivores have entirely disappeared. The native rodents and edentates are greatly reduced. In their places, artiodactyls, perissodactyls, rodents of northern origin (squirrels, cricetids), rabbits, and placental carnivores are fully entrenched and constitute, in number of genera, about half of the recent fauna.

The main determinants in this process were, first, ecological status and, second, place of origin. Ecological uniques tended to survive (Fig. 8). It is true that glyptodonts and ground sloths, after spreading over both continents, became extinct and that they apparently were ecological uniques. The question of their extinction involves some other and not properly understood factor, and it is part of a larger question that cannot be discussed here. The smaller, likewise or even more strictly ecologically unique relatives of these animals, armadillos, tree sloths, and anteaters, did survive. So did the monkeys, ecological uniques with respect to North America, and most of the truly ecologically unique old native rodents.

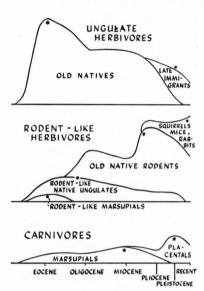

When ecological vicars met, one or the other generally became extinct (Fig. 9). In South America, old native ungulates disappeared and ungulates of northern origin survived. Many old native rodents (about half the generic lines) became extinct and rabbits, squirrels, and field mice survived. Marsupial carnivores became extinct and placental carnivores survived. The fact that in each case the survivors were of northern origin cannot be pure coincidence. It is not explanatory to say that the animals from North America were "superior" or "more progressive," and such statements would be hard to substantiate by any objective evidence from their anatomy, for instance.

FIG. 9. Development in South America of ecological vicars, similar in adaptation to invading types from North America. Height of the graph in each case represents the relative number of known genera. The time scale at the bottom applies to all graphs. Top and bottom graphs show simple, total replacement of old groups by late invaders from North America. The more complex middle graph shows total replacement of old rodent-like marsupials (Polydolopidae) by other old native rodent-like forms, partial replacement of old rodent-like ungulates (mainly typotheres and hegetotheres) by old native true rodents, and then partial replacement of most of the latter by rabbits and true rodents in the late invasion from North America. Surviving old native rodents are, in the main, ecologically unique, with no closely similar competitors among the late invaders. * = apogee.

The ultimate factors have not been and probably cannot be designated, but a generalized explanation presents itself. North American animals had intermittently throughout the Age of Mammals and almost continuously in its later part been involved in the flux and intermigration of the World Continent. Those extant in the Plio-Pleistocene were the ones that had been successful in a long series of competitive episodes. They were specialists in invasion and in meeting competitive invaders. South American mammals had competed among themselves in the early Tertiary, but by about the end of the Oligocene they had essentially completed a process of parceling out the ecological opportunities among a number of practically noncompeting lines. Thereafter until the late Pliocene they met no impact from outside their own closed economy, and when it came, they had not evolved the required defenses.

Thus the recent South American mammalian fauna is a complex agglomeration, in spite of the fact that processes of ecological adjustment have again reduced it to an essentially balanced economy. It may all be ultimately derived from North America, and some of the evidence to that effect has been summarized. This evidence is suggestive but inconclusive for the oldest elements, stronger for the mid-Cenozoic elements, and conclusive and unquestioned for the latest elements. Even if all did have the same geographic origin, there are the three quite distinct broad faunal strata. Their different times of entry into South America complicate the picture, not only because of corresponding differences in differentiation within that continent, but also because each stratum was drawn from a different sort of World Continent fauna. Differentiation, replacement, intermigration, complex stratification, divergent specialization, and other processes were constantly going on in the World Continent, and the strata of South American mammals sampled this sequence at three very different levels.

The static zoogeographic picture in a classical sense, of current resemblances and differences of regional faunas, is further complicated by differential regional extinction. Pumas link North and South America in nonhistorical zoogeography because they now occur on both continents, and camels separate the faunal regions, because they occur in South but not in North America. But in the Pleistocene pumas and camels occurred throughout both continents and in the Pliocene their ancestors were present in North but not in South America. Final analysis of the present relationships of South and North American faunas must involve this factor as well as the factor of stratification.

In Table II an attempt is made to analyze the now extant South American mammals with respect to their geographic history and their present relationships to mammals in the recent North American fauna (north of the tropical zone).

This analysis is on a family level. More refined analysis, to genera or below, would involve some changes of status in the last stratum. Central America, with its peculiar faunal history and its intermediate faunal types, is not involved in this comparison, which is based on the fully South American and the temperate-zone North American faunas. Special consideration of Central America is now necessary.

The Role of Central America

There is and doubtless always has been considerable difference between regional faunas within South America. The faunas of the Patagonian pampas, the Andine punas, and the tropical rain forests are strikingly distinct. They are, nevertheless, regional varieties or differentiates of a general South American fauna and they share much the same sort of differences from and resemblances to the general fauna of temperate North America. There have not, during the Cenozoic, been any absolute barriers between regions within South America, and no outstanding effects of isolation are historically evident in separate parts of the

TABLE II—ANALYSIS OF ZOOGEOGRAPHIC RELATIONSHIPS OF SOUTH
AMERICAN RECENT MAMMALS, WITH RESPECT TO NORTH AMERICA

I. Oldest South American faunal stratum, from North America (?) in late Cretaceous-Paleocene.
    A. Collaterals (strongly differentiated) from same level present in North America.
        1. Without late level spread and recent presence in North America: caenolestids (North American collaterals: opossums). (Some students would place the caenolestids under IB1 and the opossums under IB2; this may be correct but seems unlikely at present.)
        2. With late level spread, etc.: none.
    B. Ancient stock extinct in North America.
        1. Without late level spread and recent presence in North America: none.
        2. With late level spread, etc.: armadillos (N. A. distribution restricted).
II. Intermediate South American faunal stratum, from North America in Oligocene.
    A. Collaterals (well differentiated) from same level present in N. A.
        1. Without late level spread, etc.: "hystricomorphs" or caviomorphs except porcupines (differentiated N. A. collaterals: sewellel, squirrels, etc.).
        2. With late level spread, etc.: porcupines.
    B. Ancient stock extinct in North America.
        1. Without late level spread, etc.: monkeys. (No collaterals in N. A. wild fauna, but man could be considered as such.)
        2. With late level spread, etc.: none.
III. Late South American faunal stratum, from North America in late Pliocene and Quaternary.
    A. Collaterals from same level (here poorly differentiated and representing essentially the same immediate stock) present in N. A. Late level spread back to N. A. possible in some cases, but in that event part of the same general episode of intermigration as emplacement of the South American stratum: opossums (history somewhat questionable, sometimes considered IB2, but probably belonging here), shrews (marginal and with slight penetration in S. A.), rabbits, squirrels, cricetids, dogs, bears, raccoons, weasels, cats, peccaries (marginal and with slight penetration in N. A.), deer.
    B. Collaterals extinct in N. A.: tapirs, camels. (Peccaries, listed under A, are marginal between A and B.)

continent. At most there has been a sort of climatic zoning by which animals once more widespread have become confined to particular, areally definable environments (primates to tropical forests, camels to mountains and cold plains, etc.), or the faunas of deteriorating environments have been progressively impoverished (in Patagonia, for example). Mid-Cenozoic faunas lately found in Colombia (cooperatively by the

Colombian government and the University of California, under the direction of R. A. Stirton) have interesting regional differences from contemporaneous Patagonian faunas, but are definitely of the same general type and reveal no unexpectedly exotic groups. An old idea that northern and southern South America were separated by a Tertiary sea barrier and had quite distinct faunal histories, an idea still current among a few students but long rejected by others, is thus conclusively proved false.

There are, nevertheless, two regions of (broadly speaking) Latin America and of the Neotropical Region of static zoogeography that have had faunal histories decidedly different from that of South America: Central, or in a somewhat broader sense Middle, America and the West Indies. The development of the West Indian fauna is one of the most fascinating topics of historical zoogeography and has been the subject of long, sometimes bitterly polemic discussion involving fundamental principles of this science. It is, however, of minor importance for the present broader theme and cannot be considered here. The West Indies have been a faunal dead-end. There is little evidence that they have had a reciprocal influence on the larger faunas of the continental mainlands.

Middle America, on the contrary, has had an essential and striking role in the development of the faunas of all the Americas. A few admirable studies of the static, modern zoogeography of parts of the region have been made, and some attention has been given to historical aspects, but full evaluation is lacking and too little thought has been given to this subject. A cause for relative neglect has been the extreme paucity of primary historical documents. With one possible exception of no present value, no pre-Pliocene nonaquatic fossil has ever been found in tropical Middle America. There is one known, rather small but extremely important, early Pliocene mammalian local fauna, from Honduras (found and described by P. O. McGrew and associates), and there are several scattered Pleistocene faunules, of considerable interest but still lacking forms (especially the smaller mammals) that would be more fully enlightening.

Direct and conclusive study will require a good sequence of Central American land faunas, including vertebrate microfaunas, from Miocene, at latest, to recent. There is no assurance, nor even any considerable probability, that such a sequence remains to be discovered. It is nevertheless possible to evaluate the role of this region with some assurance, even if without adequate detail, on the basis of the scraps of local, direct evidence and the increasingly imposing array of indirect evidence.

The recent fauna of Central America is essentially like that of South America. The same faunal strata occur there, although, as already noted, their ages and relationships with respect to the area occupied are here different. Environmental conditions in Central America are similar to those of adjacent tropical South America. With union of these two areas, the resulting neotropical fauna has occupied territory as far as the environmental similarity extends. This is roughly as far as the climate can be called "tropical" in broad terms, and the line conventionally bounding the Neotropical Region to the north has been drawn at the equally conventional boundary of tropical climates, delimiting an area extending to and stopping with the hot Mexican lowlands. This is, indeed, merely a critical line within a broad transitional zone and not a localized barrier. Few distributions stop precisely at the line. Starting far north of it, say in Colorado or New Mexico, and pro-

TABLE III—FAMILIES OF RECENT LAND MAMMALS IN SELECTED PARTS OF NORTH, CENTRAL, AND SOUTH AMERICA

	New Mexico	Costa Rica	Guianas
Didelphidae	X	X	X
Soricidae	X	X	O
Cebidae	O	X	X
Callithricidae	O	O	X
Myrmecophagidae	O	X	X
Bradypodidae	O	X	X
Dasypodidae	X[1]	X	X
Ochotonidae	X	O	O
Leporidae	X	X	X
Sciuridae	X	X	X
Geomyidae	X	X	O
Heteromyidae	X	X	O
Castoridae	X	O	O
Cricetidae	X	X	X
Zapodidae	X	O	O
Erethizontidae	X	X	X
Caviidae	O	O	X
Hydrochoeridae	O	O	X
Dasyproctidae	O	X	X
Echimyidae	O	X	X
Canidae	X	X	X
Ursidae	X	O	O[2]
Procyonidae	X	X	X
Mustelidae	X	X	X
Felidae	X	X	X
Tapiridae	O	X	X
Tayassuidae	X[1]	X	X
Cervidae	X	X	X
Antilocapridae	X	O	O
Bovidae	X	O	O

X Present. O Absent.
[1] Present but marginal.
[2] Absent here, but present elsewhere equally deep in South America.

gressing to regions far south of it, say to Ecuador or the Guianas, animals mainly neotropical in distribution rather steadily become more frequent, and those mainly nearctic less frequent. In detail, Central America also has local differentiation, with numerous species and some genera (but no higher categories among mammals and few among other animals) confined to that area.

The place of Central America within the broad outlines of static recent zoogeography is well displayed by comparison of the mammalian families of New Mexico, Costa Rica, and the Guianas, each area with the same number of families (twenty-one). About half the families (ten fully and two more marginally) are common to all three areas but generally with different species and sometimes with different genera in each. Six families occur in New Mexico only, as among these three areas, and three in the Guianas only. These are the most definitely nearctic and neotropical groups, respectively. Costa Rica has no families that do not occur either in New Mexico or in the Guianas. It has three families in common with New Mexico but not the Guianas and six with the Guianas but not New Mexico, and is thus intermediate in this respect but somewhat more like the Guianas, justifying inclusion in the Neotropical Region (see Table III).

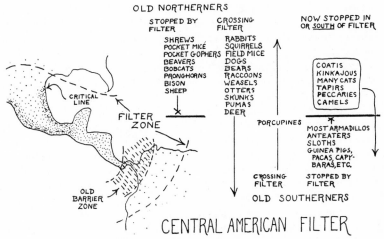

OLD NORTHERNERS

STOPPED BY FILTER	CROSSING FILTER	NOW STOPPED IN OR SOUTH OF FILTER
SHREWS	RABBITS	
POCKET MICE	SQUIRRELS	
POCKET GOPHERS	FIELD MICE	
BEAVERS	DOGS	COATIS
BOBCATS	BEARS	KINKAJOUS
PRONGHORNS	RACCOONS	MANY CATS
BISON	WEASELS	TAPIRS
SHEEP	OTTERS	PECCARIES
	SKUNKS	CAMELS
	PUMAS	
	DEER	

FILTER ZONE

CRITICAL LINE

PORCUPINES

MOST ARMADILLOS
ANTEATERS
SLOTHS
GUINEA PIGS,
PACAS, CAPY-
BARAS, ETC.

OLD BARRIER ZONE

CROSSING FILTER	STOPPED BY FILTER

OLD SOUTHERNERS

CENTRAL AMERICAN FILTER

Fig. 10. Diagram of middle America as a faunal filter. The examples given are from the recent fauna of land mammals. For some groups the action of the filter was different in the Pleistocene.

Middle America may be considered statically as a transition zone and historically as, successively or intermittently, a barrier and a migration route, but these simple and usual characterizations hardly begin to express its true role and importance.

As a transition zone and migration route, the role is not merely that of a habitat and a pathway. Middle America is a faunal filter (see Fig. 10). Its ecological characteristics, in the broadest sense, determined which stocks were involved in faunal interchanges between North and South America and which are now immobilized to north and to south. The filtering action is not sharply localized. It begins well to the north (and west), roughly at the edge of the lower Sonoran life zone in southwest United States, and also reaches far to the south and east, more or less to the edge of the Guiana highlands and thence southward and westward. From these quite indefinite outer edges, the filtering action becomes denser toward the central critical line, which now approximates the border of the central Mexican plateau. It probably had about the same or at times a more southerly position in the Pleistocene, but in parts of the Tertiary it may have been considerably farther north.

At present some northern groups, such as the shrews, pocket mice, and pocket gophers, penetrate well into the filter zone, but not beyond its vague southeastern edge. Others, such as the bobcats, bison, and sheep, have stopped near its attenuated northern border. For other northern forms, the filter zone has been essentially an open passage: rabbits, squirrels, dogs, otters, pumas, and many others among recent animals, and also horses, mastodons, and some other fairly recently extinct groups. Most of the old southerners, South American mammals of the first and second faunal strata, are now stopped somewhere within the zone: most armadillos, all anteaters and tree sloths, all the old native South American rodents except the porcupines. One armadillo (*Dasypus novemcinctus*) is peculiar in that a generation or so ago it stopped at about the northern edge of the filter zone but in the last few years has spread well beyond this. A related form (*Dasypus bellus*, now extinct) was even more widespread in North America in the Pleistocene, when there were also a few other old southerners (glyptodonts, ground sloths, capybaras) unaffected by the filter. It is also interesting that the filter was in some cases permeable for ancestral forms but now completely separates their differentiated northern and southern descendants, for instance in the cases of the porcupines and the bears.

Most peculiar in this respect are the rather numerous animals clearly of ultimate northern origin and yet now stopped in or *south* of the filter zone: coatis, kinkajous, the numerous kinds of South American cats other than the puma, short-faced bears, tapirs, peccaries (reaching the extreme northern edge of the filter, but hardly beyond), camels, and other lesser differentiates. Superficially one can say simply that such groups happened to become extinct in North but not in South America, a statement but not an explanation. For most of them, at least, there is a more explanatory probability: the particular populations and lines involved were native to Middle America, adapted to environmental conditions prevailing there and over much of South America and not adapted to or *immediately* derived from North America above the present filter zone. In some cases there are complications requiring modifications of or additions to this general theory (for instance, for the bears, páramo tapirs, and camels), but even these need not be flatly exceptional or contradictory, and for most groups involved the theory is a simple, elegant, and sufficient explanation of their peculiar distributional history.

It is an obvious, but nevertheless frequently unappreciated, fact that immigrants from North to South America did not come from the continent as a whole or from its broad, now temperate zone, best known to us both paleontologically and neontologically, but only from Central America. With local and geologically brief interruptions for part of it, Central America has been continuous with the North American land mass throughout the Cenozoic. Marine barriers were mostly in the extreme southeastern part of Central America and the major barrier, especially toward the end of the Cenozoic, was in what is now part of South, not Central, America (in western Colombia). Thus Central or broadly Middle America must have had a fauna mainly or purely North American in origin and in broad faunal type until toward the end of the Pliocene, a conclusion usefully attested by the one known Tertiary land fauna from Central America, early Pliocene in age and entirely North American in affinities. Nevertheless, Middle America must have been an important center of regional faunal differentiation within the North American general fauna.

Even in the early Cenozoic, when climatic zoning was less sharp than now, such zoning did exist, and Middle America has by astronomical and meteorological necessity always been the warmest (or most evenly warm) and tropical part of North America. It must long have been a center of adaptation and local radiation of faunal elements specifically adapted to its special conditions, not only climatic but also edaphic, floral, etc. This special local fauna was the one, and the only one, available for spread to South America, in all of the faunal strata of the latter region. Some Central American differentiates have succeeded in spreading northward (jaguars in the Pleistocene, for instance, and probably a number of otherwise mysterious newcomers in more northern fossil fields throughout the Cenozoic). Spread southward, when geographically possible, was more general and rapid because northern South America is more like Middle America in climate and associated factors. The Tertiary sea barrier did not follow a climatic zonal boundary, and when connection was established the incorporation of Central America into the South American and of South America into the Central American faunal zone was rapid and reciprocal.

Thus may be readily explained neotropical differentiation within many groups of old northern origin, the roots of which have not been found among the fossils from higher latitudes in North America. The more distinctively neotropical forms (at levels mainly of specific to generic differentiation) in many families may be inferred to have been Middle American differentiates: numerous noncaviomorph rodents, some dogs, the southern procyonids (*sensu lato*), most of the southern cats and most of the deer, among others. There is also discernible, on these grounds, a minor stratification *within* the broad late stratum of the South American fauna, between forms which had been longer in Middle America and more differentiated there, and those newer or less isolated in that region. Thus the coatis (*Nasua*) are inferred to be older and their allies the true raccoons (*Procyon*) younger Middle American forms, or among the deer the brockets (*Mazama*) may be older and the closer allies of our white-tails (*Odocoileus*) younger there. In some such cases there are other factors to consider, especially the possibility and timing of spread northward from Middle America. Here emphasis can only be placed on broader aspects of the historical role of Middle America and details cannot further be discussed. In fact, these details have not yet been adequately studied, if at all, from this point of view.

THE BEARING OF THE LIVING METASEQUOIA ON PROBLEMS OF TERTIARY PALEOBOTANY

By Ralph W. Chaney

Department of Paleontology, University of California, and Research Associate, Carnegie Institution of Washington

Read before the Academy, April 26, 1948

The discovery of huge living trees in California in 1769, followed by the naming and description of the coast redwood, *Sequoia sempervirens*, by Endlicher in 1847,[1] served as a prelude to the recognition of fossil redwoods in many parts of the northern hemisphere. Leafy shoots from the Oligocene of France, originally assigned to *Taxites langsdorfii* by Brongniart[2] were correctly transferred to the genus Sequoia by Heer in 1855.[3] Heer also identified as members of this genus specimens sent to him from the collections of polar explorers, from Tertiary deposits in Greenland, Iceland, Spitzbergen, Siberia, Sachalin, northern Canada and Grinnell Land.[4] Bringing to North America much of the tradition of European paleobotany, Lesquereux recognized several species of fossil Sequoia in the western United States, including the widely distributed *S. langsdorfii*.[5] During ensuing years the occurrence of Sequoia has been widely noted over the northern hemisphere, at middle latitudes in rocks assigned to middle Tertiary, and at high latitudes in rocks of older Tertiary and Cretaceous age. From the pattern of its occurrence during these later periods of earth history, the paths of its migration southward have been charted.[6,7] Its environment in past ages has been reconstructed from comparisons with the modern habitat of the coast redwood in California and Oregon.

A fossil cone described as *S. heerii* by Lesquereux[8] from beds of Oligocene age on Medicine Lodge Creek (Sage Creek), Montana, differs from other American cones referred to Sequoia in its attachment on a "naked pedicel." Lesquereux believed that the absence of needles on this "pedicel" (if it had had needles it could not have been properly so designated) had resulted from maceration. In later years identical stalked cones have been found at other Tertiary localities in western North America, such as Bridge Creek, Oregon, and Elko, Nevada; some of the cones figured by Heer as *S. nordenskioldi* from the Eocene of Spitzbergen,[9] and as *S. langsdorfii*[10] and *S. brevifolia*[11] from the Eocene of Greenland are also borne on stems lacking needles. For some time it has been apparent that this type of Sequoia cone is readily distinguishable from those of the living species and of other American fossil species; one of my students has even suggested that there are differences sufficient to justify establishing a new genus.[12]

In 1936 Endo[13] pointed out for the first time a significant character in a

Reprinted by permission of the author and the National Academy of Sciences from Proceedings of the National Academy of Sciences, 34, 503–515 (1948).

cone of this type, assigned to *S. japonica* from later Tertiary deposits of Japan and Korea. His description and remarks are as follows:

"Description: Cone rather small, spherical, ca. 16 mm. in diameter; cone-scales ca. 16 in number, arranged in 4 longitudinal rows, each row with 4 scales; escutcheon hexagonal, transversely grooved and radially wrinkled, 10 mm. wide, 3 mm. high. Peduncle stout, 2 mm. in diameter.

"Leaves with decurrent base, sessile, arranged in 2 lines; linear, bluntly mucronate at apex, 10 mm. long, 2 mm. wide; upper surface slightly furrowed along the midrib.

"Remarks: The arrangement of the cone-scales in the present species is in longitudinal rows, while being usually spiral in most other species. It has this characteristic feature in common with the cones from the Miocene of John Day valley, once described by Lesquereux as belonging to *Sequoia langsdorfii;* unfortunately the latter is too imperfect for farther comparison with the present materials."

Endo's use of the term "peduncle" is unfortunate, since the stems to which the cones are attached appear in at least two specimens (figures 6, 13) to bear leaves. They may best be considered leafy shoots bearing terminal cones. An obscure photograph (figure 12) of a vegetative shoot shows its needles in opposite position, although Endo does not mention this feature in his description of the leaves. In fact, many fossil shoots with oppositely placed needles had been figured as far back as the days of Heer with no reference to this readily observable character.

It remained for Miki[14] to found a new genus, Metasequoia, in 1941 on the basis of stalked cones and leafy shoots from Pliocene deposits at Osusawa and elsewhere in the clay beds of Central Hondo. His description and discussion (in altered sequence) are here quoted:

"Character: Cone pedunculate, scale decussate, shield-form; peduncle with distichous scars of leaves and scaly leaves at the base. Shoot deciduous; leaf distichous, linear, obtuse, petiolate; stomata parallel to the midrib.

"The remains have usually been referred to Sequoia or Taxodium, indeed the cone is like that of Sequoia and the foliage shoot is somewhat like those of Taxodium.

"The cones were never found connected to branches, but as the leaf-scars on the peduncle are also distichous, it is conceivable that the cones and the shoots belonged to the same plant. The foliaged shoots seem to be lateral branches shedding in autumn, because their length is usually constant and the proximal end is covered by scaly leaves, although they have no scaly bud on the top and the branches two or more years old have two or more bud scars on the nearly same point as in Fig. 8 Ge.

"The cone is distinguished from that of Sequoia by the decussate arrangement of scales and by the delicate peduncle having scale leaves at the base. The foliaged shoot differs from Sequoia by distichous arrangement of leaves and by the brittle petiole. At a glance the shape of the shoot of fragmental remain seems to be Taxodium or Cephalotaxus but it differs from Taxodium by distichous leaf and parallel arrangement of stomata on it and from Cephalotaxus by short delicate shoot without scaly bud at the terminal and by the obtuse top of leaf.

"The decussate arrangement of cone-scales is not found in living Taxodiaceae, but a common character in Cupressaceae. The shedding of lateral foliaged shoot with linear leaves is common in Glyptostrobus and Taxodium. So it is sure that the remains belong to Taxodiaceae but as the characters do not harmonize with those of the living forms, a new genus Metasequoia is established."

Since several of the cone-stems which he figures (*A*—*g, h, i, j, k*) show scaly leaves or leaf scars, it seems clear that they are modified leafy shoots rather than peduncles. Miki uses the term "distichous" to describe the position of needles on the foliage shoots; whether he meant to indicate their opposite position (and I am inclined to believe from his phrasing that he did) is uncertain, but in any event the term carries no such implication; Sargent[15] even defines "distichous" as "leaves arranged alternately in two vertical ranks," though the word may be equally well used for opposite position. The significant feature of Miki's description is his recognition of the association of cones bearing decussate scales with leafy shoots which were deciduous. He assigns two species to Metasequoia, of which one, *M. disticha*, was originally described as *S. disticha* by Heer[16] from the Eocene of Spitzbergen on the basis of leafy shoots. The second, *M. japonica*, is the species originally described by Endo as *S. japonica* from Miocene and Pliocene deposits in Japan and Korea; it is distinguished from *M. disticha* by the shape and fewer numbers of its cone-scales, distinctions which may not prove to be of specific significance in the light of our present knowledge of the genus. Miki's assignment of these fossil cones and shoots to a new genus, and his conclusion that even though they do not occur in direct attachment they are parts of the same deciduous plant, represent an outstanding discovery in Tertiary paleobotany. It is all the more remarkable, coming as it did only a few years before a second major discovery.

Miki's paper had probably not been read by any paleobotanist or botanist outside of Asia when it was announced, in the spring of 1946, that three trees of Metasequoia had been found living in Central China. Tsang Wang, attached to the Bureau of Forestry of the Ministry of Agriculture, had brought back to Nanking specimens collected at the village of Mo-tao-chi, in eastern Szechuan, about 140 miles northeast of Chungking. This material was studied by W. C. Cheng, Professor of Forestry at National Central University, and H. H. Hu, Director of the Fan Memorial Institute of Biology, both of whom have a wide knowledge of the living plants of China. They soon realized that it represented no known living tree, and comparisons showed that the cones and leafy shoots were essentially the same as those described by Miki from fossil specimens in Japan. Additional collecting by C. J. Hsueh in 1946 resulted in the discovery of several additional trees, and greatly augmented the material available for study. During the fall of 1947, C. T. Hwa, also a student of Professor Cheng, spent several months in the region, with financial support provided by the Arnold Arboretum of Harvard University through the coöperation of E. D. Merrill,[17] and with a small grant from the University of California.

In the region to the south, in western Hupeh, Hwa found several hundred additional trees of Metasequoia, made a comprehensive collection of the woody plants of this general area, and brought out a large quantity of viable seeds. With adequate material for study at hand, Hu and Cheng have recently published an account of this new tree under the name *M. glyptostroboides*.[18] In an earlier paper, Hu[19] had mentioned the discovery of this living tree in his brief discussion of another fossil species, *S. chinensis*, which had been described by Endo from the Oligocene flora of Fushun, Manchuria;[20] Hu correctly transferred it to the genus Metasequoia on the basis of its stalked, decussate-scaled cones. The leaves and cones of the living trees of Metasequoia, as described by Hu and Cheng, differ in no essential respects from those of the fossils on which Miki based his generic description. But there are four additional characters, of particular interest to paleobotanists, which are mentioned by these authors: (1) "opposite, distichously arranged foliage shoots"; (2) "leaves—opposite"; (3) "staminate flowers axillary and terminal, opposite, on racemose or paniculate flowering branchlet-system"; (4) cone-bearing twigs "with decussate linear leaves before maturity, and with conspicuous leaf scars and with persistent bracts at the base in winter." This paper by Hu and Cheng, describing the occurrence and external characters of *M. glyptostroboides*, represents a major contribution to the botany of China and of the world.

With this significant information regarding Metasequoia, both fossil and living, coming over from Japan and China, I have reëxamined with graduate students at the University of California[21] the abundant conifer material in our Tertiary collections from the western United States, and later the collections at the United States National Museum. We have also studied the descriptions and illustrations of Heer and others, covering material from Cretaceous and Tertiary horizons elsewhere in the northern hemisphere. All of the specimens previously referred to *S. heerii*, and many of those assigned to *S. langsdorfii* and several other fossil species, have the cone or foliage characters of Metasequoia. In addition, staminate aments like those of the living species have been found in the Bridge Creek flora (Oligocene) of Oregon, and the Elko flora (Miocene) of Nevada, in association with typical cones and leafy twigs of Metasequoia. These fossil aments and twigs from Nevada had previously been referred to Taxodium.[22] It has become increasingly apparent that many of the specimens assigned to Sequoia and Taxodium from the Cretaceous and Tertiary floras of North America are properly referable to Metasequoia. A generic revision of some of these is now in preparation, under the auspices of the American Philosophical Society and the Carnegie Institution of Washington. At this time it seems desirable to rewrite the description of Metasequoia on the basis of the paleobotanical evidence. In this description and the following discussion the data provided by fossil specimens will be the primary consideration, though in some cases our knowledge of corresponding parts of the living tree has enabled us better to interpret them. All consideration of fossil stems is here omitted, since study of the wood of Metasequoia, modern and fossil, has not progressed to a point where significant distinguishing characters between it and Sequoia have been noted.

*Genus Metasequoia Miki.—Description.—*Foliage shoots straight, decussate; alternate pairs which come out from top and bottom of branch are twisted approximately 90° into horizontal plane of laterally disposed pairs so that all lie along one plane on branch, in opposite pairs; pairs originating in vertical plane often missing and represented by scars preserved on top surface of branch; diverging at angles approaching 90°, commonly ranging in length up to 8 cm., deciduous. Needles decussate, twisted with their decurrent bases to form two oppositely paired ranks, closely spaced, diverging at angles approaching 90° in typical, mature specimens; up to 1.8 cm. long, averaging about 8 mm., longest on proximal half of shoot and gradually reduced in length toward its tip; up to 2 mm. in width; obtusely tipped, narrowed and twisted at point of attachment to decurrent base; midrib well defined, with stomata parallel to it on ventral surface. Staminate cones ovate, up to 5 mm. long, with decussate bracts; closely spaced, sessile and decussate on elongate spikes; rotated into one plane so that they appear to be attached in opposite pairs. Ovulate cones globose to ovoid or elliptic, up to 2 cm. long and 1.5 cm. wide, averaging 1.5 by 1.2 cm. (at one American locality (Mollala) they are globose, 1.6 to 2.4 cm. in diameter, open cones slightly broader); cone-scales 12 to 24, decussate, peltate on broad-based stalks, discs lenticular to hexagonal, with transverse, medial grooves. Seeds about 3 mm. long, 1 mm. wide, the surrounding wings asymmetrical, notched at the apex, with over-all length of 4 to 5 mm., width of 3 to 3.5 mm. Cones terminal on stout, straight or curved shoots; cone-bearing shoots probably lateral, up to 4 cm. long and 2 mm. in diameter, more slender at the middle, bearing scaly leaves at base in complete specimens, rarely with scaly leaves or leaf-scars preserved along the shoot, probably widely spaced and evidently decussate.

*Discussion.—*It is unusual to find leafy shoots attached to branches in the fossil record. Their position is decussate in every instance, though the shoots that come out at right angles to the plane of the branch are commonly missing, and may be represented only by scars which show on the exposed surface of the slab. These fossil shoots average somewhat longer than those of the living *M. glyptostroboides* which we have examined. Some specimens, especially those from Elko, Nevada, and Mollala, Oregon, both of Miocene age, have slender, curving shoots with needles more

openly spaced and directed distally at higher angles than the typical specimens from Bridge Creek and other localities; studies of foliage of living
trees have not progressed to a point where we can determine whether
there is corresponding variation in *M. glyptostroboides*. Differences of
opinion have been expressed regarding the mode of attachment of the
needles. I agree with Stebbins[23] that their position is decussate; this
may be readily observed at the tips of young shoots on seedlings which
we have growing in Berkeley. The older shoots on herbarium specimens,
as well as the leafy shoots preserved as impressions on our fossils, also show
clearly the alternating position of attachment of successive pairs of needles
and the twisting of their decurrent bases to bring all the pairs of needles
into a single plane. Thomas Morley, graduate student in botany at the
University of California, has at my suggestion sectioned the stem of a leafy
shoot of the living *M. glyptostroboides* (sheet No. 753369, Univ. Calif.
Herbarium). He finds the leaf gaps opposite at each node, with each
successive pair at right angles to the pair below. However, in alternating
nodes the leaf gaps and the decurrent leaf bases are twisted approximately
90°, which brings all the points of attachment of the needles into essentially the same plane along the shoot. An original decussate arrangement
is thus confirmed by Morley's slides. No difficulty has been experienced
in recognizing the opposite position of the needles in well-preserved fossils
of Metasequoia; under low magnification the relations of needles and
leaf bases to the shoot are as clear as with modern material; both living
and fossil specimens are distinguishable at a glance from leafy shoots of
Sequoia·and Taxodium in which the needles are alternately disposed along
the shoots. Like the pairs of needles, the decussately attached staminate
cones are twisted into a single plane along the twig so that they are disposed in opposite or nearly opposite pairs. The staminate cones of a fossil
specimen from the Oligocene Bridge Creek flora of Oregon are much smaller
than those from Elko, and appear to represent a less-developed stage;
in the living species there is a similar range in size. A specimen from Elko
shows six spikes, in close association like those of the living species. The
considerable range in size and shape of the ovulate cones, and in the
numbers of their cone-scales, is no wider than is to be found in cones of
the living species, and we have no present basis for determining whether
such variation will provide criteria for recognizing two or more species.

As stated in the description, needles are commonly lacking from the
cone-bearing shoots, and even their attachment scars are difficult to make
out on most fossil specimens. The scars are readily visible on shoots of the
living plant, and needles may remain in attachment while the cone is on
the tree. When it has fallen, the needles are shed; the fossil record is
made up exclusively of cones which have fallen to the ground, and the
presence of needles on their shoots is not to be expected. Since this dis-

cussion deals with fossil material, in which the cones and leafy shoots are not commonly attached to branches, we have had to qualify certain of our statements regarding their mode of attachment. However, there is little doubt that this follows the general pattern of the living *M. glyptostroboides*, in which the vegetative and reproductive shoots, and their needles and scales, are prevailingly decussate.

A survey of the characters of Metasequoia as seen in fossil material, and a comparison of these characters with those of Sequoia and Taxodium, provides the following bases for distinguishing this Chinese genus:

(1) Leafy shoots decussate, disposed distichously in opposite pairs along the branches in Metasequoia; spiral, disposed distichously and alternately in Sequoia and Taxodium.

(2) Leafy shoots deciduous in Metasequoia and Taxodium; remaining on the branches 3 to 4 years in Sequoia.

(3) Needles decussate on the shoots of Metasequoia, twisted and disposed distichously in opposite pairs; spirally disposed, commonly distichous, on the shoots of Sequoia and Taxodium.

(4) Stomata in parallel bands on each side of the midrib in Metasequoia and Sequoia; irregularly transverse in Taxodium.

(5) Staminate cones decussate on spikes, twisted into distichous, opposite pairs, in Metasequoia; spirally disposed on spikes in Taxodium; solitary in the axils of terminal needles in Sequoia.

(6) Pistillate cones terminal on elongate, probably lateral, leafy shoots in Metasequoia (they are lateral in the living species), the needles widely spaced, deciduous, leaving a naked cone-shoot on shedding; terminal on short scaly shoots which develop at the ends of leafy shoots of the preceding year in Sequoia; cones at the ends of branches in Taxodium.

(7) Cone scales decussate in Metasequoia; spirally disposed in Sequoia and Taxodium.

Our conclusion that Metasequoia rather than Sequoia was the dominant conifer of the Arcto-Tertiary Flora, whose southward migration from high latitudes has been so well established,[6, 7] calls for reconsideration of the paleoecology and floristics of the Tertiary period. It is of primary significance to note that it was not an evergreen but a deciduous conifer which ranged northward to latitude 82° in Grinnell Land during the Eocene. The deciduous habit of Metasequoia was wholly consistent with that of the majority of its angiosperm associates in the older Tertiary floras from high northern latitudes. This same group of trees, only slightly altered in composition, is widely known at middle latitudes, both in North America and Asia, during middle Tertiary time. The need for determining the associates of the living *M. glyptostroboides* becomes at once apparent, for they may represent a closer approach to the Arcto-Tertiary Flora than any modern vegetation as yet studied. It is necessary also to learn as much as possible about the modern environment of Metasequoia, to serve as a guide for the reconstruction of its habitats in past ages.

In February and March, 1948, with Dr. Milton Silverman, Science Writer for the San Francisco *Chronicle*, I made a brief trip to western Szechuan and eastern Hupeh under the auspices of the Save-the-Redwoods League, and with the cordial coöperation of Chinese scientists and of Chinese and American officials. It was our good fortune to have accompanying us C. T. Hwa who had previously collected extensively in this area. The redwoods of China live in valley bottoms and slopes at altitudes from 4000 to 4450 feet. The discovery trees at Mo-tao-chi, Szechuan, including the largest tree observed[24] with a diameter of 64 inches above the buttress and a height of 98 feet, are growing in the midst of rice-paddies, and no other trees occur within 100 yards. But in the valley of Shui-hsa-pa, in western Hupeh, scores of Metasequoias were observed not only on the borders of rice-paddies on the floodplain, but extending up ravines under conditions which appeared to be relatively natural.[25] This is in no sense a forest, for trees occur largely in isolated ravines in association with other conifers and with deciduous hardwoods which show every evidence of being second growth. These associates had been widely noted at corresponding elevations during our 5-day trip into the area, and the plant formation has been described by Cheng[26] as occurring between 400 and 2000 meters elevation in this area. Among the more common hardwoods noted in immediate association with Metasequoia are chestnuts (*Castanea henryi* and two other species), a small-leafed oak (*Quercus glandulosa*), sweet gum (*Liquidambar formosana*), and cherry (Prunus) of an undetermined species. An evergreen shrub related to our spice-bush (Lindera) is one of the most abundant members of the understory. On adjacent higher slopes the birch (*Betula luminifera*) and the beech (*Fagus longipetiolata*) are common, and in one ravine there is a large tree of katsura (*Cercidiphyllum japonicum*, var. *chinensis*). Four evergreen conifers, *Cunninghamia lanceolata*, *Cephalotaxus fortunei*, *Pinus massoniana* and *Taxus chinensis*, are of regular occurrence here, and small fan palms (*Trachycarpus fortunei*) were noted at various places in the Shui-hsa-pa area. This assemblage is essentially the same as that recorded in the fossil record of the Eocene from high latitudes; many of the figured specimens of Metasequoia from Greenland and Alaska have on the same slabs leaf impressions of katsura or birch; the Oligocene and Miocene floras from the John Day Basin of Oregon and other localities in the western United States include all of the angiosperm genera (except the palm) above recorded, in association with fossils of Metasequoia. Numerous genera which are common members of the Arcto-Tertiary Flora, both in the Eocene of high latitudes, and in middle Tertiary deposits at middle latitudes, have not yet been noted in immediate association with Metasequoia at Shui-hsa-pa; however, our field work was of limited duration and carried on at a season unfavorable for easy recognition of deciduous trees. We already know that species of Alnus, Acer, Carpinus, Ostrya and Ulmus have been observed within a few miles of Metasequoia trees, and it is probable that other genera known in the fossil record will be recorded during the field season of 1948 while Professor Cheng and his associates are working in this region.

Prior to the study of the trees of this region, the nearest surviving equivalents of the Arcto-Tertiary Flora which I have seen are the mixed bald cypress (Taxodium)—hardwood forest of the Wabash river valley in Illinois and Indiana, and the hardwood forests with associated conifers at middle altitudes on the Island of Hondo in Japan. The occurrence in the Shui-hsa-pa region of Metasequoia and Cercidiphyllum now restricted to Asia,[27] together with many angiosperm genera which occur today in North America as well, gives these groves in the ravines of western Hupeh a closer resemblance to the Eocene floras of Greenland, Spitzbergen and Alaska, and to the Oligocene-Miocene floras of Oregon and Manchuria than any living group of plants known to me. Not only has Metasequoia come down through the ages to survive in Central China, but the whole assemblage of which it is a part has had a long geologic history, and has participated in wide migrations. During these movements covering thousands of miles, and continuing for millions of years, some genera have disappeared and others have been added; minor changes in leaf or fruiting characters which are the basis for specific distinctions have appeared; but the Arcto-Tertiary Flora as we know it from early Tertiary rocks at high northern latitudes is so fully represented in the Metasequoia groves of Central China that there can be no question as to the holarctic origin of this modern vegetation.

That being the case, we may turn to this region for suggestions regarding the physical environment occupied by the Arcto-Tertiary Flora at many localities in the northern hemisphere during past ages. The nearest station which provides climatic data is Chungking, 140 miles to the southwest, and at an elevation more than 3000 feet lower. Annual precipitation here (43-year record) is 43.1 inches, of which 2.3 inches fall in the winter, 11.1 inches in the spring, 17.7 inches in the summer, and 12 inches in the autumn. The mean annual temperature (44-year record) is 66.2°F., ranging from a low of 48.6° in January to a high of 84.4° in August; the mean monthly minimum (6-year record) ranges from 35° in January to 70° in August, and the extreme lowest recorded temperature in 25 years is 28.9°; the mean monthly maximum (6-year record) ranges from 59° in January to 104° in August, and the extreme highest recorded temperature in 25 years is 111°. Relative humidity averages about 82% (16-year record), and there is little monthly variation. It seems probable that at

Shui-hsa-pa, 4000 feet in elevation, there is higher rainfall and a wider range in temperature. At the time of my visit in March, temperatures were mild and light rains fell daily. Villagers reported that there is no snow or frost, and the general aspect of the understory, made up of evergreen shrubs in the Lauraceae, Theaceae, Euphorbiaceae and Palmae, is suggestive of winter temperatures which rarely fall below freezing. Discussing the climate of the Red Basin of Szechuan, on the eastern rim of which our area is located, Cressey has stated:[28] "The climate is temperate and mild. Despite the location in the interior of the continent, it is protected from extremes of temperature by the surrounding mountains, and the contrast between summer and winter is not great. Summer temperatures seldom exceed 100°F., while during the winter the thermometer does not usually drop below freezing."

The only vegetation in North America which is closely comparable with Metasequoia and its associates of Central China is the bald cypress-hardwood forest of the south Atlantic coastal plain and the Gulf of Mexico,

TABLE 1

SHOWING PRECIPITATION AND TEMPERATURE IN REGIONS OCCUPIED BY METASEQUOIA, TAXODIUM AND SEQUOIA

| | ALTI-TUDE, FEET | PRECIPITATION, INCHES | | | | | FAHRENHEIT TEMPERATURE | | |
		WINTER	SPRING	SUMMER	AUTUMN	ANNUAL	MEAN ANNUAL	EXTREME MAX.	MIN.
Chungking	754	2.3	11.1	17.7	12.0	43.1	66.2	111	28.9
Brunswick, Ga.	14	9.3	9.8	18.6	12.0	49.7	68.4	103	13.0
Glennville, Ga.	175	9.7	9.9	17.4	9.9	46.9	67.1	106	11.0
Hammond, La.	44	14.9	14.0	18.1	11.2	58.5	67.5	106	1.0
Eureka, Calif.	62	19.5	10.2	1.0	8.3	39.0	51.6	85	20.0

extending northward up the Mississippi Valley to Illinois and Indiana. This is a lowland forest, reaching a maximum altitude of about 475 feet in the valley of the Wabash River. At latitudes corresponding to Shui-hsa-pa in Louisiana and Georgia, this forest lives within a few tens of feet of sea level, ranging up to about 200 feet in Georgia. As in Central China, precipitation is well distributed and adequate over all this region (table 1), with more than half falling in the spring and summer months. In the southeastern United States at the latitude of Shui-hsa-pa, temperatures show essentially the same mean average, but the extreme minima are much lower.

The bald cypress, T. distichum, of the American forest has its best development in swamps and on swamp borders, but its occurrence with hardwoods on moist floodplains more closely resembles the environment of Metasequoia in Central China. All of the angiosperm associates in the groves at Shui-hsa-pa have been noted with the exception of Cercidiphyllum and Trachycarpus which are confined to Asia; Sabal takes the place of the latter genus in the southern United States.   In spite of their geographic separation and marked topographic differences, the general aspect of the Taxodium-hardwood forest is surprisingly similar to that of the Metasequoia-hardwood assemblage.   This resemblance is the more significant since during middle Tertiary time Taxodium and Metasequoia lived together in western North America and in northeastern Asia, in association with the same angiosperms; during early Tertiary time, these two conifers were widely distributed at high latitudes and with the same genera of hardwoods.   Taxodium is almost as widely distributed in the Arcto-Tertiary Flora as Metasequoia.   We conclude that this forest type had its origin at the north, in Eocene and Cretaceous time, in a region with a summer-wet and winter-cool climate; the deciduous habit of all the dominant trees, including Metasequoia and Taxodium, is consistent with such a climate.   By Oligocene and Miocene time, a similar forest was widely established as far south as Oregon and Nevada, and down into Japan and Manchuria.   By the end of the Miocene, Metasequoia appears to have disappeared from this continent; with a changing climatic regime in western North America, the surviving Taxodium-hardwood forest has been confined to southeastern North America.   In Asia Taxodium is rare or absent in Pliocene floras; here Metasequoia has continued down to the present, though it is now confined to a limited area where environmental factors are favorable.   This tree is reproducing on a limited scale, but its continued existence will be determined by the pressure put upon it by a people whose land, fuel and timber resources are wholly inadequate.   A conservation committee has recently been organized in Nanking, and we may hope for its success in protecting some of the groves in which Metasequoia and its associates are living.   Glyptostrobus, a close relative of Taxodium, has survived in the lowlands of South China.   Sequoia, the living genus most similar to Metasequoia, is likewise a relict genus, restricted to the California and Oregon coast.   Here the rainfall regime is wholly different from that in Central China, though the temperature, somewhat lower at this more northerly latitude, resembles that of western Szechuan in its equability (table 1).   Our present knowledge of the Tertiary floras of Europe indicate that Heer was correct in his original reference of material from the Miocene of Switzerland to this genus, and that Sequoia rather than Metasequoia lived on this continent during the Tertiary period. Wide-spread submergence in western Europe at this time appears to have provided living conditions which favored Sequoia, although Metasequoia may be found in the fossil record of the Tertiary interior, farther to the east.

Having in mind the deciduous habit of Metasequoia and Taxodium, the deciduous hardwood associates of these genera, both in living forests and in the fossil record, and the modern environments in Central China and southeastern North America. we may suggest certain physical conditions which may have been best suited to the origin and development of the Arcto-Tertiary Flora. A summer-wet climate appears to have been the primary requisite, with a total annual rainfall in excess of 40 inches. Moderate temperature seldom falling below freezing is also indicated, though a winter characterized by lower temperatures is indicated by the prevailing deciduous habit. The apparent absence of polar ice-caps during at least the early part of the Tertiary period, and postulated ocean circulation, makes it reasonable to accept the occurrence of Metasequoia and its associates as far north as Grinnell Land; possibly it was the darkness of the arctic night rather than low winter temperatures which brought about the annual shedding of the leaves of these trees, a habit which has been retained in Metasequoia even though winter temperature in its habitat in Central China seems not to make the deciduous habit a modern necessity. It is doubtful whether the present altitude of the Metasequoia occurrence, at about 4000 feet, has always been an essential requirement. More probable is the assumption that the high valleys occupied by these trees provide the only existing habitat which is suitable. Farther to the north at lower altitudes, extremes of temperature or precipitation characterize the climate of China, and although the fossil record shows that Metasequoia has lived there in the past, it can no longer do so. The limited area in eastern Szechuan and western Hupeh where the trees are known to have survived is surrounded by mountain ranges which protect them from the climatic extremes which characterize other inland environments. An equable climate rather than a high altitude appears to be the determining factor in the modern occurrence of Metasequoia.

We may summarize our current knowledge of the fossil occurrence and history of the genus Metasequoia as follows:

(1) Many of the fossil leaves and cones from the Cretaceous and Tertiary rocks of high northern latitudes, and from middle latitudes in North America and Asia, which have previously been referred to Sequoia and Taxodium, are now known to be Metasequoia on the basis of recent descriptions of fossil and living members of this genus in Asia.

(2) Vegetative and reproductive units in the fossil record differ in no essential respect from those of the living *M. glyptostroboides* of Central China. Like those of this tree, they are characterized by the decussate arrangement of their shoots, leaves and scales, and by the deciduous habit of leafy and cone-bearing shoots.

(3) Occurrence of Metasequoia in the Arcto-Tertiary Flora, at high latitudes in the Eocene epoch, at middle latitudes in the Oligocene and Miocene, provides evidence of the northern origin of this Flora, and of its southward migration during the Tertiary period.

(4) Survival of Metasequoia in Central China, in association with many of the hardwood genera recorded with it in the fossil records of the

northern hemisphere, provides a basis for reconstructing the climatic conditions under which the Arcto-Tertiary Flora had its origin and subsequent migration. A humid climate with summer rainfall, and with moderate temperatures not regularly falling below freezing, may be suggested as best suited to this deciduous forest during its past history.

[1] Endlicher, S., *Syn. Conif.*, 197–198 (1847).

[2] Brongniart, A., *Prodrome Hist. Veg. Foss.*, 108 (1828).

[3] Heer, O., *Flora Tert. Helv.*, **1**, 54, pl. 20, f. 2; pl. 21, f. 4 (1855).

[4] Heer, O., *Flora Foss. Arct.*, 7 vols. (1868–1883).

[5] Lesquereux, L., *U. S. Geol. Surv. Terr.*, VII, 76 (1878).

[6] Chaney, R. W., *Bull. Geol. Soc. Am.*, **51**, 473 (1940).

[7] Chaney, R. W., *Ecol. Mon.*, **17**, 144–146 (1947).

[8] Lesquereux, L., *U. S. Geol. Surv. Terr.*, VII, 77, pl. 7, f. 13 (1878).

[9] Heer, O., *Flora Foss. Arct.*, **2, 3**, 36, pl. 4, f. 4a (1870).

[10] Heer, O., *Ibid.*, **2, 4**, 464, pl. 43, f. 1 (1869).

[11] Heer, O., *Ibid.*, **3, 3**, 5, pl. 2, f. 8 (1874).

[12] Ashley, J. F., in an unpublished report, written in 1938 when a graduate student, he suggested that stalked cones from Elko might be placed in a genus intermediate between Sequoia and Taxodium.

[13] Endo, S., *Proc. Imper. Acad.* (*Tokyo*), **12**, 172, f. 5, 7–13 (1936).

[14] Miki, S., *Jap. J. Bot.*, **11**, 261–263, f. 8 (1941).

[15] Sargent, C. S., *Manual of Trees of North America*, p. 894 (1922).

[16] Heer, O., *Flora Foss. Arct.*, **4, 1**, 63, pl. 12, f. 2a; pl. 13, f. 9–11 (1876).

[17] Merrill, E. D., *Arnoldia*, **8**, 1–8 (1948).

[18] Hu, H. H., and Cheng, W. C., *Bull. Fan. Mem. Inst. Biol.*, **1**, 153–161, pl. 1 (1948).

[19] Hu, H. H., *Bull. Geol. Soc. China*, **26**, 105–107 (1946).

[20] Endo, S., *Jap. J. Geol. and Geog.*, **6**, 27–29, pl. 7 (1928).

[21] Acknowledgment is due T. R. Pray and R. H. Shan for their assistance.

[22] Lesquereux, L., op. cit., 73, pl. 6, f. 13.

[23] Stebbins, G. L., *Science*, **108**, 95–99 (1948).

[24] Hwa reports seeing a tree more than 7 feet in diameter and over a hundred feet tall near Shu-hwi-chang, Hupeh.

[25] It is not possible to determine, in our present state of knowledge, that any of the Metasequoia trees are truly native. However, their association with the same conifers and angiosperms at several places strongly indicates that they have a natural place in this plant formation.

[26] Cheng, W. C., *Trav. For. Toulouse*, **1**, 150 (1939).

[27] *Ginkgo biloba* is also living here, but was noted only near villages and is probably not native.

[28] Cressey, G. B., *China's Geographic Foundations*, pp. 312–313 (1934).

EVOLUTION OF THE PSILOPHYTE PALEOFLORA

Daniel I. Axelrod

University of California, Los Angeles 24

Received August 12, 1958

Introduction

A century has now elapsed since Sir John William Dawson described the nude plant, *Psilophyton,* from the Devonian rocks of Gaspe (1859). Comprising an exceedingly ancient and simply constructed plant (fig. 1), it was the first fossil member of the ancient phylum Psilophyta to be discovered. At first the idea that it was a fossil plant was received with considerable scepticism but by the turn of the century, owing to the discovery of additional Devonian plants, it was generally conceded to be an authentic land plant. During the succeeding three decades numerous Devonian land plants of diverse character were described from rocks on all the continents. The problems of evolution posed by this earliest land vegetation—the Psilophyte Paleoflora— have been especially difficult to resolve. In particular, divergent views have been expressed with respect to their probable antiquity, their phylogenetic relations and their rate of evolution. Evidence afforded by more recent discoveries of new land plants in Devonian, Silurian and Cambrian rocks makes it possible to view these problems with better perspective. To understand the nature of the issues to be discussed, it is desirable first to recall certain salient features of the earliest land flora.

The oldest land plants now known are from the Early Cambrian of the Baltic region (Reissinger, 1939; Naumova, 1949), where approximately 20 spore-types of very simple construction in terms of size, shape, and sculpture are recorded. Spores of somewhat more complex character occur in the Middle and Late Cambrian of Kashmir, Spiti, and the Salt

Range in India (Ghosh and Bose, 1950; 1952; Ghosh, Sen and Bose, 1951; Jacob et al., 1953a; 1953b), and in eastern Sweden (Darrah, 1937). Approximately 60 Cambrian spore-genera are now on record, all discovered largely during the past decade.

These spores may be regarded as reproductive cells of land plants because they are cutinized. Further, at least some of the Cambrian plants were vascular since woody fragments showing scalariform tracheids, and tracheids with simple and bordered pits, occur in association with the spores in India. Most importantly, several phyletic lines appear to be represented, though their affinities in terms of modern types are difficult to judge. Naumova suggested that the spores from the Baltic region represent both Bryophyta and Pteridophyta. In the latter group she noted that one of the types is similar to spores of the *Calamariaceae* of Carboniferous age. The Indian workers (Jacob *et al.,* 1953b) report that their fossils apparently represent 6 different groups of vascular plants, chiefly primitive pteridophytes (including equisetalean types), probably seed ferns, and possibly primitive gymnosperms. That the phylum Lepidophyta was already established by the Middle Cambrian is shown by the occurrence of *Aldanophyton* in Siberia (Krystofovich, 1954), which is represented by several stems, one up to 8.5 cm. long, with spirally arranged microphyllous leaves.

Remains of land plants have not yet been recorded from Ordovician or Lower to Middle Silurian rocks. However, several genera are known from the Upper Silurian of Australia. Some are of uncertain systematic position, others have been assigned to the Psilophyta, and one (*Baragwanathia*) is a well developed lycopod (Lang and Cookson, 1935). Commencing in the Early Devonian, vascular land plants are recorded in moderate numbers, and they increased in abundance and in diversity during the rest of the period. By Late Devonian time, the following major categories had become established:[1]

PSILOPHYTA ("psilophytes")
  Psilophytales (Rhynia, Psilophyton, Horneophyton, etc.)
LEPIDOPHYTA ("lycopods")
  Baragwanathiales (Baragwanathia)
  Protolepidodendronales (Protolepidodendron, Protolepidodendropsis)
  Lepidodendronales (Archaeosigillaria, Lepidodendron, Bergeria)
ARTHROPHYTA ("horsetails")
  Hyeniales (Hyenia, Calamophyton)
  Pseudoborniales (Pseudobornia)
  Sphenophyllales (Sphenophyllum)
  Calamitales (Asterocalamites, Calamites)
PTEROPHYTA ("ferns")
  Archaeopteridales (Archaeopteris)
  Protopteridales (Protopteridium, Iridopteris, Aneurophyton, Dawsonites, Reimannia)
  Coenopteridales (Clepsydropsis, Asteropteris)
  Cladoxyales (Cladoxylon)
PTERIDOSPERMOPHYTA ("seed ferns")
  Calamopityales (Calamopitys, Stenomyelon, Diichnia)
CONIFEROPHYTA ("conifers")
  Pityales (Callixylon, Paleopitys, Archaeopitys)

Three successive evolutionary phases have been described, including the Psilophyton Flora, the Hyenia Flora, and the Archaeopteris Flora, which lived in the Early, Middle and Late Devonian respec-

---

[1] Only a few examples of genera representing these orders are given here; some, of course, are monotypic.

tively. Named for one of the more typical genera of each association, these Floras largely represent different generic assemblages though some types occur in more than one Flora. In general, contemporaneous Devonian Floras from widely separated parts of the northern and southern hemispheres include many types in common. For this reason it has generally been supposed that the vegetation of the world showed essentially no regional differentiation during the Devonian (Seward, 1933; Dorf, 1955); as we shall see, however, important vegetation provinces were already in existence.

EVOLUTIONARY SIGNIFICANCE OF DEVONIAN PSILOPHYTES

Interest in the Psilophyte Paleoflora has centered chiefly on the evolutionary significance of the most simple of known vascular plants, notably the "true" psilophytes of the Devonian, *Rhynia, Horneophyton,* and *Psilophyton.* The sporophyte of these plants consisted only of an upright axis that was adapted to life on land, including a simple vascular strand of phloem and xylem for conduction and support, stomata, cuticle, and cutinized spores: they were not differentiated into root, stem, and leaf (fig. 1). In basic morphology they are quite close to the hypothetical first land plants conceived by Lignier, Potonie, Bower, and Campbell, and serve as monuments to those superb morphologists and phylogenists who essentially described them before they were discovered.

As soon as these plants had been interpreted, chiefly on the basis of the remarkable silicified material in the Rhynie chert of Scotland (Kidston and Lang, 1917–21), it was only natural for most investigators to regard them as the actual ancestors of all higher vascular land plants. Since *Rhynia* was such a simply constructed plant (fig. 1), and closely agreed with the "prototype" of land plant which had been earlier visualized by Bower and others, it was quickly accepted

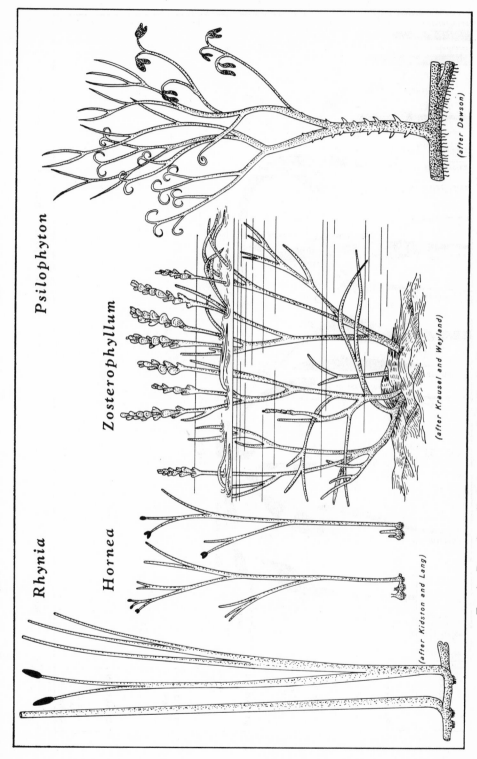

FIG. 1. Devonian psilophytes may only be bradytelic types persisting from the Precambrian.

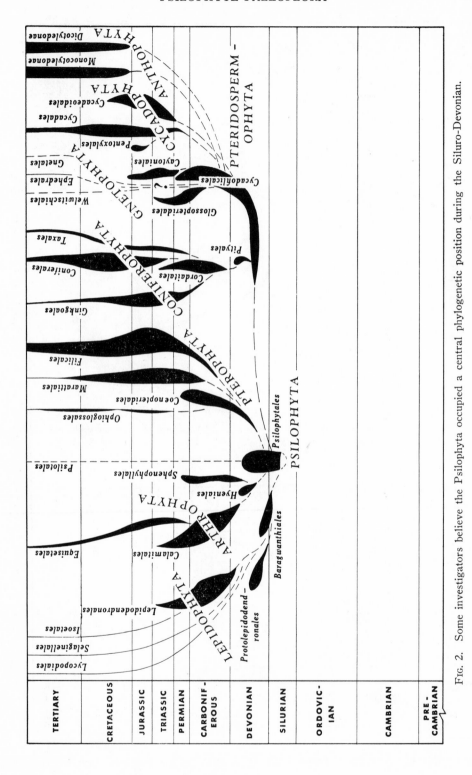

Fig. 2.   Some investigators believe the Psilophyta occupied a central phylogenetic position during the Siluro-Devonian.

as *the* ancestor of all vascular land plants (i.e. Zimmermann, 1930; Hirmer, 1927). Furthermore, since pre-Devonian vascular land plants were not then known, the increasing diversification and complexity of the Psilophyte Paleoflora during the Middle and Late Devonian led naturally to the belief that a great burst of evolutionary activity quickly followed the invasion of the previously unoccupied land (fig. 2). This presumed eruptive phase was believed responsible for the development of the successively more complex Psilophyton, Hyenia and Archaeopteris Floras (Arber, 1921; Seward, 1933). In spite of evidence to the contrary, these views are still held by a number of investigators i.e. Zimmermann, 1952; Smith, 1955; Takhtajan, 1956; Dorf, 1955).

Evidence was already available when *Rhynia* was described to show that it or other Devonian psilophytes could not be ancestral to the Lepidophyta, Arthrophyta, Pterophyta, and Coniferophyta. Actually, all living phyla of vascular plants had already evolved before Late Devonian time, except angiosperms (see list above) and possibly cycadophytes. The ancient conifers *Paleopitys* (descr. 1870) and *Callixylon* (descr. 1911) possessed complex secondary wood and were trees to judge from the fact that they are represented by logs: those of Callixylon were up to 3 feet in diameter. Most importantly, they lived contemporaneously with psilophytes. The existence of the lycopod *Protolepidodendron* (descr. 1880) in the Early Devonian should also have dispelled any doubts as to the phyletic significance of the psilophytes many years ago: if the psilophytes are ancestral (a point not proven), divergence must have taken place long before Devonian time. The discovery of the well preserved Devonian Gilboa forest in 1923, with *Aneurophyton* (*Eospermatopteris*) trees 25–40 feet tall and with 3–4 foot trunks that supported a large crown of fronds like those of tree ferns, should

also have raised doubts as to the phyletic significance of the Rhynie psilophytes which had just been described. The later discovery of *Baragwanathia* in the Late Silurian of Australia—a plant very close in fundamental structure to the living *Lycopodium selago*—also gives us a clue as to the evolutionary status of the Devonian psilophytes. Another vane pointing in the same direction is the fact that the Cambrian *Aldanophyton* resembles certain species of *Drepanophycus* of the Early Devonian (Leclercq, 1956), which lived approximately 170 million years later. Finally, the discoveries of woody plants in the Cambrian which are more complex than *Rhynia* firmly establishes the fact that Silurian and Devonian psilophytes could not be ancestral to all vascular land plants.

If we accept the views of phylogenists of the *Rhynia*-school, notably Zimmermann and his supporters, then according to our present information it took over one billion years to evolve the structurally simple *Rhynia* from algal ancestors, yet only 15 to 20 million years (or less) to transform *Rhynia* into lepidodendrons, calamites, and cordaites, 75 million years (or less) to evolve cycadophytes and ginkgophytes, and 150 million years (or less) to develop magnolias, palms, and sycamores. To those who still construct phyletic charts showing the divergence of all vascular plant phyla from Late Silurian and Early Devonian psilophytes (fig. 2) we may appropriately point out that such a scheme is not in agreement with geologic evidence as to the antiquity of the phyla concerned, or with our present understanding of the nature of the evolutionary process.

The chief reason that the Devonian and Silurian psilophytes have been considered primitive, ancestral types by many investigators is simply that the nature of the evolutionary process, as viewed over long spans of geologic time, was still obscure only 15 years ago. Simpson's (1944; 1953) brilliant analysis of the tempo and mode of evolution, as based on a synthesis of genetic and paleontologic data, has paved the way for a reappraisal of the early land plants. The true significance of the Silurian and Devonian psilophytes is to be found in our answer to the fundamental question which was earlier posed by Eames (1936), and more recently by others (Berry, 1945; Leclercq, 1954; 1955; Andrews and Alt, 1956) : are the Devonian psilophytes archaic and ancestral, or are they only ancient, simple plants? There is now good evidence to show that they are ancient, simple plants which persisted long after their derivatives—*if any*—went on to explore other evolutionary avenues. They represent slowly-evolving (bradytelic) forms, types fully comparable to *Chara, Selaginella, Equisetum, Ginkgo, Araucaria, Marattia, Schizaea, Platanus,* and *Sassafras* in the plant kingdom, and to *Lingula, Limulus, Sphenodon, Didelphus,* and *Latimeria* in the animal world, all of which have persisted essentially unchanged for scores of millions of years (fig. 1).

The psilophytes were adapted to comparatively stable environments, chiefly the near-coastal swampy lowlands of a world in which the climate was mild into high latitudes during most of the Early and Middle Paleozoic, and probably earlier. Such an ecologic occurrence—in a geologically stable, common, and persistently widespread environment—explains readily the reported similarity of vegetation over the world in the Devonian (Seward, 1933; Dorf, 1955). However, we now know that plants which were transported into these lowland basins from the hinterlands comprised numerous forms that belonged to diverse vegetation types which were in the uplands, and further, these plants were more complex than those living in the lowlands which comprise the bulk of the record. The diversity and complexity of vegetation that existed in the continental interiors during the Devonian is indicated clearly by the rich spore floras which

have now been described from Canada (Radforth and McGregor, 1954) and Germany (Thompson, 1952). The New Albany shale flora of the Kentucky-Indiana-Tennessee area (Hoskins and Cross, 1952) provides additional evidence. It comprises 30-odd genera, represented chiefly by wood transported by large rivers from the hinterland to a stagnant, lagoonal site of deposition. Numerous, highly complex types from the interior (including *Callixylon* logs) occur in association with the simple psilophytes which were chiefly of coastal swamp occurrence. Generally similar relations are shown also by the Devonian flora of Spitzbergen (Hoeg, 1942), and by a recently collected Devonian flora from east-central Nevada (UCLA coll.).

In these connections, it is pertinent to recall that the early Paleozoic plant record is much less complete than that of animals. This is chiefly because the hard parts of the recorded animal phyla are more readily preserved than are the leaves, seeds, or stems of plants. The great abundance and diversity of marine invertebrates in the early Paleozoic, as compared with the rarity of plants, is only a natural consequence of the record: it does not mean there were few or no plants. Those plants which may once have been preserved in continental sediments have largely been destroyed due to subsequent erosion, for nonmarine rocks do not last so long in the record as the marine. By contrast, the marine invertebrates lived at the sites of deposition which have been preserved. Furthermore, plants growing near the shores of the major geosynclines in which the bulk of the record accumulated had, in general, comparatively little hard tissue which would favor their preservation: the near-shore area in those times apparently was an ecologic refuge for ancient types which required continuously mild temperature to judge from their simple structure. More advanced forms with woody trunks and other hard parts were evolving principally in the more distant uplands, in areas of environmental diversity, and hence were so remote from the sites of deposition that most of them did not get into the lowland record, though occasionally some of them did (i.e. *Paleopitys, Callixylon*).

The fossil record thus supports the belief that the plants of the continental interiors were more highly evolved than the contemporaneous psilophytes which lived near the shore. The psilophytes were highly adapted to these lowland sites in which the environmental-organism relations were essentially unchanging, conditions now considered necessary for bradytelic lines (Simpson, 1944; 1953; Stebbins, 1950). The view that most Devonian lowland plants are relict types which express various experiments in different ways of life, and which evolved long before the Devonian, not only comes closer to the actual situation as judged from stratigraphic and phylogenetic evidence, but is consistent with current opinions as to the nature of the evolutionary process. On this basis we may conclude that the successive phases of the Devonian lowland vegetation, as recorded by the Psilophyton, Hyenia, and Archaeopteris Floras (Arber, 1921; Dorf, 1955), represent no more than the replacement of different ecologic units migrating from upland into lowland areas, and not evolutionary change as such. Analogous replacements are well documented for the Late Pennsylvanian (Elias, 1933), and also for the Tertiary as shown by the time-space relations of the Arcto-Tertiary, Neotropical-Tertiary, and Madro-Tertiary Geofloras (Chaney, 1947; Axelrod, 1939; 1958).

These interpretations give us a clue as to why the evolutionary relations of plants represented in the Devonian floras have become increasingly difficult to assess, as judged from the comments of various investigators (i.e. Hoeg, 1942; Andrews and Alt, 1956). The problem may be attributed partly to the fact that comparisons are being made between plants from lowland and upland areas which represent types in different ("primitive," "advanced") stages of evolution; further, some of those from the uplands represent members of lineages which had not previously been in the lowlands, and hence are wholly new to us (i.e. *Siderella*). In addition, part of the problem has been due to convergence in the evolution of the plant body in these ancient groups. We have thus been including in some of our taxa, such as *Psilophyton*, plants of diverse affinities (*see* Leclercq, 1954).

Since the Devonian land flora was composed of many plants, of which we have now examined only a few, and which represent diverse branches of several phyletic stocks, they could scarcely be expected always to provide evidence of types intermediate to previously known genera. Attempts to classify them into a so-called natural system would lead obviously to unsatisfactory results because during the adaptive radiation of major groups evolution leads to a phyletic branching so complex that any central line or trunk was essentially nonexistent. Since phyletic charts which have been assembled from ample paleontological data regularly suggest an evolutionary pattern more nearly resembling an intricately branched shrub—not a tall, sparsely branched tree—the inherent difficulties of placing accurately a series of disconnected twigs (fossils) in their proper position is apparent.

PRECAMBRIAN ORIGINS OF THE LAND FLORA

Since vascular land plants had already attained some diversity of type by the Early Cambrian, their earlier evolution must have taken place in Precambrian time. This brings up the problem as to whether the phyla of vascular plants evolved from the Psilophyta at that early date (or at any other time), or whether they have all had independent origins. In seeking an answer to this problem, we must remember that most authorities have assumed that the Tracheophyta (to which these phyla belong) is a "natural" group: it is composed of plants having independent sporophytes with an open system of growth and vascular tissue. Is this sufficient to make it a "natural" alliance in terms of phylogenetic relations? (*also see* Bold, 1957). Has Nature been so rigid that vascular tissues evolved only once, and in only one line—the Psilophyta —from which the other phyla have diverged?

Actually, the record supports the belief that xylem and phloem elements may have developed repeatedly in different phyla, much like the cuticle, cutinized spores, heterospory, spines, seed habit, secondary wood, leaves or roots. It is pertinent that there are near-vascular Devonian plants which do not belong to any known phylum. *Crocalophyton,* a plant considerably larger and more complex than *Rhynia,* had a complex internal structure. Its apical meristem of indecisive character formed conducting cells that can be termed pre-tracheids. As Andrews and Alt (1956) have noted, had it evolved much further it would have given rise to a unique plant, and certainly one far removed from the simple *Rhynia. Nematophyton, Prototaxites* (3-foot trunks), and their relatives were near-vascular plants, with longitudinally aligned conducting cells. Their derivatives, if any, would also have been types quite unlike *Rhynia* which has been visualized as the prototype of all vascular plants. The great diversity of the psilophytes themselves, some of which (*Yarravia, Sciadophyton*) are far removed from *Rhynia,* also suggests that other evolutionary lines may have evolved vascular systems independently. Further, there are a number of genera which are often included provisionally in the psilophytes (i.e. *Schizopodium, Barinophyton, Gosslingia*) because they are "primitive types" that do not fall into any other group (*see* Arnold, 1947; Andrews and Mamay, 1955, for comments on morphology). They may well represent ancient stocks which are now extinct that developed vascular tissues independently of

Rhynia: at least their morphology is sufficiently different in basic character to make their derivation from *Rhynia* seem most unlikely.

Such data make it probable that vascular tissue has evolved repeatedly in different phyla. This brings us back to the old question, which has been raised again in recent years (Eames, 1936; Berry, 1945; Andrews, 1947; Andrews and Alt, 1956), as to whether there were several transmigrations to land by plants of different basic alliances represented in an ancient, and largely extinct, algal plexus. Eames has rightly emphasized the fact that the variety of body type and sporangium position in the psilophytes is foreshadowed in the existing higher algae (Eames, 1936). No doubt there were many other novel algal types in earlier times, of which we have no record, that resembled psilophytes even more closely in these respects.

In this connection it is pertinent that although morphological studies suggest that such groups as the lycopods, arthrophytes and ferns are natural phyla, this is not true of the Psilopsida, a clear definition of which has not been achieved (*see* Leclercq, 1954, pp. 302–307). In general, those ancient, simple plants which do not fit well into the other phyla have been relegated to the psilophytes. Clearly, the evolutionary significance of the group cannot be resolved until we decide what the Psilophyta is in terms of accurate definition. If we confine to it *Rhynia* and *Horneophyton,* for example, and place the others in isolated groups of presently unknown affinity, then perhaps our ideas of morphology and evolution will at least express what we know. A clue as to how we might then view the psilophytes is provided by examples of the evolutionary history of certain living plants. The present day *Isoetes* apparently culminates the reduction series *Sigillaria-Pleuromeia-Nathorstiana-Isoe-tites-Isoetes* which extends down into the Carboniferous, a span of some 300 million years. Since the history of vascular plants ranges into the Precambrian, fully 200 million years below the Devonian, is there any reason why some of the Devonian psilophytes are not reduced, simplified members of ancient lines? The living *Selaginella* and *Lycopodium* are essentially unchanged from the related *Selaginellites* and *Lycopodites* of the Carboniferous. The *Aldanophyton-Drepanophycus* line of evolution appears to be another example of a bradytelic line (Leclercq, 1956, p. 112), persisting from the Middle Cambrian into the Devonian. May not some psilophytes also represent bradytelic types of ancient isolated lines which largely became extinct in the Devonian? The cycadeoids and caytonias were large, diversified groups which died out in the Early Cretaceous. Is it not possible that some psilophytes comprise the last members of more ancient stocks which earlier in their history also were highly diversified, though comparatively primitive plants? And if vascular plants have had diverse sources in the algae, can not some of our "problem" psilophytes represent members of ancient, isolated, small phyla which have long been extinct?

Perhaps we have been too inclined to stuff all "primitive" land plants into the Psilopsida. Although most investigators are now agreed that the group is "unnatural," let us remember that Nature did not make it so. May we not be on sounder grounds from an evolutionary viewpoint if we entertain more seriously the possibilities that (1) all the phyla of vascular plants may extend back through a general "psilophytic stage" to independent (and unknown) algal sources (fig. 3), and that (2) other phyla of plants which are now extinct may also have included psilophytic plants. On this basis, the Psilophyta as now conceived may represent an ancient group of *unrelated* plants in various primitive ("psilophytic") stages of evolution which developed from diverse algal alliances. Since all phyla of vascular plants have passed through a primitive stage, then it must follow that

all of them at some time have been "psilophytic"; but it does not follow that they were all derived from psilophytes.

TIME OF TRANSMIGRATION

One problem that has been frequently raised is: Why did it "take so long" for plants to transmigrate from sea to land (Andrews and Mamay, 1955)? Actually, there is no concrete evidence to suggest that it did. The problem lies partly in understanding the nature of the record. The bulk of the unmetamorphosed Lower Paleozoic and Precambrian sedimentary section now available for study is marine, not continental: hence few records of land plants would be expected in it. Whilst they may once have been preserved in the nonmarine section, most of it has been eroded and the record is lost. Judging from the inferred nature of Cambrian land plants, the late Proterozoic land flora may have been nearly as complex as that which has been preserved in the Late Silurian to Middle Devonian rocks. But rather than being in the low lands, it probably was in the more distant uplands of environmental diversity, areas propitious for rapid evolution. Pertinently, plants in general seem to have evolved in much the same manner as animals, at least in terms of the broader aspects of tempo and mode (Stebbins, 1952). As Simpson has shown, the major phyla of vertebrates—"fishes," amphibia, reptiles, birds, mammals—took on the order of 40 to 50 million years to evolve from their respective ancestral types. Modern ferns, cycadophytes, and angiosperms required fully as long to diverge from their earlier forerunners (Axelrod, 1952). From his critical researches on the evolution of the coniferophytes, Florin (1949) has concluded that the Cordaitae, Ginkgoinae, Coniferae and Taxineae probably were already distinct by the Late Devonian-Mississippian. This suggests the ancestry of the group probably extends into the Silurian. Further, the occurrence of coniferous trees with 3-foot trunks (i.e. *Callixylon*) in the

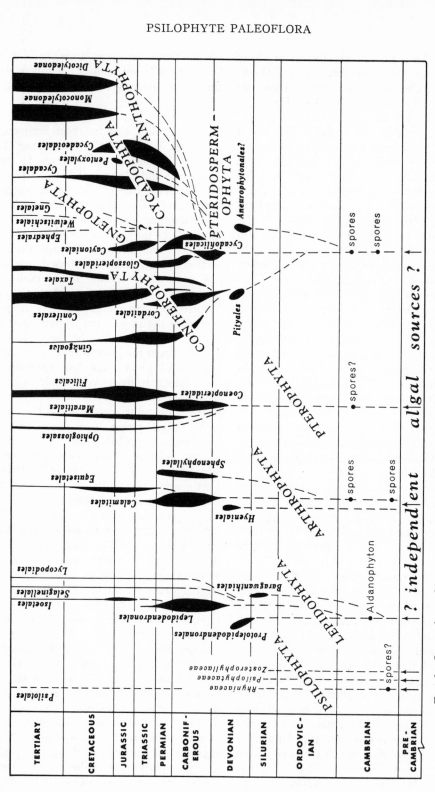

FIG. 3. Increasing evidence suggests that these plant phyla probably had independent algal sources (*cf.* fig. 2).

Middle Devonian probably means that the basic conifer type diverged from its ancestral seed-fern plexus by Early Silurian, if not in Ordovician time. Viewed in this light, the report of spores resembling those of seed ferns in the Cambrian is not at all surprising (Andrews and Alt, 1956, p. 365), but is fully to be expected.

The future discovery of a Precambrian vascular land flora of complex nature should therefore not amaze us, at least not in terms of its actual existence. It would appear that the times of transmigration fall far down in the Precambrian because algae were already in existence approximately a billion years prior to the Cambrian. The great morphological diversity of algae is well recognized, and they most probably were quite varied in the later Precambrian. If we assume that a number of algal groups were invading the lands during the Precambrian, then the apparent great diversity and high degree of organization of the Cambrian land flora is readily accounted for, and the Devonian psilophytes become ancient, slowly-evolving types of diverse alliances which were persisting in a "psilophytic stage" of evolution, some of which may be members of phyla now extinct.

These facts and inferences lead to the suggestion that our view of the Psilophyte Paleoflora has been much too narrow. As we bring early land plants into sharper focus in terms of their geologic, ecologic, and evolutionary relations, it seems clear that our phyletic charts need extensive revision, possibly on the order suggested here (fig. 3). Obviously, no final answers can be given to these problems that still surround the origins of the Psilophyte Paleoflora, and they will be with us for years to come. They deserve careful consideration from a broadened outlook, and with an open system of thinking that can only come when we are free of the shackles of a rigid phyletic dogma. We may hope that new evidence from the Cambrian, and from the still older, and as yet undiscovered, land plants of Precambrian time will illuminate more clearly the early history of the terrestrial flora, a history which we can now but dimly perceive.

SUMMARY

Evidence is reviewed which suggests that the salient evolutionary features of the earliest vascular land flora—the Psilophyte Paleoflora—included the following:

1. The Psilophyte Paleoflora was already in existence in Precambrian time.

2. The phyla of vascular plants may well represent unrelated groups that developed independently from different algal sources which migrated to land during the Precambrian, passing through a "psilophytic" stage early in their history.

3. The Late Silurian and Devonian psilophytes, and many of their associates, are not primitive and ancestral, but are ancient bradytelic types. They comprise members of different alliances which probably had persisted essentially unchanged since the Precambrian, surviving in mild, lowland sites close to sea level.

4. The reported similarity of vegetation across the earth during the Devonian applies only to the floras of the swampy lowlands. Vegetation in the adjacent uplands was diverse in composition, and largely included plants which were morphologically far advanced beyond the simple psilophytes.

5. The presumed "rapid evolution" of the Devonian flora is due to a misinterpretation of the record. Rather than comprising successive evolutionary stages, the Psilophyton, Hyenia, and Archaeopteris Floras represent only the replacement of lowland by more highly adapted upland floras which had evolved in areas of environmental diversity far removed from the lowlands where the record accumulated, and long before the Devonian.

LITERATURE CITED

ANDREWS, JR., H. N. 1947. Ancient plants and the world they lived in. Comstock Publ. Co., New York. 279 pp.
——, AND S. H. MAMAY. 1955. Some recent advances in morphological paleobotany. Phytomorphology, 5: 373–393.
——, AND KAREN S. ALT. 1956. *Crocalophyton:* a new fossil plant from the New Al-

bany shale, with some comments on the origin of land vascular plants. Ann. Missouri Bot. Gard., 43: 355–378.

ARBER, E. A. N. 1921. Devonian floras. Cambridge Univ. Press. 109 pp.

ARNOLD, C. A. 1947. An introduction to paleobotany. McGraw-Hill Book Co. 433 pp.

AXELROD, D. I., 1939. A Miocene flora from the western border of the Mohave desert. Carnegie Inst. Wash. Pub. 516.

——. 1952. A theory of angiosperm evolution. EVOLUTION, 6: 29–60.

——. 1958. Evolution of the Madro-Tertiary Geoflora. Bot. Rev., 24: 433–509.

BERRY, E. W. 1945. The beginnings and history of land plants. Johns Hopkins Univ., Studies in Geol., 14: 9–91.

BOLD, H. C. 1957. Morphology of plants. Harper & Bros. 699 pp.

CHANEY, R. W. 1947. Tertiary centers and migration routes. Ecol. Monogr., 17: 139–148.

DARRAH, W. C. 1937. Spores of Cambrian plants. Science, n. s., 86: 154–155.

DAWSON, J. W. 1859. On fossil plants from the Devonian rocks of Canada. Geol. Soc. London, Quart. Jour., 15: 477–488.

DORF, E. 1955. Plants and the geologic time scale. in The Crust of the Earth. Geol. Soc. Amer. Spec. Paper 62: 575–592.

EAMES, A. J. 1936. Morphology of vascular plants: Lower groups. McGraw Hill Book Co. 433 pp.

ELIAS, M. K. 1933. Late Paleozoic plants of the Midcontinent region as indicators of time and of environment: Internat. Geol. Congr., Report of 16th session, U.S.A., 1: 691–700.

FLORIN, R. 1949. The morphology of *Trichopitys heteromorpha* Saporta . . . . Acta Horti Bergiani, 15: 79–109.

GHOSH, A. K., AND A. BOSE. 1950. Microfossils from the Cambrian strata of the Salt Range, Punjab. Trans. Bose Res. Inst., 18: 71–78.

—— AND ——. 1952. Spores and tracheids from the Cambrian of Kashmir. Nature, 169: 1056–1057.

——, J. SEN AND A. BOSE. 1951. Evidence bearing on the age of the Saline Series in the Salt Range of Punjab. Geol. Mag., 88: 129–132.

HIRMER, M. 1927. Handbuch der Palaeobotanik. 708 pp. Munich.

HOEG, A. O. 1942. The Downtonian and Devonian Flora of Spitzbergen. Norges Svalbard.-OG Isharvs-Undersokelser, Oslo, 1–228.

HOSKINS, J. H., AND A. T. CROSS. 1952. The petrification flora of the Devonian-Mississippian black shale. The Paleobotanist, 1: 215–244.

JACOB, K., MRS. CH. JACOB AND R. N. SHRIVASTAVA. 1953a. Evidence for the existence of vascular land plants in the Cambrian. Current Sci., 22: 34–36.

—— AND —— AND ——. 1953b. Spores and tracheids of vascular plants from the Vindhyan System, India: the advent of vascular plants. Nature, 72: 166–167.

KIDSTON, R., AND W. H. LANG. 1917–21. Old Red Sandstone plants showing structure from the Rhynie chert bed, Aberdeenshire, pts. I–V. Roy. Soc. Edinb., Trans., 51–52.

KRYSTOFOVICH, A. N. 1954. Discovery of lycopodiaceous plants in the East-Siberian Cambrian. Dokladi Akad. Nauk U. S. S. R., 91: 1377–1379. (in Russian)

LANG, W. H., AND I. C. COOKSON. 1935. On a flora including vascular land plants associated with *Monograptus* in rocks of Silurian age from Victoria, Australia. Phil. Trans. Roy. Soc. London, ser. B, 224: 421–449.

LECLERCQ, S. 1954. Are the Psilophytales a starting or a resulting point? Svensk Bot. Tidskrift, 48: 301–315.

——. 1955. Evidence of vascular plants in the Cambrian. EVOLUTION, 10: 109–114.

NAUMOVA, S. N. 1949. Spores of the Lower Cambrian. Bull. Acad. Sci. U. S. S. R., 4: 49–56. (trans. from Russian)

RADFORTH, N. W., AND D. C. McGREGOR. 1954. Some plant microfossils important to Pre-Carboniferous stratigraphy and contributing to our knowledge of the early floras. Canadian Jour. Bot., 32: 601–621.

REISSINGER, A. 1939. Die "Pollenanalyse" Angedehnt auf alle Sedimentgesteine der geologischen Vergangenheit. Paleontolographica, B, 84: 1–20.

SEWARD, A. C. 1933. Plant life through the ages. Cambridge Univ. Press. 607 pp.

SIMPSON, G. G. 1944. Tempo and mode in evolution. Columbia Univ. Press. 237 pp.

——. 1953. The major features of evolution. Columbia Univ. Press. 434 pp.

SMITH, G. M. 1955. Cryptogamic botany. v. 2. Bryophytes and Pteridophytes. McGraw-Hill Book Co. 399 pp.

STEBBINS, JR., G. L. 1950. Variation and evolution in plants. Columbia Univ. Press. 643 pp.

TAKHTAJAN, A. L. 1956. Telomophyta 1. Psilophytales-Coniferales. Academia Scientiarum U. S. S. R., Instit. Botanicum. 488 pp.

THOMPSON, P. W. 1952. Beitrag zur Kenntnis der Sporomorphenflora im Unter- und Mitteldevon. Paleont. Z., 25: 155–159.

ZIMMERMANN, W. 1930. Phylogenie der Pflanzen. Jena.

——. 1952. Main results of the "Telone Theory." The Paleobotanist, 1: 456–470.

EVOLUTION OF THE NESTS OF BEES

Charles D. Michener

University of Kansas, Lawrence, Kansas

Nests or other objects constructed by animals provide an opportunity to see a sort of summation of results of certain of the behavior patterns of the animals as expressed over a considerable length of time. Most bees are solitary, each nest being constructed by a single adult female; but for social bees a nest permits observation of the results of behavior, not of a single individual, but of several to many (a maximum of probably 100,000).

Although 20,000 or more species of bees exist in the world, nests of relatively few have been found and described. Even among those that have been described, it often happens that characteristics which one would especially like to know about have not been recorded. Nevertheless, so much is known about bee nests that no full account can be given here.

Bees are essentially a group of sphecoid wasps that has abandoned predatory habits and makes use of pollen instead of insects and spiders as the principal protein source. The accompanying dendrogram (Fig. 1) gives some idea of the classification and probable phyletic relationships among the various groups of bees, as understood from morpholocigal evidence.

CELLS

The only almost invariable constant of a bee or wasp nest is the presence of one or more brood cells. A cell is the cavity in which one (or rarely more) young is reared. In the sphecoid wasps, from which bees undoubtedly arose, the most common type of cell is an unlined cavity in the ground. Some sphecoid wasps construct cells in pith or make exposed nests of mud (like those of mud daubers), but these are

Contribution number 1230 from the Department of Entomology of The University of Kansas. Preparation of this paper was greatly facilitated by grant number G11967 from the National Science Foundation.

developments parallel to those that have occurred among bees, and it seems highly likely that the most primitive bees were ground nesting, like the majority of sphecoid wasps and bees. In most nonsocial forms the construction follows a strict sequence, as follows: excavation, lining (if it occurs), provisioning, oviposition, and closure. The same sequence is then repeated for the next cell. Sakagami and Michener (1962) have described the breakdown of this typical chain of operations in halictid bees, even solitary species of which usually work on several cells during the same period, and of course simultaneous construction of many cells is the rule in some thoroughly social bees such as *Apis*.

Lining: As has been indicated, sphecoid wasps do not ordinarily line their cells. Apparently ancestral bees acquired not only pollen-feeding habits and the necessary structures to permit such habits, but also the behavior patterns, structures, and glands necessary to line cells. All of the primitive (most wasplike) bees line their cells in more or less elaborate ways. The family Colletidae contains those bees in which the glossa is short and broad, like that of wasps. All species of the family apply a secreted membranous lining on the inner walls of the cells. The material is tough and waterproof, translucent to transparent, cellophane-like, sometimes with recognizable silk strands imbedded in the translucent or transparent matrix. The equivalent membrane in the other primitive families of bees (most Andrenidae and Halictidae, Fig. 4, right) as well as in some of the Anthophoridae is more delicate, often brown, more waxlike in appearance, although not or only partly soluble in wax solvents. These secreted linings are painted onto the inner walls of the cells by the mouthparts of the female bee and are presumably, at least in part, salivary secretions. It is not surprising

that cell plugs, with which cells are closed
after oviposition, ordinarily are not water-
proofed on their inner surfaces with any
such material but in the related genera
Anthophora and *Amegilla* most of the inner wall of the plug is lined with the
secreted lining. It appears that the female
bee leaves a small hole in the plug as she
constructs it, and finally, probably by in-
serting her glossa through the hole, applies the lining material to the inside of
the plug surface. The final pellets of earth
that close the small hole in the plug are
unlined.

Presumably the secreted cell lining used
by burrowing bees is related to maintenance of the proper humidity within the

cell. The texture and humidity of the
pollen provided for the growing larva appears to be very important for most species; the larva dies if too much water is
absorbed into the food mass or if it dries
out and becomes too hard. This matter
would appear to be far more critical for
bees, in view of their use of a mixture of
pollen and nectar or honey as larval food,
than for wasps since the provisions provided for most wasp larvae already have
their own epicuticular and other water-
control mechanisms. Proper humidity is
also important for the larval and pupal
stages themselves.

The presumed primitive (for bees) secreted cell-lining has been lost in various

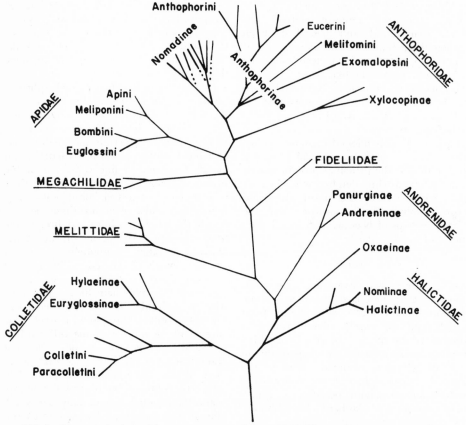

FIG. 1. Diagram of relationships among groups of bees. To facilitate reference from the text,
names of some tribes and subfamilies not mentioned in the text are omitted although the
branches are included. (Modified from Michener, 1944, Bull. Am. Mus. Nat. Hist.)

bees. In the Panurginae, some species (genus *Nomadopsis*) have such a lining, and in addition the subspherical food mass is covered by a very delicate secreted membrane, apparently similar to that applied to the inner walls of the cell. Rozen (1958), however, states that the cell lining is permeable to water, a condition which perhaps explains the non-permeable covering of the food mass. In other members of the same group of bees *(Perdita)* the cell lining is abandoned altogether (Michener and Ordway, 1963), and the food mass is perhaps surrounded by a thin membrane as in *Nomadopsis*. Of course the feeding of the larvae immediately breaks such a membrane and exposes the food mass to the air within the cell, but part of the food mass retains the protection for some time after the larva begins to eat.

The cells with thin secreted linings usually have these materials applied to extraordinarily smooth surfaces of the substrate (usually soil). Such smooth surfaces cannot, apparently, be constructed merely by excavation. At least it is true that with a few exceptions, such as *Colletes,* these bees excavate cells that are considerably larger than the ultimate cell size. They bring earth from elsewhere in the nest and form an earthen lining often as much as one or two mm thick. This lining of worked substrate (usually earth) is frequently recognizable because, consisting of earth from another part of the nest, differs in color from that surrounding it. Also, it is usually of very fine texture and is firmly tamped by the pygidial area of the bee. Only after the inner surface is made extraordinarily smooth, much smoother than one would think possible, is the secreted lining applied. The earthen lining is sometimes permeated by liquid applied at about the same time as, and perhaps as part of, the secreted lining (Batra, 1964). As a result, the earthen lining is sometimes quite firm, and in forms such as *Melitoma (Anthophoridae)* intact earthen cells can be separated from the substrate.

It is interesting that the behavior patterns involved in the construction of such cell walls and their secreted linings—patterns apparently essential for the survival of the more primitive bees such as most of the short-tongued forms of the families Colletidae, Andrenidae, and Halictidae as well as some of the long-tongued Anthophoridae—should have been abandoned independently in various specialized, long-tongued bees.

A great many bees, particularly those in the families Megachilidae and Apidae (that is, in the most specialized families of long-tongued bees), have abandoned the thin secreted cell-lining and do not make the smooth lining of worked substrate or the secreted lining. In Megachilidae the cell lining may be partly the substrate in which the cell is constructed but it is always partly, and usually wholly, made of other materials brought into the nest from the outside, for example leaf pieces, chewed leaf material, resin, pebbles, etc. In the Apidae the relatively thick cell walls are made of resin (Euglossini) or of wax *(Apis, Bombus)* or of a mixture of the two (Meliponini).

Cocoons: In nearly all of the forms in which the thin secreted cell-lining of the more primitive families of bees has been abandoned, it appears to have been replaced by a cocoon spun by the mature larva. This cocoon is in many ways similar to the thin cell-lining. It consists of a layer of silk fibers to which is applied a liquid which hardens as a matrix surrounding the fibers, making the cocoon impervious except frequently for a small area, perhaps serving for ventilation. Those bees in which the thin cell-lining is applied by the adults virtually never construct cocoons as larvae, except for some anthophorids (e.g., Eucerini). Perhaps the lining and cocoon-making materials are produced from the same glands which mature in the late larval stage in some forms, and in the adult in others, and function in both stages in some anthophorids. Probably the importance of the cocoon is maintenance of proper humidity for the late larval stage and the pupa. Many bees live for months or even for several years in the late larval (prepupal) stage.

Sphecoid wasps, like most Hymenoptera, usually spin cocoons as mature larvae. It seems that the line leading to the bees lost this behavior, and probably used the same materials in the adult stage for the secreted cell-linings. However, most of the highly evolved long-tongued bees reverted to cocoons and no longer make secreted cell-linings. The salivary spinnerets of bee larvae are associated with this picture; they are well developed only in the cocoon-spinning specialized families of bees (Michener, 1953a).

Food masses: It seems reasonable to consider in a discussion of constructs by bees the food mass with which each cell is provisioned. In all the members of the family Colletidae (those with the cellophane-like cell-linings), the food mass is liquid and even watery. It fills the bottom part of the waterproof cell. The relatively small amount of pollen in such material is responsible for its liquid state and is presumably a primitive feature. In two groups of colletids (Euryglossinae and Hylaeinae) the polled is carried from the flowers back to the nest along with the liquid nectar in the crop instead of on the outside of the body of the bee. This is quite possibly the primitive manner of collecting pollen for bees, although in all other groups it is carried in a scopa made up of hairs on the hind legs, the abdomen, or sometimes in part on the propodeum.

In bees other than Colletidae, the provisions contain a higher percentage of pollen so that they are firmer. In many bees (Halictidae, Andrenidae, Xylocopinae, and others) the provisions are quite firm, obviously consisting largely of pollen. In such forms, there is an interesting series of shapes for the pollen mass, all apparently related to the curious matter of allowing this mass to contact the inner wall of the cell in the minimum possible area. The reason for this is not obvious but may have something to do with the control of humidity in the food mass or the inhibition of mold which may tend to start its growth

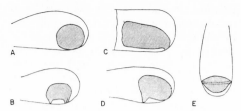

FIG. 2. Diagrams of cells of certain bees which make firm pollen masses (shaded) showing ways in which contact of these masses with the cell walls is minimized. a, *Lasioglossum inconspicuum*; b, *Dasypoda plumipes* (after Malyshev, 1935); c, *Xylocopa valga* (after Malyshev, 1935); d, *Exomalopsis chionura* (after Rozen and MacNeill, 1957; relation of cell size to pollen mass was not illustrated by those authors and is possibly incorrect); e, *Nomia triangulifera* (After Cross and Bohart, 1960).

at points where the cell wall and the pollen mass are in contact. In any event, pollen masses have the shapes described as follows (Fig. 2):

1) The most frequent shape is spherical or subspherical. Obviously such a mass will have a relatively limited area in contact with the cell wall. This shape is found in most Andrenidae and Halictidae. (2) In some species of *Nomia* (Halictidae) the pollen mass is flattened and provided with a projecting rim around the circumference so that it is supported in the lower part of the vertical cell by this rim, the bottom of the pollen mass thus not reaching the bottom of the cell. (3) In the Xylocopinae the food mass is loaf-like; the upper end (in a vertical cell) of the loaf is in contact with and attached to the cell wall but the remainder is not, the posterior end being free or supported by the egg (*Ceratina australensis*, see Michener, 1962) or the posterior end may have a small area of contact with the cell wall. (4) In *Exomalopsis* (Anthophoridae) the pollen mass is in contact with the cell at its rounded posterior end; the anterior end is supported by a median projection (Rozen and MacNeill, 1957). (5) The most remarkable shape is that made by *Dasypoda* (Melittidae), in which the pollen mass is supported by three short legs projecting from it, thus constituting a tripod (Malyshev, 1935).

(6) The activities of the larva also contribute to reduction of the contact of provisions with the surface of the cell, for in various bees, especially Panurgini, the larva works under the food mass and feeds with the food supported on its venter. (7) The provisions made by some long-tongued bees (e.g., *Anthophora,* Meliponini, some Megachilidae) are soft, semi-liquid, and flow; therefore they fill the lower part of a cell. In their texture such provisions are presumably independent reversions toward the liquid colletid type.

Of course in those few bees in which food to the larvae is provided gradually instead of by mass provisioning, there is no preservation problem. However, the only bees which exhibit this behavior are *Apis, Bombus* (in part and sometimes only to a limited degree), and *Allodape* (Xylocopinae) and its relatives; these probably constitute not over 400 of the 20,000 species of bees.

Cell shape: The cells of bees do vary in shape, but in general, particularly in the bees that are thought to be most primitive (Paracolletini and Euryglossinae), the cells are homomorphic—that is, all are more or less of the same shape. This is the commonest situation. However, various groups have acquired a degree of plasticity in cell shape, which then conforms more or less to the shape of the cavity in which the cell is located. Some members of the primitive family Colletidae, including especially those that nest in pith (e.g. *Hylaeus*) and also the ground nesting bees of the genus *Colletes,* make burrows into the substrate and then divide the burrows by means of transverse partitions made of the cellophane-like material already described as characteristic of cell linings in this family. The result is that the innermost cell, that is, the cell farthest from the surface or nest entrance, has its distal end rounded to fit the rounded end of the burrow, whereas the other cells have both ends truncated. In other colletids, e.g. some forms of *Hylaeus* and its relatives such as *Meroglossa,* the cells are sometimes made in the same way but using the burrow of

a beetle or other insect in twigs or in wood. The volume of the various cells is more or less constant, hence they are shorter in portions of the burrow having large diameters than in portions having small diameters. (By no means do all bees which construct cells in series, end to end, have heteromorphic cells. For example, the Xylocopinae regularly construct cells in series, but the partitions between the cells are so shaped that the distal end of each cell is rounded just like the distal end of the apical cell of the series.)

Many primitive bees (most Paracolletini, Halictidae, Andrenidae) have homomorphic cells which are flatter on one side (the lower side in the case of horizontal cells) than on the other (Fig. 2a). Such cells are called bilaterally symmetrical by Malyshev (1935). Radially symmetrical cells (round in cross-section), however, occur in some Colletidae and in almost all of the long-tongued families, and are modified as hexagonal in *Apis.* At least in the latter families and possibly also in Colletidae, radial symmetry must be derived from bilateral.

Certain bees, principally or exclusively in the family Megachilidae (e.g., *Osmia lignaria*), make heteromorphic cells whose shape corresponds to cavities that the bees happen to have discovered and used. Thus, in at least two families (Colletidae and Megachilidae), the generally homomorphic form of bee cells has been abandoned, obviously independently.

The wax cells of *Bombus* are a most extraordinary development. They are somewhat variable in size and shape, and therefore heteromorphic, but are unique among the bees in that in most species they contain a cluster of eggs or immature stages instead of only one, and in that they grow (i.e. wax is added to them) as their contents grow. At first such a cell need only enclose the eggs, because no large quantity of provisions is placed in the cell; thus the larvae are fed progressively instead of by mass provisioning.

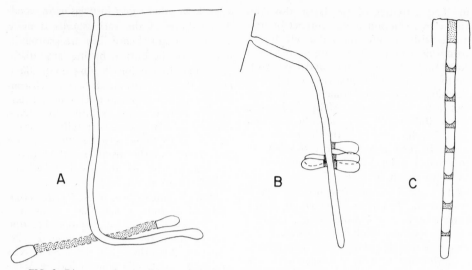

FIG. 3. Diagrams of nests of bees. a, *Andrena erythronii* in ground; b, *Lasioglossum guaruvae* in earth bank; c, *Hoplitis pilosifrons* in pithy stem.

NESTS

Because of its widespread occurrence through the more primitive families of bees, I believe that the primitive type of bee nest consists of a burrow entering the soil, and giving rise at its lower end to laterals, each ending in a single cell (Fig. 3A) (See Michener and Lange, 1957). This sort of nest is also widely distributed among sphecoid wasps. The lateral burrows are built one at a time so that at first the nests will have only the main burrow continued as one lateral ending in a cell. When that cell is provisioned and sealed, a second lateral is started, the soil from which is used to fill the first. The result is that there is rarely more than one lateral open at a time, although if one considers all the earth-filled laterals, there may be several radiating from the lower end of the main burrow. Such nests are well known in the ground-nesting Colletidae, Andrenidae, and in some of the Anthophoridae.

Many Halictidae have such nests, differing in that the main burrow extends downward below the level of the laterals. In other Halictidae, however, there is a tendency to concentrate the cells or save work

by shortening the laterals until the cells arise without laterals from the walls of the main burrow. Further developments in the Halictidae, as detailed by Sakagami and Michener (1962), include: (1) concentration of the cells in limited spaces (Fig. 3B); (2) excavation of burrows around the cells or around portions of them so that there are only thin walls between the burrows and the interiors of the cells; and (3) expansion of these burrows to form a space around the cluster of aggregated cells, the cell cluster often being supported only by a few earthen pillars or only by rootlets which pass through the cell cluster. Such clusters are small combs of cells, usually made of earth. Photographs of such nests are shown in Figure 4.

It is interesting that this air space or vault surrounding the cell cluster has arisen independently in several groups of the subfamily Halictinae, as well as in the genus *Nomia* in the Nomiinae, and even in the subterranean nests of the distantly related genus *Proxylocopa* (Xylocopinae). Such a space surrounding the cell cluster occurs also in the halictine, *Augochlora*, which nests in rotting wood. The function of this space is unknown, but it seems that it must play some role related to the

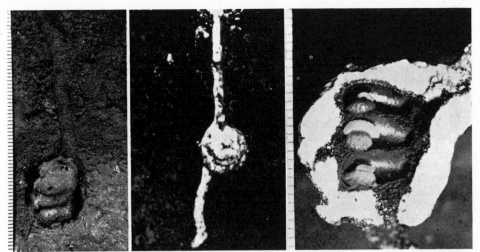

FIG. 4. Nests of *Augochlorella striata* in soil. Left, nest opened to show cell cluster and burrow leading down to it (photo by Ellen Ordway); center, nest pored with plaster of Paris, then excavated to show form of whole nest (photo by C. W. Rettenmeyer); right, cell cluster opened and showing smooth linings of three adjacent cells, very thin earthen cell walls, and earth pillars supporting cell cluster in air space here filled with white plaster of Paris. (Immature stages shown are an egg in the upper cell and larvae in the others.) (Photo by C. W. Rettenmeyer.) Scales are in millimeters.

environmental conditions within the cells. It certainly is not a labor-saving device since it obviously requires considerable work to construct it. The thinness of the earthen walls of the cells is sometimes noteworthy; in some genera they are consistently less than one-half a millimeter thick, and one can see the details of the shapes of all cells from the outside of the cell cluster.

In burrowing halictids which do not make such cell clusters, the cells are excavated into the substrate and lined with worked earth and a secreted lining, as described above. Some of those which make cell clusters construct the cells in the same way and then excavate the earth from around the group of cells. Others, however, excavate the space and then build the cells within it. The constructed wall in this case appears to be homologous to the earthen lining added to excavated cells. Intermediate conditions are known, as described especially by Stockhammer (1964) for *Augochlora*, in which the bee sometimes excavates part of a cell into the substrate and then continues the walls outward into the nest cavity with independent walls as a constructed cell. In spite of such intermediates, however, the diversity of the methods of producing the cells in those bees which isolate a cell cluster from the surrounding earth (or rotten wood) emphasizes the independent origin of such cell clusters in various phyletic lines.

The shortening of lateral burrows and clustering of cells as seen in many halictids may originally have been a matter of economy of labor. An entirely different development of a similar sort which arose repeatedly was the habit of placing cells in series end to end. Sometimes such an arrangement can be seen in lateral burrows, each of which thus contains two to several cells [*Pseudagapostemon* (Halictidae), see Sakagami and Michener, 1962; some *Andrena*, see Michener and Rettenmeyer, 1956]. In other cases no lateral burrows are constructed, but cells are placed end to end in the main burrow or its branches (e.g., *Hylaeus*, some *Colletes*, Xylocopinae, many Megachilini, Fig. 3C).

Still another interesting labor-saving device is re-use of cells after refurbishing.

Curiously, this seemingly simple device seems to have arisen as a regular arrangement only in some of the Halictidae that make clusters of cells (Sakagami and Michener, 1962) and in the genus *Apis*.

Many bees tend to start their nests in pre-existing holes in the substrate, and as has been indicated, some always use such cavities instead of making their own. These are labor-saving arrangements of a different sort. The family Megachilidae includes many which consistently use pre-existing holes and rarely or never dig or gnaw their own. The family Megachilidae also includes nearly all the bees (except the social ones) in which the cells are no longer constructed in the substrate but are placed on the surfaces of materials in fairly exposed situations. Presumably this development was possible only among bees using more or less weather-resistant foreign materials (resin, pebbles, mud) in cell construction. Examples include the genus *Dianthidium* which builds nests of pebbles and resin on boulders or branches of trees or bushes, and *Chalicodoma* which constructs mud nests on cliffs or buildings. For such an exposed nest, the cells and the nest are synonymous; there is no other part of the nest. For the majority of bees, however, the nest is much more than merely the cells.

In some nonsocial bees, all of the cells that a female produces are located in a single nest. From the standpoint of economy of labor, this is the best arrangement. In others, however, the female may disperse her cells in several nests. For example, in *Megachile brevis* the female moves from place to place, sometimes over distances of several miles, making nests with one to several cells in different places (Michener, 1953b). In *Andrena erythronii* the female remains in the same vicinity but nonetheless constructs two or three nests during her life, each containing a few cells (Michener and Rettenmeyer, 1956). In *Anthocopa papaveris* (Megachilidae) (Malyshev, 1935) and *Perdita maculigera* (Andrenidae) (Michener and Ordway, 1963) each nest burrow ends in only

a single cell (rarely two in the first mentioned species). The number of nests made by each such bee is unknown, but must be several. Since the bees listed are quite unrelated, the tendency for multiplicity and simplification of nests must have arisen independently in various groups.

Reduction of nest structure reaches its extreme in the primitively social xylocopine genus *Allodape* and its relatives. Here the nest itself is nothing but a burrow, usually in the pith of a stem. The young are reared together in it, there being no separate cells for them (Sakagami, 1960).

By contrast, in some bees the number of cells per nest is very large. This is particularly true in the social forms. Sociability has arisen independently in various bees. Even in the Halictinae, social behavior including a worker caste and an increased number of cells has arisen several times. In this group, neither nest nor cell structure is influenced by the social behavior, except for the more extensive burrow system and larger number of cells in nests containing more bees. Thus there are both solitary and social forms with cells scattered through the earth, with cells gathered into clusters, and with cells in clusters or combs surrounded by air spaces.

Even within a single species of facultatively or temporarily social halictine, the cells and nests are essentially the same whether made by a single bee or by a colony. Batra (1964) has seen that the cells in the nests of a social halictine, *Lasioglossum zephyrum*, are excavated by several bees and that several individuals may cooperate in lining and provisioning. Yet a single bee of the same species can do the same job. The bees in such nests have little contact with one another and it is probable that the stimuli that result in appropriate construction are those from the nest itself. There is no evidence for integration of activities through contacts among members of the colony, such as is obvious in socially more specialized insects including the Meliponini and *Apis*. Communication is therefore not direct, but by way of the construct. In a nest occupied by a single bee, constructed features must also serve as stimuli for further constructing, i.e., it is as though the bee communicates with itself. Similar stimuli evidently result in similar construction activity whether there is only one bee or a colony.

Among the most interesting bees are those of the family Apidae. Some Euglossini are solitary, constructing their cells of resin, sometimes mixed with bits of bark, in pre-existing cavities *(Euglossa, Euplusia).* Some species of *Euglossa* (e.g. *E. dodsoni)* construct an exposed nest of resin in which they place their cells; in other words, they make their own cavity for the cells instead of finding one. Among the close relatives of *Euglossa* is the genus *Eulaema,* in at least some species of which there is a certain amount of social organization since several individuals which are probably workers are involved in the construction of each mud cell and in its provisioning. (C. Dodson, personal communication.) Such nests may contain numerous individuals and occupy large cavities in the soil, in wood, in termite nests, or in other situations.

The related bumblebees *(Bombus)* make use of similar cavities or abandoned nests of small mammals, and secrete wax for construction. In *Bombus* we encounter for the first time pots made of wax (and old cocoons) for storage of food material for the consumption of adults. Food supplies discussed above were in brood cells and for the use of larvae (although limited autumnal storage of food for adult consumption is known in the nest burrows of Xylocopinae) .

Such storage pots are also characteristic of the stingless bees (Meliponini) which exist in large permanent colonies with a social organization equivalent in complexity to that of the common honeybee. The nests of most stingless bees are found in large cavities. One of the architectural features which seems to be of evolutionary interest is the arrangement of the brood cells. In the Australian species of the subgenus *Plebeia* of the genus *Trigona,* the cells are spherical and clustered together

in a mass which is surrounded by a thin wax and resin involucrum. It seems quite possible that this is the primitive cell arrangement (see Michener, 1961). In another species of the same subgenus found in northern Australia and New Guinea, the cells are arranged in concentric layers with spaces between them. It is possible that from such an arrangement the usual meliponine nest organization with a series of horizontal combs of cells (Fig. 5, left) may have arisen. In all such nests there is a wax and resin involucrum surrounding the brood chamber which contains the combs. Independently, in several different subgenera of *Trigona* and the derived genus *Lestrimelitta,* the neat arrangement of cells into combs appears to have broken down. Derivation from ancestors with cells in combs is suggested by the vertically elongate cells like those crowded into combs, in contrast to cells of the Australian *Plebeia* thought to have the primitive cell arrangement for the group. In those forms in which the combs are partly or entirely disorganized to form clusters of cells, the involucrum is absent. The significance of the disappearance of the involucrum and the breakdown of the combs appears to be adaptation to small spaces for nesting. Nests of these species with clusters of cells are to be found in large hollow stems, in crevices in logs, in small spaces between boards in the walls of houses (Fig. 5, right), and in similar situations where a nest organized into combs surrounded by an involucrum could not possibly be accommodated. It is interesting that in some species whose involucrum is virtually absent, small patches of it are sometimes constructed. These would appear to be vestigial structures (resulting from "vestigial behavior") having no functional significance in the nest as it is used by the bees today.

From the standpoint of cell arrangement, the most remarkable of the Meliponini is the African *Dactylurina.* In this genus the brood cells, instead of forming horizontal combs or clusters as in other members of the group, and instead of be-

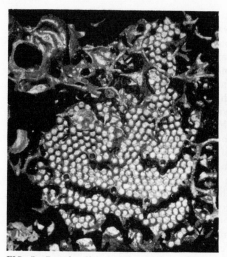

FIG. 5. Brood cells of *Trigona*. Left, horizontal combs of *Trigona carbonaria*, with large honey pots (one open) at upper left; right, sheet of cells of *Trigona wybenica* filling space between two boards, showing how most species which do not make combs can crowd their nests into small spaces.

ing vertically elongate as in most members of the group, are horizontal and form vertical combs with cells facing in both directions just as in the genus *Apis*. In other features the nests of these bees are similar to those of other Meliponini.

The brood cells of *Apis* are arranged as in *Dactylurina* but there are two sizes, one for males, the other for workers. The occasional very different brood cells for queens are comparable to those that occur in the genus *Trigona* of the stingless bees.

Honeybees are remarkable for the fact that, unlike the bumblebees and the stingless bees, they do not have honey pots but store provisions for adult consumption in cells similar to the brood cells. Perhaps this is related to the fact that the presumably primitive species of the genus *Apis* do not nest in cavities as do their relatives but construct nests in the open, hanging from a large branch or an overhanging rock or ledge. In such situations, large and rather delicate honey pots might be easily destroyed by natural forces. It is true that the more specialized species of *Apis* such as the common honeybee do nest in cavities, but this is probably a derived rather than a primitive nesting site for the genus,

as judged from behavioral evidence relating to communication.

A comparable evolutionary development in stingless bee nests is the progressive independence of the nests from the cavities usually used as nesting sites by members of that group. Nests in cavities are surrounded by batumen layers. The thick walls of cerumen (a mixture of resin, wax, and sometimes mud or other materials) cut off the hollow (for example, in the trunk of a tree) and form a cavity of proper size for the nest; thin walls of lining batumen cover the inside of that portion of the hollow used for the nest. Some nests (e.g., *Trigona cupira*) are partially exposed, being constructed in hollows in banks or in trees, one side of which is open. In such cases the batumen is much elaborated on the exposed side of the nest, being several layers thick with airspaces between. Finally, in certain species such as *Trigona corvina*, the nest is constructed in the open, surrounding the branch of a tree. In such cases the batumen layers are numerous, sometimes forming a multilayered insulating and protective barrier as much as 20 cm thick surrounding the whole nest except for the entrance hole.

Although relatively few of the nests of the 20,000 species of bees in the world are known, it is very obvious that nest structures have some taxonomic value. It is often easy to recognize the tribe or genus of a bee by its nest structure. Such characteristics, however, are useful at all levels, from the species to the family. Indeed, Kerfoot (1964) has described what appear to be subspecific differences in the shape of the pollen mass in *Nomia nevadensis*.

Comparative studies of nests designed to add to our knowledge of affinities among groups of bees are primarily useful if one can recognize homologous structures among the various nests.

The structures of bee cells or nests result from the interactions of the behavioral patterns of the bees with the environment in which the nest is constructed. It is legitimate to ask to what extent the nest structure can be considered a reflection of species specific behavior patterns of the insect, and to what extent is it a response to the environment in which the insect finds itself. It is at least possible to point out that, with exceptions in the Colletidae and Megachilidae and of course cells producing different castes in social bees, the shape and structure of cells are very uniform within each species. The arrangement of the cells and the formation of the whole nest may vary greatly with the local variations in the substrate or the nest environment. Indeed, Stockhammer (1964) was able to find virtually all possible arrangements of cells and of the surrounding vault in nests of *Augochlora* in different situations in logs and in artificial nests. The cells themselves, at least internally, varied but little, in spite of the impressive flexibility in nest architecture.

Furthermore, among different kinds of bees, cells are often quite similar although the nest structure may be very different. Batra (1964) and Stockhammer (1964) have observed the behavior patterns involved in cell construction and cell lining in species of different genera (*Lasioglos-sum* and *Augochlora*) of the family Halictidae in nests constructed in substrates between two sheets of glass in a bee room where the insects have been maintained under laboratory conditions. Nests of these two bees are extremely different, although the cells are similar. It is quite obvious that the behavior patterns involved in the construction of the cells can be recognized and homologized in bees of the two genera. It therefore seems entirely legitimate to homologize the parts of the cells. For example, the smooth, worked lining of substrate material; the thin secreted lining; the inner end; the cell opening; the lower rather flat side of the cell as distinguished from the other, more concave sides; and the cell plug all seem to be homologizable between the two genera of Halictidae. The flat side of the cell is particularly significant in this case because in the cells which have such a surface, it is typically the lower one. However, in various Halictidae, the cells become slanting or even vertical (see Sakagami and Michener, 1962). Even when the cells are vertical, one of the sides is flatter than the rest. It is to this side that the pollen mass is attached in a vertical cell, being somehow stuck to the smooth, waxy surface. In horizontal cells it is held in position on this surface by gravity alone. The evidence of homology is strengthened by this sort of observation, as well as by the common behavior patterns involved in the construction of the various features of the cells.

On the other hand, cells of more distantly related bees such as *Megachile* and *Apis* are constructed by means of largely different movements on the part of the insect and by use of entirely different materials. The cells, moreover, have different shapes, and in *Apis* they are not plugged in the same way after oviposition, for there is progressive feeding of the larvae. It is difficult to speak of homology of the details of the structure, as one can do when comparing the two species of Halictidae. However, it would be unreasonable to feel that the cells as wholes are not homologous among all bees (exceptions are *Allodape* and its relatives, see Sakagami, 1960).

The problem in homologizing these constructs of bees is exactly comparable to that in homologizing structures. The difficulty or impossibility of defining the idea of homology in a satisfactory way is the same for constructs as for morphological features. For example, it is possible to homologize fine details of the fore limbs of two mammals, but on comparing one of them with the pectoral fin of a fish, only general statements about homologies can be made. Clearly, however, it seems as reasonable to speak of homologous constructs as it is to speak of the homologous structures of the organism itself.

One of the noteworthy features of the nests of many bees, especially of the Halictidae and the social Xylocopinae related to *Allodape,* is the constriction of the entrance. The nest burrows are originally dug with a constricted entrance, and the bees replace the constriction in the event that it is destroyed. It is obvious that the long-lived bees such as these would have special needs for nest defense; similar constrictions are weak or absent in the majority of the burrowing bees which are solitary and whose nests are open only for brief periods in each generation. Some such bees have other protective devices such as tumuli of loose dirt completely closing the nest entrances. The noteworthy feature of the entrance constrictions is the exactly parallel way in which they are used for protection in the unrelated Halictidae and Xylocopinae. In both groups, guard bees commonly occupy the entrances, consistently if more than one bee is in the nest at the same time. The guard normally has her head in the entrance, her body down in the burrow. At any disturbance, she bites at the disturbing object, often without touching it. If the disturbance continues, she will turn and block the entrance with the dorsal apical portion of her abdomen; this action is practical only in a nest having a constriction at the entrance but a relatively large burrow diameter just below the entrance. In this position the bee is difficult to dislodge and we have seen her successfully prevent the entrance of ants, mutillid parasites, etc. The constricted entrance and the associated behavior patterns seem to have arisen independently in at least the two unrelated groups of bees mentioned above. Superficial examination would suggest that they are homologous, but the great taxonomic differences and absence of comparable behavior among other, and more or less intermediate, groups suggest that this is not the case.

SUMMARY AND CONCLUSIONS

Bee nests include or consist of cells for rearing young. Nests also serve as resting places and often as wintering places for adults (mostly for females). Among thoroughly social bees, nests include storage places for food for adults as well as for larvae. Primitive nests are branching burrows, each branch ending in a cell lined with impervious material and containing liquid food for the larva. Labor-saving grouping of cells ultimately leads to series of cells end to end along a burrow, or to clusters or comblike arrangements. Adaptation to pre-existing cavities leads to cells of various shapes rather than of the same shape, as in most bees. Many other features of the cells, the food mass, and the nest as a whole have evolved, and it is easy to cite instances which can be described as convergence, parallelism, reversion to a structure made by an ancestral type, simplification of structure, vestigial structures, and the like. Most features have arisen more than once, if our understanding of bee phylogeny is at all correct. In general, influence of the substrate is minimal on cells but may be very great on gross nest form or the manner of cell clustering. Flexibility of behavior serving to take advantage of local differences in the substrate is so great that in nests of a single species virtually all possible arrangements of cells can be found in rotten wood, but species that nest in more homogeneous substrates probably possess less potential for flexibility.

There is no obvious relationship between the development of social organization and the nest architecture, except that the larger the social groups, the more cells are present. The organization of the nest and the structure of the cells is similar in social groups and their close solitary relatives (if extant). This means that there are distinctive features of nest structure in the various taxa of bees, and that these features are more conservative than the degree of social organization, a conclusion at first surprising considering the complex of interactions among individuals that would seem necessary to make a society effective. However, communication among individuals of primitively social bees seems largely based upon stimuli of the construct, without contact among individuals of the colony. The same stimuli must guide construction in nests of related non-colonial bees, the bee making features which later cause it to do something else. In that case, it is as though the bee is communicating with itself; in a colony, features made by one bee may have their effect on another. In this light, similar constructs would be expected whether made by a lone individual or by a colony.

Comparative studies of nests show not only distinctive features of the taxa from subspecies to superfamily, but also homologies among nest structures. Such homologies can be supported in detail for related forms by ontogony, behavior patterns involved in construction, as well as relative position, appearance, and function of nest parts but suffer from the same problems of definition as homologies of structural parts of organisms themselves.

REFERENCES

(Review or recent works which can serve as guides to other literature, rather than historically significant works, are cited in most cases.)

Batra, S. W. T. 1964. Behavior of the social bee, *Lasioglossum zephyrum*, in the nest (Hymenoptera:Halictidae). Insectes Sociaux, in press.

Cross, E. A., and G. E. Bohart. 1960. The biology of *Nomia (Epinomia) triangulifera* with notes on other species of *Nomia*. Univ. Kansas Sci. Bull. 41:761-792.

Grandi, G. 1961. Studi di un entomologo sugli Imenotteri superiori. Boll. Instituto Ent. Univ. Bologna 25:1-659.

Kerfoot, W. B. 1964. Observations on the nests of *Nomia nevadensis bakeri* with comparative notes on *Nomia nevadensis arizonensis* (Hymenoptera: Halictidae). J. Kansas Entomol. Soc., in press.

Malyshev, S. I. 1935. The nesting habits of solitary bees. Eos 11:201-309.

Michener, C. D. 1944. Comparative external morphology, phylogeny and a classification of bees. Bull. Am. Mus. Nat. Hist. 82:157-326.

————. 1953a. Comparative morphological and systematic studies of bee larvae with a key to the families of hymenopterous larvae. Univ. Kansas Sci. Bull. 35:987-1102.

————. 1953b. The biology of a leaf-cutter bee (*Megachile brevis*) and its associates. Univ. Kansas Sci. Bull. 35:1659-1748.

————. 1961. Observations on the nests and behavior of *Trigona* in Australia and New Guinea (Hymenoptera, Apidae). Am. Mus. Novitates 2060:1-46.

————. 1962. The genus *Ceratina* in Australia, with notes on its nests (Hymenoptera:Apoidea). J. Kansas Entomol. Soc. 35:414-421.

Michener, C. D., and R. B. Lange. 1957. Observations on the ethology of some Brazilian colletid bees (Hymenoptera, Apoidea). J. Kansas Entomol. Soc. 30:71-80.

————. 1958. Observations on the ethology of neotropical anthophorine bees (Hymenoptera: Apoidea). Univ. Kansas Sci. Bull. 39:69-96.

Michener, C. D., and E. Ordway. 1963. The life history of *Perdita maculigera maculipennis* (Hymenoptera:Andrenidae). J. Kansas Entomol. Soc. 36:34-45.

Michener, C. D., and C. W. Rettenmeyer. 1956. The ethology of *Andrena erythronii* with comparative data on other species (Hymenoptera, Andrenidae). Univ. Kansas Sci. Bull. 37:645-684.

Rozen, J. G. 1958. Monographic study of the genus *Nomadopsis* Ashmead (Hymenoptera: Andrenidae). Univ. California Publ. Entomol. 15:1-202.

Rozen, J. G., and C. D. MacNeill. 1957. Biological observations on *Exomalopsis (Anthophorula) chionura* Cockerell, including a comparison of the biology of *Exomalopsis* with that of other anthophorid groups (Hymenoptera : Apoidea). Ann. Entomol. Soc. Am. 50:522-529.

Sakagami, S. F. 1960. Ethological peculiarities of the primitive social bees, *Allodape* Lepeltier (sic) and allied genera. Insectes Sociaux 7:231-249.

Sakagami, S. F., and C. D. Michener. 1962. The nest architecture of the sweat bees (Halictinae). Univ. Kansas Press, Lawrence. 135 p.

Stockhammer, K. A. 1964. Manuscript in preparation on *Augochlora pura*.

THE SIGNIFICANCE OF FLORAL CONSTANCY AMONG BEES OF THE GENUS DIADASIA (HYMENOPTERA, ANTHOPHORIDAE)

E. G. LINSLEY AND J. W. MACSWAIN

University of California, Berkeley

Received November 9, 1957

The bee genus *Diadasia* Patton is a relatively large group of solitary or gregarious ground nesting species. It occurs only in the Western Hemisphere and is abundantly represented in southwestern United States and Mexico and in the arid and semi-arid portions of South America, but is rare in the moist tropics (Michener, 1954). Biological characteristics of *Diadasia* have been discussed elsewhere (Linsley, MacSwain and Smith, 1952, 1956; Linsley and MacSwain, 1957). It is the object of the present paper to emphasize the role that food habits and flower relationships may have had in evolution and speciation in the group.

As with most organisms, food habits have played an important role also in the evolution and speciation of bees. The choice of larval food, as is usually the case with plant feeding insects, is made by the adult. The bee larva, to survive, must accept the food since it is unable to make an alternative choice. The larval food is pollen, usually mixed with some nectar, gathered from flowers by the female bee. However, bees visit flowers for a variety of reasons, other than pollen collecting. Flowers provide adult food (especially nectar) for both sexes of all species, the site of mating for many, and a male sleeping place for others. Of all these functions, the collection of pollen by females invokes the most consistently specific response to flower species, although, in some cases, the mating search by males may be equally so. Bees in which the females are highly specific in their choice of pollen sources are termed oligolectic, those which are not specific, polylectic.

Flower constancy in the collection of pollen is a characteristic of bees in general. Two principal forms of constancy are involved. The first is characteristic of individual bees which, on one or several successive trips, may gather pure or nearly pure loads of pollen from a single kind of plant, although the species as a whole may be polylectic and not sharply limited in the kind and number of pollen sources utilized. This type of constancy has long been known to floral biologists, students of insect behavior, and research workers in certain production aspects of agriculture. It is characteristic of social bees (e.g. *Apis, Bombus, Melipona*), semi-social bees (e.g. *Halictus*), and many solitary bees (e.g., some *Anthophora, Andrena, Megachile*). The second kind of constancy was partially recognized by Loew (1886) and was more clearly defined by Robertson (1925).[1] It is adaptive in nature and is characteristic of species, genera, and even higher groups of bees. This form of flower constancy is

[1] Loew (1886) observed differences in the flower visiting habits of bees with tongues of about equal length (thus presumably with the same nectar sources available) and designated *monotropic, oligotropic* and *polytropic* types, depending upon whether they visited a single species of plant, related species of plants, or unrelated plants, respectively. Originally, Robertson adopted Loew's terminology but limited the application of the terms to flower visits for pollen. Later [Robertson (1925)] he proposed the parallel terms *monolectic, oligolectic* and *polylectic* for use in reference to pollen visits of bees, restoring Loew's terminology to its original meaning. The first two conditions are not significantly different and we have dropped the term *monolectic*.

TABLE 1. *Known pollen sources for North American species of* Diadasia

Malvaceae				Cactaceae esp. Opuntia	Compositae esp. Helianthus	Convolvulaceae Convolvulus	Onagraceae Clarkia
Sphaeralcea	Callirhoe	Sidalcea	Sida				
D. diminuta (Cresson)	D. afflicta (Cresson)	D. nigrifrons (Cresson)	D. consociata Timberlake	D. australis (Cresson)	D. enavata (Cresson)	D. bituberculata (Cresson)	D. angusticeps Timberlake
D. laticauda Cockerell				D. opuntiae Cockerell			
D. lutzi Cockerell				D. rinconis Cockerell			
D. martialis Timberlake							
D. mexicana Timberlake							
D. nitidifrons Cockerell							
D. olivacea (Cresson)							
D. palmarum Timberlake							
D. sphaeralcearum Cockerell							
D. tuberculifrons Timberlake							
D. vallicola Timberlake							

termed oligolecty, and is reflected in physiological and morphological adaptations which sharply limit the number and kind of pollen sources normally utilized by bees with this inherited characteristic.

The general subject of flower constancy has been comprehensively reviewed by Grant (1950) and certain phases have been discussed recently by Michener (1954). The latter author comments on difficulties associated with the definition of the term oligolecty. For purposes of the present discussion oligolectic species may be defined as those in which the individual members of the population, throughout its range and in the presence of other pollen sources, consistently and regularly collect pollen from but a single plant species or from a group of similar or related plant species, turning to other sources, if at all, only when there is a local shortage or absence of that pollen. Such species exhibit physiological adaptations to the host flower such as short flight seasons which are more or less synchronized with the blooming period of the host plants, or sometimes special diurnal flight periods coinciding with unusual times of pollen availability. Also morphological adaptations may exist for the extraction or carrying of the pollen or to facilitate the simultaneous extraction of nectar from the pollen plant.

A substantial number of flower records have been published for species of *Diadasia* (cf. Cockerell, 1898, *et seq.;* Timberlake, 1939, *et seq.*), mostly without distinguishing between pollen and nectar visits. Thus, from a survey of the literature, one might conclude that several of the species of *Diadasia* gather pollen from a variety of plants, but this does not appear to be the case. Michener (1936, 1937) has contributed a number of critical flower records and his catalogue of species (Michener, 1951) is particularly valuable since it includes not only significant records from the literature but reflects firsthand knowledge of the flower relationships of these insects.

Present knowledge of the pollen sources for the North American species of *Diadasia* (table 1) indicates that this genus is composed of species which are oligolectic. The majority of these are associated with plants of the family Malvaceae, mostly with species of the genus *Sphaeralcea*. Presumably these bees evolved in geographic isolation, appropriate conditions for which undoubtedly existed and still exist in the peripheral and isolated mountain ranges of the areas of southwestern United States and northern Mexico where this group of bees is most abundant, as are their host plants (Kearney, 1935). Subsequently, a number of these have spread into the same areas (perhaps since the advent of agriculture and the construction of roads) and now appears to be wholly or partially sympatric and associated with similar or identical pollen sources. If this pattern is to remain relatively stable in terms of the environment, some means presumably will be developed for minimizing the competition for food which results. In andrenid bees of the subgenus *Onagrandrena,* and among certain species of *Ptilandrena* this is accomplished by a partial division of the diurnal period in which the pollen is available (Linsley, MacSwain and Smith, 1955; Linsley and MacSwain, 1956). Our data are not precise enough to reveal whether this situation obtains in *Diadasia,* although, in a locality where two species were taking pollen from the same flowers, we noted that *D. olivacea* seeks nectar at the flowers an hour before the first *D. diminuta* appear, possibly setting the stage for such a development.

In view of the association of most *Diadasia* with Malvaceae, the restriction of *D. enavata* to Compositae, *D. angusticeps* to Onagraceae and *D. bituberculata* to Convolvulaceae, suggests the possibility of sudden and abrupt changes in pollen sources. The first two species exhibit morphological adaptations of the tibial scopa for the gathering and carrying of pollen grains from their respective plant sources (plumose hairs for small pollen grains of the Compositae in the former case, stiff non-plumose hairs in the second case for extracting the spherical pollen grains of Onagraceae, which are bound together by viscin threads. *D. bituberculata,* on the other hand, has elongated, specialized mouthparts suitable for extracting nectar from the deep flower of *Convolvulus,* while simultaneously gathering pollen. A similar specialization occurs in the species of the related genus *Melitoma* which are associated with flowers of *Ipomoea.* Whether these represent subsequent adaptations or perfection of pre-adapted features cannot now be determined. In 1952, on the Borrego Desert of California we found a female of the cactus oligolege, *D. australis californica* taking pollen from *Phacelia,* when pollen from the few locally available blooms of cactus had been exhausted, indicating that this species, at least, will turn to distantly related plants in the face of a local shortage of the usual pollen source. A second female, taken from *Phacelia* flowers at the same time, was not gathering pollen from that plant, yet she had less than a dozen grains of cactus pollen on her body.

It is interesting to note that species now included in the megachilid genus *Lithurge* somewhat parallel the flower relationships of *Diadasia.* The North American species are all associated with Cactaceae (Michener, 1951, 1954). Of the Old World species *L. dentipes* (Smith) collects pollen from *Hibiscus* (Malvaceae), *L. fuscipennis* (Lepeletier) and *L. chrysurus* (Fonsc.) from Compositae (Malyshev, 1930).

In conclusion, we would like to reemphasize that oligolecty is a relative phenomenon. Properly understood, and used with a knowledge of mating habits and certain other biological characteristics it provides explanations for many evolutionary phenomena in the bees. Thus, it may be regarded as a mechanism which permits the survival of large numbers of sympatric species in those groups which have this characteristic (most *Perdita, Andrena,* etc.) by assuring that in years of pollen shortage, competition for that which is available will be among members of the *same* species. In years when the appropriate pollen is completely lacking, the less adaptable species will become locally extinct, fragmenting the species geographically and the stage may be set for geographic speciation resulting in *closely related allopatric species with the same pollen plant*. With the breakdown of geographical barriers permitting these species to come together the result is a group of *closely related sympatric species with the same pollen plant*. On the other hand, the adaptable species, for example, those without specialized pollen collecting apparatus, or those which are preadapted for another flower, will presumably be able to change their food habits and, if the flowers are the site for mating, isolation can become effective and provide a mechanism for speciation resulting in *closely related sympatric or allopatric species with quite different pollen plants*. In *Diadasia*, available evidence suggests that, at various times in the past, each of these mechanisms may have played important roles in the evolution of species now found in North America. Furthermore, these processes appear to be in active operation today, presumably to produce the new forms of tomorrow.

Summary

At least thirteen of the North American species of *Diadasia* are oligolectic visitors to plants of the family Malvaceae, especially of the genus *Sphaeralcea*. Presumably most of these species evolved in geographic isolation in the peripheral and isolated mountain ranges of southwestern United States and northern Mexico, where the bees and their pollen plants abound, and have subsequently been brought together through the advent of agriculture and man-made roads which favor both. However, three species are oligoleges of *Opuntia* (Cactaceae), one each of *Clarkia* (Onagraceae), *Convolvulus* (Convolvulaceae) and of *Helianthus* (Compositae), suggesting speciation associated with a sudden change of pollen plants. Data derived from a study of one of the cactus-visiting species indicate a possible mechanism by which this might have occurred.

Literature Cited

Cockerell, T. D. A. 1898. On some panurgine and other bees. Trans. American Ent. Soc., 25: 185–198.

——. 1905. *Diadasia* Patton; a genus of Bees. American Naturalist, 39: 741–745.

——. 1906. The North American bees of the family Anthophoridae. Trans. American Ent. Soc., 22: 63–116.

——. 1914. Bees visiting *Helianthus*. Canadian Ent., 46: 409–415.

Grant, V. 1950. The flower constancy of bees. Botanical Rev., 16: 379–398.

Kearney, T. H. 1935. The North American species of *Sphaeralcea* subgenus *Eusphaeralcea*. Univ. Calif. Publ. Botany, 19: 1–128, 12 pls., 1 fig.

Linsley, E. G., and J. W. MacSwain. 1956. Further notes on the taxonomy and biology of the andrenine bees associated with *Oenothera*. Pan-Pacific Ent., 32: 111–121.

——. 1957. The nesting habits, flower relationships, and parasites of some North American species of *Diadasia* (Hymenoptera, Anthophoridae). Wasmann Jour. Biol. 15: 199–235.

Linsley, E. G., J. W. MacSwain and R. F. Smith. 1952. The bionomics of *Diadasia consociata* Timberlake and some biological relationships of emphorine and anthophorine bees (Hymenoptera, Anthophoridae). Univ. Calif. Publ. Entomology, 9: 267–290, pls. 1–6.

——. 1955. Observations on the nesting habits and flower relationships of some species of *Melandrena* (Hymenoptera). Pan-Pacific Ent., 31: 178–185.

——. 1956. Biological observations on *Ptilothrix sumichrasti* (Cresson) and some related groups of emphorine bees (Hymenoptera, Anthophoridae). Bull. So. Calif. Acad. Sci., 55: 83–101, 2 pls.

Loew, E. 1886. Weitere Beobachtungen über den Blumenbesuch von Insekten an Freilandpflanzen der Botanischen Gartens zu Berlin. Jahrbuch des Königlichen Botanischen Gartens und des Botanischen Museums zu Berlin, 4: 93–178.

Malysev, S. J. 1930. Nistgewohnheiten der Steinbienen, *Lithurgus* Latr. (Apoidea). Zeitschr. f. Morph. u. Ökol. d. Tiere, 19: 116–134, 9 figs.

Michener, C. D. 1936. Some western anthophorid and nomiine bees. American Mus. Novit., 876: 1–4.

——. 1937. Records and descriptions of North American bees. Ann. Mag. Nat. Hist., (10) 19: 393–410, 1 fig.

——. 1951. Emphorini, *in:* Muesebeck, Krombein and Townes, Hymenoptera of America north of Mexico. U. S. Dept. Agr., Agr. Mon. No. 2: 1218–1221.

——. 1954. Bees of Panama. Bull. Amer. Mus. Nat. Hist., **100**: 1–175, 155 figs.

Robertson, C. 1925. Heterotropic bees. Ecology, **6**: 412–436.

Timberlake, P. H. 1939. New species of the genus *Diadasia* from California (Hymenoptera, Apoidea). Bull. Brooklyn Ent. Soc., **34**: 11–16.

——. 1940. New species of bees of the genus *Diadasia* from California (Hymenoptera, Apoidea). Bull. Brooklyn Ent. Soc., **35**: 22–30.

——. 1941. Synoptic table of North American species of *Diadasia* (Hymenoptera, Apoidea). Bull. Brooklyn Ent. Soc., **36**: 2–11.

A FOSSIL ANT COLONY:
NEW EVIDENCE OF SOCIAL ANTIQUITY*

By EDWARD O. WILSON AND ROBERT W. TAYLOR
Biological Laboratories, Harvard University

The fossil remains which will be described below are of exceptional interest for two reasons: (1) they are the first ant fossils to be reported from Africa south of the Sahara and (2) they comprise what appears to be a fragment of a colony preserved as a unit, thus constituting the first fossil insect colony ever recorded. From the sample we have been able to make measurements of the worker polymorphism and certain deductions concerning the biology and social structure of an ant species as it lived in the lower Miocene over 30 million years ago.

We are indebted to the Trustees and Director of the Coryndon Museum for the opportunity to study this unique material, which was collected by Dr. and Mrs. L. S. B. Leakey in the Lower Miocene deposits of Mfwangano Island, Lake Victoria, Kenya. Professor A. E. Emerson first identified the specimens as ants, realized their potential significance, and forwarded them to us for examination. The research program of which the study became a part is currently supported by Grant No. GB 1634 from the National Science Foundation.

Oecophylla leakeyi Wilson and Taylor, new species
(Subfam. Formicinae, Tribe Oecophyllini)

Diagnosis. Distinguished from all other known species of the genus, living and fossil, by the large size of both worker subcastes; by the massive, cordate head of the major worker; and by the presence of well developed ocelli in the major worker. All of these characters are illustrated in Figure 2.

The mesosoma is stouter than in the two living species *(longinoda, smaragdina)* and in the Miocene species *sicula;* in this regard its structure is closer to the Eocene species *brischkei.* The petiole is not well enough preserved in any of the *leakeyi* specimens to permit a meaningful comparison with the same structure in other species. The gaster has the form typical of all other known members of the genus.

The *holotype* is the major worker head illustrated in Figure 2 and Plate 11. Its maximum width taken perpendicular to the long axis is

---

Manuscript received by the editor April 21, 1964.

Reprinted by permission of E. O. Wilson and the Editor from
PSYCHE, **71**, 93–103 (1964).

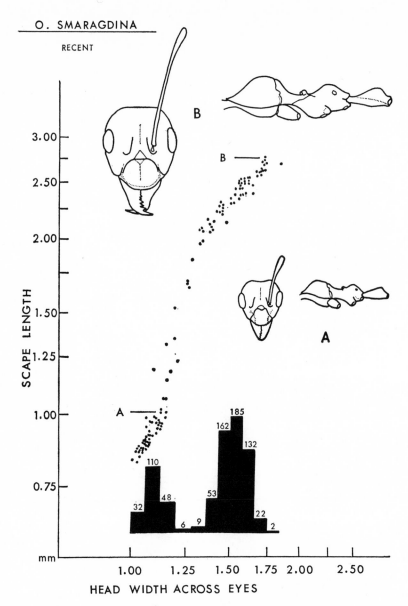

Figure 1. *O. smaragdina.* (For explanation see opposite page).

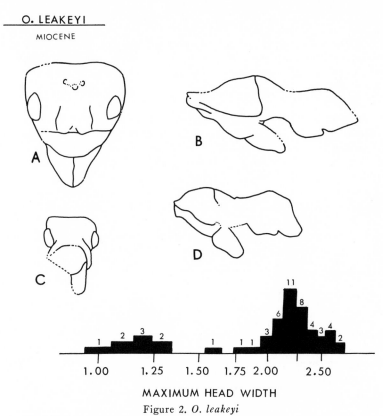

MAXIMUM HEAD WIDTH

Figure 2. *O. leakeyi*

Figures 1-2. *The comparison of worker polymorphism in the Miocene Oecophylla leakeyi with that in the living O. smaragdina.* In Figure 1 (opposite page), the size frequency curve of a large random sample from a single colony of *O. smaragdina* from Assam is given in head width units plotted logarithmically. The mesosomas and petioles of selected minor and major workers are also shown, as well as the double logarithmic plot of the scape length against head width. (Modified from Wilson, 1953). In figure 2 (above) similar data from the fossil *leakeyi* colony are given in scale with Figure 1. Pupal worker head widths are used but are closely comparable to adult worker head widths. Scape length could not be measured in this material. A, head of holotype major worker (imaginal), B, mesosoma and petiole of a major worker (imaginal), C, head of a minor worker (pupal), D, mesosoma and petiole of a minor worker (imaginal).

2.36 mm.; its length, taken from the posteriormost level of the occiput to the anteriormost level of the clypeus, is 2.19 mm. This specimen agrees well in size and structure with the heads of entire worker pupae. There can be no doubt that it is from a worker specimen.

Material examined. A total of 438 specimens, including 197 larvae (perhaps including some prepupae), 105 worker pupae, 24 worker heads, 48 worker mesosomas, and 64 worker gasters. Even if the various worker body parts are assumed to have resulted from dismemberment of a smaller number of workers, the total number of individuals represented in the collection is at least $197 + 105 + 64 = 366$. All of these pieces were collected together by Dr. and Mrs. Leakey in a volume of matrix about 2 feet square and several inches thick, in a Lower Miocene Deposit on Mfwangano Island, near Rusinga Island, in the Kavirondo Gulf neighborhood of Lake Victoria, Kenya. The geology of this and similar deposits in the area has been briefly reviewed by Chesters (1957). The holotype and some paratypes will be deposited in the British Museum (Natural History). Other paratypes will be placed in the ant collection of the Museum of Comparative Zoology, Harvard University, and in the Centre for Prehistory and Paleontology, Coryndon Museum, Nairobi, Kenya.

The Zoogeography of *Oecophylla*

The genus is represented by two living species: *O. smaragdina* (Fabricius) which ranges from India to the Solomon Islands and Queensland; and *O. longinoda* (Latreille), which occurs throughout most of tropical Africa. These are the famous "weaver ants" whose workers employ the mature larvae as shuttles to bind the nests together. The nests are always arboreal and consist of clusters of green leaves folded over and fastened together with larval silk. A single mature colony usually occupies many such nests scattered through one or more trees. The colonies are highly territorial, defending their trees against other ant species and larger invading animals. The workers are exclusively arboreal in their foraging, collecting varied insect prey and attending coccids. The two species are very similar in both morphology and behavior, but sufficient minor differences in morphology exist to justify their specific separation. Over most of their ranges both species are very abundant and highly adaptable. They occur in rain forests, groves of crop trees, and even shade trees along urban streets. The most complete and general studies of the biology of the genus are contained in the works by Ledoux (1950, 1954) on *O. longinoda*. Bhattacharya (1943) and Brown (1959) have reported on special aspects of the ecology and physiology of *O. smaragdina*. Variation and taxonomic relationships of the two species are discussed in the reviews of Emery (1921) and Wheeler (1922).

Oecophylla is well represented in Tertiary fossil deposits. *O. brishkei* Mayr, which closely resembles the modern forms, is moderately abundant in the Baltic amber, of Eocene age. It was represented by 50, or 0.4% of all of the 11,678 Baltic amber ants examined by G. Mayr and W. M. Wheeler jointly (Wheeler, 1914). A second, more divergent species, *O. brevinodis* Wheeler, was represented in the collections by a single specimen. Another species, *O. sicula* Emery, has been described from Upper Miocene deposits in Sicily. The species thus far mentioned form a morphocline in the increase of length of the legs, antennae and petiole, and the narrowing of the metathoracic constriction. This morphocline, which follows the geologic sequence, runs as follows: *brevinodis* → *brischkei* → *sicula* → *longinoda* (together with *smaragdina*). It seems reasonable to conclude that the species exhibit the approximate phylogenetic succession that must have occurred in the evolution of the modern species of the genus. *O. leakeyi* is a somewhat divergent member with reference to this succession, in its larger size and retention of ocelli in the major worker caste. It would appear to fall nearest to *brischkei* in the degree of mesosomal and appendage elongation. Two other species have been named on the basis of queens found in the Miocene shales of Europe: *O. obesa radobojana* (Heer) from Radoboj, Croatia; and *O. praechara* (Foerster) from Brunstatt, Alsatia. The precise relationships of these forms cannot be determined, although Mayr (cited by Wheeler, 1914) stated that *radobojana* cannot be distinguished from *smaragdina*. No New World fossils of *Oecophylla* are known, and the genus is notably absent from the rich Miocene collections from Florissant, Colorado, described by Carpenter (1930).

In sum, the picture that emerges of *Oecophylla* is that of a morphologically stable Old World genus that has persisted through most of the Tertiary with very little speciation. *Oecophylla* is related to at least two other relict, arboricolous Old World genera that date to the Eocene: *Dimorphomyrmex* and *Gesomyrmex*. Furthermore, it is not far distant from *Gigantiops,* a remarkable terricolous genus now limited to the South American rain forests. It seems appropriate to regard *Oecophylla* as both specialized and caught in an evolutionary cul-de-sac. We can speculate that its unique specializations have permitted it to remain abundant and widespread — but at the expense of blocking further significant evolution and speciation.

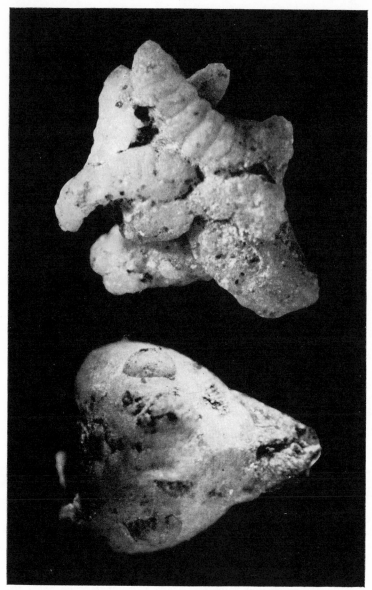

The Polymorphism and Inferred Biology
of *Oecophylla leakeyi*

There are good reasons to regard the Mfwangano Island material as a sample from a single colony, perhaps the contents of one nest preserved intact. In evidence is the fact that such a large number of specimens in all stages of development were recovered from a volume of roughly only one cubic foot of rock. Also, and equally important, many of the immature forms are beautifully preserved in clusters. A single group of newly hatched larvae are joined together in a typical "microlarval pile" (Plate 10). These groupings could have been preserved only if the colony had been subjected to a minimum of disturbance prior to fossilization.

When we measured the head widths of all of the adequately preserved pupal workers (the measurable adult workers were too few for our purposes) the results were startling. As shown in Figures 1 and 2 the size-frequency distribution is of essentially the same form as in the living species *O. smaragdina*. This particular distribution includes the following two important features: the separate distributions of the minor and major worker castes are nearly but not completely non-overlapping, and the majors are *more numerous* than the minors. So far as is known, the *Oecophylla* type of distribution is peculiar to the genus among living ants (Wilson, 1953). The polymorphism in *O. longinoda* was shown independently by Weber (1949) and Ledoux (1950) to be correlated with a division of labor in which the majors do most of the foraging and nest defense and the minors serve more as nurses. The allometry of the living *Oecophylla*, involving a narrowing of the metathoracic constriction with increase in size (instead of the reverse), is also unusual if not unique among living ant species. The same kind of allometry is exhibited by *O. leakeyi*. Thus *O. leakeyi* possessed the same unusual and quite specialized features of worker polymorphism retained by the modern members of the genus. This first direct demonstration of the nature of polymorphism in an extinct ant species shows *Oecophylla* to be conservative not only in morphology but in basic social organization.

But this is not the end of the story. Further findings indicate that the *leakeyi* nest was arboreal, just as in modern species. Numerous larvae, pupae, and adults are attached directly to well preserved leaf frag-

---

EXPLANATION OF PLATE 11

Left: head of holotype major worker, *O. leakeyi. Right:* fossilized microlarval pile of *O. leakeyi*. The maximum diameter of the larval pile is approximately 3.4 mm.

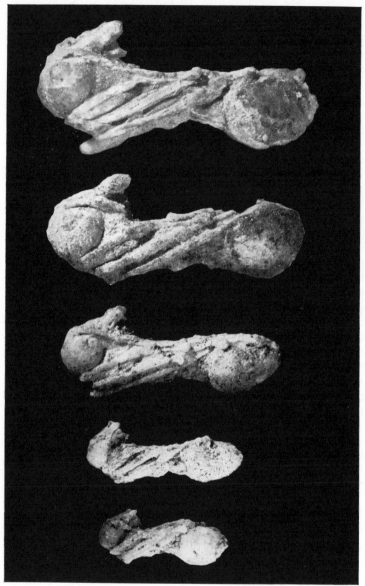

WILSON AND TAYLOR — FOSSIL ANT COLONY

ments. Also, the *leakeyi* pupae are not enclosed in cocoons, a negative character shared with the modern species of the genus. The absence of cocoons is a rare and probably derived character within the sub-family Formicinae (Wheeler, 1915). Cocoons are omitted by many of the diverse species of *Polyrhachis* that are arboreal and use silk produced by their larvae for nest construction. They are also omitted by certain twig-dwelling species belonging to such genera as *Campono-tus (Colobopsis)* and *Gesomyrmex;* the latter genus is included on the basis of a single naked pupa recorded by Wheeler (1929). Cocoons are also lacking in two related terricolous genera, *Prenolepis* and *Paratrechina.* The great majority of formicine genera, however, are both terricolous and cocoon-makers. The absence of cocoons is, there-fore, correlated, but not perfectly, with the arboricolous habit. Addi-tional evidence favoring the proposition that the *leakeyi* colony was arboricolous is the very fact that the colony was preserved intact. It is very difficult to imagine how a subterranean or log-nesting colony could have been preserved as a unit; but it is much easier to imagine how an arboreal nest, especially the kind constructed by modern *Oeco-phylla,* could have broken off, dropped into the water, and been pre-served with little further disturbance. The small ratio of workers to immatures suggests that the former were able to escape in part while the latter remained trapped inside the drowned nest.

Although the foregoing considerations are admittedly tenuous, some-thing more definitive can be said about the habitat in which the *leakeyi* colony lived. The species was part of a rich arthropod fauna. The Leakeys *(in litt.)* found it in association with many hundreds of other soft-bodied insects of diverse orders, as well as arachnids. Very little of this interesting fauna has been studied. There is also abundant associated plant material. In a preliminary study of the Mfwangano and Rusinga Islands plant fossils, Chesters (1957) discerned a mini-mum of 17 families and 21 genera of which five are fern genera. The majority of the fossils represent living African tropical genera. "Much of the material awaiting detailed examination will probably prove to be unidentifiable owing to its mode of preservation as crystalline casts. But the report here published does give a representative picture of a Miocene flora closely akin to that of tropical Africa at the present day. . . . The large number of lianas suggests a gallery-type forest in which trees festooned with climbers overhung the water-course."

EXPLANATION OF PLATE 12

Fossil pupae of *O. leakeyi* of various sizes. The actual total length of the smallest specimen is about 4.0 mm.

SUMMARY

Oecophylla leakeyi Wilson and Taylor is described as a new species. It is from the Lower Miocene deposits of Mfwangano Island, Kenya, and is the first species of fossil ant described from Africa south of the Sahara. The type series, which contains worker subcastes, pupae, and larvae in all stages of development, is interpreted as comprising a colony fragment, the first ever recorded as a unit in the social insects. From statistical and morphological studies of the three-dimensional specimens it is concluded that the worker polymorphism conforms to the essential features that uniquely characterize the living *Oecophylla* species within the modern ant fauna. This constitutes direct evidence of the stability of a specific social system through a considerable period of time, i.e. 30 million years or longer. Other evidence is cited which suggests that the *leakeyi* colony also resembled the modern species of *Oecophylla* in that it nested arboreally in tropical rain forest.

LITERATURE CITED

BHATTACHARYA, G. C.
    1943. Reproduction and caste determination in aggressive red-ants, *Oecophylla smaragdina,* Fabr. Trans. Bose Res. Inst., Calcutta, 15: 137-156.

BROWN, E. S.
    1959. Immature nutfall of coconuts in the Solomon Islands. II. Changes in ant populations and their relation to vegetation. Bull. Ent. Res., 50: 523-558.

CARPENTER, F. M.
    1930. The fossil ants of North America. Bull. Mus. Comp. Zool. Harvard, 70: 1-66.

CHESTERS, K. I. M.
    1957. The Miocene flora of Rusinga Island, Lake Victoria, Kenya. Paleontographica, (B) 101: 30-71.

EMERY, C.
    1921. Formiche tessitrici del genere *Oecophylla* fossili e viventi. Rend. Acad. Sci. Inst. Bologna, (1920-21): 99-105.

LEDOUX, A.
    1950. Étude du comportement et de la biologie de la fourmi fileuse (*Oecophylla longinoda* Latr.). Ann. Sci. Nat. Zool. (11) 12: 314-461.

    1954. Recherches sur le cycle chromosomique de la fourmi fileuse Oecophylla longinoda Latr. (Hyménoptère *Formicoidea*). Insectes Sociaux 1: 149-175.

WEBER, N. A.
    1949. The functional significance of dimorphism in the African ant, *Oecophylla.* Ecology, 30: 397-400.

WHEELER, W. M.
    1914. The ants of the Baltic amber. Schrift. Phys. Ökon. Ges. Königsb., 55: 1-142.

    1915. On the presence and absence of cocoons among ants, the nest-spinning habits of the larvae and the significance of the black cocoons among certain Australian species. Ann. Ent. Soc. Amer., 8: 323-342.

    1922. Ants of the American Congo Expedition. A contribution to the myrmecology of Africa. Bull. Amer. Mus. Nat. Hist., 45: 1-270.

    1929. The identity of the ant genera *Gesomyrmex* Mayr and *Dimorphomyrmex* Ernest André. Psyche, 36: 1-12.

WILSON, E. O.
    1953. The origin and evolution of polymorphism in ants. Quart. Rev. Biol., 28: 136-156.

SOME PROBLEMS AND GUIDING PRINCIPLES OF ANGIOSPERM PHYLOGENY*†

ROBERT F. THORNE

Rancho Santa Ana Botanic Garden, Claremont, California

PROBLEMS

Major problems faced by the angiosperm phylogenist are the inadequate fossil record, the prevalence of convergent evolution, the extreme modification of some angiosperms, and the limited training of most phylogenists. These are the most serious, though by no means the only, problems retarding the development of a phylogenetic classification of the flowering plants.

The relatively soft tissues of flowering plants provide no bones, no chitonous exoskeleton, and no calcareous shells for fossilization. Furthermore, lack of mobility prevents plants from being mired in the "fossil-traps" that have been so productive of animal remains. Most angiosperms do, however, have some woody tissues, resistant pollen grains, a waxy coating on the leaf epidermis, and often hard fruits or seeds, all of which are amenable to fossilization. There is, therefore, a meagre fossil record which goes back to the Lower Cretaceous (Scott, Barghoorn, and Leopold, 1960), but it is incomplete for most groups and unknown for the remainder.

This fragmentary record is so inadequate that it has been claimed that we botanists have no right to use the word "phylogeny" in connection with angiosperm evolution above the species level. In the strict sense that "phylogeny" refers only to phyletic lines based upon complete series of fossils in a continuous time sequence, the critics are correct. Our reconstruction of the evolutionary history of the flowering plants must be largely inferential and hypothetical. However, as Grant (1959) has cogently stated, the basic philosophy and ultimate aims of both paleontologists and neontologists are the same, though their methodologies are necessarily different. We are all attempting to develop a phylogenetic classification of past and present life. Most botanists prefer to use "phylogeny" in the broader sense, and that is the way I am using the term here.

Our forced preoccupation with contemporary plants to work out hypothetical lineages and inferred relationships has certain compensations, perhaps overlooked by some paleontologists. Because the angiosperms are a large and relatively modern group, there is a wealth of living forms. We have very numerous "living-fossils" and non-missing-links, particularly in the Old

*Contribution to a Symposium on Principles and Methods of Phylogeny. Presented at the meeting of the American Society of Naturalists, cosponsored by the American Society of Zoologists and the Society of Systematic Zoology. American Association for the Advancement of Science, Philadelphia, Pa. December 27, 1962.

†I am indebted to Professors Verne Grant and Richard Benjamin of Rancho Santa Ana Botanic Garden for many helpful suggestions in the preparation of this paper.

World tropics. This abundance of phylogenetic relicts compares most favorably with the relatively few coelacanths, lungfishes, tuataras, and leiopelmids of the vertebrate zoologists. Furthermore, the greatly variable rates and directions of evolution within the tissues and organs of individual plant species present innumerable examples of primitive features retained in otherwise highly divergent groups and specialized features developed in primitive angiosperms. Comprehensive studies of these primitive taxa and the conservative features in more specialized taxa enable us to recognize ancestral conditions and the direction of evolutionary trends. Conclusions drawn from such observations are most reliable when supplementary information can be gained from angiosperm fossils and comparative studies of non-angiospermous vascular plants.

The prevalence of convergent evolution in the angiosperms, as in many other plant and animal groups, creates another serious problem for the phylogenist. Much of the artificiality of our various classifications can be attributed to the failure of some taxonomists to recognize convergence in such evolutionary stages or conditions as anemophily, dioecism, sympetaly, epigyny, zygomorphy, parasitism, epiphytism, and other adaptations to extreme habitats and to relatively limited means of nutrition, pollination, and dissemination (figures 1 and 2). The Glumiflorae, Geraniales, Sapindales, Parietales, Polemoniales, and Rubiales of Engler and Diels (1936), the Ranales, Urticales, Rhoeadales, and Sarraceniales of Cronquist (1957), and the Herbaceae, Dilleniales, Rosales, Pittosporales, Thymelaeales, Aristolochiales, Tamaricales, Myrtales, Hamamelidales, Celastrales, and Lamiales of Hutchinson (1959) appear to be artificial taxa in which convergent groups have been united. These groupings are listed here because they are widely accepted and even taught by many botanists.

It is often difficult to decide whether shared characteristics are due to common ancestry or to convergent evolution. The decision must depend upon the maximum correlation of multiple, unrelated characteristics in different organs of the plant at all stages of its development, the study of series, and the selection of those features that are least labile and least divergent within the investigated taxon. Many of the criteria given by Simpson (1961) for recognition of convergence or parallelism versus homology in animal evolution are also applicable to plant taxa. Greater use of the rapidly accumulating information on comparative stem, leaf, and seed anatomy, embryology, palynology, cytogenetics, host-parasite relationships, food plant preferences of phytophagous insects, phytochemistry, serology, physiology, ecology, biogeography, and paleobotany would eliminate much of the polyphyleticism in flowering plant classification.

As the mass of relevant data becomes otherwise unmanageable, the use of electronic computers may become helpful and even necessary. However, the developing neo-Adansonian method among some numerical biologists (Sokal, 1961; Sneath, 1961) of giving equal taxonomic weight to each characteristic seems to be a retrograde step in taxonomy. It entirely ignores the critical importance of conservative features and apparently overlooks the evolution of closely associated characteristics linked genetically or through the

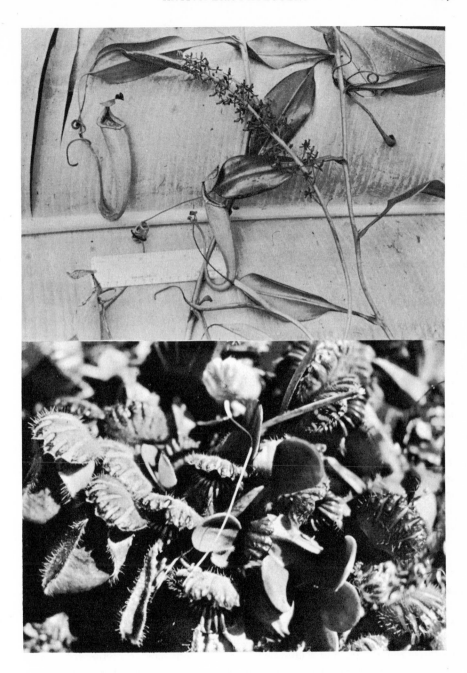

FIGURE 1 (above). A tropical pitcher-plant, Nepenthes, Nepenthaceae, from the Finisterres of New Guinea. Each pitcher terminates a tendril at the end of a flat blade-like petiole.

FIGURE 2 (below). The southwest Australian pitcher-plant, *Cephalotus follicularis* Labill., Cephalotaceae, related to the Saxifragaceae but quite unrelated to either the Nepenthes of figure 1 or the American pitcher-plants of the Sarraceniaceae. The three unrelated pitcher-plant families are a rather startling example of convergence.

guidance of natural selection (Stebbins, 1951). I cannot agree with these workers nor with other empiricists (Gilmour, 1940; Blackwelder and Boyden, 1952) that classifications based upon phylogenetic relationships are undesirable or are less useful than "natural" or artificial arrangements. The primary objective of systematists is the development of a classification of all organisms that reflects phylogenetic relationships as accurately as can be determined from fossil series or from educated inferences (Benson, 1962; Myers, 1952, 1960; Porter, 1959; Starrett, 1958; Simpson, 1961; and many others). To many of us, taxonomic work would be a very sterile occupation if we had to be merely specimen and fact finders, accumulators, and filers. Evolutionary studies add meaning, stature, and excitement to our science.

The extreme structural modification of many angiospermous taxa has frequently prevented phylogenists from determining relationships and ultimate origins. The prevailing trend toward structural reduction often results in such simplified tissues and organs that clues to relationships are largely or completely obscured. Parasitic taxa, groups adapted to extreme habitats, such as submersed aquatics (figure 7) and desert-dwellers, and anemophilous families are especially divergent from their presumed ancestral stock. We have far too many taxa of uncertain position awaiting careful study and more refined techniques of phylogenetic analysis.

Few, if any, systematists are trained broadly enough to interpret correctly the vast amount of comparative anatomical, embryological, palynological, and many other kinds of data currently available. Even fewer of us are adequately equipped to gather directly from the plants all the kinds of data that make it possible to draw valid inferences about their relationships.

Other problems impede the attainment and the acceptance of a reasonably phylogenetic classification of the flowering plants, not the least of which is the attitude of those botanists who disregard overwhelming evidence presented to correct the misplacement of various taxa. However, available space can be used more effectively here in the discussion of a few applications of some of the guiding principles of angiosperm phylogeny that I have published elsewhere (Thorne, 1958).

PRINCIPLES

Ancestral features and trends of divergence can be recognized in the tissues and organs of existing angiosperms. This principle has been established by comprehensive comparative studies in such primitive orders as the Annonales (Magnoliales of some authors), Nymphaeales, and Hamamelidales (including such relicts as Trochodendron, Tetracentron, Euptelea, Cercidiphyllum, Eucommia, and Platanus). An excellent sample of the voluminous literature of these investigations is afforded by the studies of the Winteraceae (Bailey, 1944; Bailey and Nast, 1943–1945; Nast, 1944), Degeneria (Bailey and Smith, 1942), Himantandra (Bailey, Nast, and Smith, 1943), Magnoliaceae (Canright, 1952–1960), Monimiaceae (Money, Bailey, and Swamy, 1950), and Trochodendron and Tetracentron (Bailey and Nast, 1945; Nast and Bailey, 1945).

An acceptable description of the probable appearance and characteristics of the immediate angiospermous ancestors of these most primitive living flowering plants can be synthesized from the data presented in the above papers. Briefly, these early angiosperms, associated with gymnosperms and ferns in warm, humid, Lower Cretaceous forests, must have been trees with alternate, evergreen, simple leaves, vesselless wood, and strobiloid, bisexual, radially symmetrical flowers. These primitive flowers, probably borne singly, consisted of separate, numerous, spirally arranged sporophylls subtended by poorly differentiated perianth members. The laminar microsporophylls were supplied with three vascular bundles and with two pairs of submerged, linear microsporangia producing monosulcate pollen grains. The stalked, elongate, conduplicate or involute, laminar megasporophylls had stigmatic, unsealed margins and many adaxially scattered, anatropous, crassinucellate ovules with two integuments. The nectarless flowers were pollinated by beetles or other unspecialized insects seeking pollen or specially produced food-bodies. The ripened follicular fruit had many seeds with showy sarcotestas, which were sought out and disseminated locally by birds or small arboreal or terrestrial animals. The seeds contained a single, rudimentary, poly- or dicotyledonous embryo embedded in abundant perisperm and endosperm. No living angiosperm species or family combines all these primitive features, but all can be found in a relatively few relict species in the three orders mentioned above. *Zygogynum vieillardii* Baill., a New Caledonian montane endemic of the Winteraceae, illustrated by a flowering branch in figure 3, approaches this hypothetical ancestral angiosperm in many of its features. *Asimina triloba* (L.) Dunal (figure 4) of the Annonaceae, the pawpaw of our eastern American deciduous forests, is somewhat more divergent in most of its characteristics; however, like the related annonalian native species of Magnolia, Liriodendron, Illicium, Schisandra, and Calycanthus, it should remind us that not all the angiospermous relicts are restricted to the humid forests of southeastern Asia and its adjacent archipelagoes.

Presumably in the ancestors of a modern angiosperm group the ancestral condition of a particular characteristic can be no more advanced than its condition in the existing derivative species most primitive for that characteristic. It is therefore logical to seek clues to relationships among the least divergent members of a taxon and in the most conservative organs of these primitive plants, not among the highly specialized, often convergent tips of phyletic branches. That exceptional, rare, or otherwise unique members of a taxon may be more critical for phylogenetic inferences than the hundreds of more specialized species of the same taxon is well illustrated by Saruma of the Aristolochiaceae and Platystemon and Meconella of the Papaveraceae.

The Aristolochiaceae, or birthworts, are a sizable family of mostly tropical vines or herbs, best known in the United States through Aristolochia, the Dutchman's-pipe vine, and Asarum, the wild-ginger. The birthworts are sometimes treated as a separate order or are allied with such peculiar families as the parasitic Rafflesiaceae and Hydnoraceae and the tropical

FIGURE 3 (above). A flowering branch of *Zygogynum vieillardii* Baill., a small tree of the New Caledonian mountains belonging to the relict family Winteraceae.

FIGURE 4 (below). A flowering branch of pawpaw, *Asimina triloba* (L.) Dunal, a small relict tree species of the Annonaceae, photographed on May 13, 1962, on a wooded slope along the Mississippi River north of Keokuk, Iowa. Note the trimerous, radially symmetrical perianth and numerous stamens.

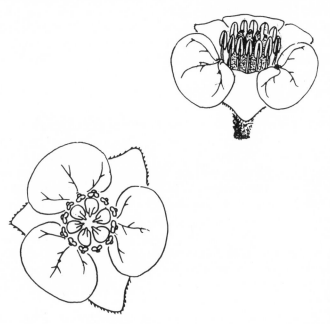

FIGURE 5 (above). A flower of *Aristolochia labiata* Willd., a Brazilian species photographed in the Botanic Garden at Lae, New Guinea. The calyx is bilaterally symmetrical, gamosepalous, and petaloid.

FIGURE 6 (below). Diagrams of the flower of *Saruma henryi* Oliv., a monotypic relict of the Aristolochiaceae from Hupeh, China. Diagrams drawn by Howard Pfeifer from the type description and drawings in Hooker's "Icones Plantarum."

pitcher-plants, Nepenthaceae (figure 1) (Hutchinson, 1959). The largest genus, Aristolochia (figure 5), with no petals, with a highly specialized, bilaterally symmetrical, gamosepalous, petaloid calyx, inferior ovary, and lianous habit, offers few clues to family relationships. *Saruma henryi* Oliv., a monotypic, phylogenetic relict from Hupeh, China, is, however, a non-missing-link which does provide adequate information about the family's relationships. It is a perennial caulescent herb with radially symmetrical flowers (figure 6) with trimerous green sepals and conspicuous, distinct petals, essentially apocarpous and semi-superior gynoecium, monosulcate pollen grains, follicular fruit producing seeds with a rudimentary embryo in abundant endosperm, and other primitive features of the Annonales. Its nearest living relatives outside the Aristolochiaceae seem to be the Annonaceae, including our *Asimina triloba* (figure 4).

In view of the other evidence, it is significant that among the swallow-tail butterflies of the Papilioninae (Munroe, 1953) the larvae of the three tribes Papilionini, Graphiini, and Troidini have as their dominant food plants respectively the Lauraceae, Annonaceae, and Aristolochia. The Lauraceae are unquestionably close relatives of the Annonaceae. Munroe stated, "Although the dominant food plants of the Graphiini are Anonaceae, a number of species in several groups share the lauraceous food plant with the basal Papilionini on the one hand and the most primitive Hesperoidea on the other.... The Troidini differ sharply from the other two tribes in feeding almost without exception on Aristolochia." Presumably the food preferences of closely related insect larvae might indicate similar phytochemistry in the food plants, and by inference, close relationship among those plants.

In California, where the poppy family, Papaveraceae, is abundantly represented, the genera Platystemon and Meconella serve in their reproductive characteristics as connecting links between the Papaveraceae and the Berberidales (Ranales in the strict sense), as Saruma does between the Aristolochiaceae and the Annonales. Some of the poppies and closely related fumitories, Fumariaceae, have evolved rather specialized capsular fruit dehiscing by valves and strikingly similar to those of the mustards, Brassicaceae. Apparently, because of the common parietal placentation, often dimerous perianth parts, and the specialized capsules, the poppies and fumitories are often combined with the mustards and capers, Capparaceae, in the Rhoeadales. There is, nevertheless, little supporting evidence for the close relationship of these two groups. This is one of the many examples among the angiosperms of classification being based upon the results of convergent evolution. The primitive ranunculoid flowers and fruit of Platystemon and Meconella, on the other hand, show their berberidalian relationships in their radially symmetrical, trimerous petals and sepals and their numerous stamens that apparently develop centripetally. Their many lightly coherent carpels are functionally or internally apocarpous and in Platystemon are separate at maturity, and their seeds have a minute embryo in copious endosperm. Further convincing evidence is presented by the berberidalian anatomy of the stem and leaf stomata, morphology of the pollen grains, and abundance of alkaloids, including berberin and protopine, in the tissues. Alkaloids are not abundant in the mustards and capers though the pungent mustard oils are. This use of relevant evidence from several botanical disciplines gives conclusive evidence of the relationships of the family and indicates the divergence and specialization of the capsule with its valvular dehiscence.

Because all organs of a plant at all stages of its development can produce useful phylogenetic information, data must be assembled and evaluated from all possible biological sources. The Cactaceae are another family that illustrates the value of this approach. Often treated near the Cistales (Parietales) in an order of their own, the cacti are certainly good members of the Chenopodiales (Centrospermae), as evidenced by their possession of such chenopodialian features as anomalous secondary thickening from successive cambia in the stem, succulence of leaf and stem, peripheral, curved embryo surrounding the central perisperm, and betacyanins in the flowers. The embryological evidence alone (Maheshwari, 1950) is overwhelming for the close relationship of the cacti to the Portulacaceae, Aizoaceae, and other members of the order. Placement of the cacti near the Cistales is presumably due to the convergence of the two groups in their parietal placentation and general similarity in gross floral anatomy.

Clues to relationships and direction of evolutionary trends in a taxon can often be obtained from study of vestigial rudiments of organs or rudiments of vascular supply to missing or greatly modified organs. If rudiments cannot be found upon examination of a few specimens of a species or of a few species of a genus or family, careful investigation of a large series of specimens of the same or related species may reveal the occasional presence of the vestiges. Sporadic specimens of the usually apetalous *Asarum canadense* L. can be found with minute, subulate petals. Members of the Salicaceae are ordinarily completely dioecious, without any vestiges of the missing sex organs. In both Salix and Populus, however, occasional trees can be found with catkins containing both male and female flowers or even structurally bisexual flowers. Staminodia or carpellodia, as rudiments of the missing sex organs, are commonly present in unisexual flowers. Most angiosperm families possess at least some species with structurally bisexual flowers or have relationship to other families possessing species with bisexual flowers. With the additional fact that most of those angiosperms that are considered primitive on the basis of other characteristics have bisexual flowers, we can confidently assert that monoecism and dioecism in the flowering plants are derived (Parkin, 1951, 1957).

Evolution often tends strongly toward reduction or loss of parts as well as toward greater complexity and elaboration of parts. Simple structures and simple plants when investigated have usually proved to be examples of reduction rather than of retention of primitive features. Besides being bisexual, the primitive flower was apparently subtended by a perianth, probably first of undifferentiated bract-like sepals and later by both protective, green sepals and attractive, white or colored petals. Wind-pollinated flowers usually lack petals and often lack sepals, yet perianth rudiments, like the bristles or scales in the sedges, Cyperaceae, the scale-like lodicules in the grasses, Poaceae, and the nectar-producing glands in Salix (some species of which are insect-pollinated), are often recognizable. Well-developed perianths in the more primitive, insect-pollinated relatives of wind-pollinated species, often in the same family or even the same genus, furnish strong evidence for this evolutionary reduction or total loss of perianth members.

Submersed or floating aquatic species tend to show the most extreme evolutionary reduction. The Ceratophyllaceae (figure 7), hornworts or coon-tails, among the most abundant submersed aquatics in fresh water, lack roots completely and possess much dissected leaves and simple, reduced flowers. Their relationship to the Nymphaeaceae, water-lilies, was traced by examination of specialization series in the Nymphaeaceae, as represented by the genera Nelumbo (figure 8), Brasenia, and Cabomba, and by compara-tive studies in the two families of the stamens, carpels, seeds, leaves, and stems (wholly without vessels and probably primitively so).

The smallest and most highly reduced flowering plants of all are the Lemnaceae, tiny floating aquatics called duckweeds. Wolffia, for example, consists of a pin-head-sized globose thallus, which produces an inflorescence consisting of one uniovulate pistil and one or two stamens. One might con-sider the search for lemnaceous relatives nearly hopeless, but studies of series of less reduced Lemnaceae and specialized aquatic members of the Araceae, particularly Pistia, and careful embryological investigations of both families rather conclusively showed that the duckweeds are merely greatly reduced aroids, meriting treatment in the same order Arales. Simi-larly, the Typhaceae and Sparganiaceae, cattails and burreeds, appear to be basically wind-pollinated, marsh-dwelling aroids, to be treated as an adja-cent order Typhales. In view of similarities in habit, habitat, inflorescence, and fruit, it is probably significant that *Sparganium eurycarpum* Engelm., Sparganiaceae, and *Acorus calamus* L., sweet-flag of the Araceae, have been shown by Parmelee and Savile (1954) to be hosts to the same rust *Uromyces sparganii* Clint. & Peck (with aecial stage on *Hypericum vir-ginicum* L.). Rusts are usually rather host-specific.

Three large, wind-pollinated, graminoid families of monocotyledons, the Poaceae, Cyperaceae, and Juncaceae, grasses, sedges and rushes respec-tively, are often associated ecologically and systematically. Some sys-tematists treat the Juncaceae as related to the Liliaceae, and most ally the Cyperaceae with the Poaceae. Actually the grasses form a distinct order Poales, resembling in many basic ways the Commelinaceae, the day-flowers and spiderworts, and allied families in the Xyridales. The rushes and sedges, on the other hand, are closely related to each other and only dis-tantly to the grasses through their mutual common origin with the Xyridales. The Liliaceae are only distantly related to these families through their common origin as monocotyledons from some ancient dicotyledonous stock. The close alliance of the rushes and sedges, despite the rather dissimilar flowers and fruit of the big, well-known, specialized genera, is suggested by

FIGURE 7 (above). Flowering and fruiting plants of the hornwort, *Ceratophyllum demersum* L., Ceratophyllaceae, a rootless, submersed aquatic with much dissected leaves. In many basic respects it resembles Cabomba of the Nymphaeaceae.

FIGURE 8 (below). Flower and leaves of the water-lotus, *Nelumbo lutea* (Willd.) Pers., Nymphaeaceae. Although hardly similar in appearance to the hornwort of figure 7, the lotus is rather closely related to it and also belongs in the order Nymphaeales.

the similar flowers of their primitive southern hemisphere genera and by their similar growth habit and seeds. The clinching evidence for their close relationship comes from their embryology and cytology. The Juncaceae produce pollen grains in tetrads, the Cyperaceae single grains. However, embryological studies have revealed that the sedge pollen grain is actually a monad containing the usual vegetative and generative cells plus three nonfunctioning nuclei of the other three microspores of the tetrad. After division of the pollen mother cell nucleus, no microspore walls are produced (Maheshwari, 1950). Further, members of both the Juncaceae (Luzula) and the Cyperaceae (Carex, Eleocharis) have chromosomes with diffuse centromeres, a rather rare condition among angiosperms, resulting in much aneuploidy (Håkansson, 1954, 1958; Davies, 1956).

The rates and directions of evolution vary greatly in the different organs of each angiospermous species. Even the most primitive genera and families show some highly divergent characteristics. The Old World species of Drimys, Sect. Tasmannia of the Winteraceae, which of all living angiosperms retain perhaps the most impressive collection of primitive features, have achieved functional dioecism. Magnolia and others of the larger primitive genera supply highly instructive series of species showing many trends of structural modification in their reproductive organs. Platystemon and Meconella, mentioned above, retain in their reproductive structures the most primitive features in the Papaveraceae; yet, both genera consist of highly specialized, small, opposite-leaved, annual herbs. Romneya, Dendromecon, and other woody members of the family, though possessing various primitive features in the stem and foliage, have relatively divergent flowers and fruit. On the other hand, such highly advanced taxa as the Lamiaceae, mints, and Asteraceae, composites, have rather primitive features in many of their species. Although most of their representatives are herbs, some species possess the primitive tree or shrub habit. Some tropical composites and mints are large timber trees. The mints retain bisexual flowers with a superior ovary though the composites, with bisexual to unisexual or neutral flowers often in the same inflorescence, are completely epigynous. Consequently, it is more exact to refer to a taxon as "primitive" or "advanced" only in reference to specified characteristics.

Although evolutionary trends are sometimes reversed under changed environmental conditions, there is never return to the identical original state. Dichromena of the generally wind-pollinated sedges has returned to insect pollination, but the lost perianth has not been regained. The attractive function has been assumed by the white bases of the upper leaves clustered under the capitate spikelets (Lagerheim, 1893; Leppik, 1955). The temperate species of Salix have returned also to insect-pollination but the function of the missing petals is assumed by the showy stamens, and the perianth rudiment, as mentioned above, has become a nectary. Thus, the function of lost or greatly modified members is generally assumed by some adjacent organs. Other striking examples of biological replacement of inconspicuous or missing petals are afforded by the enlarged, showy sepal in

FIGURE 9 (above). Inflorescence of *Mussaenda erythrophylla* Schum. & Thonn., Rubiaceae, showing the much enlarged, showy red sepals. This plant, native to tropical Africa, was photographed in the Botanic Gardens at Brisbane, Queensland, Australia.

FIGURE 10 (below). Flowering branches of the poinsettia, *Euphorbia pulcherrima* Willd., Euphorbiaceae. The large, showy red leaves subtend small inflorescences called cyathea.

FIGURE 11 (above). A flowering branch of the Queensland silver wattle, *Acacia podalyriaefolia* Cunn., Fabaceae, showing the leaf-blade-like phyllodia, each of which is actually a greatly expanded petiole with possibly the midrib of a leaf which has lost its multiple leaflets in the course of evolution. Photograph taken by Fred Humphreys of Nedlands, West Australia.

FIGURE 12 (below). A flowering branch of *Acacia diptera* Lindl. of West Australia. Not only have the leaf blades disappeared in this species but the phyllodia are very small and decurrent along the flattened, winged, green stems. Photograph taken by Fred Humphreys of Nedlands, West Australia.

Mussaenda (figure 9), Pinckneya, and other genera of the Rubiaceae, showy spathes of Anthurium, Calla, and other Araceae, upper red leaves of Bougainvillea and poinsettia (figure 10), white margins of cyatheal glands in some Euphorbia species, stamen filaments in Callistemon and many other Myrtaceae, and styles in some species of Grevillea of the Proteaceae. The phyllodia (figure 11) of most Australian wattles, Acacia "Div." Phyllodineae, and the cladophylls of the Australian Jacksonia of the Fabaceae and the American Epiphyllum, Nopalochia, and other cacti have taken over the functions of missing leaf-blades. In the Australian *Acacia diptera* Lindl. and related species of the Series Alatae even the phyllodia have been largely replaced by the green, winged stem (figure 12).

Many new structures in the angiosperms have developed as modifications of or outgrowths from pre-existing structures in the proangiosperms. The subtending bracts and sepals of the angiosperm flower have apparently evolved from leaves and the petals from sterile stamens. In some instances all the perianth members seem to have been derived ultimately either from leaves or from stamens. The carpels and stamens considered "standard" in most flowers presumably are modified from leaf-like sporophylls. Floral nectaries have had most diverse origins (Fahn, 1953). Many are known to be modified from carpellodia, staminodia, and perianth members, and others are merely cells in or cellular outgrowths from the receptacle and floral organs. Special structures like the coronas in Narcissus, Passiflora, and

FIGURE 13. An umbel of flowers of *Asclepias curassavica* L., blood-flower, a tropical American milkweed. Note the elaborate corona or crown, which in the milkweeds is apparently an outgrowth from the bases of the stamens.

Asclepias (figure 13) are outgrowths from the perianth or stamens. Within the stem similar developments have taken place, with sieve tube elements in the phloem evolving from sieve cells and vessel elements and wood fibers in the xylem from tracheids. The structural modification of these cells and organs is often so extreme that it is difficult to recognize their origins.

Although it is difficult to assign evolutionary significance to the restricted or sporadic occurrence of many unusual features, their distribution in correlation with other uncommon characteristics often indicates relationship. The distribution of the betacyanins, "nitrogenous anthocyanins" of Gibbs (1945), is an excellent example. These pigments are apparently restricted to the Chenopodiales (Centrospermae), where they are correlated with such other distinctive features as were listed above in the discussion of the Cactaceae. Although often treated in other orders by some systematists, the Nyctaginaceae, Aizoaceae, Portulacaceae, Cactaceae, and Polygonaceae significantly possess most of these features that are so rare or lacking in other angiospermous taxa.

Although its significance otherwise remains obscure, no characteristic of the Annonales (Magnoliales) is so constantly present throughout that large order of fragrant, relict angiosperms as the spherical "ethereal oil" cells in the parenchymatous tissues. The Aristolochiaceae, mentioned above, possess this feature in common with the other Annonales. So also do the Lauraceae, Calycanthaceae, Canellaceae, Chloranthaceae, Saururaceae, and Piperaceae, so frequently and unnecessarily placed in other orders. The heavy development of alkaloids in the Annonales and Berberidales (including Papaveraceae), myrosin cells in the Capparales, where correlated with parietal placentation and capsular fruits, the peculiar monosporic tetranucleate embryo sac of the Onagraceae, and internal phloem and vestured pits of vessels in the Gentianales (excluding the Oleaceae but including the Rubiaceae) are only a few of the pertinent examples that might be cited here.

The distribution of trends or tendencies toward the possession of certain characteristics can often be a most helpful clue in the search for relationships. In some families of the Santalales (including the Celastrales) there is only a tendency toward parasitism; in others, particularly the Balanophoraceae and the Loranthaceae in part, parasitism has become complete. Partial parasitism in the Scrophulariaceae becomes complete parasitism in the closely related Orobanchaceae. A tendency toward wind pollination in the Hamamelidales, expressed in Liquidambar, Altingia, and Platanus, becomes complete dependence on anemophily in presumably related groups like Casuarina, the Betulaceae, and most Fagaceae. Although probably associated with succulence and various physiological phenomena, the tendency of the members of the Chenopodiales to thrive under conditions of high alkalinity or salinity in the substrate is phyletically significant. It also helps to explain the predominance of these plants in maritime and desert areas.

SUMMARY

Such major problems for the angiosperm phylogenist as the inadequate fossil record, the prevalence of convergent evolution, the extreme reduction or other modification of some angiosperms, and the incomplete training of most phylogenists are discussed.

A few selected examples of the application of some guiding principles to the search for relationships and origins in the Angiospermae are presented. The probable features of the immediate common ancestor of the most primitive living angiosperms are listed. Brief consideration is given to the phylogenetic relationships of the Aristolochiaceae, Papaveraceae, Cactaceae, Ceratophyllaceae, Lemnaceae, Sparganiaceae, Poaceae, Cyperaceae, Juncaceae, Chenopodiales, and Annonales.

LITERATURE CITED

Bailey, I. W., 1944, The comparative morphology of the Winteraceae. III. Wood. J. Arnold Arboretum 25: 97–103.

Bailey, I. W., and C. G. Nast, 1943a, The comparative morphology of the Winteraceae. I. Pollen and stamens. J. Arnold Arboretum 24: 340–346.

1943b, The comparative morphology of Winteraceae. II. Carpels. J. Arnold Arboretum 24: 472–481.

1944a, The comparative morphology of the Winteraceae. IV. Anatomy of the node and vascularization of the leaf. J. Arnold Arboretum 25: 215–221.

1944b, The comparative morphology of the Winteraceae. V. Foliar epidermis and sclerenchyma. J. Arnold Arboretum 25: 342–348.

1945, The comparative morphology of the Winteraceae. VII. Summary and conclusions. J. Arnold Arboretum 26: 37–47.

1945, Morphology and relationships of *Trochodendron* and *Tetracentron*. J. Arnold Arboretum 26: 143–154.

Bailey, I. W., C. G. Nast and A. C. Smith, 1943, The family Himantandraceae. J. Arnold Arboretum 24: 190–206.

Bailey, I. W., and A. C. Smith, 1942, Degeneriaceae, a new family of flowering plants from Fiji. J. Arnold Arboretum 23: 356–365.

Benson, L., 1962, Plant taxonomy. Methods and principles. Ronald Press, New York. 494 p.

Blackwelder, R. E., and A. Boyden, 1952, The nature of systematics. Systematic Zool. 1: 26–33.

Canright, J. E., 1952, The comparative morphology and relationships of the Magnoliaceae. I. Trends of specialization in the stamens. Am. J. Botany 39: 484–497.

1953, The comparative morphology and relationships of the Magnoliaceae. II. Significance of the pollen. Phytomorphology 3: 355–365.

1955, The comparative morphology and relationships of the Magnoliaceae. IV. Wood and nodal anatomy. J. Arnold Arboretum 36: 119–140.

1960, The comparative morphology and relationships of the Magnoliaceae. III. Carpels. Am. J. Botany 47: 145–155.

Cronquist, A., 1957, Outline of a new system of families and orders of dicotylendons. Bull. Jardin Botan. l'Etat [Bruxelles] 27: 13–40.

Davies, E. W., 1956, Cytology, evolution and origin of the aneuploid series in the genus Carex. Hereditas 42: 349–365.

Engler, A., and L. Diels, 1936, Syllabus der Pflanzenfamilien. 11th Edition. Gebruder Borntraeger, Berlin. 419 p.

Fahn, A., 1953, The topography of the nectary in the flower and its phylogenetical trend. Phytomorphology 3: 424–426.

Gibbs, R. D., 1945, Comparative chemistry as an aid to the solution of problems in systematic botany. Trans. Roy. Soc. Can., 3rd series, Sect. 5, 39: 71–103.

Gilmour, J. S. L., 1940, Taxonomy and philosophy, p. 461–474. In J. Huxley [Ed.], The new systematics. Oxford Univ. Press, Oxford.

Grant, V., 1959, Natural history of the Phlox Family. Vol. 1. Systematic botany. Martinus Nijhoff, The Hague. 280 p.

Håkansson, A., 1954, Meiosis and pollen mitosis in x-rayed and untreated spikelets of Eleocharis palustris. Hereditas 40: 325–345.

1958, Holocentric chromosomes in Eleocharis. Hereditas 44: 531–540.

Hutchinson, J., 1959, The families of flowering plants. 2 volumes. Oxford Univ. Press, Oxford.

Lagerheim, G. de, 1893, Note sur une Cyperacee entomophile. (Dichromena ciliata Vahl). J. Botany 7: 181–183.

Leppik, E. E., 1955, Some viewpoints on the origin and evolution of flowering plants. Acta Biotheoret. 11: 45–56.

Maheshwari, P., 1950, An introduction to the embryology of angiosperms. McGraw-Hill, New York. 453 p.

Money, L. L., I. W. Bailey and B. G. L. Swamy, 1950, The morphology and relationships of the Monimiaceae. J. Arnold Arboretum 31: 372–404.

Munroe, E., 1953, The phylogeny of the Papilionidae. Proc. Pacific Sci. Congr. Pacific Sci. Assoc. 7th. 4: 83–87.

Myers, G. S., 1952, The nature of systematic biology and of a species description. Systematic Zool. 1: 106–111.

1960, Some reflections on phylogenetic and typological taxonomy. Systematic Zool. 9: 37–41.

Nast, C. G., 1944, The comparative morphology of the Winteraceae. VI. Vascular anatomy of the flowering shoot. J. Arnold Arboretum 25: 454–466.

Nast, C. G., and I. W. Bailey, 1945, Morphology and relationships of Trochodendron and Tetracentron. II. Inflorescence, flower and fruit. J. Arnold Arboretum 26: 267–276.

Parkin, J., 1951, The unisexual flower—a criticism. Phytomorphology 2: 75–79.

1957, The unisexual flower again—a criticism. Phytomorphology 7: 7–9.

Parmelee, J. A., and D. B. O. Savile, 1954, Life history and relationship of the rusts of Sparganium and Acorus. Mycologia 56: 823–836.

Porter, C. L., 1959, Taxonomy of flowering plants. W. H. Freeman, San Francisco. 452 p.

Scott, R. A., E. S. Barghoorn and E. B. Leopold, 1960, How old are the angiosperms? Am. J. Sci. 258-A: 284–299.

Simpson, G. G., 1961, Principles of animal taxonomy. Columbia Univ. Press, New York. 247 p.

Sneath, P. H. A., 1961, Recent developments in theoretical and quantitative taxonomy. Systematic Zool. 10: 118–139.

Sokal, R. R., 1961, Distance as a measure of taxonomic similarity. Systematic Zool. 10: 70–79.

Starrett, A., 1958, What is the subspecies problem? Systematic Zool. 8: 111–115.

Stebbins, G. L., 1951, Natural selection and the differentiation of angiosperm families. Evolution 5: 299–324.

Thorne, R. F., 1958, Some guiding principles of angiosperm phylogeny. Brittonia 10: 72–77.

A METHOD FOR DEDUCING BRANCHING SEQUENCES IN PHYLOGENY[1,2]

Joseph H. Camin and Robert R. Sokal[3]

Department of Entomology, The University of Kansas, Lawrence

Accepted May 3, 1965

With the advent of relatively objective classifications, such as the phenetic classifications produced by the operational techniques of numerical taxonomy (Sokal and Sneath, 1963), it was inevitable that biologists would wonder what phylogenetic conclusions could be drawn from them and with what reliability. If these phenetic taxonomies did not reflect all of the elements of phyletics (Sokal and Camin, 1965), could techniques be devised for deducing the latter? For example, could operational methods be devised for deducing the cladistic relationships among taxa, so that, given the same initial information, different investigators would obtain the same results? By cladistic relationships we mean the evolutionary branching sequences among taxonomic units without regard to phenetic similarities among them or to an absolute time scale.

There is no question that phylogenies could probably be reconstructed without error for any taxonomic group if complete fossil sequences for that group were available. However, can cladistic reconstructions be carried out with any degree of reliability if only characters of recent forms are considered? Several recent studies have also considered this question from different points of view (Doolittle and Blombäck, 1964; Edwards and Cavalli-Sforza, 1964; Simpson, 1963; Throckmorton, 1965; Wilson, 1965).

Since 1962 a group at the Entomology Department of The University of Kansas has been examining the principles by which phylogenies are constructed conventionally, as well as the relation between the principles and practices of phylogeny and those of taxonomy, both orthodox and numerical. In addition to the authors, the group includes G. W. Byers and C. D. Michener and several graduate students. The study was based on a group of imaginary animals possessing a number of morphological characteristics generated by one of us (JHC) according to rules known so far only to him, but which are believed to be consistent with what is generally known of transspecific evolution. Genetic continuity was accomplished by tracing the drawings of the animals from sheet to sheet, permitting the preservation of all characters except for such modifications as were desired. Although the study is still in progress, it has already led to an empirical method which we believe capable of deducing probable cladistics from the characters of existing organisms.

Detailed studies of subsets of the assemblage of hypothetical animals by orthodox phylogenetic methodology resulted in differing, but internally consistent, cladistic schemes, the choice among which was not apparent to those uninitiated in the true phylogeny. Comparison by Camin of these various schemes with the "truth" led him to the observation that those trees which most closely resembled the true cladistics

---

[1] This paper was presented on December 29, 1964, at a symposium entitled "Interactions between numerical and orthodox taxonomies" at Knoxville, Tennessee, before the Society of Systematic Zoology.

[2] Contribution No. 1261 from the Department of Entomology, The University of Kansas, Lawrence. Research for this paper was supported by NSF Grant G 21011.

This investigation also was supported in part by a Public Health Service research career program award (No. 3-K3-GM-22, 021-01S1) from the National Institute of General Medical Sciences to Robert R. Sokal.

[3] We are indebted for constructive comments and criticisms to W. A. Clemens, P. R. Ehrlich, C. D. Michener, F. J. Rohlf, P. H. A. Sneath, the Biosystematics Discussion Group and the Evolutionists at The University of Kansas.

invariably required for their construction the least number of postulated evolutionary steps for the characters studied. Subsequently we examined the possibility of reconstructing cladistics by the principle of evolutionary parsimony. The following technique seems capable of doing this.

Technique

The technique requires a conventional data matrix as used for numerical taxonomy (Table 1). The columns of this matrix represent the *operational taxonomic units* (OTU's), which can stand for any taxonomic unit from individual through species up to higher categories. The rows of the matrix represent characters scored into different *character states* as qualitative or quantitative subdivisions of each character, differing among the OTU's.

The basic assumptions underlying character coding are fundamental to the entire technique and must be carefully examined.

1. We assume that characters can be expressed in discrete states differing among at least some of the OTU's of the study.

2. The character states can be arrayed in some logical order. If the characters are quantitative (*e.g.,* counts of bristles, segments, or leaves, or increments of size) linear order for the states is easily accomplished. Qualitative characters (shapes, colors, etc.) may require some ingenuity as well as some arbitrariness in coding states. If a logical order cannot be found for a qualitative character, the states may have to be recoded as several two-state characters. For details of this procedure see Sokal and Sneath (1963, p. 74ff).

From our knowledge of evolutionary processes the following three asumptions are not valid for all cases, although they are probably true for the majority of characters and taxa. Thus, they are only working assumptions which, as we shall show, can themselves be tested by the technique and may be relaxed in certain instances.

3. It is assumed that we have knowledge of the direction of the evolutionary trends within characters, and therefore the character states can be arrayed in a presumed evolutionary sequence from primitive (ancestral) to derived. In the linear sequence of character states, 1, 2, 3, 4, 5, 6, the presumed evolutionary sequence may be from 1 to 6, or from 6 to 1, or from 3 in two directions (toward 1 as well as toward 6). The primitive character state in these three examples would be 1, 6, or 3, respectively. For convenience, the primitive state is coded zero, derived states

positively or negatively, as required (see Table 1).

4. The ancestral state arose only once in the taxa at hand. Wilson (1965) has called such character states *unique.* Derived character states may, however, have arisen repeatedly in different branches of the group studied.

5. Evolution is irreversible, *i.e.,* a line, having attained a derived character state, cannot return to a character state ancestral to the derived one.

Under these assumptions the minimum number of evolutionary steps necessary to evolve c states of a character is $c - 1$. The number of character states and the minimum number of evolutionary steps necessary for each character are shown in Table 1. The most parsimonious cladistic dendrograms for characters 5 and 6 are shown at the bottoms of Tables 2A and 2B. We suggest the term *cladogram* to distinguish a cladistic dendrogram from a phenetic one which might be called a *phenogram.*[4] The principles of our approach are best illustrated during a preliminary step in the computations, the calculation of the so-called compatibility matrix.

All characters in the study are fitted to the pattern of the cladogram of each character. By this we mean that we compute the number of evolutionary steps required to arrive at the correct character states for all the OTU's in the study via the various cladistic patterns provided. The pathways of a pattern cladogram are unidirectional from the base of the dendrogram to the tips. Since changes in character states are irreversible (assumption 5) an evolutionary step in a character affects all pathways beyond that step. Provisionally any time several branches come off a stem at the same place a single evolutionary step suffices to produce the same change in any or all branches. Evolutionary steps increasing character state codes are shown graphically as short lines crossing the stems, while those decreasing the character state codes are shown as X-marks across the stems. They are marked with the num-

---

[4] Ernst Mayr (1965) has independently suggested the same terms with identical meanings. Arnett (1963) has used *phenogram* for a profile-type summary of characters.

TABLE 1. *Data matrix.*

				t OTU's				Character states (*c*)	Minimum steps (*c* − 1)
	7	8	13	14	15	25	28		
1.	1	0	1	0	1	1	1	2	1
2.	1	1	0	0	0	2	0	3	2
3.	1	1	1	2	0	2	2	3	2
4.	3	2	0	0	3	1	0	4	3
5.	1	1	2	1	0	1	3	4	3
6.	1	0	0	0	0	−1	0	3	2
7.	0	0	0	0	−1	0	1	3	2
									15

(*n* Characters)

ber of the character which they represent (Fig. 1). Each mark represents a character state increment or decrement of 1 only. To indicate a change from state 3 to 5, for example, two marks must be shown on a stem. The state code at the base of the dendrogram is assumed to be 0 (primitive) for all characters. It is convenient to set up the data in a *pattern table* as shown in Table 2. This arranges the OTU's by the state codes of the characters that form the bases for the patterns (*e.g.*, characters 5 and 6). The character state codes inside the table are the columns of the data matrix in Table 1 rearranged in the new order. The cladogram at the bottom of the table may be helpful, although we have not generally found it necessary for our computations.

Fitting character 1 to the pattern of character 5 (Table 2A) we find that it possesses state 1 in OTU 15. A mark cannot be placed at the base of the cladogram because OTU's 8 and 14 are coded 0 and would be changed by such an evolutionary step. A positive mark is therefore placed on the branch to OTU 15. A single step suffices to change OTU's 7 and 25 to character state code 1. The mark for this step cannot be placed on the stem leading to the cluster (7–25) as it would raise all members of the cluster to state 1. We therefore place the marks over the cluster as shown in Fig. 1, heavy cross lines indicating changes for the stems concerned and thin lines connecting the heavy ones to indicate that these comprise a single step. Such clusters may then be resolved later in the

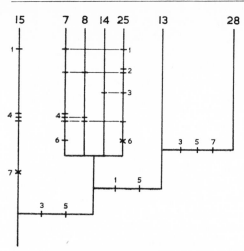

FIG. 1. Pattern cladogram of character 5. This cladogram follows the pattern shown in Table 2A. Numbers at the tips of the branches are code numbers of OTU's. The evolutionary steps for each character are marked on the branches. Evolutionary steps increasing character state codes are shown as lines across branches, those decreasing character state codes as X-marks. The number of the character represented is next to each mark. Single steps affecting several members of a cluster are diagrammed as heavy cross lines which indicate changes for the stems concerned, connected by thin lines to indicate that these comprise a single step.

procedure. Finally a mark before the point where OTU's 13 and 28 separate will raise these to code 1. These marks and those for fitting the other characters to pattern 5 are shown graphically in Fig. 1.

Character 2 needs a single positive mark to raise OTU's 7, 8, and 25 to state code 1 and a second for OTU 25 only, to raise it to code 2. Character 3 has a step prior to cluster (7–25) raising all OTU's other than 15 to code 1. A single positive mark raises OTU's 14 and 25 to code 2 and another raises OTU 28 to code 2. In character 4, because OTU's 14, 13, and 28 are at state 0, three separate positive steps are required to change OTU 15 to code 3. One step will raise OTU's 7, 8, and 25 to state 1, a second will raise OTU's 7 and 8 to state 2, and a third will raise OTU 7 to state 3.

Character 5, being the pattern character,

TABLE 2. *Sample pattern tables.*

To demonstrate the method of computing the number of necessary evolutionary steps and the measure of compatibility between the various characters and patterns constructed according to other characters. The cladograms at the bottoms of the tables are the most parsimonious pathways for evolution of characters 5 and 6, respectively, whose states are underlined in the tables.

A. Pattern table of character no. 5.

	OTU's							Total steps	Extra steps
	15	7	8	14	25	13	28		
1.	1	1	0	0	1	1	1	3	2
2.	0	1	1	0	2	0	0	2	0
3.	0	1	1	2	2	1	2	3	1
4.	3	3	2	0	1	0	0	6	3
5.	0̲	1̲	1̲	1̲	1	2̲	3̲	3	X
6.	0	1	0	0	−1	0	0	2	0
7.	−1	0	0	0	0	0	1	2	0
								21	6

Characters (row label on left side)

B. Pattern table of character no. 6.

	OTU's							Total steps	Extra steps
	25	8	13	14	15	28	7		
1.	1	0	1	0	1	1	1	2	1
2.	2	1	0	0	0	0	1	3	1
3.	2	1	1	2	0	2	1	4	2
4.	1	2	0	0	3	0	3	6	3
5.	1	1	2	1	0	3	1	4	1
6.	−1̲	0̲	0̲	0̲	0̲	0̲	1̲	2	X
7.	0̲	0	0	0	−1	1	0̲	2	0
								23	8

Characters (row label on left side)

requires only the minimum number of steps as indicated. In character 6 a single positive and a single negative step change OTU's 7 and 25 to codes 1 and −1, respectively. Finally, character 7 needs a positive and a negative step to change OTU's 28 and 15 similarly. The total number of steps required for any one character to fit a given pattern is listed to the right of the pattern table (Table 2A). After a little practice the number of steps required can be written down simply by inspection of the pattern table.

Some additional problems in evaluating the number of evolutionary steps are illustrated by Table 2B which is a pattern table based on character 6, showing a V-shaped evolutionary trend. Evolutionary steps now have to be calculated in both directions from the pivotal stem. Parsimony may result by following the provisional rule on branches arising from one place on the stem. For example, a single step may turn the left and right arms or the pivotal stem and one of the arms in the same direction. For character 1 in Table 2B a single step turns OTU's 25 and 7 to character state 1

and a second step turns OTU's 13, 15, and 28 to state 1, leaving OTU's 8 and 14 at state 0. Thus two evolutionary steps are required to fit character 1 to the pattern of character 6.

Subtracting the minimum number of steps $(c − 1)$ for each of the characters (see Table 1) from the total number of steps yields the extra number of steps necessary to fit a given character to a pattern. These values are shown in the last column of each pattern table (Table 2). Whenever this value is 0, the character is compatible with the pattern provided. The number of extra steps is a measure of the incompatibility of the character to any given pattern. A check on the computation is provided since the sum of the total necessary steps minus the sum of the extra steps must give the sum of the minimum number of steps, $\Sigma(c − 1)$. When all (n) characters have been fitted to the n patterns (one for each character) the numbers of extra steps for each pattern are assembled in a *compatibility matrix* (Table 3). The diagonal elements of the compatibility matrix are zeros since, obviously, every character is compatible with its own pattern. They are indicated by X's and excluded from the computation. Rows and columns of this matrix are summed in two ways. The number of zeros is counted (and recorded as "compatibilities") and the numbers of extra steps are summed.

The compatibility matrix provides information of two kinds. It shows which characters provide "good" patterns and thus are relatively close to the presumed correct cladogram. Such characters would have high column compatibilities, i.e., have a large number of characters compatible with their pattern and consequently few extra steps in their column. The compatibility matrix also supplies us with information about "poor" characters which are those whose patterns have relatively few characters compatible with them and call for a large number of extra steps, and which also fit poorly to most other patterns, showing few compatibilities and. requiring many extra steps. Thus in Table 3 the pattern of character 4 has only 2 compatibilities and requires 11 extra steps by the other characters in order to conform to it. In addition, character 4 is incompatible with all other patterns and requires 18 extra steps to fit it to the patterns of the other characters. Such characters may be poor because of miscoding of their character states. The latter can arise from errors in transcription of data (such a case occurred in the analysis of the horses discussed below), or by an incorrect interpretation of the evolutionary trends in character states. Coding a character 0, 1, 2, 3 implies that evolution has proceeded in steps from 0 to 3. If, in fact, evolution proceeded from state 3 to 0, the compatibility matrix would show the miscoded character to be poor as a pattern and in fitting other patterns. The assumption of irreversibility of evolutionary steps may not be true in a specific case. When state 2 of a character arose from state 1 as well as by reversion from state 3, the character will show up as miscoded, if we consider all OTU's exhibiting the operationally homol-

TABLE 3. *Compatibility matrix.*

		Patterns							Compati-bilities	Extra steps
		1	2	3	4	5	6	7		
Characters	1.	X	2	2	2	2	1	1	0	10
	2.	1	X	1	2	0	1	0	2	5
	3.	2	2	X	4	1	2	1	0	12
	4.	2	3	4	X	3	3	3	0	18
	5.	1	1	1	3	X	1	1	0	8
	6.	0	0	0	0	0	X	0	6	0
	7.	0	0	0	0	0	0	X	6	0
Compatibilities:		2	2	2	2	3	1	2	14	–
Extra steps:		6	8	8	11	6	8	6	–	53

ogous character state 2 as identical. Thus the method provides a check on some of its assumptions. If we knew which instances of apparent state 2 were really reversions from state 3, we could recode these as state 4 to preserve the linear sequence, which would improve the pattern and fit of this character in the compatibility matrix. It has therefore been our practice to exclude characters which show few compatibilities and large numbers of extra steps in their columns and rows on the assumption that these characters are miscoded. The reconstruction of the cladogram is then carried out without considering these characters which are later fitted separately to the reconstructed cladogram. Frequently reexamination of poor characters and fitting them to the final reconstruction in their own most parsimonious sequence will reveal the source of miscoding and permit their use in subsequent studies.

A number of different approaches to the reconstruction of the cladogram have been developed. None work perfectly so that they directly provide the most parsimonious solution. All methods provide a *procladogram*, which represents a state of considerable parsimony but must be adjusted by inspection or preferably a systematic program of trial and error to change it to the final most parsimonious arrangement. Our first approach fitted all characters to the cladogram of a good pattern as defined above, making adjustments as necessary. The steps necessary to fit

TABLE 4. *The monothetic method for reconstructing cladograms.*

A. Data matrix for group A (Table 1) with characters 6 and 7 recoded and character 4 omitted.

	OTU's							Cycle 1, Step 1
Characters	7	8	13	14	15	25	28	
1	1	1	0	1	0	1	1	OTU's 14 and 15 have
2	1	1	0	0	0	2	0	6 zeros each. Removal
3	1	1	1	2	0	2	2	of OTU 14 leaves no
5	1	1	2	1	0	1	3	"non-zero" rows. Re-
6+	1	0	0	0	0	0	0	moval of OTU 15 leaves
6-	0	0	0	0	0	1	0	rows 3 and 5 non-zero
7+	0	0	0	0	0	0	1	and 7- all-zero. There-
7-	0	0	0	0	1	0	0	fore, remove OTU 15.
Number of zeros	3	5	5	6	6	3	4	

B. Data matrix A with OTU 15 removed.

	OTU's						Cycle 1, Step 2
Characters	7	8	13	14	25	28	
1	1	0	1	0	1	1	
2	1	1	0	0	2	0	
3	1	1	1	2	2	2	Subtract unity
5	1	1	2	1	1	3	from rows 3
6+	1	0	0	0	0	0	and 5; delete
6-	0	0	0	0	1	0	row 7-.
7+	0	0	0	0	0	1	
7-	0	0	0	0	0	0	

C. Data matrix B with unity subtracted from rows 3 and 5 and row 7- deleted.

	OTU's						Cycle 2, Step 1
Characters	7	8	13	14	25	28	
1	1	1	0	1	0	1	1	Recompute number of ze-
2	1	1	0	0	2	0	ros for remaining OTU's.
3	0	0	0	1	1	1	OTU's 8 and 14 have 6 ze-
5	0	0	1	0	0	2	ros each. Removal of either
6+	1	0	0	0	0	0	8 or 14 leaves no non-zero
6-	0	0	0	0	1	0	rows. Removal of both 8
7+	0	0	0	0	0	1	and 14 leaves row 1 non-
Number of zeros	4	6	5	6	3	3	zero. Therefore, remove OTU's 8 and 14 together.

D. Data matrix C with OTU's 8 and 14 removed.

	OTU's				Cycle 2, Step 2
Characters	7	13	25	28	
1	1	1	1	1	
2	1	0	2	0	Subtract unity from
3	0	0	1	1	row 1. Row 1 be-
5	0	1	0	2	comes all-zero, so de-
6+	1	0	0	0	lete.
6-	0	0	1	0	
7+	0	0	0	1	

E. Data matrix D with row 1 deleted.

	OTU's				Cycle 3, Step 1
Characters	7	13	25	28	
2	1	0	2	0	Recompute number of zeros for
3	0	0	1	1	remaining OTU's. OTU 13 has
5	0	1	0	2	5 zeros. Removal of OTU 13
6+	1	0	0	0	leaves no non-zero rows. Simi-
6-	0	0	1	0	larly for OTU 7 with 4 zeros.
7+	0	0	0	1	Removal of OTU's 7 and 13
Number of zeros	4	5	3	3	leaves row 3 non-zero. There- fore, remove OTU's 7 and 13.

F. Data matrix E with OTU's 7 and 13 removed

	OTU's		Cycle 3, Step 2
Characters	25	28	
2	2	0	
3	1	1	Subtract unity from row 3.
5	0	2	Row 3 becomes all-zero, so
6+	0	0	delete. OTU's 25 and 28 are
6-	1	0	a terminal bifurcation.
7+	0	1	

all characters are marked on the chosen pattern cladogram (Fig. 1). Branches of this basic cladogram are rearranged if this achieves greater parsimony of evolutionary steps. The basic outline of the tree is retained but the provisionally shared steps

in cluster (7–25) must be resolved. In small studies, such as this one, it is simplest to make a frequency distribution of steps shared by OTU pairs, triplets, etc., which are subsets of a cluster. Not counting character 4, as explained in the results for Group A, we find that OTU's 8 or 14 have only one shared step with OTU 25 which, however, has 2 steps in common with OTU 7. Since OTU 8 shares a step with both OTU's 7 and 25, OTU 14 is least related to the cluster and becomes its basal branch. The origin of the stem for OTU 14 is at the same point as that for the stem leading to OTU's 13 and 28 because there are no steps common to all of cluster (7–25) that do not also affect OTU's 13 and 28. The joint step of OTU's 14 and 25 (character 3) cannot be made compatible with such an arrangement and, therefore, must be an example of parallelism. Next to arise from the stem bearing the rest of the cluster is OTU 8 because it shares one step with OTU's 7 and 25. The latter share two steps and represent the terminal branches of the former cluster.

The completed reconstruction can be inspected in Fig. 2. In this cladogram evolutionary steps for characters 8 through 12 are also added. These were not included in the data matrix or the computation, because they occurred in the derived state in only one OTU each. The steps for these characters are compatible with the general cladogram and emphasize that OTU 25 is very specialized.

In larger clusters, frequency distributions of shared steps are more tedious without a digital computer. Another approach consists of a single-linkage cluster analysis (Sokal and Sneath, 1963) of the OTU's based on the number of common evolutionary steps.

The third approach is the monothetic method which works directly from the original data matrix. However, all characters having both positive and negative states must be recoded as two characters as shown in Table 4A for the data matrix of Table 1. Although the method is monothetic in operation, its results are polythetic (Sokal and Sneath, 1963, p. 13). The steps are as follows.

1. Zero states are counted for each OTU (column). This provides some measure of "primitiveness," as OTU's with greater numbers of characters in state "0" should branch off the main trunk of the cladogram near its base.
2. The OTU with the greatest number of zeros is removed and the remaining data matrix is checked for rows (characters) without zeros. (If there are ties for largest number of zeros, the first of the tied OTU's is removed.)
3. If no "non-zero" rows appear, the OTU with the next largest number of zeros is removed (or the second of the tied OTU's is removed) and the previously removed OTU column is placed back into the matrix.
4. If there are still no non-zero rows, then

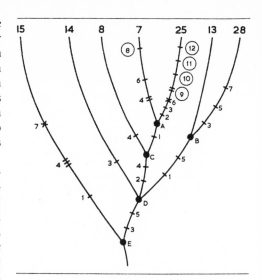

FIG. 2. Reconstruction of cladogram of Group A of the hypothetical animals, based on the pattern cladogram of Fig. 1. The OTU's and evolutionary steps are indicated as in Fig. 1. Characters 8 through 12 (circled) were not included in the data matrix (Table 1) or Fig. 1 because they occurred in the derived state in only one OTU each. The total number of evolutionary steps, not counting characters 8 through 12, is 23 compared with the minimum number of 15 steps from Table 1. The ancestors of the OTU's at the tips are indicated by black circles and identified by capital letters. Their probable character states can be easily obtained from the cladogram by going from the base to the ancestor. Thus for ancestor C, characters 1 through 7 will be in states 0, 1, 1, 1, 1, 0, 0, respectively.

the first and second OTU's are removed simultaneously. If this still leaves no non-zero rows, the OTU columns are placed back into the matrix and the OTU with the next largest number of zeros is removed. If no non-zero rows appear, the third and first, third and second, or all three OTU's are removed in that order. This process is systematically continued until at least one non-zero row appears (Table 4A).
5. When a non-zero row appears after the removal of one or more OTU's, the OTU or OTU's whose removal from the matrix produced a non-zero row is drawn as a branch from the base of the procladogram (Fig. 3A).
6. Unity (1) is then subtracted from each character state code in each non-zero row (Table 4B). This is repeated, if the row remains non-zero after the subtraction of one. Another branch, the main trunk of the procladogram, is drawn adjacent to the branch bearing the removed OTU or OTU's and evolutionary steps

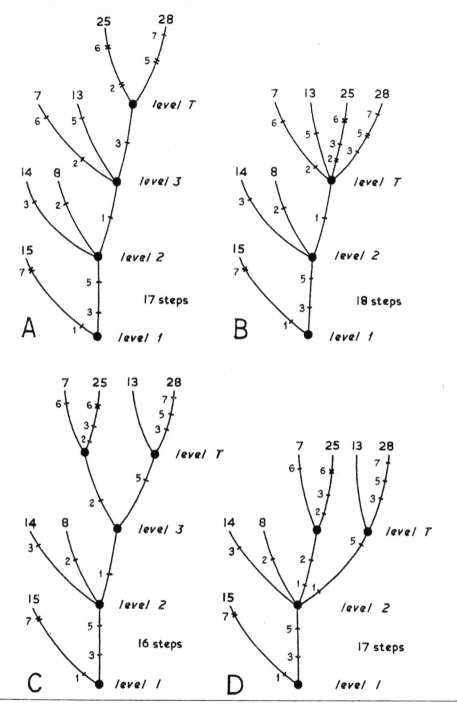

FIG. 3. Steps in the reconstruction of the cladogram of Group A (Fig. 2) by the monothetic method. Symbolism as in earlier figures. Level numbers and T refer to levels of furcation from 1 to terminal level. A. Procladogram resulting from monothetic technique illustrated in Table 4. Total number of evolutionary steps is 17. B. OTU 25 moved down one branching point; 18 evolutionary steps result. C. OTU's 25 and 7 grouped as are OTU's 13 and 28. Achieved parsimony of 16 steps. This is equally parsimonious but not identical to cladogram in Fig. 2. Addition of character 4 to this cladogram and further adjustments for parsimony result in a cladogram identical to Fig. 2. D. Branch bearing OTU's 7 and 25 move down one branching point; 17 evolutionary steps result. If OTU's 8, 7, and 25 are now rearranged so that they share their common step for character 2, the cladogram of Fig. 2 is obtained.

representing the subtraction of one are drawn on that trunk with a number beside it for identification representing the character affected (Fig. 3A). At this time, any rows which are left all-zero may be removed from the matrix and dropped from subsequent consideration. Steps for such characters are placed on the branch leading to the removed OTU's (Fig. 3A).

7. The number of column zeros for the remaining OTU's is recomputed and the process is repeated through a second cycle (Tables 4C and 4D) and continued until the reconstruction of the procladogram is completed (Tables 4E and 4F).

8. When the procladogram (an initial approximation of the most parsimonious solution) is completed, all character states (evolutionary steps) are added to the cladogram and final readjustments for greater parsimony are made (Fig. 3A).

Because all of the methods devised so far yield only good approximations of the most parsimonious solution, it is necessary to test for parsimony and to make adjustments when these are indicated. This can best be practiced with a systematic procedure. First remove all internodes, *i.e.*, segments of stems between furcations, which do not bear any evolutionary steps because there is no reason to assume separate branching points in the absence of intervening evolutionary steps. Next move all common evolutionary steps found on adjacent branches to the base stem of these branches. This practice is parsimonious by making one evolutionary step do the work of two. Finally, and of most consequence, is the trial and error moving of branches which we shall illustrate in Fig. 3. From the procladogram resulting from the monothetic method (Fig. 3A) we try moving one of the terminal branches, the branch carrying OTU 25 or OTU 28, down one furcation to the furcation level 3 indicated in Fig. 3A. This now becomes furcation level T (the terminal level) and OTU's 25, 28, 7, and 13 all emerge from this point

(Fig. 3B). While our original procladogram required 17 evolutionary steps, the new adjustment requires 18 steps, and is thus moving away from the intended direction. However, we can now check members of the cluster 25, 28, 7, and 13, for common steps which can be removed to base stems. We find in Fig. 3C that OTU's 25 and 7 can be placed together with character step 2 made common, and OTU's 28 and 13 can be joined with character step 5 in common. This necessitates parallel steps in OTU's 25 and 28 for character 3, which previously was a common step, but we have now reduced the number of steps for the cladogram to 16. This is the same number required by the true cladogram but Fig. 3C is not the correct solution. Moving the branch which bears OTU's 7 and 25 in Fig. 3C from furcation level 3 to level 2 (Fig. 3D) will result in an equally parsimonious cladogram which is the same as Fig. 2, the correct solution. This illustrates an important point. Different, but equally parsimonious solutions may occur and in order to distinguish between them one must have added information from further characters. When character 4 was laid on the cladogram of Fig. 3C, without correcting it for apparent miscoding, this took an additional eight steps. Further rearrangement following the principles outlined above reduced the added steps for character 4 to only seven and yielded the correct solution. However, when character 4 is fitted and recoded in its most parsimonious sequence to either the cladogram of Fig. 3C or of Fig. 2, it results in only four additional steps and the two solutions remain equally parsimonious. Therefore, in such cases, additional characters must be sought in order to find the most probable solution to the cladogram and to the recoding of character 4.

We should point out that the small studies reported in this paper are based on very few characters and decisions on alternative cladograms are frequently taken on the saving of a single step. When more characters are studied, such decisions generally are more soundly based. However, even in larger studies equally parsimonious solutions may occur in certain portions of the tree, where the determination of structure depends on very few evolutionary steps.

Three computer programs have been developed by Ronald Bartcher for carrying out the above methods of numerical cladistics. The first program calculates a compatibility matrix, finds the optimal pattern, and then fits the characters to this pattern. A second program carries out the monothetic method of finding a procladogram. The third program parctices parsimony on a cladogram for any given data matrix. The output is shown as an actual cladogram with the evolutionary steps marked in. These programs, called CLADON I, II, and III, respectively, were prepared in FORTRAN IV, for the IBM 7040 with 16K memory, at The University of Kansas Computation Center. As currently written they can handle 30 OTU's and 50 characters. Persons interested in obtaining copies of CLADON for adaptation to their computational equipment are invited to write to the authors. To provide some idea of running time, four of the reconstructions reported in this paper (including one with 14 characters) took approximately one-half minute at a cost of $1.50 by CLADON I, or two minutes ($6.00) by CLADON II including drawing of cladograms. Attempts to improve parsimony by CLADON III (unsuccessful—apparently correct solutions were obtained by either CLADON I or II) took five minutes.

RESULTS

The technique was applied experimentally to data from several hypothetical cases, including Group A, seven OTU's from Camin's imaginary animals, which furnished the illustrative example of the technique section. Data from several groups of real organisms were also analyzed.

Group A

The cladogram of Fig. 2, which was obtained directly from the compatibility matrix (Table 3), proved to be entirely correct. Besides leading to the reconstruction, the compatibility matrix provides additional information of interest. Characters which provide poor patterns usually fit well to many other patterns and are, therefore, usually compatible with the optimal pattern (e.g., characters 2, 6, and 7). Some characters which provide poor patterns may fit only moderately well to other patterns. This usually indicates some lack of parsimony, i.e., parallel evolution for that character (e.g., characters 1 and 3 in Table 3 and Fig. 2). We have already noted character 4 which provides a poor pattern and also fits quite poorly to most other patterns. In view of these considerations, we excluded character 4 from procedures for finding the cladogram. However, as we have seen in the monothetic method, it was necessary to employ character 4 in order to obtain the correct solution. That it is not unduly discordant can be seen from the moderate number of extra steps in rows and columns. Nevertheless, when equally parsimonious solutions occur, it is probably preferable to seek additional new characters in order to resolve such solutions. Examination of the true phylogeny of the OTU's in Group A revealed an error in tracing the forms, which unintentionally produced reversibility in character 4. When character 4 is recoded to fit the cladogram of Fig. 2 in its most parsimonious sequence, reversibility plus parallelism is revealed.

Another use of a reconstructed cladogram is to predict the character states of the ancestral forms at the branching points (see Fig. 2). Because no evolutionary changes have taken place since OTU 28 branched off their common ancestral stem, OTU 13 is identical with the ancestral form B, for the characters under consideration. This relationship presents a method for introducing fossil forms into a study along with recent forms. All OTU's which show no evolutionary steps subsequent to their last point of branching can be considered ancestral to all OTU's derived subsequent to the branch. An analysis of

Group A, including fossils *A* through *E*, again resulted in the correct cladogram.

Two other studies of simulated phylogenies showed that cladograms with little or moderate amounts of parallelism were reconstructed without error. Further work with hypothetical phylogenies led to the following tentative conclusions.

1. If reversible characters greatly outnumber irreversible ones, the most parsimonious tree will probably be incorrect. However, if the reversible characters are not highly correlated with each other, the compatibility matrix will provide criteria for removing them prior to the reconstruction and, if the remaining irreversible characters are numerous enough to give the correct cladogram, the most parsimonious tree will be correct.

2. Parallel or miscoded convergent characters (Sokal and Camin, 1965) will not be detected as such when they outnumber divergent characters and will show as recent divergences in the most parsimonious tree. If divergent characters are more numerous than others, the most parsimonious tree will show all evolutionary steps correctly.

Fossil Horses

W. A. Clemens of the Zoology Department, The University of Kansas, kindly provided us with data on lineages of fossil horses. These lineages are reputedly among the best known in the animal kingdom. He chose species within those genera believed to represent some of the major lines of horse evolution (see Fig. 4), although the actual species are not necessarily in the direct cladistic lines. Characters chosen (Table 5) were among those considered significant by authorities in the field and for which data on all species used in the analysis were available. Table 6 shows the data matrix and the compatibility matrix from which the reconstruction shown in Fig. 4 can be obtained. Presumed ancestral forms are shown circled and by dashed stems.

The reconstruction of equid cladistics is correct according to the studies of Stirton

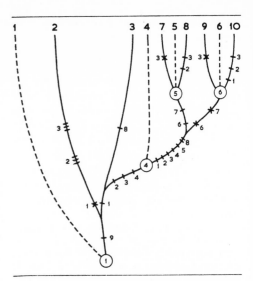

FIG. 4. Reconstructed cladogram of the fossil horses based on data in Table 6. The OTU code numbers and evolutionary steps are indicated as in Figs. 1 and 2. Character 3 has been recoded as explained in the text. Dashed branches represent OTU's ancestral to others in the study. Their code numbers are also shown in circles at points of branching. There are 31 evolutionary steps in this cladogram, compared with a minimum number of 20 (Table 6). OTU numbers represent the following fossil horse species: 1. *Mesohippus barbouri* Schlaikjer, Oligocene, data from Schlaikjer (1932, 1935). 2. *Hypohippus osborni* Gidley, Miocene, data from Gidley (1907) and Osborn (1918). 3. *Archaeohippus blackbergi* (Hay), Miocene; following White (1942), *A. nanus* is regarded as a synonymous species. Generic reference follows Stirton (1940). Data from Simpson (1932), White (1942), and Bader (1956). 4. *Parahippus pristinus* Osborn, Miocene, data from Osborn (1918). 5. *Merychippus (Merychippus) seversus* (Cope), Miocene, data from Downs (1956, 1961). 6. *Merychippus (Protohippus) secundus* Osborn, Miocene, data from Osborn (1918). 7. *Nannipus* cf. *minor* (Sellards), Pliocene, data from Lance (1950). 8. *Neohipparion occidentale* (Leidy), Pliocene, data from Gregory (1942). 9. *Calippus placidus* (Leidy), Pliocene, data from Gidley (1906, 1907) and Osborn (1918). 10. *Pliohippus mexicanus* Lance, Pliocene, data from Lance (1950).

(1940) and of Simpson (1951). During the analysis two characters appeared to be miscoded. One of these (character 7) was discovered to have been erroneously transcribed and is shown corrected in Table

TABLE 5. *Characters and character states of fossil horses.*

	Character State Codes*			Character State Codes*	
	A	B		A	B
Character 1. FEET:			**4. CROCHET:**		
3 toes, all supporting, phalanges broad	−1	0	Absent or present in only a few individuals	0	0
3 toes, lateral digits reduced in size and slightly shorter than middle digit, phalanges broad	0	−	Present, but prefossette closure not complete	1	−
			Prefossette closure complete	2	1
3 toes, lateral digits reduced in size and slightly shorter than middle digit, phalanges narrow	1	1	**5. CEMENT:**		
			Absent or irregularly developed	0	0
3 toes, lateral digits distinctly shorter	2	2	Present	1	1
1 toe, laterals reduced to splints	3	3	**6. FOSSETTES:**		
			With simple borders	−1	−1
2. LENGTH OF METATARSAL III:			Fossette closure not complete	0	0
Less than 140 mm	0	0	With complex borders	1	1
140 to 169 mm	1	−	**7. PROTOCONE:**		
170 to 200 mm	2	1	Linked to protoselene	−1	−1
Greater than 200 mm	3	2	Fossette closure not complete	0	0
3. AVERAGE CROWN LENGTHS (anteroposterior) of 4th upper premolar and 2nd upper molar:			Separated from protoselene	1	1
			8. CROWN HEIGHT:		
Less than 14.5 mm	0	0	Brachydont	0	0
14.5 to 16.9 mm	1	1	Hypso-brachydont	1	1
17.0 to 20.9 mm	2	−	Hypsodont	2	2
Greater than 20.9 mm	3	2	**9. METALOPH AND ECTOLOPH:**		
			Not connected	0	−
			Connected	1	0

* Column A. Character states for entire study. Column B. Character states for restricted study of species from genera represented in late Miocene or early Pliocene faunas (species 2, 3, 7, 8, 9, and 10), recoded when necessary.

6A. The other was character 3, average crown length of two cheek teeth, which Clemens, unknown to us, deliberately had coded from the point of view of operational homology, *i.e.,* from smallest to largest, in order to test the method. It is generally assumed from fossil evidence that each of the subgenera of *Merychippus,* here represented by OTU's 5 and 6, gave rise to at least one lineage of horses of larger size and another lineage in which there was a reduction in size. Interestingly this interpretation is sustained by character 3, reflecting changes in dimensions of the dentition, but not character 2, length of metatarsal III. This might be an artifact reflecting the choice of OTU's.

If the characters are operationally coded, reversals of evolutionary trends tend to confound the true cladogenesis of the data. When the compatibility matrix indicated character 3 to be miscoded, it was laid aside until after the cladogram had been reconstructed from the other characters. However, within clusters (5, 7, 8) and (6, 9, 10) we were unable to differentiate species 5 and 7 or 6 and 9. The generally accepted phylogenetic interpretation of the evolutionary changes for character 3 emerged automatically when the assumption of irreversibility was relaxed and the character was fitted most parsimoniously to the cladogram. Thus by a consistent application of the technique the originally miscoded character was recognized and contributed to the final reconstruction.

For a subsequent analysis of "recent" forms we selected six species from genera represented in late Miocene or early Pliocene faunas (species 2, 3, 7, 8, 9, and 10). Although some of the ancestral genera (species 1, 4, 5, and 6) survived into this period, their characteristics were assumed to be unknown. However, the predicted characteristics of the ancestral genera are correct and the cladogram emerges as before. Character 9 was not used since it is invariant in this analysis. Thus, no prediction could be made about the nature of character 9 for OTU 1. Also, since species 5 and 6 were not included, it was not possible to infer the evolutionary changes of character 3 correctly.

Other Organisms

The Fusulinidae, a group of paleozoic protozoa were analyzed using data obtained from Dunbar (1963), Dunbar and Henbest (1942), and Dunbar and Skinner (1937) by Roger Kaesler of the Geology Department at The University of Kansas. Cladograms of genera as well as species corresponded well with ideas on cladistic relationships expressed by Dunbar. Studies of 25 species of bees of the *Hoplitis* complex and of 24 genera of Mecoptera (scorpionflies) were also carried out using recent material. In both instances the cladograms obtained by our method corresponded well with ideas on cladistic relationships expressed by authorities in the field. Separate publications on all of these studies are in preparation. Such studies are continuing and are suggesting methods for analyzing OTU's of supraspecific rank.

DISCUSSION

General Considerations

From the findings reported above it would appear to be possible to deduce cladistic sequences from the characteristics of recent organisms. It may be argued that the cladistic solutions obtained from recent organisms merely reflect the thinking of

TABLE 6. *Fossil horses.*

A. Data matrix.

				OTU's							Character states (c)	Minimum steps (c-1)
	1	2	3	4	5	6	7	8	9	10		
1.	0	-1	1	1	2	2	2	2	2	3	5	4
2.	0	3	0	1	2	2	2	3	2	3	4	3
3.	0	3	0	1	2	2	1	3	1	3	4	3
4.	0	0	0	1	2	2	2	2	2	2	3	2
5.	0	0	0	0	1	1	1	1	1	1	2	1
6.	0	0	0	0	1	-1	1	1	-1	-1	3	2
7.	0	0	0	0	1	-1	1	1	-1	-1	3	2
8.	0	0	1	0	2	2	2	2	2	2	3	2
9.	0	1	1	1	1	1	1	1	1	1	2	1
												20

(row label at left: Characters)

B. Compatibility matrix.

				Patterns						Compatibilities	Extra steps
	1	2	3	4	5	6	7	8	9		
1.	X	4	5	1	1	1	1	1	0	1	14
2.	5	X	1	3	3	4	4	3	0	1	23
3.	6	1	X	3	3	5	5	3	0	1	26
4.	1	3	4	X	1	1	1	1	0	1	12
5.	0	1	2	0	X	0	0	0	0	6	3
6.	1	2	4	0	0	X	0	0	0	5	7
7.	1	2	4	0	0	0	X	0	0	5	7
8.	1	3	5	1	1	1	1	X	0	1	13
9.	0	1	1	1	1	1	1	1	X	1	7
Compatibilities:	2	0	0	3	2	2	2	3	8	22	–
Extra steps:	15	17	26	9	10	13	13	9	0	–	112

(row label at left: Characters)

the taxonomists who furnished us with the data. This is true in a general sense. However, the method proposed here tests the assumptions behind character coding. Repeatedly, through our methodology, we have been able to point out to our colleagues errors in their reasoning about evolutionary trends in characters.

While evolutionists probably have a relatively thorough understanding of modes of evolutionary change, assumptions about the relative frequencies of these phenomena may be in error. We therefore do not know how frequently assumptions 3, 4, and 5 about character coding will be valid in any given study.

The correctness of our approach depends

on the assumption that nature is indeed parsimonious. Alternative, equally parsimonious solutions may appear and the choice between them may not be evident from the data at hand. While the addition of a single new character may permit a decision, we should be on our guard against relying too firmly on the cladograms so obtained. Far-reaching decisions about stems are sometimes taken on the weight of a single evolutionary step. Partly this has been due to our choice of few characters for the analyses which initially were carried out by hand. While it is remarkable that even with few characters we obtained results consistent with the known facts, it is obvious that more characters would make decisions on junctions less likely to be dependent on the presence or absence of single evolutionary steps. The larger studies with more extensive suites of characters currently being processed by computer should lead to firmer cladograms. The probability of correctness of any portion of the tree varies with the relative reliability of our interpretation of any one character and with the number of characters and character states on which it is based.

The method as described above assumes equal probability of all evolutionary steps[5] after the characters have been coded. The method of coding characters and our initial assumptions about the evolutionary trends do reflect judgments based on biological knowledge of the material. The criteria by which this may be done have been outlined by several authors (Hennig, 1957; Maslin, 1952). Thus in actuality all evolutionary steps are not assumed to be equally probable.

The method proposed here is not substantially different from the conventional cladistic approaches of phylogenists. It simply quantifies and systematizes these procedures, making them objective in the process and permitting them to be put on

---

[5] This point has been called to our attention by E. C. Minkoff, Harvard University.

a computer. Thus, they have the same relation to conventional (cladistic) phylogeny that numerical taxonomy has to conventional phenetic taxonomy. Just as the study of numerous characters and the preparation of dendrograms in numerical taxonomy enhance knowledge and understanding of systematic relationships, so an analysis of cladogenesis along the lines proposed here leads systematists to critical tests of their ideas and assumptions about a phylogeny.

The proposed method does not weight characters equally in the construction of the cladogram, since compatible characters are preferred over those that are incompatible. Characters with few states tend to be more compatible than those with many. Since evolutionary steps are equally weighted, those with more states will be more heavily weighted. However, the weighting procedure agrees with the principles of numerical taxonomy (Sokal and Sneath, 1963); it is automatic and *a posteriori*, based on the entire available evidence rather than on *a priori* or character-by-character weighting as employed in conventional phylogenetic procedures.

Technical Points

The method illustrated here and several variations currently being investigated are empirical approaches to finding the most parsimonious cladogram. A possible pattern cladogram might be a phenogram, if phenetics is closely related to cladistics. However, cladograms and phenograms will be similar only when similarities are due to recent divergence. It is to be expected that the two types of dendrograms will not be entirely alike because they measure different aspects of phyletic relationship. Locating the cladogram requiring the minimum number of evolutionary steps by trial and error is a stupendous computational task, but might be made manageable by a Monte Carlo method. We have therefore attempted to reach a near parsimonious solution by one of the methods reported above, before applying trial and error improvements. An analytical mathematical solution which would give the single most parsimonious cladogram is a difficult mathematical problem.

We do not yet know how to evaluate all of the information in the compatibility matrix. It indicates when some of our assumptions, such as irreversibility in evolution, are wrong. The matrix may also point out cases in which the basic assumption of evolutionary parsimony is invalid.

A feature for changing the primitive state of a character can be built into the computer program to try a variety of assumptions adopted by the operator to reveal the most parsimonious, internally consistent evolutionary pattern. In this way we could investigate hypotheses about evolutionary trends in the character. There seems to be no fundamental obstacle to assuming more complicated evolutionary trends than the V-shaped ones discussed above. Thus a character coded

$$-2 \leftarrow -1 \leftarrow 0 \rightarrow 1 \rightarrow 2 \rightarrow 3 \rightarrow 4$$
$$\downarrow \qquad\qquad \downarrow$$
$$-2' \qquad\qquad 3'$$
$$\downarrow$$
$$4'$$

could be included in the computations.

We have as yet no technique for dealing with cases of hybridization. Similarly, we have not yet explored the consequences of missing data for character states of given OTU's. These could be handled by adding the characters to the cladogram after the construction is complete, in the same way in which we now add the characters which differ in a single state for one OTU only. The cladogram might then provide a means of predicting the missing character states as it does for the character states of ancestral forms.

Implications for Systematics

The development of a technique for deducing cladistic relationships among organisms appears to furnish a base for classification alternative to the phenetic system espoused by numerical taxonomy. Since the present method appears to be the "phyletic" one professed by orthodox taxonomists, it might appear that classifications should be established on the basis of it or a similar method. However, we have pointed out elsewhere (Sokal and Camin, 1965) that phyletic relationships are always a composite of phenetic, cladistic, and chronistic relationships not always clearly separated in the minds or writings of systematists and that systematics as a whole must be based on all of these considerations. The degree to which phenetics and cladistics coincide is not yet known, although we may assume it to be considerable. Since no operational system for combining phenetic and cladistic relationships is available we must choose between a phenetic or cladistic basis for classification. We distinguish here between "systematics" and "classification," the former including not only the study of the order of living things but also the causes and processes bringing this about, while classification is simply the arrangement of organized nature into categories for the convenience of biologists. For a variety of reasons, detailed elsewhere (Sokal and Camin, 1965), it would seem that a phenetic basis is preferable for classification in this narrow sense until an operational system, combining cladistics and phenetics can be established.

Comparison of phenograms with cladograms may lead to the resolution of phenetic resemblance into its components discussed by us in detail in Sokal and Camin (1965). If by a comparative cladistic and phenetic study of a group of organisms it has been shown that an apparently similar character in two organisms could not possibly be due to primitive patristic similarity, it must therefore be a case of parallelism (derived patristic similarity) or of classical convergence. This will stimulate biologists to a study of the underlying structural and physiological phenomena which lead to an apparently identical result. Such studies may permit the separation of parallelisms from divergence and may facilitate the recognition of characters which have been miscoded as convergent. The joint consideration of chronistics, cladistics, and phenetics will also enable objective measurement of evolutionary rates.

SUMMARY

A method is described for reconstructing presumed cladistic evolutionary sequences of recent organisms and its implications are discussed. Characters of the organisms to be studied are presented in a data matrix of the type employed in numerical taxonomy with the character states arrayed according to a presumed evolutionary sequence. The reconstruction proceeds on the hypothesis that the minimum number of evolutionary steps yields the correct cladogram. The method has been programmed for computer processing.

LITERATURE CITED

ARNETT, R. H., JR. 1963. The phenogram, a method of description for studies on *Oxacis* (Coleoptera, Oedemeridae). Coleopt. Bull., 17: 6–18.

BADER, R. S. 1956. A quantitative study of the Equidae of the Thomas Farm Miocene. Bull. Mus. Comp. Zool., 115: 47–78.

DOOLITTLE, R. F., AND B. BLOMBÄCK. 1964. Amino-acid sequence investigations of fibrinopeptides from various mammals: evolutionary implications. Nature, 202: 147–152.

DOWNS, THEODORE. 1956. The Mascall fauna from the Miocene of Oregon. Univ. California Publ. Geol. Sci., 31: 199–354.

——. 1961. A study of variation and evolution in Miocene *Merychippus*. Contrib. Sci., Los Angeles County Mus., 45: 1–75.

DUNBAR, C. O. 1963. Trends of evolution in American fusulines. *In* Von Koenigswald, G. H. R., *et al.* (eds.), Evolutionary trends in Foraminifera. Elsevier Publ. Co., New York, pp. 25–44.

DUNBAR, C. O., AND L. G. HENBEST. 1942. Pennsylvanian Fusulinidae of Illinois. Bull. Illinois State Geol. Surv., 67: 1–218.

DUNBAR, C. O., AND J. W. SKINNER. 1937. Upper Paleozoic ammonites and fusulinids. 2. Pernian Fusulinidae of Texas. Univ. Texas Bull., 3701: 517–825.

EDWARDS, A. W. F., AND L. L. CAVALLI-SFORZA. 1964. Reconstruction of evolutionary trees. *In* Phenetic and phylogenetic classification. Systematics Assoc. Publ., 6: 67–76.

GIDLEY, J. W. 1906. New or little known mammals from the Miocene of South Dakota. Bull. Amer. Mus. Nat. Hist., 22: 135–153.

——. 1907. Revision of the Miocene and Pliocene Equidae of North America. Bull. Amer. Mus. Nat. Hist., 23: 865–934.

GREGORY, J. T. 1942. Pliocene vertebrates from Big Spring Canyon, South Dakota. Univ. California Publ. Geol. Sci., 26: 307–446.

HENNIG, W. 1957. Systematik und Phylogenese. Ber. Hundertjahrfeier Deutsch. Entomol. Ges., pp. 50–70, Berlin.

LANCE, J. F. 1950. Paleontología y estratigrafía del Plioceno de Yepomera, Estado de Chihuahua. Iª parte: Equidos, excepto Neohipparion. Bol. Inst. Geol. Mex., 54: 1–83.

MASLIN, T. P. 1952. Morphological criteria of phylogenetic relationships. Syst. Zool., 1: 49–70.

MAYR, E. 1965. Numerical phenetics and taxonomic theory. Syst. Zool., 14: 73–97.

OSBORN, H. F. 1918. Equidae of the Oligocene, Miocene, and Pliocene of North America; iconographic type revision. Mem. Amer. Mus. Nat. Hist. (n.s.), 2: 1–330.

SCHLAIKJER, E. M. 1932. The osteology of *Mesohippus barbouri*. Bull. Mus. Comp. Zool., 72: 391–410.

——. 1935. Contributions to the stratigraphy and palaeontology of the Goshen Hole area, Wyoming. IV. New vertebrates and the stratigraphy of the Oligocene and early Miocene. Bull. Mus. Comp. Zool., 76: 97–189.

SIMPSON, G. G. 1932. Miocene land mammals from Florida. Bull. Florida Geol. Surv., 10: 7–10.

——. 1951. Horses. The story of the horse family in the modern world and through sixty million years of history. Oxford Univ. Press, New York, 247 pp.

——. 1963. The meaning of taxonomic statements. *In* S. L. Washburn [ed.], Classification and human evolution. Aldine, Chicago, pp. 1–31.

SOKAL, R. R., AND J. H. CAMIN. 1965. The two taxonomies: areas of agreement and of conflict. Syst. Zool., in press.

SOKAL, R. R., AND P. H. A. SNEATH. 1963. Principles of numerical taxonomy. W. H. Freeman and Co., San Francisco and London, 359 pp.

STIRTON, R. A. 1940. Phylogeny of North American Equidae. Univ. California Publ. Geol. Sci., 25: 165–198.

THROCKMORTON, L. H. 1965. Similarity versus relationship in *Drosophila*. Syst. Zool., in press.

WHITE, T. E. 1942. The lower Miocene mammal fauna of Florida. Bull. Mus. Comp. Zool., 92: 1–49.

WILSON, E. O. 1965. A consistency test for phylogenies based on contemporaneous species. Syst. Zool., in press.

CONSTRUCTION OF PHYLOGENETIC TREES

A method based on mutation distances as estimated
from cytochrome c sequences is of general applicability.

WALTER M. FITCH AND EMANUEL MARGOLIASH

Biochemists have attempted to use quantitative estimates of variance between substances obtained from different species to construct phylogenetic
trees. Examples of this approach include studies of the degree of interspecific
hybridization of DNA (1), the degree of cross reactivity of antisera to purified
proteins (2), the number of differences in the peptides from enzymic digests of
purified homologous proteins, both as estimated by paper electrophoresis-
chromatography or column chromatography and as estimated from the amino
acid compositions of the proteins (3), and the number of amino acid replacements between homologous proteins whose complete primary structures had
been determined (4). These methods have not been completely satisfactory because (i) the portion of the genome examined was often very restricted, (ii)
the variable measured did not reflect with sufficient accuracy the mutation
distance between the genes examined, and (iii) no adequate mathematical
treatment for data from large numbers of species was available. In this paper
we suggest several improvements under categories (ii) and (iii) and, using
cytochrome c, for which much precise information on amino acid sequences is
available, construct a tree which, despite our examining but a single gene, is
remarkably like the classical phylogenetic tree that has been obtained from
purely biological data (5). We also show that the analytical method employed
has general applicability, as exemplified by the derivation of appropriate relationships among ethnic groups from data on their physical characteristics
(6,7).

DETERMINING THE MUTATION DISTANCE

The *mutation distance* between two cytochromes is defined here as the
minimal number of nucleotides that would need to be altered in order for the
gene for one cytochrome to code for the other. This distance is determined by
a computer making a pairwise comparison of homologous amino acids (8). For

Dr. Fitch is an assistant professor of physiological chemistry at the University of
Wisconsin Medical School in Madison. Dr. Margoliash is head of the Protein Section
in the Department of Molecular Biology, Abbott Laboratories, North Chicago,
Illinois.

each pair a *mutation value* is taken from Table 1 which gives the minimum number of nucleotide changes required to convert the coding from one amino acid to the other. The table is derived from Figure 2 of Fitch (9) except that, as a result of the work of Weigert and Garen (*10*) and Brenner, Stretton, and Kaplan (*11*), the uridyl-adenosylpurine trinucleotide is now treated as a chain-terminating codon. This change of codon meaning, although it does not affect the method of calculation, does cause the mutation values for amino acid pairs involving glutamine with cysteine, phenylalanine, tyrosine, serine, and tryptophan to become 1 greater than in the table previously published (*12*). Also, misprints involving the leucine-glycine and valine-cysteine pairs have been corrected. To maintain homology, deletions, all of which occur near the ends of the chains, are represented by X's. The amino- and carboxyl-terminal sequences in which deletions occur are shown in Table 2. Thus all cytochromes are regarded as being 110 amino acids long. If the homologous pairing includes an X, no mutation value is assigned.

TABLE 1

Mutation values for amino acid pairs. Each value is the minimum number of nucleotides that would need to be changed in order to convert a codon for one amino acid into a codon for another. The table is symmetrical about the diagonal of zeros. Letters across the top represent the amino acids in the same order as in the first column and conform to the single-letter code of Keil, Prusik, and Sŏrm (*21*).

	A	C	E	F	G	H	I	L	M	N	O	P	Q	R	S	T	U	V	W	Y
Aspartic acid	0	2	2	2	1	1	2	1	3	1	1	2	2	2	2	3	2	1	2	1
Cysteine	2	0	2	1	3	2	3	2	3	2	1	2	3	1	1	1	2	2	2	1
Threonine	2	2	0	2	2	2	1	1	1	1	2	1	2	1	1	2	2	2	1	2
Phenylalanine	2	1	2	0	3	2	3	2	2	2	1	2	3	2	1	2	1	1	1	2
Glutamic acid*	1	3	2	3	0	2	1	1	2	2	2	2	1	2	2	2	2	1	3	1
Histidine	1	2	2	2	2	0	2	2	3	1	1	1	1	1	2	3	1	2	2	2
Lysine*	2	3	1	3	1	2	0	2	1	1	2	2	1	1	2	2	2	2	2	2
Alanine	1	2	1	2	1	2	2	0	2	2	2	1	2	2	1	2	2	1	2	1
Methionine	3	3	1	2	2	3	1	2	0	2	3	2	2	1	2	2	1	1	1	2
Asparagine	1	2	1	2	2	1	1	2	2	0	1	2	2	2	1	3	2	2	1	2
Tyrosine	1	1	2	1	2	1	2	2	3	1	0	2	2	2	1	2	2	2	2	2
Proline	2	2	1	2	2	1	2	1	2	2	2	0	1	1	1	2	1	2	2	2
Glutamine*	2	3	2	3	1	1	1	2	2	2	2	1	0	1	2	2	1	2	3	2
Arginine*	2	1	1	2	2	1	1	2	1	2	2	1	1	0	1	1	1	2	2	1
Serine	2	1	1	1	2	2	2	1	2	1	1	1	2	1	0	1	1	2	1	1
Tryptophan	3	1	2	2	2	3	2	2	3	2	2	2	2	1	1	0	1	2	3	1
Leucine	2	2	2	1	2	1	2	2	1	2	2	1	1	1	1	1	0	1	1	2
Valine	1	2	2	1	1	2	2	1	1	2	2	2	2	2	2	2	1	0	1	1
Isoleucine	2	2	1	1	3	2	2	2	1	2	2	3	2	1	3	1	1	1	0	2
Glycine	1	1	2	2	1	2	2	1	2	2	2	2	2	1	1	1	2	1	2	0

* Recent evidence indicates that AUA codes for isoleucine rather than methionine. As a consequence of this, the mutation values in Table 1 relating isoleucine to arginine, glutamate, glutamine and lysine should each be reduced by 1.

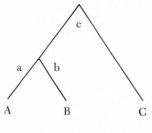

Mutation Distances

	B	C
A	24	28
B		32

FIGURE 1. Calculation of observed mutation distances. The upper apex represents a hypothetical ancestral organism that divided into two descending lines, one of which subsequently also divided. Thus we have three present-day species, A, B, and C. The number of observable mutations that have occurred in a particular gene since the A and B lines of descent diverged are represented respectively by a and b. The number of mutations that separate the lower apex and C is represented by c. The sums of $a + b$, $a + c$, and $b + c$, then, are the mutation distances of the three species as currently observed.

For each possible pairing of cytochromes, the 110 mutation values found are summed to obtain the minimal mutation distance. For purposes of calculation, these mutation distances are proportionally adjusted to compensate for variable numbers of pairs of residue positions in which at least one member contains an X. For example, the number of X-containing amino acid pairs occurring between the *Saccharomyces* and *Candida* cytochromes c is 1, whereas that between two mammalian cytochromes c is 6. Thus the known mutation distance of the former pairing is multiplied by 110/109 whereas that of the latter is multiplied by 110/104. The results for 20 known cytochromes c, rounded off to the nearest whole number, are shown in the lower left half of Table 3.

The basic approach to the construction of the tree is illustrated in Figure 1, which shows three hypothetical proteins, A, B, and C, and their mutation distances. There are two fundamental problems: (i) Which pair does one join together first? (ii) What are the lengths of legs a, b, and c?

As a first approximation, one solves problem (i) simply by choosing the pair with the smallest mutation distance, which in this case is A and B, with a distance of 24. Hence A and B are shown connected at the lower apex in Figure 1. To solve the second problem, one notes that the distance from A to C, 28, is 4 less than the distance from B to C. Hence there must have been at least 4 more countable mutations in the descent of B from the lower apex than in the descent of A. Thus if $a + b = 24$ and $b - a = 4$, then $a = 10$, $b = 14$, and therefore $c = 18$. Note that an exact solution is obtained from which a reconstruction of the mutation distances precisely matches the input data.

When information from more than three proteins is utilized, the basic procedure is the same, except that initially each protein is assigned to its own subset. One then simply joins two subsets to create a single, more comprehensive, subset. This process is repeated according to the rules set forth below until all proteins are members of a single subset. A phylogenetic tree is but a graphical representation of the order in which the subsets were joined.

In the present case, we start with 20 subsets, each subset consisting of a single cytochrome c amino acid sequence. To determine which two subsets

TABLE 2

Areas of cytochromes *c* involving deletions. The first seven and the last four amino acids of the cytochromes *c* for the 20 species studied are shown. Deletions are represented by X's. Sequences are reported in the single-letter code of Keil *et al.* (*21*), a key to which is provided in Table 1.

Amino terminal positions 1–7	Organism	Carboxyl terminal positions 107–110
PLPFGQY	*Candida*	LXSI
XEGFILY	*Saccharomyces*	LXCG
XXYFSLY	*Neurospora*	LELX
XXYVPLY	Moth	SEXI
XXYVPLY	Screwworm fly†	LSEI
XXXXXXY	Tuna	LESX
XXXXXXY	All other vertebrates	No deletions

† Reexamination by Chan of the carboxyl terminal tetrapeptide of the screwworm fly cytochrome *c* has eliminated the serine shown in Table 2. It would therefore appear that where a deletion is necessary in this region, it is best placed terminally.

should be joined, all possible pairwise combinations of subsets are in turn assigned to sets *A* and *B*, with all remaining subsets in each case assigned to set *C*. In each alternative test all proteins are thus a part of one of the three sets. The three sets are treated exactly as in the preceding example, except that now the mutation distances used are averages determined from every possible pairing of proteins, one from each of the two sets whose average mutation distance is being calculated.

One arbitrarily accepts, from among all the possible pairings examined, that assignment of protein subsets to sets *A*, *B*, and *C* which provides the lowest average mutation distance from *A* to *B*. The leg lengths are then calculated and recorded. Henceforth the proteins of *A* and *B* so joined are treated as a single subset, and the entire procedure described in the preceding paragraph is repeated. Thus the number of subsets, originally equal to the number of proteins (N), is reduced by 1 with each cycle. In this fashion, after $N-1$ joinings of subsets, the initial phylogenetic tree will have been produced. Because average mutation distances are now being used, the solutions obtained are very unlikely to permit an exact reconstruction of the input data.

TESTING ALTERNATIVE TREES

Because of the arbitrary nature of the rule by which proteins are assigned to sets *A* and *B*, the initial tree will not necessarily represent the best use of the information. To examine reasonable alternatives, one simply constructs another tree by assigning an alternative pair of protein subsets to sets *A* and *B* whenever the mutation distance between the two subsets is not greater by

TABLE 3

Minimum numbers of mutations required to interrelate pairs of cytochromes c. Values in the lower left half of the table are mutation distances as determined from the amino acid sequences and, prior to rounding off, were used to derive Figure 2. Values in the upper right half of the table are reconstructed distances found by summing the leg lengths in Figure 2. The references cited in the last column are to studies of the amino acid sequences of the cytochromes c of the indicated species.

Protein	1	2	3	4	5	6	7	8	9	10	11	12	13	14	15	16	17	18	19	20	Species
1		1	13	15	15	13	11	14	15	15	16	16	17	29	29	30	33	64	62	68	Man (22)
2	1		12	15	14	12	11	13	15	14	15	15	16	28	29	29	32	63	61	67	Monkey (*Macacus mulatta*) (23)
3	13	12		10	9	8	6	7	13	13	13	14	15	27	27	30	30	61	59	65	Dog (24)
4	17	16	10		1	5	10	11	15	15	16	16	17	30	30	31	31	64	62	68	Horse (25)
5	16	15	8	1		4	9	10	14	14	15	15	16	29	29	32	32	62	61	67	Donkey (26)
6	13	12	4	5	4		7	8	13	12	13	13	14	28	29	30	30	61	59	65	Pig (27)
7	12	11	6	11	10	6		7	11	11	12	12	13	24	25	29	29	60	57	63	Rabbit (30)
8	12	13	7	11	12	7	7		13	13	14	14	15	27	25	28	28	60	57	63	Kangaroo (*Canopus canguru*) (28)
9	17	16	12	16	15	13	10	14		3	3	4	8	26	27	28	31	62	60	66	Pekin duck (*Anas platyrhynchos*) (29)
10	16	15	12	16	15	13	8	14	3		4	3	8	26	27	28	31	61	59	65	Pigeon (29)
11	18	17	14	16	15	13	11	15	3	4		2	9	27	28	31	31	62	60	66	Chicken (17)
12	18	17	14	17	16	14	11	13	3	4	2		9	28	29	31	30	62	60	66	King penguin (*Aptenodytes patagonica*) (29)
13	19	18	13	16	15	13	11	14	7	8	8	8		30	30	38	33	63	61	67	Snapping turtle (*Chelydra serpentina*) (31)
14	20	21	30	32	31	30	25	30	24	24	28	28	30		38	34	37	66	66	72	Rattlesnake (*Crotalus adamanteus*) (32)
15	31	32	29	27	26	25	26	27	26	26	26	27	27	38		35	38	68	66	73	Tuna (33)
16	33	32	24	24	25	26	23	26	25	26	26	28	30	40	34		16	59	56	63	Screwworm fly (*Haematobia irritans*) (29)
17	36	35	28	33	32	31	29	31	30	31	31	30	33	41	41	16		59	56	63	Moth (*Samia cynthia*) (34)
18	63	62	64	64	64	64	62	66	66	66	62	65	61	72	58	59	62		60	66	*Neurospora* (*crassa*) (35)
19	56	57	61	60	59	59	59	58	62	62	62	61	65	69	66	63	60	57		56	*Saccharomyces* (*oviformis*) iso-1 (36)
20	66	65	66	68	67	67	67	68	66	66	66	65	67	69	65	61	61	57	41		*Candida* (*krusei*) (37)

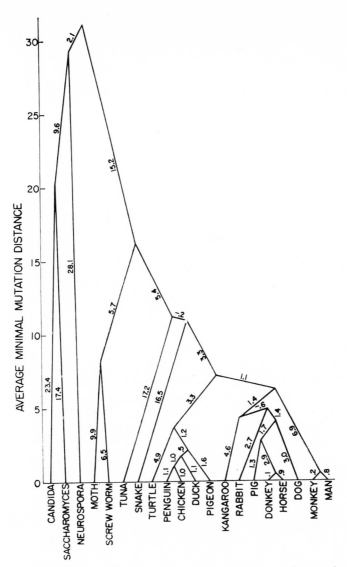

FIGURE 2. Phylogeny as reconstructed from observable mutations in the cytochrome *c* gene. Each number on the figure is the corrected mutation distance (see text) along the line of descent as determined from the best computer fit so far found. Each apex is placed at an ordinate value representing the average of the sums of all mutations in the lines of descent from that apex.

some arbitrary amount than that between the members of the initial pair used in constructing the initial phylogenetic tree (*13*). The tree that is less satisfactory on the basis of criteria set forth below is discarded, and other alternatives are tested.

The best of 40 phylogenetic trees so far examined is presented in Figure 2.

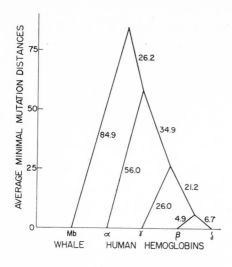

FIGURE 3. A gene phylogeny as reconstructed from observable mutations in several heme-containing globins. See Figure 2 for details. The percent "standard deviation" (7) for this tree is 1.33.

Each juncture is located on the ordinate at a point representing the average of all distances between the juncture and the species descendant from it. The mutation distance to any one descendant may be more or less than the ordinate value.

By summing distances over the tree, it is possible to reconstruct values (upper right half of Table 3) comparable to the original input mutation distances (lower left half of Table 3). The 20 species are indicated in the last column; the identifying numbers in the first column and the top row of the table may be used as coordinates. Thus the tabulated values interrelating the human and horse cytochromes at coordinates (1,4) and (4,1) are mutation distances of 17 and 15 respectively, the former being the input datum, the latter having been obtained from the tree by reconstruction. If the absolute difference between two such mutation distances $| (i,j) - (j,i) |$ is multiplied by 100 and divided by (i,j), the result is the percentage of change from the input data. If such values are squared and the squares are summed over all values of $i < j$, the resultant sum (Σ) may be used to obtain the percent "standard deviation" (7) of the reconstructed values from the input mutation distances. The number of mutation distances summed is $N(N-1)/2$, or 190 for our case. If this number is reduced by 1, divided into the sum Σ, and the square root taken, the result is the percent "standard deviation." Since the standard deviation is a larger number than the standard error, the probable error, or the average deviation, the percent "standard deviation" is used here, it being less likely to create overconfidence in the significance of a result (7).

THE STATISTICALLY OPTIMAL TREE

In testing phylogenetic alternatives, one is seeking to minimize the percent "standard deviation." The scheme shown in Figure 2 has a percent "standard deviation" of 8.7, the lowest of the 40 alternatives so far tested. The percent "standard deviation" for the initial tree was 12.3.

In addition to using a gene product to discover evolutionary relationships among several species, one can similarly delineate evolutionary relationships among different genes. Our procedure constructs, from the amino acid sequences of human alpha, beta, gamma, and delta hemoglobin chains and whale myoglobin (15), the gene phylogeny shown in Figure 3. The overall result is as Ingram had previously indicated (15). A cautionary note may be derived from this. A wildly incorrect result could easily be obtained if the presence of multiple, homologous genes were not recognized and a phylogeny were constructed from sequences which were coded for, say, half by genes for alpha hemoglobin chains and half by genes for beta hemoglobin chains. This results from the speciation having occurred more recently than the gene duplication which permitted the separate evolution of the alpha and beta genes.

The method described can also be used to develop treelike relationships by employing data which are very different in character from mutation distances. For example, the physical characteristics of human beings have been used to construct a tree relating several ethnic groups (Fig. 4; 6).

Although we are examining the product of but a single gene, and a rather small one at that, the phylogenetic scheme in Figure 2 is remarkably like that constructed in accord with classical zoological comparisons (5). There are only

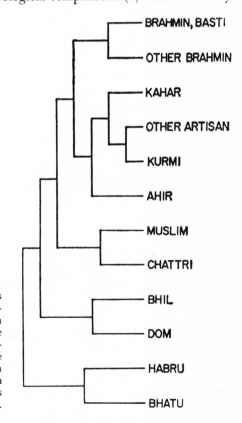

FIGURE 4. Relations among various tribes and castes of India. The data used to construct this scheme are the D^2 values given by Rao (6). This figure is in principle like Figure 2 except that, to prevent misinterpretation of the physical significance of the numbers one obtains, branching is shown as a rather uniform step function which preserves the relationships but obliterates the quantitative distances of the ordinate.

BRAHMIN, BASTI

OTHER BRAHMIN

KAHAR

OTHER ARTISAN

KURMI

AHIR

MUSLIM

CHATTRI

BHIL

DOM

HABRU

BHATU

three noticeable deviations, discussed below, and these may well be changed as more species are added to the list. Of even greater value would be sequences from other genes, since special environmental effects may easily cause the convergence of one or several genes in phylogenetically disparate organisms. Hemoglobin amino acid sequences may soon be available in great enough numbers to prove useful in this respect.

Almost all the alternative phylogenetic schemes tested involved rearrangements within the groups birds (16, 17) and nonprimate mammals (14, 18, 19). With respect to the birds, it will be noticed that the penguin is closely associated with the chicken, whereas one might have expected that all the "birds of flight" (Neognathae) would be more closely related to each other than to the penguin (Impennae). This discrepancy is probably related to the very small numbers of mutations involved. In this regard, it is interesting to note that on the basis of a micro-complement-fixation technique using antisera to several purified enzymes, Wilson et al. (2) found that the duck is more closely related to the chicken than is the pigeon. This agrees with our findings.

In the second group, the kangaroo is shown closely associated with the nonprimate mammals, whereas most zoologists would maintain that the placental mammals, including the primates, are more closely related to each other than to the marsupials.

A third anomaly is that the turtle appears more closely associated with the birds than to its fellow reptile the rattlesnake. Although it is true that the snake is involved in seven of the nine instances where the reconstructed values differ from the input mutation distances by more than 4 mutations, this cannot account for the anomaly, which in fact results from the close similarity of the turtle's cytochrome c amino acid sequence to those of the birds.

Thus the phylogenetic tree in Figure 2 is imperfect. Nevertheless, considering that only one gene product was analyzed and that no choices were made other than those dictated by the statistical analysis, the results are very promising, and a phylogeny based upon a quantitative determination of those very events which permit speciation, namely mutations, must ultimately be capable of providing the most accurate phylogenetic trees.

ELAPSED TIME AND EVOLUTIONARY CHANGE

It should be pointed out that the ordinate of Figure 2 represents the minimum number of mutations observable. Since multiple mutations in a single codon are not likely to produce mutation values as large as the actual number of mutations sustained, Figure 2 is greatly foreshortened with respect to the actual number of mutations (20). The possibility of obtaining an ordinate scale denoted as actual mutations by applying a correction factor, using the relative frequencies of codons observed to have sustained one, two, and three nucleotide changes, must await reliable statistical information on the relative probabilities that given amino acid substitutions will permit the progeny to compete successfully in their environment. Any meaningful correction of this sort is

TABLE 4. Descent of the mammalian cytochromes. Changes in amino acids are shown in capital letters with one or two under-linings to indicate that one or two nucleotide replacements had to occur to produce the indicated change. In general, unchanging amino acids are not repeated, but occasionally it has been necessary to relist an unchanged amino acid because a mutation appear-ing in one line of descent did not apply to other lines listed further down the page. Such unchanged amino acids are shown in lower case. The lines of descent are shown on either side of the table. The following rules were used in formulating each amino acid position of the ancestral sequences: Choose the amino acid so that the changes in the codon during descent require (i) the small-est overall number of mutations; (ii) the fewest segments containing multiple mutations (that is, two lines with one mutation each are preferred to one line with two mutations); (iii) the fewest sequential mutations (that is, one mutation in each of two lines following a branch point is preferred to one mutation before and one after the branch point); (iv) the fewest back mutations; (v) the fewest kinds of amino acids. Rule (i), where applicable, took priority over all others and rule (ii) took priority over the re-mainder. It was not found necessary to choose among the last three rules. The ancestral mammalian cytochrome c sequence shown was derived from the amino acid sequences of all 20 cytochromes c.

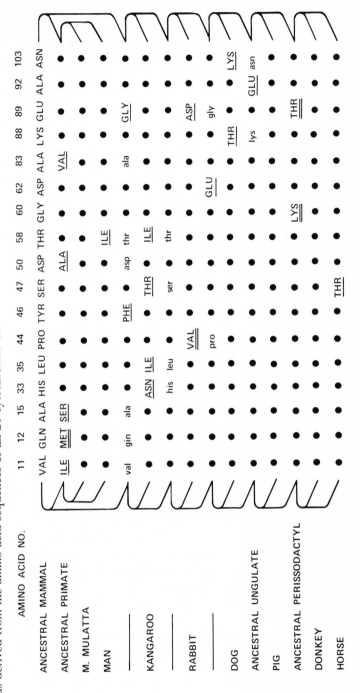

AMINO ACID NO.	11	12	15	33	35	44	46	47	50	58	60	62	83	88	89	92	103
ANCESTRAL MAMMAL	VAL	GLN	ALA	HIS	LEU	PRO	TYR	SER	ASP	THR	GLY	ASP	ALA	LYS	GLU	ALA	ASN
ANCESTRAL PRIMATE	ILE		MET	SER													
M. MULATTA																	
MAN																	
KANGAROO	val	gln	ala	his	leu	pro	PHE		ALA	ILE					GLY		
RABBIT				ASN	ILE	VAL		THR		ILE							
DOG												GLU	VAL	ASP			LYS
ANCESTRAL UNGULATE														THR		GLU	
PIG											LYS			lys	gly		
ANCESTRAL PERISSODACTYL																	
DONKEY															THR		asn
HORSE																	THR

precluded at present by the lack of such statistical information, but its importance may be emphasized by noting that such a correction would yield an ordinate in Figure 2 in which equal numbers of mutations would correspond to equal intervals of time, as long as the rate at which mutations are fixed, averaged for many lines of descent over very long periods of evolutionary history, does not vary appreciably (20).

It should be noted that the method does not assume any particular value for the rate at which mutations have accumulated during evolution. Indeed, from any phylogenetic ancestor, today's descendants are equidistant with respect to time but not, as computations show, equidistant genetically. Thus the method indicates those lines in which the gene has undergone the more rapid changes. For example, from the point at which the primates separate from the other mammals, there are, on the average, 7.5 mutations in the descent of the former and 5.8 in that of the latter, indicating that the change in the cytochrome c gene has been much more rapid in the descent of the primates than in that of the other mammals.

The method allows negative mutation distances, and a few were observed in some of the discarded phylogenetic schemes. Their absence from the best-fitting scheme would indicate that there were no significant evolutionary reversals in this gene.

One highly desirable goal is the reconstruction of the ancestral cytochrome c amino acid sequences. The procedure, though not difficult, is dependent upon the phylogenetic tree on which these sequence data are arranged. Given the present scheme (see Fig. 2) one can reconstruct the ancestral proteins. A reconstruction of the ancestral amino acid sequences for the mammalian portion of tree is shown in Table 4. One can then ask such a question as "What are the mutations required to account for the difference between the cytochromes c of the ancestral primate and of the ancestral mammal?" The data in Table 4 clearly identify the mutations as occurring in positions 17, 18, 21, 56, and 89. In a similar manner, the monkey and human lines are distinguished by a single mutation in the human line which resulted in the substitution of isoleucine for threonine at position 64.

There is presently no detectable relationship between the primary structures of cytochrome c and those of hemoglobins (12). Nevertheless, the reconstruction and comparison of the ancestral amino acid sequences may reveal a homology that cannot be detected in present-day proteins. The employment of such ancestral sequences may be generally useful for detecting common ancestry not otherwise observable.

Note added in proof. Since this article was accepted our attention has been called to several earlier papers which present some of the important concepts discussed here. Sokal and his collaborators (38) have for several years been studying various ways of producing treelike relationships from quantitative taxonomic information. In an interesting application of this type of technique, using the amino acid sequences of fibrinopeptides from several ungulates, R. F. Doolittle and B. Blombäck (39) constructed such a tree and specifically indicated how knowledge of the genetic code would be useful for more precise constructions.

Jukes (*40*, fig. 3) has presented the Ingram scheme of the hemoglobin gene duplications and placed upon the various legs estimates of the numbers of nucleotide substitutions. His figure is not essentially different from Figure 3 of this article.

REFERENCES AND NOTES

1. B. J. McCarthy and E. T. Bolton. *Proc. Natl. Acad. Sci. U.S.* **50**, 156 (1963).
2. A. C. Wilson, N. O. Kaplan, L. Levine, A. Pesce, M. Reichlin, W. S. Allison, *Fed. Proc.* **23**, 1258 (1964); C. A. Williams, Jr., in *Peptides of Biological Fluids*, H. Peeters, Ed. (Elsevier, New York, 1965), p. 62; M. Goodman, *ibid.*, p. 70; A. S. Hafleigh and C. A. Williams, Jr., *Science* **151**, 1530 (1966).
3. R. L. Hill, J. Buettner-Janusch, V. Buettner-Janusch, *Proc. Natl. Acad. Sci. U.S.* **50**, 885 (1963); R. L. Hill and J. Buettner-Janusch, *Fed. Proc.* **23**, 1236 (1964).
4. E. Margoliash, *Proc. Natl. Acad. Sci. U.S.* **50**, 672 (1963); E. L. Smith and E. Margoliash, *Fed. Proc.* **23**, 1243 (1964); E. Margoliash and E. L. Smith, in *Evolving Genes and Proteins*, V. Bryson and H. Vogel, Eds. (Academic Press, New York, 1965), p. 221.
5. A. S. Romer, *Vertebrate Paleontology* (Univ. of Chicago Press, Chicago, ed. 2, 1945).
6. Our procedure may be compared with the "cluster analysis" approach as formulated by A. W. F. Edwards and L. L. Cavalli-Sforza [*Biometrics* **21**, 362 (1965)]; their approach is, in one sense, the reverse of that we have used, since cluster analysis starts with all the elements as members of the same subset and proceeds to subdivide that subset into successively smaller but more numerous subsets until each element is the sole member of its own subset. In terms of Figure 2, Edwards and Cavalli-Sforza constructed their tree from the top down, whereas we built ours from the bottom up. Edwards and Cavalli-Sforza report testing their method on C. R. Rao's data [*Advanced Statistical Methods in Biometric Research* (Wiley, New York, 1952)] on physical characteristics of 12 Indian castes and tribes. Rao had used these data to postulate relationships among the castes and tribes. Although the nature of these data is quite different from that of ours, the formal mathematical problems are very much alike, and we have used the D^2 values of Rao, as did Edwards and Cavalli-Sforza, to find the best tree. Edwards and Cavalli-Sforza's tree has a percent "standard deviation" (7) of 32.6. Our result, shown in Figure 4, has a percent "standard deviation" of 29.2 and, except that it possesses greater detail, conforms to the conclusions drawn by Rao.
7. The quotation marks are placed around "standard deviation" because the data used in its formulation here are not statistically independent as is generally required. This is evident in that only 20 amino acid sequences determine the 190 mutation distances utilized.
8. The homology may be found by aligning the cysteine residues which bind the heme. Excellent examples of this may be seen in Figure 10 of E. Margoliash and A. Schejter, *Advan. Protein Chem.* **21**, 114 (1965).

9. W. M. Fitch, *J. Mol. Biol.* **16**, 1 (1966).
10. M. G. Weigert and A. Garen, *Nature* **206**, 992 (1965).
11. S. Brenner, A. O. W. Stretton, S. Kaplan, *ibid.*, p. 994.
12. W. M. Fitch, *J. Mol. Biol.* **16**, 9 (1966).
13. It will be recognized that once the first tree is calculated, the number of computations required for alternatives becomes greatly reduced. For example, if instead of the tree shown in Figure 2 one wishes to test a tree which differs only in the order in which the chicken, duck, and penguin are joined, the only legs in need of recalculation are those five descending to these birds from the avian apex.
14. The cow (*18*) and sheep (*19*) cytochromes *c* are identical with that of the pig (*27*).
15. V. M. Ingram, *The Hemoglobins in Genetics and Evolution* (Columbia Univ. Press, New York, 1963); A. B. Edmundson, *Nature* **205**, 883 (1965).
16. The cytochrome *c* of the turkey (*29*) is identical with that of the chicken (*16*).
17. S. K. Chan and E. Margoliash, *J. Biol. Chem.* **241**, 507 (1966).
18. K. T. Yasunobu, T. Nakashima, H. Higo, H. Matsubara, Λ Benson, *Biochim. Biophys. Acta* **78**, 791 (1963).
19. S. K. Chan, S. B. Needleman, J. W. Stewart, E. Margoliash, unpublished results.
20. This is analogous to the relationship between numbers of amino acid replacements and the evolutionary time scale discussed by E. Margoliash and E. L. Smith in *Evolving Genes and Proteins*, V. Bryson and H. Vogel, Eds. (Academic Press, New York, 1965), p. 221.
21. B. Keil, Z. Prusik, F. Sörm, *Biochim. Biophys. Acta* **78** (1963).
22. H. Matsubara and E. L. Smith, *J. Biol. Chem.* **238**, 2732 (1963).
23. J. A. Rothfus and E. L. Smith, *ibid.* **240**, 4277 (1965).
24. M. A. McDowall and E. L. Smith, *ibid.* p. 4635.
25. E. Margoliash, E. L. Smith, G. Kreil, H. Tuppy, *Nature* **192**, 1125 (1961).
26. O. F. Walasek and E. Margoliash, unpublished results.
27. J. W. Stewart and E. Margoliash, *Can. J. Biochem.* **43**, 1187 (1965).
28. C. Nolan and E. Margoliash, *J. Biol. Chem.* **241**, 1049 (1966).
29. S. K. Chan, I. Tulloss, E. Margoliash, unpublished results.
30. S. B. Needleman and E. Margoliash, *J. Biol. Chem.* **241**, 853 (1966).
31. S. K. Chan, I. Tulloss, E. Margoliash, *Biochemistry* **5**, 2586 (1966).
32. O. P. Bahl and E. L. Smith, *J. Biol. Chem.* **240**, 3585 (1965).
33. G. Kreil, Z. *Physiol. Chem.* **334**, 154 (1963).
34. S. K. Chan and E. Margoliash, *J. Biol. Chem.* **241**, 335 (1966).
35. J. Heller and E. L. Smith, *Proc. Natl. Acad. Sci. U.S.* **54**, 1621 (1965).
36. Y. Yaoi, K. Titani, K. Narita, *J. Biochem. Tokyo* **59**, 247 (1966).
37. K. Narita and K. Titani, *Proc. Japan Acad.* **41**, 831 (1965).
38. R. R. Sokal, *Syst. Zool.* **10**, 70 (1961); F. J. Rohlf and R. R. Sokal, *Univ. Kansas Sci. Bull.* **45**, 3 (1965); J. H. Camin and R. R. Sokal, *Evolution* **19**, 311 (1965).
39. R. F. Doolittle and B. Blombäck, *Nature* **202**, 147 (1964).
40. T. H. Jukes, *Advan. Biol. Med. Phys.* **9**, 1 (1963).
41. This project received support from grants from NIH (NB-04565) and NSF (GB-4017) to W.M.F. We thank Peter Guetter and Daniel Brick for valuable technical assistance.

SECTION V

The Evolution of Man

DOBZHANSKY, THEODOSIUS. 1961. Man and natural selection. Am. Scient. **49**: 285–299.

LE GROS CLARK, WILFRED E. 1959. The crucial evidence for human evolution. Proc. Am. Phil. Soc. **103**: 159–172.

TOBIAS, PHILLIP V. 1965. Early man in East Africa. Science **149**: 22–33.

WASHBURN, S. L. 1950. The analysis of primate evolution with particular reference to the origin of man. Cold Spr. Harb. Symp. Quant. Biol. **15**: 67–78.

BARTHOLOMEW, GEORGE A., JR., and JOSEPH B. BIRDSELL. 1953. Ecology and the protohominids. Am. Anthrop. **55**: 481–498.

FREMLIN, J. H. 1964. How many people can the world support? New Scient. **24**: 285–287.

Much of our interest in evolution stems naturally from interest in ourselves and in mankind generally. In studying the evolution of other organisms we feel that a better understanding can be gained of our own origins, and of our "place in nature."

Many of the tools available for the direct study of the evolution of other organisms are more or less denied to us for the study of human evolution. Our ability directly to manipulate human populations in experimental situations is severely limited for cultural reasons. An even more serious constraint is biological. Organisms with a generation time of more than twenty years are not ideal subjects for the study of evolution in process. In spite of these difficulties, some excellent work has been done on microevolution in populations of *Homo sapiens*. Perhaps the best known is the work on the evolutionary dynamics of sickle-cell anemia and related subjects by Allison and his coworkers (e.g., Allison, 1959). A paper by Allison on the population genetics of hemoglobin characters is reprinted in the Spiess book *Papers on Animal Population Genetics*. In addition, considerable attention has been given by geneticists to the inheritance of blood types and of congenital malformations, and much of the resultant data have been of interest to the evolutionist (for a general summary, see the excellent book by Stern, 1960).

Attention has in particular been focused on the role of mutation in the genetic system of man and other organisms, and intense controversy has been generated about what has become known as the question of "genetic load." One of the foundation papers on this question, "An estimate of the mutational damage in man from data on consanguineous marriages" by Morton, Crow, and Muller, also appears in the Spiess text.

Another area in which studies of human populations have been very important in shaping evolutionary thinking is that of the interpretation of geographic variation. Geographic variation in such characters as skin color, hair color, hair type, tooth size, body build, frequency of genes controlling color blindness, blood and hemoglobin types, and so forth, tends to be explainable in terms of geographically varying selection pressures (see, for instance, Brace, 1964) as well as migration and, perhaps in some cases, genetic drift. As one would expect, variation in skin color (related to the amount of insolation) does not coincide with variation in the frequency of genes for sickling hemoglobin (related to the geographic distribution of *falciparum* malaria and possibly other factors). Such *discordant* variation, superbly documented in *Homo sapiens*, has been found in most organisms which have been investigated. It has led biologists to the realization that subspecies or "races" based on variation in one or two arbitrarily selected characters usually are not meaningful evolutionary units. Unfortunately, cultural factors, themselves the product of evolution, have made it very difficult for scientists to deal objectively with the taxonomy of human variation (see Ehrlich and Holm, 1964).

Included is a general paper by Dobzhansky,* "Man and Natural Selection," which touches on many of the subjects mentioned above, and gives this eminent biologist's views on such subjects as the uniqueness of man and his evolutionary future.

Much of the interest in human evolution has centered on the fossil record of man. This interest developed at a time when there was debate as to whether or not man had evolved, and the search was on for a "missing link." It has not diminished appreciably in spite of the discovery of hundreds of fossils which could claim this title. Two papers dealing with the physical evidence for human evolution are included. That by Le Gros Clark,* although almost a decade old, is a reasonable summary of the overall picture as it is still viewed by many workers. Tobias's paper* deals with more recent East African finds whose interpretation is now disputed (for a view somewhat different from that of Tobias, see Robinson, 1965).

More general papers on human origins are those of Washburn* and of Bartholomew and Birdsell.* Washburn takes a broad view of primate evolution and compares in some detail man's anatomical features with those of his primate relatives. Bartholomew and Birdsell, in contrast, take a primarily ecological approach to the biology of the earliest "men." In the past few years there has been an upsurge of interest in the behavior of nonhuman primates in nature (see, for instance, DeVore, 1965). Although such studies are outside of the scope of this collection, they are of great interest to evolutionists, and already they are providing rich sources of data for those interested in understanding man's cultural evolution.

We think that Fremlin's article* is a particularly fitting finale. He shows us quite clearly one possible ending of the hominid line—indeed of organic evolution. Suggestions of a less distant denouement of human evolution may be found in a recent article by Ehrlich (1967). Man has gained mastery over his environment—from the point of view of future evolution, the critical question is whether he will gain mastery of himself.

BIBLIOGRAPHY

Allison, A. C. 1959. Metabolic polymorphisms in mammals and their bearing on problems of biochemical genetics. Amer. Nat. **93:** 5–16.

Brace, C. L. 1964. A nonracial approach towards the understanding of human diversity. In A. Montagu (ed.), *The Concept of Race.* Free Press of Glencoe, New York, pp. 103–152.

DeVore, I. (ed.). 1965. *Primate Behavior.* Holt, Rinehart & Winston, New York.

Ehrlich, P. R. 1967. Paying the piper. New Scient. **36:** 652–655.

———, and R. W. Holm. 1964. A biological view of race. In A. Montagu (ed.), *The Concept of Race.* Free Press of Glencoe, New York, pp. 153–179.

Robinson, J. T. 1965. Homo "habilis" and the Australopithecines. Nature **205:** 121–124.

Stern, C. 1960. *Principles of human genetics.* 2nd ed. W. H. Freeman, San Francisco.

* Paper included in this section.

MAN AND NATURAL SELECTION*

By THEODOSIUS DOBZHANSKY

Man's Evolutionary Uniqueness

BY CHANGING what man knows about the world, he changes the world he knows; and by changing the world in which he lives, he changes himself. Herein lies a danger and a hope; a danger because random changes of the biological nature are likely to produce deterioration rather than improvement; a hope because changes resulting from knowledge can also be directed by knowledge.

The human species, _Homo sapiens,_ mankind, is the unique and most successful product of biological evolution, so far. This has sometimes been questioned, I suspect without too much conviction on the part of the doubters, perhaps only to mock man's pretensions or to challenge his values. But man _is_ the most successful product of evolution, by any reasonable definition of biological success. Man began his career as a rare animal, living somewhere in the tropics or subtropics of the Old World, probably in Africa. From this obscure beginning, mankind multiplied to become one of the most numerous mammals, for there will soon be about three billion men living. Numbers may not be an unadulterated blessing, but they are one of the measures of biological success of a species.

Moreover, man has spread and occupied all the continents and most islands, except for the frozen wastes of Antarctica and of the interior of Greenland; he has learned to traverse seas and oceans and deserts; he is well on the way towards control or elimination of the predators and parasites which used to prey on him; he has subdued and domesticated many animal and plant species, made them serve his needs and his fancies, broadened enormously the range of utilizable food supplies, and learned to make use of a variety of energy sources. Modern man lives no longer at the mercy of wild beasts and vagaries of the climate; he has reached a status where his continuation as a species is in no danger, except perhaps as a result of man's own folly or of a cosmic accident.

The evolutionary uniqueness of man lies in that in mankind the biological evolution has transcended itself. With man commences a new, superorganic, mode of evolution, which is the evolution of culture. Culture is a tremendously potent instrument for adaptation to the environment. A very large part of the evolutionary progress, both biologically and culturally, has come from adversity. Life faces environments which are more often niggardly than bountiful, more frequently inimical than benign. For life to endure, it must develop defences and adaptations. Biological adaptation occurs through natural selection;

* A Sigma Xi-RESA National Lecture, 1960–1961.

new genes arise through mutation, sexual recombination creates new combinations of genes, and natural selection acts to multiply the successful genetic endowments and to reduce the frequencies of the unsuccessful ones. In man and in man alone, adaptation may occur also through alteration of culture. Many species of mammals have become adapted to cold climates by growing warm fur; man alone has achieved the same end by donning fur coats. Birds have mastered the air by becoming flying machines; man has conquered the air by building flying machines.

Biological and cultural evolutions of man are not independent; they are interdependent. The superorganic has an organic basis. Formation and maintenance of culture presuppose a human genotype. Even the most clever ape cannot learn human culture. Some writers have jumped to the conclusion that the genetic development of the human species was completed before culture appeared, and that the evolution of culture has replaced biological evolution. This is not true. The two evolutions go together, interacting and usually mutually reinforcing each other. There is feedback between genetics and culture. Culture is an adaptive mechanism supplemental to, but not incompatible with, biological adaptation. To be sure, adaptation by culture proved to be more efficacious, and, before all else, more rapid than adaptation by genes. This is why the emergence of the genetic basis of culture was the master stroke of the biological evolution of the human species. The genetic basis of culture should be improved or at least maintained. It should not be allowed to deteriorate.

Natural Selection, Struggle, and Fitness

Man has not only evolved; for better or for worse, he is also evolving. Is he to become a superman or a demigod? Or will the fate in store for him be like that of so many successful species of the past, which eventually declined and became extinct? Long-term prophecies do not expose the prophets to the risk of being proved wrong too soon. I nevertheless do not wish to indulge here in prophecies or in designing utopias. I wish rather to investigate some of the evolutionary forces currently at work in the human species.

According to the theory set forth by Darwin and Wallace more than a century ago, adaptation occurs in biological evolution by way of the process of natural selection. Does natural selection operate in modern mankind? This has to be answered obviously in the negative, if by "natural" you mean a world uninhabited and uninfluenced by man. But it is here that we must proceed with the greatest caution. What, indeed, is selection, and when is a selection "natural" and when is it not? Darwin said that natural selection is the outcome of the survival of the fittest in the struggle for life. "Struggle" suggests strife, contention, competition. Darwin himself wrote that " . . . from the war of nature, from famine and death, the most exalted object we are capable of conceiving, the higher animal, directly follows."

However, natural selection does not ineluctably depend on any of these things. Birch (1957) has defined competition thus: "Competition occurs when a number of animals (of the same or different species) utilize common resources the supply of which is short; or if the resources are not in short supply, competition occurs when the animals seeking these resources nevertheless harm each other in the process." Natural selection may, however, take place when resources are not limiting, if the carriers of some genes possess greater reproductive potentials than others. Some cases have been observed in experiments with animals and plants when a genotype superior under competition is inferior in the absence of competition, or vice versa.

And who is the "fittest," whose survival results in natural selection? Does natural selection make us fit for life in the society of other men, or for wisdom, or for good will, or for unselfishness? It does not necessarily ordain any of these qualities. Darwinian fitness is a measure of the reproductive proficiency. Its guiding principle is "be fruitful, and multiply, and replenish the earth." It is quite indispensable to distinguish Darwinian fitness from excellence in human estimation. The two may go hand in hand, but sometimes they may be in opposition.

It is man and man alone who can probe, scrutinize, and question the wisdom of the evolutionary process which brought him into being. He may improve what nature hath wrought. When man chooses the individuals who are to become parents of the succeeding generation he practices artificial selection. According to Lerner (1958), artificial selection is a process which has a goal that can be visualized. Any selection which is not artificial is natural selection.

Mutation and the Normalizing Natural Selection

There are several forms of natural selection operating in the human species, as well as in other organisms. Although the distinctions between these forms of selection are neither absolutely rigid nor always clear-cut, they are helpful for straight thinking about evolutionary problems. Stabilizing (Schmalhausen 1949) or normalizing (Waddington 1957) natural selection is the simplest and most obvious. It is a conservative force; it counteracts the spread in populations of detrimental mutants, hereditary diseases, and weaknesses of various kinds. Failure, or at least relaxation, of the normalizing selection in human populations leads to fears that an insidious process of genetic decay is at work in the human species. Is there a basis for these fears?

Mutations continue to arise in man, even as they have been arising since the dawn of life. Some mutants cause grave and even fatal hereditary diseases, such as retinoblastoma, hemophilia, epiloia, etc. Others cause malformations, such as achondroplasia, arachnodactyly, or brachydactyly. Still others, and probably a majority of mutants, cause small and unspectacular changes in the appearance or physiology or behavior of their carriers. Small mutations are difficult to study quantitatively. Not enough is known about them, even in Drosophila and in other organisms more favorable for experimentation than man. Large mutations are certainly more often deleterious than useful, at least in the environments in which the species normally lives, and at least in homozygous condition. A useful major mutant is like a needle in a haystack; it may be there but it is notoriously hard to find among the many harmful ones. It is tempting to suppose that all or most small mutations will also be harmful, in various small and devious ways. This is what geneticists who are adherents of the "classical" hypothesis of the population structure believe to be the case. The evidence on which this belief rests is not fully convincing (see below).

A brief consideration of some examples of the operation of the normalizing selection in man will be useful at this point. Achondroplasia or chondrodystrophy are formidable names for a rather common type of dwarfism in man, caused by the presence of a single dominant mutant gene. Achondroplasts have bodies and heads of about normal size, but their limbs are very short. Some achondroplastic dwarfs are born in families in which at least one of the parents is a dwarf. Such dwarfs evidently inherit the genes for the abnormality from the affected parents. But some dwarfs are children of parents of normal stature; these dwarfs carry the dominant gene for dwarfism newly arisen by mutation. Mørch has recorded the birth of eight dwarf mutants among about 94 thousand children in Denmark; this indicates that about one sex-cell per 24,000 sex cells produced by normal parents transports a newly arisen gene for achondroplastic dwarfism, a mutation rate of the order of 4×10^{-5} per generation.

The genes for achondroplastic dwarfism newly arisen by mutation are introduced into the gene pool of human populations; this happens relentlessly in every generation. Does it follow that the dwarfism will grow more and more widespread in the course of time? Not necessarily. The spread of the genes for dwarfism is opposed by natural selection. Mørch found that the achondroplastic dwarfs in Denmark produce only about twenty per cent as many children as do their nondwarf brothers and sisters. This means that the adaptive value, or the Darwinian fitness, of the achondroplastic dwarfs is only 0.2 normal; it can also be said that the gene for the dwarfism is opposed by a normalizing natural selection of a magnitude of 0.8.

How does natural selection operate on this gene? Why do the dwarfs produce so few children? It turns out that this is chiefly because many of them remain unmarried. And their failure to find mates is not due to a weakened sexual drive but to their external appearance being not in accord with what is regarded in our society as handsomeness or attractiveness. Here, then, is an example of a natural selective process which operates not by causing early death of the carriers of certain genes, but acting instead via certain culturally conditioned forms of human behavior. A person who remains childless may be described as genetically "dead"; but childlessness is a form of "genetic death" which does not immediately produce a cadaver.

Some mutant genes are, to be sure, eliminated by a normalizing selection acting through "genetic death" which is also real death. Retinoblastoma is a form of cancer of the eye, which afflicts infants and children; unless the eyes are removed promptly by a surgical operation early death is inevitable. Neel and Falls found the mutation from the normal to the dominant mutant gene causing retinoblastoma to be about as frequent as that causing the achondroplastic dwarfism (see above). Before the invention of surgery which saves the lives of retinoblastomatic children, the normalizing selection was eliminating in every generation all the mutant genes for retinoblastoma which arose in that generation (i.e., in the sex-cells which gave rise to that generation). The surgery may be said to frustrate this normalizing selection; the retinoblastomatics, though blind, grow up and become capable of being parents of children one-half of whom will now inherit the gene for retinoblastoma. The retinoblastomatics, like the achondroplasts, are now of two kinds—those due to new mutations and those having inherited the gene from their parents.

Genes which reduce the Darwinian fitness of their carriers less dramatically than do the genes discussed above are nevertheless also opposed by normalizing selection. Predisposition to diabetes mellitus, or at least to some of its forms, seems to be inherited through a recessive gene. The same seems to be true of some forms of myopia (short-sightedness). We do not know either the mutation rates which produce these genes, nor the selection rates which oppose their spread. What is of interest for our purposes is that these selection rates doubtless vary greatly depending on the environment. Myopia is likely to be more incapacitating to people engaged in some occupations (i.e., hunters or automobile drivers) than in others (i.e., handicraftsmen or clerks), and besides myopia can be "cured" by wearing glasses. The onset of diabetes mellitus may be early or late in life; it may thus strike after the close of the reproductive age, and thus fail to reduce the number of the children produced and hence to reduce the Darwinian fitness. And some forms of diabetes may be "cured" by insulin therapy.

Now, to "cure" a hereditary disease obviously does not mean to change the genes which have caused it. Health and disease refer however to the states of well-being or infirmity of a person; a person consulting his doctor does not ask the latter to alter his genes, but only to advise how to change the environment in a way such that the genes with which the person has been born will react by producing a reasonable state of well-being. A myopic wearing glasses, or a diabetic having received his insulin injections, is no longer incapacitated, or at least less so than both were before the "cure." The relief of the incapacitation may however increase their Darwinian fitness, and mitigate the severity of the normalizing natural selection.

The "Normal" Man

The removal of a mutant from a population is called a genetic death or, less dramatically, genetic elimination. The death of a child with retinoblastoma eliminates from the population one mutant retinoblastomatic gene. When an achondroplastic dwarf fails to marry, or raises a family with fewer children than he would have if he were not a dwarf, a mutant gene for achondroplasia is eliminated. The classical hypothesis of population structure assumes that there exists for every biological species, or may appear or be produced in the future, one normal, or best, optimal genetic endowment. This genetic endowment would give the ideal, the normal, the archetypical man, or the ideal Drosophila fly, or the ideal corn plant—the man, the Drosophila, the corn as they ought to be. The way to produce this normal man is to let the normalizing natural selection remove, eliminate, purge from the population all the mutant genes. What then would remain would be the ideal constellation of genes.

This hypothesis has the advantages of simplicity, though not necessarily of accuracy. It is a product of typological thinking, which has, to be sure, venerable antecedents. It goes back to Plato's eternal ideal types. Many scientists find the appeal of the typological mode of thought irresistible. Indeed, if the classical hypothesis were justified, the problem of the guidance of the biological evolution of the human species would be theoretically simple, however difficult it might still remain in practice. We would have to arrange for the normalizing natural selection to protect the ideal normal human genes from contamination by mutations. Or, to put it in positive rather than negative terms, we might strive to obtain a mankind in which everybody would be a carrier of the normal genetic endowment. The three billion humans, or whatever numbers this "normal" mankind might contain, would then be as similar genetically as identical twins. But they would presumably be strong and healthy and happy identical multitudes!

Diversifying Natural Selection

Fortunately or unfortunately, depending upon one's point of view, the classical hypothesis of population structure is perhaps only a half-truth. That it is true to some extent is clear enough. Harmful mutants do arise, and some of them seem to be unconditionally harmful. It is hard to imagine an enviroment in which retinoblastoma could possibly be harmless, not to speak of usefulness. Accumulation of such mutants in human populations can only augment human misery. To counteract this accumulation, one could, conceivably, reduce the mutation frequencies, or else eliminate the mutants as painlessly as possible. Unfortunately, for the time being, man has learned how to increase the mutability by exposure to high-energy radiations and by other means, but not how to decrease the mutation rates (Muller 1950, 1960).

The concept of a single genetic endowment, ideal or optimal for each living species, is however a typological fiction. No living individual, and certainly no population and no species, exist in absolutely uniform environments. Environments vary in time and in space. How does life solve the problem of adaptation to a multiplicity of environments? There are two possible solutions, and, with its habitual opportunism, evolution has used them both. The first is the genetically-conditioned physiological and developmental plasticity. The organism reacts to changes in the environment by adaptive modifications. For example, the human body has physiological mechanisms which enable it to conserve an almost constant internal temperature despite external temperature variations. In man, the most important kind of plasticity is his educability. Most humans can be trained for, and can acquire skills to perform passably in, any one of the many employments which most human societies have to offer.

Secondly, a population facing a diversity of environments may become genetically diversified. Natural selection favors different genetic endowments in different environments. This is the diversifying (also called disruptive, Mather 1955) form of natural selection. Instead of one perfect genotype, diversifying selection favors many genotypes; it favors genetic polymorphism. A population which abounds in genetic variety has a better grip on a complex environment than a genetically uniform population; polymorphism is one way of exploiting the environment more fully.

Diversity and Equality

Adaptations by way of plasticity and by way of genetic diversity are not mutually exclusive. They are complementary. Culture is by far the most potent adaptive mechanism which has emerged in the evolution of life. Its potency is due to its being transmitted by teaching and learning, instead of by genes. The ability to be trained, and to become competent in whatever occupation a person meets his opportunity, increases the social and usually also the biological fitness. Genetic specialization for one vocation may confer very high fitness for that particular vocation. But educability permits a choice of vocations, and thus confers fitness in complex and changeable environments. In an evolving culture new occupations constantly arise. Who needed aircraft pilots a century ago, but how many blacksmiths are now needed in technologically advanced countries?

Culture is, however, an adaptive contrivance to make people diversified, not to make them alike. If uniformity were advantageous, genetic fixity would most likely have emerged in evolution. Genetic diversity or polymorphism joins force with developmental plasticity. I could have probably learned many kinds of jobs other than that I actually fixed upon. But no amount of effort and training could make me a first-rate wrestler or sprinter or painter or concertmaster. I just do not possess the genetic wherewithal for these occupations. Other people do, and this genetic diversity enriches the store of man's capabilities. It is the leaven of cultural progress.

The facts of biology are compatible with the lofty vision of human equality. All men have been born equal; they certainly are not all alike. It is nonsense to think that only identical twins can be equals. Human equality is not predicated on identity, or even on identity of ability. It presupposes, however, something approaching an equality of opportunity to develop whatever socially useful gifts and aptitudes a person's genes have provided him with, and which he may choose to develop.

Culture fosters a multitude of employments and functions to be filled and served; equality of opportunity stimulates division of labor rather than sets it aside; it enables every person to choose among occupations for which he is qualified by his abilities. It is wrong to think that equality of opportunity makes genetic variation unimportant. It does precisely the opposite. It makes the differences between people reflect meaningfully their genetic differences. Inequality of opportunity acts, on the contrary, to hide, to distort, and to stultify the genetic diversity.

Balancing Natural Selection

Far from being an unfortunate deviation from the ideal state, genetic diversity is an adaptive response of life to its environment. A gene useful in one environment may cause a genetic disease in another; a mutant harmful in combination with some genes may be useful in other combinations. Some adaptively ambivalent genes increase the fitness of their carriers when in single dose, in heterozygous state, but are harmful, or even lethal in homozygotes.

The sickle-cell anemia and the Mediterranean anemia, or thalassemia, are the best known human examples. These almost invariably fatal diseases are due to homozygosis for genes which in heterozygous condition seem to confer a relative immunity to certain kinds of malarial fevers. Heterozygous carriers consequently enjoy a superior fitness, hybrid vigor, or heterosis, in countries where these particular forms of malaria are prevalent. The genes for sickle-cells and for thalassemia are common in tropical and subtropical parts of the Old World, and they have been introduced in the New World as well.

Natural selection holds the "normal" and the sickle-cell and thalassemia genes in balanced polymorphism in populations of malarial countries. This is the balancing form of natural selection. How important is balancing selection in the human species is an open issue. It may well be that many of the genes responsible for the individual differences which we observe among so-called "normal" persons, differences in facial features, body build, health, intelligence, longevity, etc., are kept in balanced polymorphism. Morton and Chung (1959) have presented evidence that the genes for the M and N blood types are maintained by balancing selection. The heterozygotes MN have a Darwinian fitness superior to MM and NN homozygotes. Just what is the advantage of the heterozygous state is unknown, nor is the nature of the drawback in homozygotes. The homozygotes are certainly viable; I am one of them. A very slight superiority in fitness in heterozygotes is, however, sufficient to maintain a balanced polymorphism.

There are grounds to suspect that the O-A-B blood types in man are also held in balanced polymorphism. The evidence for this is at present inconclusive, but recent works of Levene, Rosenfield, Morton, Crow, and others show that the genes involved are subject to a still different kind of selective pressure. This is a relative incompatability between the mother and the fetus when they differ in genetic constitution in certain ways. Such incompatibility has been known to arise because of the genes for a still different system of blood types, the Rhesus, or Rh system. An Rh positive fetus in an Rh negative mother may suffer injury or even be aborted.

Directional Natural Selection

The form of natural selection most important in the long run is directional selection. It was pivotal in Darwin's theory of evolution. Living species may respond to challenges of their environments by genetic changes. Genes once useful become inferior to others and are gradually eliminated, replaced by superior gene variants. The whole genetic system of the species is eventually rebuilt.

There is a fairly general agreement among biologists that the emergence of the human species was due in the main to directional selection. It has, however, been questioned whether directional selection, or indeed any form of natural selection, has continued to operate after the genetic basis of culture has taken shape. Now, let us admit that the success of mankind as a biological species was due precisely to man's culture being able to change ever so much faster than his genes can. Man adapts his environments to his genes more often than he adapts his genes to his enviroments. But, as pointed out, the two methods of adaptation are complementary and not alternative. Far from making human environments stable and uniform, culture increases the tempo of change. Given an environmental flux, the necessary and sufficient condition for genetic change is availability in the populations of genetic variants, some of which are better and others less well adapted to shifting environments. Natural selection will multiply the favorable and depress or eliminate the unfavorable variants.

We do not know exactly how much genetic change has taken place in mankind at different stages of its history. Modern man might or might not be able to survive, even if properly trained, in the environments of his ancestors of 100,000, or even 10,000 years ago. Or, if he survived, he might not be as efficient or as happy in those environments as his ancestors were. We do not know for sure. Neanderthal man may or may not have been capable of becoming a reasonably well adjusted citizen if raised in New York or in New Orleans. Perhaps some Neanderthals might have been fit to become Ph.D.'s and to be elected members of the Society of Sigma Xi. But, on the other hand, they may have been unfit for any now existing education. Modern women are alleged to experience greater difficulties in childbirth than did their great-grandmothers. All this is conjectural and not rigorously proved. It is, however, a fallacy to assert that what is unproved did not occur. In point of fact, some of the above changes probably did occur.

Are Culture and Natural Selection Compatible?

We have seen that several forms of natural selection operate in modern mankind. But they certainly do not operate as they did during the Stone Age, or even as they did a century ago. Neither does natural selection operate always in the same way in wild and "natural" species, quite "unspoiled" by culture. This is inevitable. Natural selection depends on environments, and environments change. Human environments have changed a great deal in a century, not to speak of millennia.

The real problem is not whether natural selection in man is going on, but whether it is going on towards what we, humans, regard as betterment or deterioration. Natural selection tends to enhance the reproductive proficiency of the population in which it operates. Such proficiency is however not the only estimable quality with which we wish to see people endowed. And besides, a high reproductive fitness in one environment does not even insure the survival of the population or the species when the environment changes.

Normalizing selection is, as we have seen, not the only form of natural selection. The relaxation of some of its functions is, however, a cause of apprehension. Medicine, hygiene, civilized living save many lives which would otherwise be extinguished. This situation is here to stay; we would not want it to be otherwise, even if we could. Some of the lives thus saved will, however, engender lives that will stand in need of being saved in the generations to come. Can it be that we help the ailing, the lame, and the deformed only to make our descendants more ailing, more lame, and more deformed?

Suppose that we have learned how to save the lives of persons afflicted with a hereditary disease, such as retinoblastoma, which previously was incurably fatal. In genetic terms, this means that the Darwinian fitness of the victims of the disease has increased, and that the normalizing selection against this disease is relaxed. What will be the consequence? The incidence of the disease in the population will increase from generation to generation. The increase is likely to be slow, generally no more than by one mutation rate per generation. It may take centuries or millennia to notice the difference for any one disease or malformation. However, the average health and welfare of the population are liable to show adverse effects of relaxed selection much sooner.

The process of mutation injects in every generation a certain number of harmful genes in the gene pool of the population; the process of normalizing selection eliminates a certain number of these genes. With environment reasonably stable, the situation tends to reach a state of equilibrium. At equilibrium, the mutation and the elimination are equal. If mutation becomes more frequent (as it does in man because of exposure to high-energy radiations and perhaps to some chemicals), or if the elimination is lagging because of relaxation of normalizing selection, the incidence of harmful mutant genes in the population is bound to increase. And take note of this: If the classical theory of population structure were correct, all harmful mutations would be in a sense equivalent. For at equilibrium there is one elimination for every mutation, regardless of whether the mutation causes a lethal hereditary disease like retinoblastoma, or a malformation like achondroplasia, or a relatively mild defect such as myopia (Muller 1950, 1960).

The problem is, however, more complex than this theory would suggest. It calls for reasearch in what Wright (1960) describes neatly as "unfortunately the unpopular and scientifically somewhat unrewarding borderline fields of genetics and the social sciences." Although at equilibrium there may be one genetic elimination for every mutation, it is unrealistic to equate the human and social consequences of different mutations. The elimination of a lethal mutant which causes death of an embryo before implantation in the uterus is scarcely noticed by the mother or by anyone else. Suffering accompanies the elimination of a mutant, such as retinoblastoma, which kills an infant apparently normal at birth. Many mutants, such as hemophilia or Huntington's chorea, kill children, adolescents, or adults, cause misery to their victims, and disruption of the lives of their families. There is no way to measure precisely the amount of human anguish; yet one may surmise that the painful and slow death of the victims of so many hereditary diseases is torment greater than that involved in the elimination of a gene for achondroplasia owing to the failure of an achondroplastic dwarf to beget children.

Looked at from the angle of the costs to the society, the nonequivalence of different mutants is no less evident. Myopia may be inherited as a recessive trait. Increases of the frequencies in populations of the gene for myopia are undesirable. Yet, it may become more and more common in future generations. However, only a fanatic might advocate sterilization of the myopics or other radical measures to prevent the spread of this gene. One may hope that civilized societies can tolerate some more myopics; many of them are very useful citizens, and their defect can rather easily be corrected by a relatively inexpensive environmental change—wearing glasses. The effort needed to eradicate or to reduce the frequency of myopia genetically would exceed that requisite to rectify their defect environmentally, by manufacturing more pairs of glasses.

Diabetes mellitus is, given the present level of medicine, more difficult and expensive to correct than is myopia. Some diabetics may nevertheless be treated successfully by insulin therapy, helped to live to old age, and enabled to raise families as large as nondiabetics. The incidence of diabetes may therefore creep up slowly in the generations to come. Now, most people would probably agree that it is better to be free of diabetes than to have it under control, no matter how successfully, by insulin therapy or other means. The prospect is not a pleasant one to contemplate. Insulin injections may perhaps be almost as common in some remote future as taking aspirin tablets is at present.

Towards Guidance of Human Evolution

Are we, then, faced with a dilemma—if we enable the weak and the deformed to live and to propagate their kinds, we face the prospect of a genetic twilight; but if we let them die or suffer when we can save them we face the certainty of a moral twilight. How to escape this dilemma?

I can well understand the impatience which some of my readers may feel if I refuse to provide an unambiguous answer to so pressing a problem. Let me however plead with you that infatuation with over-simple answers to very complex and difficult problems is one of the earmarks of intellectual mediocrity. I am afraid that the problem of guidance of human evolution has no simple solution. At least I have not found one, nor has anybody else in my opinion. Each genetic condition will have to be considered on its own merits, and the solution which may be adopted for different conditions will probably be different. Suppose that everybody agrees that the genes causing myopia, achondroplasia, diabetes and retinoblastoma are undesirable. We shall nevertheless be forced to treat them differently. Some genetic defects will have to be put up with and managed environmentally; others will have to be treated genetically, by artificial selection, and the eugenic measures that may be needed can be effected without accepting any kind of biological Brave New World.

Let us face this fact: Our lives depend on civilization and technology, and the lives of our descendants will be even more dependent on civilized environments. I can imagine a wise old ape-man who deplored the softness of his contemporaries using stone knives to carve their meat instead of doing this with their teeth; or a solid conservative Peking man viewing with alarm the new fangled habit of using fire to make oneself warm. I have yet to hear anyone seriously proposing that we give up the use of knives and of fire now. Nor does anyone in his right mind urge that we let people die of smallpox or tuberculosis, in order that genetic resistance to these diseases be maintained. The remedy for our genetic dependence on technology and medicine is more, not less, technology and medicine. You may, if you wish, feel nostalgic for the good old days of our cave-dwelling ancestors; the point of no return was passed in the evolution of our species many millenia before anyone could know what was happening.

Of course, not all genetic defects can be corrected by tools or remedies or medicines. Even though new and better tools and medicines will, one may hope, be invented in the future, this will not make all genetic equipments equally desirable. It is a relatively simple matter to correct for lack of genetic resistance to smallpox by vaccination, or for myopia by suitable glasses. It is not so simple with many other genetic defects. Surgical removal of the eyes is called for in cases of retinoblastoma; this saves the lives of the victims, but leaves them blind. No remedies are known for countless other genetic defects. Human life is sacred; yet the social costs of some genetic variants are so great, and their social contributions are so small, that avoidance of their birth is ethically the most acceptable as well as the wisest solution. This does not necessarily call for enactment of Draconian eugenic laws; it is perhaps not overoptimistic to hope that spreading biological education and understanding may be a real help. Make persons whose progeny is likely to inherit a serious genetic defect aware of this fact; they may draw the conclusions themselves.

The strides accomplished by biochemical genetics in recent years have led some biologists to hope that methods will soon be discovered to induce specific changes in human genes of our choice. This would, indeed, be a radical solution of the problem of management of the evolution of our species, and of other species as well. We would simply change the genes which we do not like, in ways conforming to our desires. Now, if the history of science has any lesson to teach us, it is the unwisdom of declaring certain goals to be unattainable. The cavalier way in which the progress of science often treats such predictions should instill due humility even in the most doctrinaire prophets. The best that can be said about the possibility of changing specific genes in man in accordance with our desires is that, although such an invention would be a great boon, it is not within reach yet. And it cannot be assumed to be achievable.

Let us also not exaggerate the urgency of the problem of the genetic management of the evolution of our species. Another problem, that of the runaway overpopulation of our planet, is far more immediate and critical. If mankind will prove unable to save itself from being choked by crowding it hardly needs to worry about its genetic quality. Although the problems of numbers and of quality are not one and the same, yet they may be closely connected in practice. As steps towards regulation of the population size will begin to be taken, and this surely cannot be postponed for much longer, the genetic problem will inexorably obtrude itself before people's attention. The questions "how many people" and "what kind of people" will be solved together, if they will be solved at all.

Some people believe that all would be well with mankind, if only natural selection were permitted to operate without obstruction by medicine and technology. Let us not forget, however, that countless biological species of the past have become extinct, despite their evolution having been directed by natural selection unadulterated by culture. What we want is not simply natural selection, but selection, natural and artificial, directed towards humanly desirable goals. What are these goals? This is the central problem of human ethics and of human evolution. Darwinian fitness is no guide here. If, in some human society, genetically duller people produce more progeny than the brighter ones, this simply means that, in the environment of that particular society, being a bit thick-headed increases the Darwinian fitness, and being too intelligent decreases it. Natural selection will act accordingly, and will not be any less "natural" on that account.

Human cultural evolution has resulted in the formation of a system of values, of *human* values. These are the values to which we wish human evolution to conform. These values are products of cultural evolution, conditioned of course by the biological evolution, yet not deducible from the latter. Where do we find a criterion by which these values are to be judged? I know of no better one than that proposed by the ancient Chinese sage: "Every system of moral laws must be based upon man's own consciousness, verified by the common experience of mankind, tested by due sanction of historical experience and found without error, applied to the operations and processes of nature in the physical universe and found to be without contradiction, laid before the gods without question or fear, and able to wait a hundred generations and have it confirmed without a doubt by a Sage of posterity."

REFERENCES

Most of the ideas and arguments presented in this article will be discussed in more detail in a book entitled "The Human Species," to be published by the Yale University Press. The references specifically mentioned in the article are as follows:

BIRCH, L. C. 1957. The meaning of competition. *Amer. Natur., 91,* 5–18.

CROW, J. F. and N. E. MORTON. 1960. The genetic load due to mother-child incompatibility. *Amer. Natur., 94,* 413–419.

LERNER, I. M. 1958. The genetic basis of selection. John Wiley, New York.

LEVENE, H. and ROSENFELD, R. E. 1961. ABO incompatibility. Progress in medical genetics. Grune and Stratton, New York.

MATHER, K. 1955. Polymorphism as an outcome of disruptive selection. *Evolution, 9,* 52–61.

MØRCH, E. T. 1941. Chondrodystrophic dwarfs in Denmark. *Opera Domo Bio. Hered. Hum. Univ. Hafniensis, 3,* 1–200.

MORTON, N. E., and C. S. CHUNG. 1959. Are the MN blood groups maintained by selection? *Amer. Jour. Human Genetics, 11,* 287–251.

MULLER, H. J. 1950. Our load of mutations. *Amer. Jour. Human Genetics, 2,* 111–176.

———. 1960. The guidance of human evolution. In S. Tax's "Evolution After Darwin," *2,* 423–462.

SCHMALHAUSEN, I. I. 1949. Factors of evolution. Blakeston, Philadelphia.

WADDINGTON, C. H. 1957. The strategy of the genes. Allen and Unwin, London.

WRIGHT, SEWALL. 1960. On the appraisal of genetic effects of radiation in man. The biological effects of atomic radiation. Summary Reports, 18–24 *Nat. Acad. Sciences,* Washington.

THE CRUCIAL EVIDENCE FOR HUMAN EVOLUTION

WILFRID E. LE GROS CLARK

Professor of Anatomy, Oxford University

(Commemoration of the Centennial of the Publication of The Origin of Species *by Charles Darwin,*
Annual Meeting of the American Philosophical Society, April, 1959)

IT HAS BEEN remarked that it is never possible ultimately to prove a scientific hypothesis—the most that one can hope to do is to disprove it. Except possibly to the more metaphysically minded, this is no doubt an extreme proposition, for plenty of examples could be adduced to illustrate a prediction based on a scientific hypothesis which has subsequently been verified. In the whole field of evolutionary studies, however, the situation is rather different. Here, past events which can never be subjected to direct observation have to be inferred from the data provided by material which is presently existing (even when it consists of relics of the past). In *The Origin of Species* Darwin did of course refer to the geological and fossil evidence for evolution, but at that time he had to stress the imperfection of the geological record, and he realized well enough that critics of his theory of evolution by natural selection would "ask in vain where are the numberless transitional links which must formerly have connected closely allied and representative species." In fact, Darwin's evidence for his theory was derived almost entirely from his observations on living organisms—their variation in nature and under domestication, the tendency of their populations to increase rapidly in numbers and the inference that they are necessarily exposed to what he termed the "struggle for existence," their geographical distribution, and so forth. All this kind of evidence (some of his critics argued), however formidable it might be in its collective and mutual reinforcement, was no more than circumstantial, or presumptive, evidence. Now, it is an interesting question, but one which is not easily answered —just at what point in the gradual accumulation of circumstantial evidence can the latter be accepted as adequate for demonstrating the truth of a proposition? Perhaps the most we can say is that, in practice, this point is mainly determined by the multiplicity of independent sources from which this evidence is derived; if several lines of argument based on apparently unrelated data converge on, and mutually support, the same general conclusion, the probability that this conclusion is correct may appear so high as to carry conviction to the mind of unbiased observers.

In the problem of human evolution, with which Darwin dealt specifically in his *Descent of Man* in 1871, although he had no fossil evidence on which he could rely and could only refer to hypothetical connecting links, he did adduce indirect evidence from a variety of sources which, he wrote, "declare in the plainest manner, that man is descended from some lower form, notwithstanding that connecting-links have not hitherto been discovered." His sources of collateral evidence were derived from comparative anatomy (which demonstrated a unity of design and a close similarity of homologous structures in man and apes), from embryology (which demonstrated that the human embryo passes through phases of early development similar to those found in lower vertebrates, from a consideration of rudimentary elements in the human body (which are unintelligible unless they are assumed to be the relics of fully developed elements which functioned in an ancestral stage of evolution), from a study of human variations (which provide the raw material for evolution by natural selection), and so forth. The cumulative effect of all this evidence was to demonstrate a vast number of facts which were only explicable on the assumption of man's descent from lower forms of life, and to show that, as with animal life in general, natural selection provided the means whereby evolution *could* have occurred. But the evidence that human evolution *did* occur— that is to say the objective and concrete evidence of intermediate stages of evolutionary development in past ages—was yet to be discovered. In a sense, it may be said that Darwin's evidence for human evolution resolved itself into conclusions which were really predictions, that is to say, predictions that in the course of time his conclusions might be

Reprinted by permission of the author and publisher from
PROCEEDINGS OF THE AMERICAN PHILOSOPHICAL SOCIETY,
103, No. 2, 159–172 (1959).

verified by the discovery of the connecting links to which he referred. Indeed, the predictive element in his conclusions was implied in his remark (in *The Descent of Man*): "Nor should it be forgotten that those regions which are the most likely to afford remains connecting man with some extinct ape-like creature, have not as yet been searched by geologists."

We may agree, then, that the verification of Darwin's line of reasoning with regard to the hypothesis of man's descent ultimately depends on the demonstration, by the concrete and objective evidence of actual fossil remains, that intermediate types actually did exist in the past such as he postulated. The facts of comparative anatomy, comparative physiology, embryology, blood reactions, etc., lead to the conclusion that man as we know him today is more closely related to the anthropoid apes than to any other group of living animals. This conclusion is given expression in the now generally accepted scheme of classification which places the human family (Hominidae) in close relationship to the anthropoid ape family (Pongidae); in fact, they are commonly grouped together in the single superfamily, Hominoidea. Such a classification carries with it the implication that, at some time in the distant past, the Hominidae and the Pongidae took their origin from a common ancestral stock and gradually became differentiated by a process of evolutionary diversification. If this is a correct interpretation of the indirect evidence presented by Darwin, we must suppose that, in tracing back the geological record of mankind, we should hope to find in regular temporal sequence a graded succession of types illustrating the evolutionary stages linking modern man with apelike ancestors. This does not mean (and Darwin himself emphasized this point very strongly) that the ancestral stock from which man is presumed to have been derived was similar in all respects to, or even closely resembled, the anthropoid apes which we know today, for the latter are also the terminal products of a long and independent evolutionary process which has led to the development of a number of specialized features peculiar to the modern apes. On the other hand, it may be inferred that the ancestral stock would have been characterized by many primitive characters such as a small brain, retreating forehead, prominent and chinless jaws, and so forth, which later became superseded in the hominid line of evolution by the development of more advanced characters, but which have been retained in the less progressive line of the anthropoid apes.

It is because the final confirmation of Darwin's ideas of the descent of man is only to be found in the fossil record that I refer to the latter in the title of my lecture as the crucial evidence. It is well to emphasize that this evidence, to be valid, must satisfy two requirements. First, it must be able to present a range of fossils showing in their anatomical structure serial gradations which link more primitive with more advanced types. Second, it must be able to demonstrate that these serial gradations are disposed in a regular time sequence—in other words that they represent a real temporal succession of types. Even the Primates of today, that is to say, the order of mammals to which man belongs, can be arranged in a *morphological* "sequence." This was emphasized many years ago by T. H. Huxley in one of his essays in *Man's Place in Nature* (1863), when he remarked "Perhaps no order of mammals presents us with so extraordinary a series of gradations as this—leading us insensibly from the crown and summit of the animal creation down to creatures, from which there is but a step, as it seems, to the lowest, smallest, and least intelligent of the placental mammals." But such a consecutive morphological series, while it carries important implications for the evolutionary argument, does not by itself set the seal to it. The important question is—are these implications confirmed by convincing evidence for an actual temporal succession of an equivalent kind? Since Darwin's time the geological record has indeed supplied much of this more direct evidence in verification of the "predictions" to which I have referred, and it is my intention in this lecture to review the evidence in brief summary.

Let us adventure on a journey backward in time and follow in retrospective order the antecedents of *Homo sapiens* so far as they have been displayed by their fossilized relics. We have not at our disposal any Wellsian time-machine, but we have an excellent substitute for it in the established succession of geological deposits which contain fossilized remains. In recent years the methods and techniques of estimating the chronological order of these deposits have been greatly elaborated, to the extent that their relative dating can often be determined with considerable assurance. This may be done by reference to relative levels of deposits superimposed the one on the other, to the varying thickness of the geological strata (which provides some indication of the relative length of time required for their deposition), to the succession of climatic changes which are known to have followed in rather regular sequence in different parts of the world and which have left their traces in the soil, and to the slow and gradual accumulation in the fossils themselves of certain chemical elements such as fluorine and uranium. These elements, it may be noted, tend to be taken up by bones which are undergoing fossilization from traces which may be present in percolating waters of the soil, and they accumulate in greater and greater quantity with the passage of time. A chemical analysis of fossils may thus provide important information for their *relative* dating. There are also methods for the determination of an *absolute* dating in terms of years. These methods are difficult of application and they are also limited in the periods of time to which they can be applied. From our present point of view it is particularly unfortunate that they are not (with techniques so far available) applicable to just that period of geological time which evidently saw some of the most significant stages in the evolution of the Hominidae. Thus, the radioactive carbon method permits the estimation of the absolute antiquity of fossils (or associated organic material) not much further back than about 50,000 years. The uranium-helium method, on the other hand, can only be used for estimating the age of much more ancient deposits, and, as far as I am aware, the most recent geological period which has been dated by this method is a stage of the Miocene period, which was about 30 million years ago. But even this distant period has some relevance to our present subject, for it was during the Miocene that many interesting types of primitive and generalized anthropoid apes flourished in the Old World (particularly in the central regions of Africa), and it has been surmised from their anatomical structure that some of these types may have provided the evolutionary material for the subsequent development of the earliest representatives of the Hominidae. Be that as it may, the earliest fossil remains so far discovered which can with certainty be termed "hominid," that is to say, which had already developed anatomical characters which are known to be quite distinctive of the Hominidae as contrasted with the related family Pongidae, occur in geological deposits laid down in the early part of the Pleistocene period. Now, methods of relative dating based on purely geological considerations show a fair agreement that the beginning of this period

began somewhere about one million years ago. Obviously, we should like to have estimates of the absolute antiquity of the early hominids which lived during this period, but it will be necessary first to discover some technique similar to the radioactive carbon method which will carry the chronological estimates a long way beyond 50,000 years ago. Until such techniques have been developed, we have to rely for estimates of antiquity during most of the Pleistocene on the methods of relative dating, and it is well to recognize that these methods can only give approximate results.[1]

I may note here that the Pleistocene can be subdivided on a relative chronological basis by reference to its climatic fluctuations. The latter half of the period (or perhaps rather more) was marked by a series of very cold cycles when much of the temperate regions of the earth became covered by glaciers and ice sheets. There were four of these glaciations, separated by three interglacial periods during each of which the climate became much warmer. The last glaciation reached its initial climax probably about 50,000 years ago, and the first glaciation is reckoned to have occurred almost half a million years ago.

Today the family Hominidae is represented by one genus only, *Homo,* and by only one species of this genus, *Homo sapiens*—that is to say, modern mankind. The geographical varieties of this species, or "races" as they are commonly termed, show considerable differences in superficial features such as skin color, hair texture, and so forth, but they are much less easily distinguished by their skeletal characters. Nevertheless, the latter do show differences, and it is well to recognize the extent of these skeletal variations in modern man when the problem arises whether a fossil human skeleton is that of *Homo sapiens,* or of some different and extinct species of *Homo.* For it has happened from time to time, by failing to recognize the wide range of individual and racial variability in our own species, some authorities have claimed that the human remains which they have discovered are those of a hitherto unknown species, and have even christened them with a new specific name. This has had the unfortunate effect of confusing and distorting the perspective of the latter-day prehistory of mankind (so far as it has

---

[1] The potassium-argon method of absolute dating, which is being currently developed by Dr. J. F. Evernden and his colleagues at the University of California, gives promise of being able to provide absolute ages in the range 50,000–1,000,000 years.

been revealed by fossil remains) to a quite ridiculous degree.

More careful and systematic comparisons have now made it clear that *Homo sapiens* has a quite respectable antiquity. For example, during the time when the Palaeolithic (Old Stone Age) culture known as the Magdalenian flourished in Western Europe, the local population was composed of people who, judging from their skull and skeleton, were similar in physical characters to modern Europeans. The Magdalenians had developed a quite rich culture, and they were responsible for some of the most beautiful examples of cave paintings and sculptures such as those found in the famous caves at Lascaux in France. They lived during the latter phases of the last glaciation in what is sometimes called the Reindeer Age (for the reason that reindeer herds occupied Europe in large numbers at that time). Now, pieces of charcoal left by the Magdalenians in one of the Lascaux caves have been analyzed for their content of radioactive carbon, and this has given an antiquity of about 15,000 years. We can go back further into the Aurignacian period which immediately preceded the Magdalenian, and still we find from a number of fossilized remains that the local population was apparently not distinguishable from modern populations of *Homo sapiens*. A radioactive carbon dating of 27,000 years has recently been reported for the period of the Aurignacian culture, and if the species *Homo sapiens* was already fully differentiated at that time the final stages of its evolutionary emergence must have occurred still earlier. We know also from fossil evidence that the species had spread widely over the earth many thousands of years ago. For example, *Homo sapiens* had certainly reached Australia, and even North America, about 10,000 years ago, and at Florisbad in South Africa there was found in 1933 a human skull, also not to be distinguished from the *Homo sapiens* type, whose antiquity has been estimated by the radioactive carbon method to have been at least 40,000 years.

The question now arises—is there any concrete evidence from the fossil record that *Homo sapiens* was actually in existence before the last glaciation of the Ice Age? Preceding the Aurignacian period in Europe there was a prolonged cultural period of the Palaeolithic termed the Mousterian, which can be conveniently divided into an Early Mousterian phase and a Late Mousterian phase (though this is really an over-simplification of the cultural

sequences which followed, and partly overlapped, each other during those times). The Early Mousterian covered the latter part of the last interglacial period and extended into the onset of the last glacial period, while the Late Mousterian coincided with the climax of the first part of the last glaciation. A fair number of fossil remains of Early Mousterian man have been found in Central Europe and also in Palestine, so that we know a good deal about their cranial and dental anatomy. A striking character is their wide variability, for while many individuals show primitive features such as strongly developed brow ridges, a somewhat retreating forehead, prominent jaws, and a feebly formed or absent chin eminence, others are very similar in their skull structure to the more primitive races of modern mankind. Further, the limb bones (so far as they are known) appear to be of quite modern type. Opinions vary on the question whether in some of their skull characters the Early Mousterians exceed the limits of variation found in *Homo sapiens*. Even if this is the case, I myself am not convinced that they exceed the limits to the extent that they can properly be assigned to another species altogether. Probably it is wise to defer a decision on this point for the present—if they are not *Homo sapiens* in the strict sense, they represent the immediate precursors of modern *Homo sapiens* and may be conveniently designated as such. But their great variability is of particular interest from another point of view.

In later Mousterian times, characterized archaeologically by the full development of the typical stone-tool industry to which the term "Mousterian" is properly attached, there existed in Europe and neighboring regions the distinctive type of man now so well known as Neanderthal man. The outstanding features of this type are the massive brow ridges, retreating forehead, large projecting jaws, absence of a chin eminence, and certain peculiarities of the occipital region and base of the skull. Some of the limb bones, also, are unusual in the thickness and curvature of their shafts and the relative size of their articular extremities. In curious contrast, the size of the brain of Neanderthal man—as indicated by the cranial capacity—was surprisingly large, on the average even larger than that of modern *Homo sapiens*. A sufficient number of Neanderthal skulls have been collected to permit of their study by statistical analysis; this has not only demonstrated their homogeneity as a local European population, it has also shown that in a number of dimensions (and proportional indices constructed therefrom) they lie outside the known range of variation of *Homo sapiens*. All these facts have led to the assumption, maintained by many (but not all) anthropologists, that Neanderthal man constitutes a distinct species, *Homo neanderthalensis*. At one time it was generally supposed that this extinct type was directly ancestral to modern man. But, as I have already mentioned, we now know that it was preceded by earlier types, and these, though showing a number of primitive features, were much more akin to *Homo sapiens*. Moreover, the fossil and archaeological record makes it clear that at the end of the Mousterian period Neanderthal man disappeared from Europe quite abruptly, to be replaced by a population of the modern *Homo sapiens* type. Presumably the latter spread into Europe from a neighboring area, perhaps the Middle East, and by replacement led to the extinction of *Homo neanderthalensis*.

Let us now return to the Early Mousterian populations and reconsider them in the light of their wide range of variability. At one end of this range are individuals which appear to presage the more extreme features of Neanderthal type; at the other end are individuals which approach so closely to primitive races of *Homo sapiens* that it is difficult to decide whether they can be taxonomically separated from this species. In other words, it seems that this degree of variability would readily have provided the raw material, so to speak, for the evolutionary diversification of what were evidently two terminal types—*Homo neanderthalensis* which became extinct, and the modern forms of *Homo sapiens*. Such a conclusion fits in quite well with the evidence relating to the temporal sequence. Some authorities, it may be noted, have been tempted to interpret the variability of Early Mousterians in terms of the coexistence of genetically different types, some of which may have interbred. But this is to complicate the picture unnecessarily and somewhat arbitrarily. The high variability of the Early Mousterians—considered as a single general population composed of regional variants —was probably related to their dispersal over Europe in small hunting communities, their exposure to changing climatic extremes, and the increasing intergroup competition for the means of survival. Such circumstances are particularly favorable for the diversifying action of the selective processes in evolution. It is interesting to note, by the way, that the first Neanderthal skull

to be studied—discovered in 1856 in a cave situated in a valley known as Neanderthal (near Düsseldorf)—was discussed at some length by T. H. Huxley in 1863; he expressed the opinion that it was "the most pithecoid of human crania yet discovered," but he concluded that, at the most, it demonstrated "the existence of a man whose skull may be said to revert somewhat towards the pithecoid type." In this statement Huxley showed a remarkable insight, for the accumulation of evidence since his time has certainly made it clear that some of the "pithecoid" features of Neanderthal man were the results of a secondary retrogression. Lastly, it should be mentioned that the Early Mousterians are sometimes referred to as "generalized Neanderthaloids," in contrast to the specialized or "classical Neanderthaloids" which constitute the species *Homo neanderthalensis*.

As far as is known at present, the "specialized Neanderthals," in the strict sense in which this term is commonly used, were limited in their geographical distribution to Europe and certain adjacent areas. But there lived at about the same time, or perhaps rather later, very similar types of prehistoric man in other parts of the world. In Rhodesia and South Africa fossil skulls have been found which also show huge brow ridges and massive jaws, and at Ngandong in Java several other skulls showing the same exaggerated features have come to light. It still remains doubtful what part, if any, was played in the evolutionary history of modern man by the populations represented by these remains. Perhaps they should provisionally be regarded as local variants of *Homo neanderthalensis*—if so, it must be supposed that this species spread very widely over the world in a comparatively short space of geological time. But, in any case, it seems unlikely that they were directly ancestral to the local races of man which now inhabit the regions where they lived (though some authorities have assumed them to be so). Like Neanderthal man in Europe, these aberrant types almost certainly became extinct without leaving direct descendants.

We now come to the problem of "pre-Mousterian man," that is to say, the nature of the populations which immediately preceded the Early Mousterians. Here we are faced with the difficulty that their fossil record is still too meagre to allow firm conclusions. A fairly complete and well-preserved skull found at Steinheim in Germany dates from the last interglacial period, or perhaps even earlier from the second interglacial period. It closely resembles the Early Mousterians and shows pronounced brow ridges of the skull, but the forehead region is quite well developed and the occipital region is full and rounded as in modern man. The cranial capacity is estimated to be less than 1,100 cc.; this comes well within the range of variation of *Homo sapiens* but is considerably below the mean value (1,350 cc.). Two fragments of skulls found at Fontéchevade in France, also reckoned to be of pre-Mousterian date, show a much closer resemblance to modern *Homo sapiens*, for the brow ridges are only moderate in size. Finally, a most important discovery was made of portions of a skull at Swanscombe in Kent in 1935—important because their antiquity may be assigned with considerable assurance to the second interglacial period which, by methods of relative dating, can hardly have been less than 100,000 years ago and may well have been more. Unfortunately, only three of the main bones forming the roof and back of the skull (the two parietals and the occipital) were found, and although they are excellently preserved they do not tell us very much. But careful anatomical and statistical studies have shown that, while in some respects they are certainly unusual, as far as can be ascertained they do not exceed the range of variation of *Homo sapiens* in their dimensions, shape, and individual structural features. They are unusual in the thickness of the skull wall and in the width of the occipital region. There is also definite evidence that the air sinuses of the face region were extensively developed, and this suggests the probability that the facial skeleton was rather massive, and that the frontal region may have had large brow ridges like the Steinheim skull. Until further remains of the contemporary population are discovered, all we can say, therefore, is that *on the evidence of the three skull bones available* Swanscombe man was probably similar to the Steinheim man, and at least very closely akin to *Homo sapiens*. The brain, incidentally, was quite large (the cranial capacity has been estimated at about 1,320 cc.), and the impressions on the inner surface of the skull bones also show that it was richly convoluted.

In our journey back in time, we have now traced primitive representatives of *Homo sapiens*, or at any rate the immediate precursors of this species, to the second interglacial period, that is to say the Middle Pleistocene. Moreover, there is no structural break in continuity through which these early types are linked in gradational series with modern *Homo sapiens*. If we now continue our journey into still greater antiquity, we come to a period, the early part of the Middle Pleistocene, when a much more primitive type of hominid was distributed over wide areas of the Old World, and at a time when (so far as we can say from the available evidence) *Homo sapiens* had not yet come into existence. So different from *Homo* was this primitive type, and so apelike in certain features of the skull and jaws, that it is usually regarded not only as a separate species of mankind, but as a separate genus, *Pithecanthropus*. The first relics of *Pithecanthropus* to be discovered were found in Java as long ago as 1891. For many years after this, in spite of expeditions which were planned to search for more remains, nothing else was found. Then, in 1937 and the following years, further fossils were brought to light, consisting of a few skulls, some jaw fragments, and a number of teeth. More extensive fossil material representing the same genus has been excavated from caves near Pekin. This was at first regarded as a separate and distinct type and was called *Sinanthropus,* but careful comparisons later made it clear that it is not to be distinguished generically from *Pithecanthropus*. The antiquity of these fossils is very great, but since their age can only be estimated by methods of relative dating, it can only be estimated to a rough approximation— probably somewhere between 200,000 and half a million years. Some of the Javanese representatives of *Pithecanthropus* are more ancient than the Chinese and (as might be anticipated from the time differential) they are in several respects more primitive in their anatomical structure.

Perhaps the most striking feature of the skull of *Pithecanthropus* is the small size of the braincase. The average cranial capacity of all known specimens taken together is only about 1,000 cc., and only about 900 cc. in the Javanese specimens considered separately. The latter actually include a skull with a capacity as low as 775 cc., which is only about 90 cc. greater than the largest so far recorded for anthropoid apes. At the same time, the brain size was evidently very variable, for in one of the skulls from Pekin the cranial capacity reached 1,200 cc., which is well within the range of variation of *Homo sapiens*. Apart from its average small size, the brain case shows a number of other characters which are obtrusively simian. For example, the cranial roof is flattened and the side walls slope downwards and out-

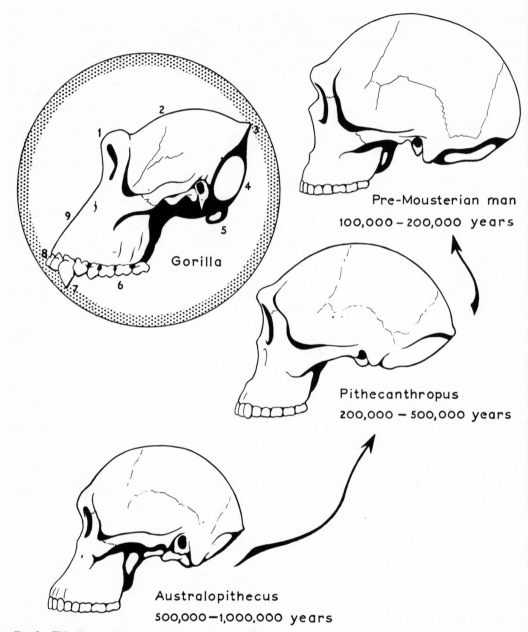

FIG. 1. This diagram illustrates the appearance of the skull in a series of fossil hominid types arranged in their temporal sequence. The antiquity of each type has been estimated by methods of relative dating and is to be regarded as no more than approximate within very broad limits. It is also to be noted that some of these types overlapped in time in different geographical regions. The representation of the genus *Australopithecus* is based on a skull found at Sterkfontein in South Africa, *Pithecanthropus* on a skull cap and portions of jaws found in Java, pre-Mousterian man on the Steinheim skull, Early Mousterian man on one of the skulls found at Mount Carmel in Palestine, and Neanderthal man on a skull found at Monte Circeo in Italy. Inset on the left is shown, for comparison and contrast, the skull of an adult female gorilla; the numerals indicate a few of the fundamental characters which, *taken in combination*, comprise a total morphological pattern distinguishing the anthropoid ape type

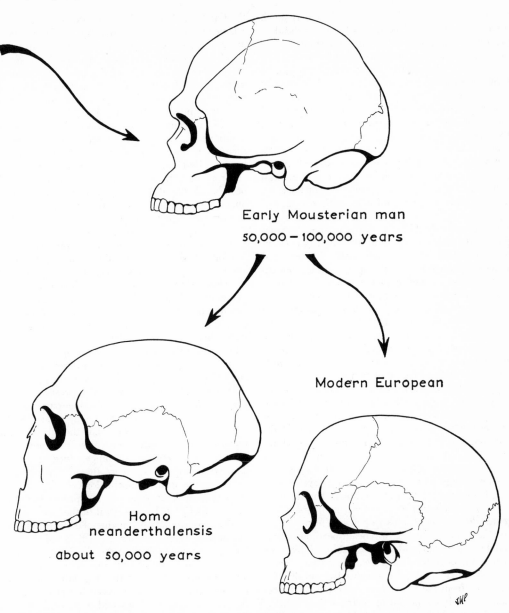

Early Mousterian man
50,000 – 100,000 years

Modern European

Homo
neanderthalensis
about 50,000 years

of skull from the hominid type of skull. The characters indicated are: (1) The forward projection of the brow ridges well beyond the front end of the brain case. (2) The low level of the cranial roof in relation to the upper border of the orbital aperture. (3) The high position of the external occipital protuberance. (4) The steep slope and great extent of the nuchal area of the occiput for the attachment of the neck muscles. (5) The relatively backward position of the occipital condyles. (6) Except in advanced stages of attrition, the teeth are not worn down to a flat, even surface. (7) The canines form conical, projecting, and sharply pointed "tusks." (8) The large size of the incisor teeth. (9) The massive upper jaw. Note, also, that in the hominid type of skull a pyramidal mastoid process of quite distinctive pattern is consistently present.

All the skulls have been drawn to the same scale, one third natural size.

wards so that the brain case as a whole is much broader towards the skull base; the forehead is markedly retreating—indeed, in some skulls a forehead can hardly be said to exist in the ordinary sense of the term; the brow ridges project to form a prominent and uninterrupted shelf of bone overhanging the eye sockets; the jaws are not only massive—they project in muzzle fashion and the lower jaw lacks any trace of chin eminence; the teeth are large, and in some individuals (though this seems to have been unusual) the canines project and partly interlock when the jaws are closed; the occipital region of the skull is marked by strong transverse crests of bone for the attachment of what must have been powerful neck muscles; the nasal aperture is low and broad; and a number of minor features in the construction of the base of the skull also approximate in some degree to the conditions generally regarded as more characteristic of the ape's than the human skull. It is interesting to note, however, that in spite of the lowly appearance of the skull, jaws, and teeth, the limb bones of *Pithecanthropus* are quite similar to those of *Homo sapiens*. Now, this serves to illustrate a most important principle of evolution—that an ancestral species or genus does not become gradually transformed *as a whole* into a descendant species or genus. It commonly happens that different parts or systems of the body evolve at different rates so that transitional stages of evolution show a mosaic of primitive and advanced characters and not an "all round" halfway stage of development. As far as the Hominidae are concerned, it is clear from the fossil record of *Pithecanthropus* that the limbs reached the final stage of their evolutionary development long before the brain, skull, and teeth had done so.

In brief, then, we may picture members of the genus *Pithecanthropus* as rather small-brained individuals with retreating forehead, beetling brows, and big jaws, but with limbs fashioned like our own. But in spite of their relatively small brains they were evidently quite advanced culturally, for we know from the traces they have left of the remains of their feasts and of their cooking hearths that those which inhabited China were skilled hunters and even knew the use of fire. They were also capable of fabricating stone implements, though of a rather crude character. It is of considerable importance for the question whether *Pithecanthropus* could have provided the ancestral basis for the subsequent evolutionary development of *Homo* to note that the remains discovered in the Far East show a fairly wide range of variation. I have already mentioned that the cranial capacity, at its upper limits, reaches close to the mean value of *Homo sapiens,* and there are similar degrees of variability in the size of the jaws, the development of the forehead region, and so forth. In fact, at one end of the range *Pithecanthropus* approaches quite closely to the Early Mousterian or Pre-Mousterian populations which I have already mentioned, and the morphological "gap" between them is almost insignificant. Unfortunately, as has so often happened in the subject of palaeoanthropology, the variants of *Pithecanthropus* have been labelled by different specific or generic names on the unwarranted assumption (or, at any rate, unwarranted on the present evidence) that they actually represent quite different types. There may be some justification for accepting the suggestion, at least provisionally, that the Javanese and Chinese populations represent different species (*P. erectus* and *P. pekinensis*), though even this distinction is doubtful. It is a well-established fact that both the genus *Homo* and also the modern genera of anthropoid apes show a high degree of variability, and if this is duly recognized the variability within the genus *Pithecanthropus* no longer appears exceptional and any further taxonomic subdivision of the genus loses its validity.

It is probable that some local representatives of *Pithecanthropus* persisted in some parts of the world after the evolutionary appearance of the genus *Homo* in other parts, but the fact remains that the earliest representatives so far known appear to have preceded the appearance of *Homo*. Thus the temporal sequence fits in with the evidence of the graded morphological series which they present, and supports the proposition that the one was probably ancestral to the other.

The most abundant remains of *Pithecanthropus* which have been discovered are those of the local populations which lived in the Far East, but there is now fossil evidence that this ancient type was by no means confined to that region of the world. For example, there have recently been found in Algeria three fossil jaws and a parietal bone of the skull which so closely resemble those of Pekin man that they are not really distinguishable in the generic sense. In spite of this, these remains have been given a new name, *Atlanthropus,* an appellation which is unfortunate not only because it seems unjustified, but also because it introduces an unnecessary complication and may obscure their real significance for human evolution. These Algerian remains were found in association with stone implements referable to the Early Acheulian phase of Palaeolithic culture, and there is reason to suppose that they date from the early part of the second interglacial period, probably more or less contemporaneously with the later Javanese fossils but antedating Swanscombe man. Another possible representative of *Pithecanthropus* is "Heidelberg man," known only from a massive lower jaw discovered in 1908, and probably of somewhat greater antiquity than the Algerian fossils. But the dentition of this species shows certain features which have led some authorities to think that its relation to *Pithecanthropus* may not be very close. Obviously, a decision on this question can only be reached when further fossil material of Heidelberg man is available for comparative study.

Thus far, it seems, we have a fossil record which, though still by no means as well documented as we could wish, does suggest a high degree of probability that from the beginning of the Middle Pleistocene onwards there has been a progressive sequence of hominid types leading almost insensibly from the primitive, small-brained *Pithecanthropus* through pre-Mousterian and Early Mousterian man to *Homo sapiens* as this species exists today. If Darwin's line of reasoning from the indirect evidence at his disposal is sound, it might be predicted that the genus *Pithecanthropus* would itself have been preceded by a type showing even more primitive and ape-like features, such as a still smaller brain, jaws of more simian dimensions, and so forth. Until 1924, we had no direct knowledge at all that any such connecting link had actually existed. In that year there was found a remarkably fine and well-preserved specimen of a new type of hominid which conformed in a most remarkable way with expectations and thus, once again, provided a verification of the predictions implied by less direct evidence. In more recent years great quantities of the fossilized remains of these creatures have been collected from cave deposits at widely different sites in the Transvaal, so that it is possible to speak with considerable assurance about their anatomical characters. Of the latter, undoubtedly the most striking is the size of the brain case, for this is not only much smaller when compared with *Pithecanthropus*, it actually overlaps the range of the modern large apes. The small brain case, combined with huge jaws, gives the whole skull a very simian appearance indeed, and it was for this reason that on their first discovery they were given the name *Australopithecus*

(which means the "southern ape"). As we know now, however, they were not apes in the strict taxonomic sense of zoological nomenclature; they were exceedingly primitive hominids which in a number of fundamental features had already developed a considerable way along the direction of hominid evolution and quite opposite to the direction of evolution which characterized the anthropoid ape family (Pongidae). In fact, they provide another excellent example of "mosaic evolution" in their combination of relatively advanced hominid features with the continued retention of primitive features inherited in common with the Pongidae from a common ancestral stock. The range of variation of the cranial capacity in *Australopithecus* has not been determined with any certainty; most of the skulls so far discovered are too incomplete, or distorted by crushing, to allow of direct estimates. Probably, however, they ranged from about 450 cc. up to about 700 cc. The higher estimates of much over 700 cc. which have been suggested for some of the specimens are too insecure to be reliable, and it is likely that they are overestimates.

It is perhaps not surprising that the earlier reports of these South African fossils were received with some scepticism and gave rise to a good deal of controversy. Because of the intense interest which they arouse, it seems almost inevitable that every discovery of fossil hominids which appears to confirm Darwin's anticipation of connecting links should be followed by controversies, and these have often been of rather a contentious and polemical character; indeed, opposing views still tend to be expressed with a vehemence which is rather unusual in scientific discussions today. No doubt this is to be explained by the fact that the problem of our own origin is by its very nature a peculiarly personal problem, so much so that even scientists may sometimes find it difficult to free their minds entirely of an emotional bias and to view the evidence quite dispassionately. In the case of *Australopithecus*, it has been the distinctively hominid characters which formed the main center of controversy, for the obviously primitive (and therefore ape-like) general proportions of the skull have never been in dispute. Let me enumerate some of the most fundamental of these hominid characters very briefly, in order to emphasize their significance for the correct interpretation of the evolutionary position of *Australopithecus*.

In their evolutionary divergence the ape line of development and the hominid line have followed in many respects very different trends. Of special significance are the contrasting trends in the dentition, for experience has shown that the comparative anatomy of the teeth can often provide particularly reliable evidence for the assessment of evolutionary affinities. In the anthropoid ape sequence of evolution, for example, the front teeth (incisors) have increased in size (leading to a broadening of the front of the jaws); as a result, the grinding teeth become disposed in rows which are parallel, or even diverge anteriorly; the canine teeth have formed powerful and projecting tusks which interlock when the jaws are closed; there is almost always a pronounced gap (diastema) in front of the upper canine to allow room for the interlocking lower canine; the front lower premolar tooth (immediately behind the canine) has accentuated the pointed and cutting (sectorial) character which is commonly found in lower Primates. In the course of hominid evolution, on the other hand, the incisor teeth remain relatively small; the dental arcade becomes evenly curved in parabolic form; the canine teeth have dwindled in size and assumed a spatulate shape—they do not project or interlock and they lie in uninterrupted series with the incisors with no abrupt contrast in their size and shape; there is normally no diastema; the front lower premolar tooth assumes a non-sectorial, bicuspid shape. In every one of these fundamental characters *Australopithecus* conforms to the hominid pattern of the dentition. The differences from the pongid type of dentition are sufficiently abrupt and clear-cut to be readily apparent simply by direct visual comparison, but they have also been abundantly confirmed by statistical analyses.

When the first australopithecine skull was found, attention was called to certain, not very conspicuous, features in which it appeared to approximate to the hominid type of skull. Later discoveries considerably reinforced the inferences drawn from these similarities, in particular an adult skull, complete except for the lower jaw and unusually well preserved, excavated in a cave at Sterkfontein near Johannesburg. This exceptional specimen has provided the opportunity for making satisfactory comparisons with extensive series of ape's skulls, and has thus served to demonstrate some rather impressive contrasts. For example, the height of the brain case in relation to the eye sockets exceeds the range of variation found in any of the apes, and so does the low position of the muscular ridge on the back of the skull for the attachment of the neck muscles. Similarly, the relatively forward position of the occipital condyles on the base of the skull (for articulation with the upper end of the vertebral column) indicates a significant approach towards the hominid condition. Together with other characters of the skull such as the conformation of the articular socket for the condyle of the lower jaw, certain structural details of the lower jaw, and the consistent presence in all the known skulls (young as well as adult) of a prominent mastoid process of typical human shape, all these anatomical details comprise a total pattern of construction which is not found in ape skulls, but which is found in hominid skulls. Thus, in spite of the simian appearance of the *general* proportions of the skull, the structural details of the latter add further support to the evidence of the dentition that the australopithecines represent an early phase in the hominid sequence of evolution.

On the basis of the early discoveries, it had been inferred from some of the features of the skull base that the australopithecines quite probably were erect, bipedal creatures, for these features appeared to indicate that the head was poised more or less evenly on the top of a vertical spinal column, and not held up by powerful neck muscles on a forwardly sloping spine as it is in apes. This indirect evidence could not by itself, of course, amount to a final proof of erect bipedalism; while it certainly justified a strong presumption that such was the case, it was at that time no more than predictive and therefore depended for its corroboration on the accession of more direct evidence. In fact, confirmatory evidence was later supplied by a detailed study of the thigh bone, and the earlier predictions finally received the most remarkable verification when specimens of the pelvis were found. Now, there is no element of the skeleton which is more distinctive of the Hominidae as compared with the large apes than the bony pelvis. In the two families it has very different proportions, which are evidently associated mainly with radical differences in posture and gait. Altogether, four different specimens of the australopithecine pelvis have been found at widely different sites in South Africa, and they all conform in their fundamental characters to the hominid pattern of construction. There can be no reasonable doubt, therefore, that the australopithecines had already achieved an erect, bipedal posture. But it should be emphasized that the pelvis shows certain differences in detail from that of *Homo sapiens*, and it may be assumed from a consideration of these differences that they had not developed the erect posture to the perfection found in modern man.[2]

When the first pelvis of *Australopithecus* was found its hominid character appeared to be in such startling contrast to the small brain of these creatures that some doubt was felt whether it actually did belong to *Australopithecus* (and not, perhaps, to some more advanced type of hominid which may have lived contemporaneously in the same region). However, apart from the fact that further excavations now appear to have eliminated this possibility, it seems that those who felt incredulous at the first discovery perhaps did not realize how common is the phenomenon of mosaic evolution, or that this phenomenon must be presumed to apply to hominid evolution in the same way that it does to that of other groups of vertebrates. After all, we know that at the *Pithecanthropus* stage of hominid evolution the limbs had already reached their final development while the skull, jaws, and brain still retained very primitive characters. From this evidence alone it might have been anticipated that the precursors of *Pithecanthropus* would show indications of a differential development of a similar type, that is to say, that the limbs would already have advanced along the hominid direction of evolution beyond the level reached by the skull, jaws, and brain.

Morphologically speaking, the genus *Australopithecus* conforms so closely to theoretical postulates for the connecting link which must be presumed to have been immediately ancestral to *Pithecanthropus,* that a true ancestral relationship seems extremely probable. The important question arises whether this inference fits into the time relationships. As the result of intensive studies of the australopithecine deposits in South Africa based on several collateral lines of evidence, it now appears certain that the most ancient remains of *Australopithecus* so far discovered did antedate *Pithecanthropus.* As I have already mentioned, the earliest representatives of *Pithecanthropus* probably date back to the beginning of the Middle Pleistocene.[3] *Australopithecus* in South Africa on the other hand, dates back to the Early Pleistocene, and it may therefore have an antiquity greater by some hundreds of thousand years. No doubt we must await further evidence for a conclusive statement on the relative time spans of *Australopithecus* and *Pithecanthropus,* but at least as far as our present information goes the inference is justified that the former was probably antecedent to the latter. In other words, the time sequence conforms with the morphological gradations represented by these fossil hominids. Of course, this general statement must not be taken to imply that the local varieties of *Australopithecus* found in South Africa were *themselves* the ancestral stock, for the genus may have had a much wider geographical distribution, and it may be that the South African types were local variants which persisted there for some time after other populations of the same genus in another part of the world had already given rise to the more advanced hominids of the *Pithecanthropus* stage of evolution.

An important aspect of *Australopithecus* is the great variability shown by different individuals and local groups, even in the circumscribed regions of South Africa in which their remains have been found. Again, as in the case of *Pithecanthropus,* there has been a tendency to interpret this variability in terms of different genera and species, and it seems to me that this has introduced the same sort of unnecessary complication into the picture. It may be emphasized again that it is the genetic fluctuation within populations that provides the basis for the selective action of the environment, and herein lies the real importance of the range of variation within the genus *Australopithecus.* As a matter of fact, some of the australopithecine specimens, at any rate as far as the jaws and teeth are concerned, approach very closely indeed to *Pithecanthropus,* so that a transition from one to the other can readily be envisaged without the need to "fill in" large gaps by hypothetical connecting links.[4]

---

[2] Some of the apparent differences may be related to individual or local group variations. For example, in two of the pelvic specimens the ischial tuberosity appears to be unusually small (though accurate measurement is rendered difficult by local erosion). But in one immature specimen from Makapan, in which the tuberosity is excellently preserved, it is closely comparable in width to that of an immature Bushman pelvis.

[3] It is important to note, when making reference to publications which are not entirely recent, that the main subdivisions of the Pleistocene have lately undergone revision. Thus, much of what used to be called Lower Pleistocene is now Middle Pleistocene, and what was once regarded as the terminal phase of the Pliocene is now taken to be Lower Pleistocene.

[4] The few specimens of australopithecine jaws here referred to were allocated by their discoverers to a separate genus, *Telanthropus.* But there appears to be no really convincing evidence that the differences which they show from other specimens of *Australopithecus* exceed, either in degree or kind, the variational limits known to exist within the single genus *Homo.*

The hominid status of *Australopithecus* has been conclusively demonstrated by extensive anatomical studies, and quite recent discoveries have now given rise to the suggestion that, in spite of the small size of the brain, the South African representatives of this genus may even have been sufficiently advanced culturally to have been capable of fashioning crude stone implements. At any rate, definite artifacts have been found embedded in breccia which also contained remains of *Australopithecus,* but which has not been found to contain any remains of a more advanced type of hominid. Clearly, this is a most exciting discovery, but perhaps not altogether unexpected. For attention had previously been drawn to quantities of baboon skulls associated with australopithecine remains, most of which show depressed fractures of the roof of the skull which suggest the possibility that they had been killed by skilful blows with an implement of some sort. The obvious inference from the discovery of the stone artifacts is that they were actually fabricated by the australopithecine individuals whose remains were found close alongside them. But there still remains the possibility that there *was* a more advanced type of hominid occupying the same region which may have been the actual tool maker, even though it has to be admitted that so far no remains of this problematical type have come to light. If, as the result of further search, it should be established that similar crude artifacts are to be found at several independent sites in association with australopithecine remains (but with no remains of any more advanced type), this would no doubt be acceptable as sufficiently good evidence of the tool-making capacity of *Australopithecus.* Naturally, the question has also been raised whether a creature with so small a brain could have possessed the intelligence required for tool-making. But this is a question which cannot at present be answered with any assurance. Taking into account the extraordinarily wide range of variation in the cranial capacity of modern man—from less than 900 cc. to about 2,300 cc. in people of apparently "normal" intelligence—and taking into account also the fact that no marked correlation has been discovered between intellectual ability and cranial capacity in normal people, it seems that within very wide limits the absolute size of the brain gives no indication of degrees of intelligence. It has to be remembered, further, that while the cranial capacity of fossil hominids can give information on the brain volume, it provides

no information of the complexity of organization of the nervous tissue of which it was composed.

We have now traced in retrospect a graded morphological series, arranged in an ordered time sequence, linking *Homo sapiens* through Early Mousterian man, pre-Mousterian man, and the small-brained *Pithecanthropus,* with the still smaller-brained *Australopithecus.* This sequence comprises a remarkable confirmation of the connecting links postulated and predicted by Darwin's hypothesis of the descent of man, at any rate as far back as the Early Pleistocene. There is no conspicuous gap in the sequence, but there still remains a serious gap covering the preceding period of the Pliocene. We know that during the early part of the Pliocene, and throughout the Miocene period before then, many interesting varieties of anthropoid apes were distributed over wide areas of the Old World, in Europe, Asia, and Africa. It is also the case that some of these fossil apes show generalized features of the skull, dentition and limb bones which might well have provided the structural basis for the subsequent emergence and differentiation of the hominid line of evolution. But as yet we have no objective evidence to show just when, or how, the emergence of this new line took place.[5]

Darwin in his time found it necessary to emphasize the imperfection of the geological record to account for the absence of many of the connecting links demanded by his conception of the evolutionary process. Since then, of course, the continual accession of fossil remains of all kinds has amplified the record enormously, and has provided much of the crucial evidence for the succession of intermediate types. But so far as human evolution is concerned, we in our time still find it necessary to emphasize its imperfection, and to re-emphasize Darwin's words, "The crust of the earth with its embedded remains must not be looked at as a well-filled museum, but as a poor collection made at hazard and at rare intervals." It is an unhappy circumstance that during the Pliocene period (which lasted about ten million years), and during the succeeding Pleistocene,

[5] Reference should be made to a fossil Primate, *Oreopithecus,* whose remains have been recovered from Early Pliocene deposits in Italy. Mainly on the basis of dental characters, this type is regarded by some good authorities as an exceedingly primitive representative of the Hominidae. But there are certain anomalous features of the dentition, as well as the paucity of material so far available, which appear to me to render such a conclusion rather doubtful for the present.

climatic changes and earth movements were accompanied by erosion and denudation of the earth's surface on a vast scale; as a result, geological deposits which may have contained valuable relics of the earlier connecting links of hominid evolution have been completely destroyed and removed. At any rate, fossiliferous Pliocene deposits in those parts of the world, such as Africa, where such connecting links may be presumed to have existed are rarely found—particularly deposits of the Upper Pliocene which was probably the critical period for tracing the course of hominid evolution which was immediately antecedent to the *Australopithecus* stage.

In view of the hazards which must always attend the preservation of fossilized remains, even under the most favorable circumstances, it is not a little remarkable that our record of the later phases of hominid evolution is as good as it is. A sequence of fossils in any other mammalian group equivalent in their close gradation to the sequence *Australopithecus → Pithecanthropus → Homo* would be regarded by most vertebrate palaeontologists as a highly satisfactory record. For even if it should prove not to represent a linear sequence of evolution (which it most probably does), it at least provides the concrete and objective evidence of a general evolutionary trend. It is an interesting fact that each discovery of a possible connecting link in human ancestry seems always to arouse more contentious and more prolonged disputation than equivalent discoveries relating to the ancestry of other mammalian species. Indeed, considered in retrospect, some of these argumentations may appear to us to savor of the ridiculous and comical, if only for the reason that such unlikely interpretations seem often to have been based on evidence the real purport of which we now accept as reasonably well assured. But, as I have already noted, the peculiarly personal nature of the study of our own origin necessarily introduces an emotional bias which tends to affect our judgment of the evidence, and this fact needs constantly to be kept in mind. Probably one of the main causes of misunderstanding in the study of hominid evolution is the use and misuse of the colloquial terms "man" and "human." Not even anthropologists always employ these terms consistently, but the main difficulty is that they are terms which in ordinary usage are commonly taken to imply very much more than the meaning attached to them by biologists when they are con-

sidering man in a strictly biological sense. It is for this reason that I would like to insist that, in discussing the evolutionary origin of our own species, the biologist should avoid altogether the terms "man" and "human"—except only where there can be no possible misunderstanding about what he means by them. Undoubtedly, also, we can approach this whole problem with much greater objectivity if we confine ourselves (even at the risk of being accused of pedantry) to the scientific terms of zoology, such as *Homo* (meaning the generic group of which *Homo sapiens* is one of the species—in fact the only surviving species), and the Hominidae (an inclusive term meaning the zoological family of which *Homo* is one of the genera).

Darwin wrote: "In a series of forms graduating insensibly from some ape-like creature to man as he now exists it would be impossible to fix on any definite point when the term 'man' ought to be used." The discovery since the publication of *The Descent of Man* of fossil types comprising mosaics of "ape-like" and "man-like" characters—in fact of just those types the former existence of which Darwin had "predicted" from the less direct evidence then available to him—now makes it clear that confusion and misunderstanding in any future discussions on hominid evolution can only be avoided if the strictest attention is paid to the customary rules of scientific nomenclature.

The very fact that it has now become necessary to emphasize this need for the most careful attention to nomenclature is surely an impressive testimony to the essential accuracy of the thesis expressed by Darwin that "man is descended from some lower form."

REFERENCES

It is inappropriate in a lecture of this kind to give a full list of references to the many books and scientific papers on human evolution which have been published. The following books are listed here for reference because they are reasonably well up to date and they provide a fairly complete bibliography of relevant publications.

BOULE, M., AND H. V. VALLOIS. 1957. Fossil men. London, Thames & Hudson.
HEBERER, G. 1956. Die Fossilgeschichte der Hominoidea. Primatologia 1:379. New York, S. Karger.
LE GROS CLARK, W. E. 1955. The fossil evidence for human evolution. University of Chicago Press.
PIVETEAU, J. 1957. Paléontologie Humaine. Traité de Paléontologie 7. Paris, Masson et Cie.
ROMER, A. S. 1941. Man and the vertebrates. 3rd ed. University of Chicago Press.

Early Man in East Africa

RECENT EXCAVATIONS IN OLDUVAI
GORGE, TANZANIA, HAVE LAID BARE A
NEW CHAPTER IN HUMAN EVOLUTION

Phillip V. Tobias*

*Department of Anatomy,
University of the Witwatersrand*

Olduvai Gorge in Northern Tanganyika (Republic of Tanzania) has in recent years thrown a flood of light on an early chapter in the evolution of man. Between 1955 and 1963, L. S. B. Leakey, M. D. Leakey, and their sons and helpers uncovered fossil bones representing no fewer than 14 individuals from various levels in the Olduvai strata (1). Although detailed descriptions are yet to be published (2), it is clear that earlier and lower mid-Pleistocene deposits of East Africa contain the remains of at least two different kinds of fossil hominids (that is, members of the Hominidae, the family of man). The first group of fossils fits comfortably into a well-defined category, the australopithecines, which have long been recognized as a partially hominized group, that is, a group possessing some characteristics like those of *Homo*. The second assemblage has proved most difficult to place in any existing category. After exploring every other possibility, we have been forced to attribute this second group of fossils to a new and lowly species of *Homo*, namely *Homo habilis*: this species represents a more markedly hominized lineage than the australopithecines and comprises a hitherto-unrecognized and even unsuspected transitional or intermediate form of early man (3).

In this article I consider the history and some of the characteristics of the new fossils, as well as their cultural and evolutionary position, and propose modifications to some existing schemes of hominid phylogeny in the light of these new discoveries.

THE OLDUVAI SEQUENCE

Before I review the new discoveries in detail, it may be useful to describe briefly the Olduvai stratigraphic succession (Fig. 1).

FIGURE 1. Schematic representation of the lower half of the Olduvai sequence, showing the approximate vertical positions of hominid fossils (numerals enclosed in squares). The potassium-argon dates are indicated near the left margin (m = million years).

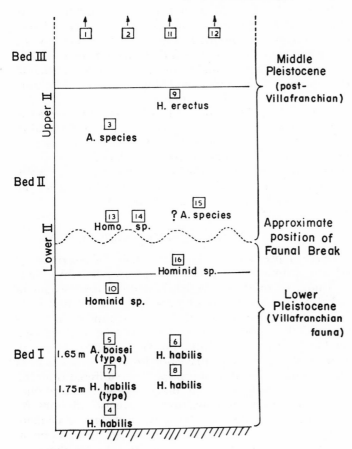

Olduvai Gorge has been cut by river action through a deep succession of old sediments, tuffs, and lavas. From the exposed strata, a remarkable series of fossils and implements has been recovered, ranging in age from Lower to Upper Pleistocene.

The strata exposed in the walls of Olduvai Gorge were divided by Hans Reck into five beds, numbered I to V, from the lowest upwards. This classification was adopted and the limits of the beds were more precisely defined by Leakey and, more recently, by Hay (4). It should be stressed, however, that these beds are not absolute stratigraphic units corresponding to sharp divisions in the Pleistocene sequence of events. Rather they are conveniently mappable units. Thus, as Hay has pointed out, two different marker beds have in various parts of the Gorge been regarded as the top of Bed I. Again, while Reck defined the base of Bed I as the basalt flows, Hay has preferred to include within Bed I the tuffs beneath the basalt. Hay thus regards the basalt flows as a constituent of Bed I in the eastern part of the Gorge.

Further, the newer analyses of fauna made by Leakey and his collaborators (5) tend to relate the fauna of the lower part of Bed II to that of Bed I and to interpret both as belonging to a final Villafranchian faunal stage. On the other hand, the fauna of the middle and upper part of Bed II is considered post-Villafranchian and so to be associated with that of Beds III and IV. The complex of Middle and Upper II, III, and IV comprises a mid-Pleistocene stratigraphic sequence.

In this presentation, the subdivision into five beds will be used to provide a background against which to consider the hominid remains.

Potassium-argon dates are available for several levels within Bed I. The span of time represented by these Beds is suggested by ages 1.75 and 1.65 million years for two levels in the lower half of Bed I. In a word, the chapters of human evolution which are dealt with here cover the period from about 2 million to about half a million years ago.

THE AUSTRALOPITHECINE CHAPTER

Exactly 40 years have elapsed since R. A. Dart published a description of a new kind of higher primate which had been recovered from a limestone fissure at Taung in South Africa (6). This discovery was one of the most remarkable, perhaps the most important, in the history of paleoanthropology. Earlier discoveries of fossilized human ancestors had shown unequivocally human affinities: this is true of the Neanderthal group and even of the earlier and morphologically more primitive Java ape-man, *Homo erectus* (or *Pithecanthropus*, as he has been called until fairly recently). But the Taung specimen differed from the others in being so much smaller-brained, bigger-toothed, and in other respects morphologically more archaic, that its precise affinities remained a cause for dispute for decades. Initially, Dart claimed no more than that it was an ape with a number of features suggesting hominization, that is, an advance in a general human direction. He therefore

TABLE 1

Dates of Discovery of Australopithecine Fossils.

1924	Taung (S. Afr.)
1936–1949	Sterkfontein Type Site (S. Afr.)
1938–1954	Kromdraai (S. Afr.)
1939	Garusi (E. Afr.)
1947–1961	Makapansgat (S. Afr.)
1948–1952	Swartkrans (S. Afr.)
1955–1959	Olduvai (E. Afr.)
1957–1958	Sterkfontein Extension Site (S. Afr.)
1964	Peninj, Lake Natron (E. Afr.)

called it *Australopithecus africanus* — simply the "southern ape of Africa."

With the wisdom of hindsight, we are today able to recognize in Dart's fossil the first real proof of the animal origins of man, the first concrete fossil evidence that Darwin's theory of the origin of species by small modifying steps and gradations from other preexisting species is applicable to man. For here was an apelike creature which showed in its anatomical makeup a greater number of resemblances to hominids than are shown by any of the existing manlike apes of Africa or Asia.

It took time, as well as the discovery of many new specimens of *Australopithecus* (Table 1), the patient study of their anatomical features, and a closer look at the living great apes, to reach the now widely accepted conclusion that the australopithecines were an early branch of the Hominidae, the family of man, rather than of the Pongidae, the family of the apes. No fewer than eight sites in Africa have yielded australopithecine fossils (Fig. 2).

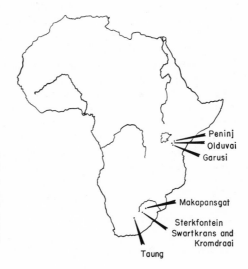

FIGURE 2. The African sites which have yielded fossilized remains of *Australopithecus,* popularly known as ape-men, near-men, or half-men. The three northern sites are in the Republic of Tanzania; the five southern sites are in the Republic of South Africa.

TABLE 2

Number of Australopithecine Teeth from Various Sites Available for Study.

Taung	24
Sterkfontein	162
Kromdraai	39
Swartkrans (35)	311
Makapansgat	55
Garusi	2
Peninj (Natron)	16
Olduvai (7)	16
Total	621

Most of the African australopithecines belong to deposits which have been classified, on comparative faunal evidence, as Lower Pleistocene. At least three sites have provided evidence that the australopithecines survived in Africa into the Middle Pleistocene — namely Swartkrans and Kromdraai in the Transvaal and Peninj (Natron) in Tanganyika.

Of all early hominid groups, the Australopithecinae are the best represented in our fossil storehouses. From the South African sites alone, no fewer than 315 australopithecine entries have been prepared for the forthcoming new edition of the *International Catalogue of Fossil Man*: some comprise a single isolated tooth, some an almost complete cranium. If we accept that all the isolated teeth from Swartkrans and Sterkfontein do indeed belong to australopithecines, the total number of australopithecine teeth now available is over 600 (Table 2). The figure for Olduvai includes only the 16 maxillary teeth of the type specimen of *A. boisei* (7), although others may need to be added to this total on further study. Juvenile and adult specimens are known, as well as male and female. Apart from age and sex variations, more than one kind of australopithecine is represented; the diversity is such that some would classify them as different genera, while others have lumped them into one genus (*Australopithecus*) with several subgenera; yet others would see them as simply different species of a single genus.

Whatever the proper classification, there is an abundance of evidence bearing on the anatomical structure and variation, the behavioral (or cultural) characteristics, and the ecological, geographical, and temporal background of the australopithecines. These lines of evidence concur in demonstrating that at least some of the known australopithecines, or of slightly earlier creatures of very similar aspect, fulfill the morphological requirements for a hypothetical human ancestor.

EAST AFRICAN AUSTRALOPITHECINES

Australopithecines have been found at three East African sites, Garusi (1939), Olduvai (1955, 1959, and ?1963), and Peninj (1964), all situated in northern Tanganyika.

The first specimen was found by Kohl-Larsen at Garusi in 1939. It comprises a fragment of upper jawbone containing both premolars. In 1943 Kohl-Larsen stated that his specimen resembled *Australopithecus* (*8*), but Weinert later reclassified it as an African species of *Meganthropus* (*9*). However, Robinson (*10*) has shown convincingly that the premolars fall within the range for the South African *Australopithecus* from Sterkfontein. This is the smaller-toothed *Australopithecus* which is usually classified today as *A. africanus*. As yet, the Garusi specimen is the only evidence we have suggesting the presence in East Africa of the gracile *africanus* species of australopithecine. The other East African australopithecines are of the larger-toothed *boisei* or *robustus* species.

The most important East African australopithecine is the specimen originally called by Leakey *Zinjanthropus boisei* (*11*) and now reclassified by Leakey, Tobias, and Napier as a species of the genus *Australopithecus*, namely *A. boisei* (*3*). For the time being the name *Zinjanthropus* is being retained to designate a subgenus within the genus *Australopithecus*. The specimen comprises a very complete cranium, including all 16 upper teeth; the wisdom teeth or third molars were still in process of erupting, suggesting that the individual was in his late teens at the time of death. A brief preliminary description has been given by Leaky (*1, 11*). Tobias (*12*) has placed on record the cranial capacity as 530 cubic centimeters; that is, the specimen's brain was no larger than that of the small-toothed *A. africanus* child from Taung. A detailed monograph on *A. boisei* will appear as part of a series of volumes on Olduvai Gorge by Leakey and his collaborators (*2*). It may be mentioned here that *A. boisei* is the biggest-toothed and most robust of all the australopithecines, exceeding in most dental dimensions even the largest-toothed of the crassident *A. robustus* group from Swartkrans in the Transvaal (Fig. 3).

It is probable that more large-toothed australopithecines are present in the Olduvai deposits. Three adult teeth, found at the site MNK II, in the lower middle part of Bed II, are for the most part of australopithecine form, shape, and dimensions (Fig. 1, hominid 15). According to Leakey (*5*), this part of Bed II is characterized by a post-Villafranchian fauna; it is early mid-Pleistocene. These teeth were referred to by Leakey and Leakey (*1*), but no attempt has yet been made to identify them specifically. Other australopithecine remains may well be present in Bed II, including the very large molar discovered in 1955, high in Bed II (*13*). Detailed studies of all these specimens are under way, and it will be some years before the complete series of full reports is published.

The third site in East Africa to yield an australopithecine is Peninj, on the west side of Lake Natron, about 80 kilometers northeast of Olduvai Gorge. Here, in January 1964, one of Leakey's assistants, Kamoya Kimeu, a member of the expedition led by Richard Leakey and Glynn Isaac, discovered a nearly complete and superbly preserved

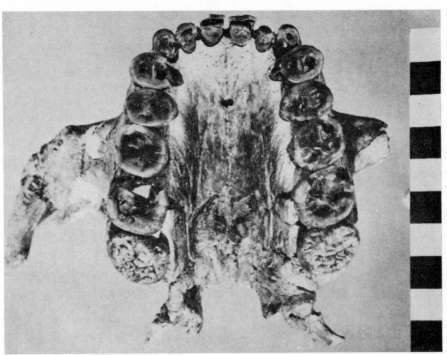

FIGURE 3. The teeth and palate of the large-toothed hominid, *Australopithecus (Zinjanthropus) boisei,* from Bed I, Olduvai Gorge.

mandible of a large-toothed australopithecine (*1*). According to Leakey's provisional identification of the fauna from this new site, it is of early mid-Pleistocene age and thus much later than the original *A. boisei* from Olduvai. It would seem to be equivalent in age to the upper part of Bed II, or even to the overlying Beds III and IV, in the Olduvai sequence. Despite this age difference, it is of interest to note that the mandibular dental arcade fits that of the maxilla of the Olduvai *A. boisei* almost perfectly and may be provisionally identified as a mandible of *A. boisei* (Fig. 4). Although age comparisons between East and South Africa are fraught with difficulties, it would seem likely that the Peninj australopithecine is comparable in age with those of Swartkrans and Kromdraai. The three sites give evidence that the large-toothed australopithecines survived in Africa well into the mid-Pleistocene (Table 3).

FIGURE 4.   Two views of the lower jawbone and teeth of a large-toothed australopithecine from Peninj, next to Lake Natron, some 80 km northeast of Olduvai Gorge. The very small front teeth (incisors and canines) and very large cheek teeth (premolars and molars) characteristic of the robust australopithecine are well shown. This mandible represents a Middle Pleistocene survivor of the African australopithecines, probably a late member of the Olduvai species, *A. boisei.*

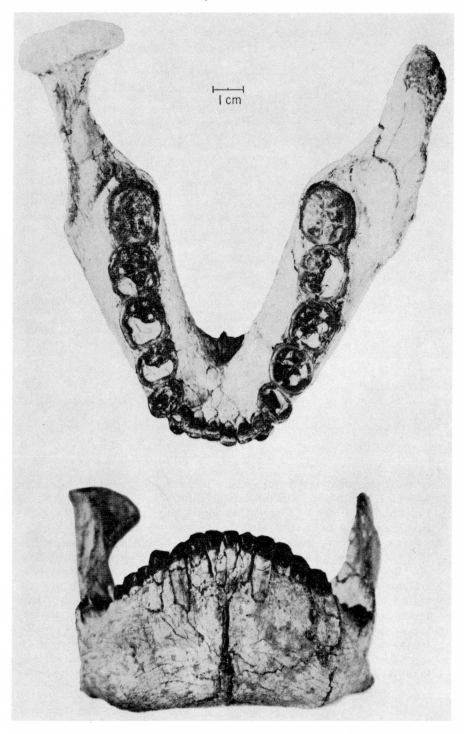

TABLE 3

Chronological and Geographical Distribution of Australopithecines. The Relative Chronological Positions of the East and South African Sites Are Uncertain, as Indicated by the Question Marks. Whereas Potassium-argon Dates Are Available for Olduvai, None Is Available for South African Sites. Comparisons of Fauna Are Valuable Among the Sites Within Each Major Geographical Zone, as Exemplified by Forthcoming New Analyses of Fauna from South African Sites by H. B. S. Cooke and from East African Sites by L. S. B. Leakey. Since Comparisons Between Fauna from the East and South African Sites Are Somewhat Vitiated by the Large Distance and Ecological Differences Between the Areas, This Scheme Must Be Regarded as Highly Provisional.

	South Africa	East Africa
	Kromdraai	?Olduvai II (Upper)
		?Peninj (Natron)
	Swartkrans	?Olduvai II (Middle)
MIDDLE PLEISTOCENE	?Sterkfontein	
LOWER PLEISTOCENE	Extension Site	?Olduvai II (Lower)
		?Garusi
	Makapansgat	
	Sterkfontein	
	Type Site	
	Taung	
		Olduvai I

UNLIKELY CLAIMANTS FOR
AUSTRALOPITHECINE STATUS

At least one other fossil from Africa has been claimed to be australopithecine, namely an incomplete cranium discovered in northern Chad and described by Coppens as an australopithecine (14). In 1963, we invited Coppens to visit South Africa and study the original australopithecine material. As a result of his study, Coppens has reached the same conclusion as Leakey and I reached independently, namely that the Chad fragment represented a more advanced hominid than *Australopithecus*. It may belong to the new species, *Homo habilis,* or even to the more advanced *Homo erectus.* The original diagnosis of the Chad fauna as very early Villafranchian is likewise being revised by Coppens; the site is apparently late Villafranchian. Unfortunately, the extremely weathered and distorted state of the Chad specimen may preclude exact comparison with other hominine remains, but it is possible that further hominid material and stone tools may yet be discovered in the area.

The possibility has been raised that the teeth and cranial fragments found outside Africa, at Ubeidiya on the Jordan River in Israel, may have belonged to an australopithecine (*15*). From a preliminary study of the scanty human remnants, generously placed at my disposal by M. Stekelis, these remains are highly likely to have belonged to *Homo* rather than to *Australopithecus,* although it may be impossible, without the discovery of further material, to attribute them to a particular species of *Homo.*

From Java has come another form of early hominid known as *Meganthropus palaeojavanicus,* of which three or possibly four mandibular fragments were found in the Djetis Beds dated to the beginning of the Middle Pleistocene (*16*). Robinson has suggested that this Javanese *Meganthropus* is simply an australopithecine (*10*). However, from a recent reexamination of the originals of *Meganthropus* I and II in comparison with original material from Africa, von Koenigswald and I concluded that, while *Meganthropus palaeojavanicus* has some strong resemblances to australopithecines, it shows several features in which it is somewhat advanced beyond the australopithecine grade (*17*). In this sense, it stands in the same relation to *Australopithecus* as does *Homo habilis* in Africa, except that *Homo habilis* has departed further from *Australopithecus* in some respects.

Another group of Asian fossils has been thought to possess australopithecine status, namely a group of isolated teeth from China attributed by von Koenigswald to *Hemanthropus peii* (*18*). Simons has suggested that these teeth are australopithecine (*19*). It is not impossible, however, that they may represent a more advanced hominid, such as *Homo habilis*; but it may be impossible to resolve the problem of their status until more specimens are recovered, including teeth in a mandible or cranium (*17*). The position of some claimants to australopithecine status is summarized in Table 4.

In sum, the case for the existence of an australopithecine stage in Asia remains unproven; the only convincing australopithecine sites remain the eight East and South African sites listed in Table 1.

THE GAP BETWEEN
AUSTRALOPITHECUS AND HOMO

Although *Australopithecus* fulfills the morphological requirements for an ancestor of man, there remains a substantial gap between the australopithecines and the most lowly representative of the hominines hitherto recognized (that is, *Homo erectus,* formerly called *Pithecanthropus, Sinanthropus, Atlanthropus,* and so on). The size of this morphological gap may best be illustrated by reference to three parameters which have shown most marked change during the process of hominization in the Pleistocene: brain size, tooth size, and tooth shape. Unfortunately, we cannot use the evidence of hand and foot bones, since we have insufficient evidence bearing on these features in *Australo-*

TABLE 4

Some Fossil Hominids Which Have Been
Claimed to Be Australopithecines.

Nature of specimen	Original designation	Revised attribution	Latest interpretation
		Swartkrans	
1 mandible, 1 mandibular fragment, and 1 radial fragment	*Telanthropus capensis*	Australopithecine (Dart, Le Gros Clark)	*Pithecanthropus* (Simonetta), *Homo erectus* (Robinson)
		Chad	
Craniofacial fragment	Australopithecine	*Homo* sp.	*Homo* sp. (unpublished)
		Ubeidiya	
2 teeth and 4 cranial fragments	Hominid	?Australopithecine	*Homo* sp. (unpublished)
		Sangiran (Djetis Beds)	
3 mandibular fragments	*Meganthropus palaeojavanicus*	Australopithecine (Robinson)	More advanced than African Australopithecine (?*Homo* sp.) (Tobias and von Koenigswald)
		China	
Isolated teeth	*Hemanthropus peii* (originally *Hemianthropus peii*)	Australopithecine (Simons)	Status not clear (?*Homo habilis*)

pithecus and in *Homo erectus*. On the other hand, good samples of braincases and endocranial casts exist for both of these groups.

From seven australopithecine crania it has been possible to make fair estimates of cranial capacity. One of these crania is the Olduvai type specimen of *A. boisei* and six are of small-toothed South African specimens. They include the child from Taung, whose estimated capacity is 500 to 520 cm³; when allowance was made for probable changes with growth, his adult capacity was estimated by various workers (*12*) as 570, 600, and 624 cm³, bigger, in fact, than any australopithecine capacity actually measured. Selecting the median value (600 cm³), we obtain an australopithecine range of 435 to 600 cm³ and a mean of 508 cm³. The range for nine *Homo erectus* crania, including 1000 cm³ for Olduvai hominid 9 (*20*), is 775 to 1225 cm³ with a mean of 978 cm³. The cranial capacity of the smallest-brained *H. erectus* was originally estimated by von Koenigswald as 750 cm³; an earlier estimate by

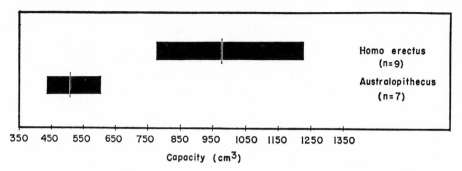

Capacity (cm³)

FIGURE 5. The ranges and means of cranial capacity in two early hominids, *Australopithecus* (including both small- and large-toothed forms) and *Homo erectus* (formerly known as *Pithecanthropus*). The largest estimated australopithecine capacity is 600 cm³ and the smallest of *Homo erectus* 775 cm³.

Weidenreich (21), subsequently disavowed by him, was 850 cm³, while Boule and Vallois give 815 cm³ (22). Most workers have accepted Weidenreich's final estimate of 775 cm³. These variations, however, reinforce an impression I gained recently when, through the courtesy of D. Hooijer and G. H. R. von Koenigswald, I examined the original Javanese crania: there is a need for reassessment of the capacities of the several Javanese crania of *Homo erectus* (23).

Figure 5 represents the ranges and the gap between the presently accepted estimates of cranial capacity for *Australopithecus* and *H. erectus*. There is an interval of 175 cm³ between the capacities of the largest-brained australopithecine and the smallest-brained *H. erectus*. However, this difference is rather meaningless unless we consider the estimated body size of the two forms. Jerison has analyzed brain size (to which cranial capacity is an approximation) into two independent components, one of which is determined by body size and the other of which is associated with improved adaptive capacities (24). Given certain assumptions, it has further been possible to estimate the number of cortical nerve cells in the brain as a whole, as well as in each of the two components. The number of "excess" nerve cells — that is, of cells over and above those which can be accounted for by body size — may then be taken as a measure of the real advancement in brain volume, irrespective of body size.

The following are estimates of the numbers of excess nerve cells based partly on Jerison's estimates and partly on my own (25):

African great apes	3.4 to 3.6 billion
Australopithecines	4.0 to 5.0 billion
Homo erectus	5.8 to 8.4 billion
Homo sapiens	8.4 to 8.9 billion

If our estimates are correct, there is a bigger gap between *Australopithecus* and *H. erectus* than between the apes and the australopithecines or between *H. erectus* and *H. sapiens*. If, instead of comparing ranges, we compare the mid-values for the groups, we obtain values of 3.5, 4.5, 7.1, and 8.65 billion for the four groups, respectively. Clearly, there is a greater distance between *Australopithecus* and *H. erectus* than between any other two consecutive groups.

To compare dental features of the two groups, it is necessary to point out that on the basis of tooth size, the australopithecines fall into two more or less well-defined subgroups. The first — represented by the fossils from Taung, Sterkfontein, Makapansgat, and Garusi — has somewhat smaller cheek teeth (premolars and molars), but somewhat larger anterior teeth (incisors and canines); this group is called *Australopithecus africanus*. The second — represented by the australopithecine fossils from Swartkrans, Kromdraai, Olduvai, and Peninj (Natron) — has larger cheek teeth and smaller front teeth; this group comprises *A. robustus* and *A. boisei* in the most recent classifications.

Figure 6 demonstrates the ranges of tooth sizes for *A. africanus* and *H. erectus*. Once more the extent of the morphological distance between the Australopithecinae and *H. erectus* is apparent. The differences

FIGURE 6. Crown areas of the maxillary (left) and mandibular (right) teeth of *A. africanus* (the australopithecine from Taung, Sterkfontein, Makapansgat, and Garusi) compared with those of *H. erectus* from Africa, Asia, and Europe. Crown area is the product of the length and breadth of the crown of a tooth; values are in square millimeters.

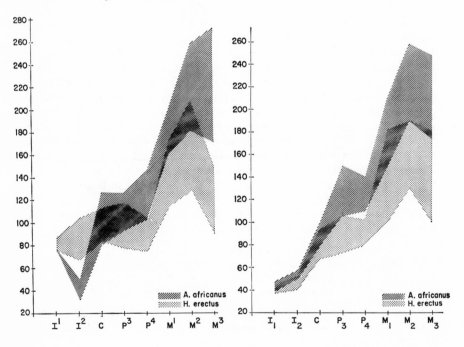

are more striking when *A. robustus* and *A. boisei* are compared with *H. erectus*.

Similarly, Figure 7 reflects variations in the shape and size of the teeth of *A. africanus* and *Homo erectus*. In a word, australopithecine cheek teeth are broader buccolingually, while hominine cheek teeth are narrower (but more elongate) from front to back.

On the basis of these three parameters, there is a clear and sizable gap between known australopithecines and *Homo erectus*. Until recently, it has apparently been tacitly assumed that *Australopithecus* graded more or less insensibly into *Homo erectus* in the manner postulated in general terms by Charles Darwin. It is therefore of no small interest to note that so large a gap exists, not only with respect to one parameter, brain size, but, in the same creatures, with respect to dental traits.

It is this gap that has been filled by *Homo habilis,* the newly discovered hominid which, with respect to the three parameters used to characterize the gap, as well as with respect to other morphological markers, lies in a largely intermediate position.

FIGURE 7. Buccolingual breadths (in millimeters) of the maxillary (left) and mandibular (right) teeth of *A. africanus* and *H. erectus*. The cheek teeth (from P3 to M3) of the australopithecines are characteristically broadened, as contrasted with those of the hominines, represented here by *Homo erectus*.

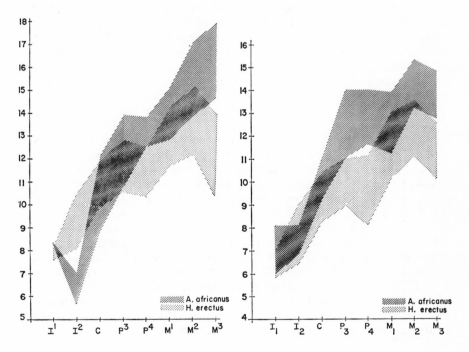

HOMO HABILIS: THE EARLY
PLEISTOCENE HOMININE

The family Hominidae may be divided into two subfamilies, the Australopithecinae and the Homininae. The term "hominine" is the common or
colloquial name connoting a member of the subfamily Homininae.

From at least four levels in Bed I and the lower (Villafranchian)
and middle parts of Bed II in the Olduvai succession have come skeletal
remains of another type of hominid (Fig. 1). This hominid differs widely
from *A. boisei,* the large-toothed australopithecine found in the same
beds. For instance, the teeth are appreciably smaller than those of *A.
boisei.* While the sizes of the teeth of *A. boisei* in general fall above the
top of the range for the South African australopithecines, the teeth of
this second hominid, especially the premolars, fall at or below the lower
end of the australopithecine range (23). Such wide divergence between
the two hominids from the same site is far in excess of what can be
attributed to sexual dimorphism: in any event, it is accompanied by
divergences in shape, proportions, and detailed morphology of the teeth,
in cranial shape and curvature, and in cranial capacity. Clearly the
second batch of fossils represents another type of hominid. In almost
all the departures of the second hominid from the australopithecine
morphological pattern, it approaches more closely to the hominine
pattern. In other words, the total pattern is more markedly hominized
than that of *Australopithecus.* To the Bed I form characterized by these
more hominized features we have given the name *Homo habilis.*

The formal naming of the species was announced by Leakey, Tobias,
and Napier on 4 April 1964 (3). The generic name implies that this
primitive hominid belonged to the genus *Homo,* while the specific name
habilis, which was suggested by R. A. Dart, means "able, handy, men-
tally skillful, vigorous," from the inferred ability of the man to make
stone tools.

In accordance with international convention in the naming of new
species, one set of remains was selected as the "type specimen" of
Homo habilis. These were the remains of a juvenile (No. 7 in Fig. 1)
whose bones — comprising a lower jaw with teeth, an upper molar
tooth, the incomplete parietal bones of the cranial vault, and a set of
hand bones — were found scattered on a single floor at the site FLK NNI
in the Olduvai Gorge (Fig. 8). In the 3 years that elapsed between his
discovery and his naming, he was known as "pre-Zinjanthropus" because the living floor on which his bones were found lies some 35 cm
below the living floor on which "Zinjanthropus" (or *A. boisei*) had been
found. The youth of the individual represented was attested by the state
of eruption of the teeth and by the signs of incomplete growth and
ossification of the other bones, thus permitting the confident association
of this group of bones as those of a single individual.

FIGURE 8. Left lateral view of the dental arcade and body of the mandible of the type specimen of the new Olduvai hominine, *Homo habilis*. In this juvenile specimen, only the first two molars have erupted. The "enamel line" on each tooth is clearly defined; areas of hypoplastic enamel are well shown on the canine tooth.

Apart from the type specimen, remains of four other individuals — three from Bed I (hominids 4, 6, and 8 in Fig. 1) and one from the middle part of Bed II (hominid 13) — were listed as "paratypes" of *Homo habilis*. Bones from two further individuals in the lower and middle parts of Bed II (hominids 14 and 16 in Fig. 1) were referred to the same species, but one of these only provisionally. All told, this batch of remains comprises some 40 teeth, two tolerably complete lower jawbones and a fragment of a third, parts of a pair of upper jawbones, varying portions of the braincases of four skulls, the hand bones of at least two individuals, foot bones, and a collarbone. In addition, two leg bones (tibia and fibula) *may* belong to *H. habilis,* but we cannot rule out the possibility that they belonged to an australopithecine.

The features which distinguish *H. habilis* remains from those of australopithecines and relate them rather to the more advanced Homininae include the capacity of the braincase, both absolutely and in relation

511

to estimated body size, the size, proportions, and shape of the teeth, the shape and size of the jaws, and the curvature of the cranial bones. In addition, the postcranial bones help us to obtain a picture of the very hominine morphological pattern of *Homo habilis*, but they do not assist in the taxonomic problem of deciding whether, for instance, the hand of *H. habilis* was closer to that of *Australopithecus* or to that of the Homininae. This is because we do not know enough about the structure of the hand in either the australopithecines or *H. erectus*.

In all those parts for which we do possess adequate comparative material for both australopithecines and early hominines, most of the bones of *H. habilis* fall at the extreme or beyond the range of variation for the australopithecines.

One important example of the greater degree of hominization shown by *H. habilis* is provided by his cranial capacity. Although the cranial vault of the type specimen is incomplete, it has been possible to estimate the capacity of the intact vault (26). The estimates range from 643 to 724 cm^3, with central values 674 and 681 cm^3. This is some 80 cm^3 more than the largest known capacity of *Australopithecus* and 95 cm^3 smaller than the smallest known capacity of *H. erectus*.

When Jerison's formulae (24) are applied to the estimate of 680 cm^3, the body size being estimated from the size of the foot bones, a value of 5.3 to 5.4 billion "excess nerve cells" is obtained. That is, the "intelligence" component of the brain of *H. habilis* has about 0.8 to 1.0 billion more neurons than that of the australopithecines, but about 1.7 to 1.8 billion fewer than that of *H. erectus* (25). Jerison's formulae thus provide striking confirmation of the evidence provided by absolute cranial capacity that *H. habilis* is a more advanced hominid than *Australopithecus* but not so advanced as *H. erectus*.

The parameter of tooth size has the same story to tell. Most of the teeth of *H. habilis* are smaller than those of most australopithecines. Thus, in 30 out of 38 comparisons, the absolute sizes of the *H. habilis* teeth lie at the extreme of the range for *Australopithecus* or outside the range.

Not only the size, but the shape of the teeth is distinctly different from that of *Australopithecus* (Fig. 9). Instead of possessing the great breadth characteristic of the teeth of the latter, the teeth of *H. habilis* are narrow and relatively elongated, this departure being found in 20 out of 30 comparisons with the australopithecine teeth. In this respect, the teeth of *H. habilis* resemble those of *H. erectus*.

In sum, *H. habilis* was a pygmy-sized hominid with a relatively large cranial capacity, reduced and narrow teeth, and a number of markedly hominine features in his limb bones. His total structural pattern was that of a creature appreciably more hominized than any of the large group of australopithecines of South and East Africa. The advanced features, moreover, were not those of an individual extreme variant, but characterized all the individuals represented over some considerable

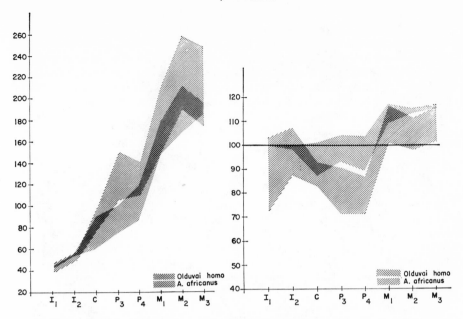

FIGURE 9. Ranges of size and shape of mandibular teeth in the *H. habilis* from Bed I and the hominine from lower Bed II compared with those of *Australopithecus africanus*. Left, crown areas (mm²). Right, the length of the tooth expressed as a percentage of the breadth. The cheek teeth (premolars and molars) of the hominines have higher indices because they are elongated and lack the characteristic australopithecine broadening of these teeth.

time. Clearly, this strain represents a distinct taxon intermediate between the most advanced *Australopithecus* and the most primitive *Homo*.

Since the original description was published in April 1964, a detailed comparison has been made between the original specimens from Tanganyika and those from Java. As a result, G. H. R. von Koenigswald and I have concluded that in the Bed II paratype of *H. habilis* (which lived some 3/4 million years later than the type specimen), the hominizing trends have been carried still further; as a result, the jaws and teeth of the later specimen (Fig. 10) closely resemble those of *H. erectus* attributed to the early Middle Pleistocene Djetis Beds of Java (17). If these features represent sequential changes, we are virtually seeing here evolution in action, with subtle intergrades from one level of hominization to the next.

CULTURAL STATUS OF HOMO HABILIS

It is accepted that cultural or ethological evidence may be added to morphological evidence in assessing the taxonomic status of a group.

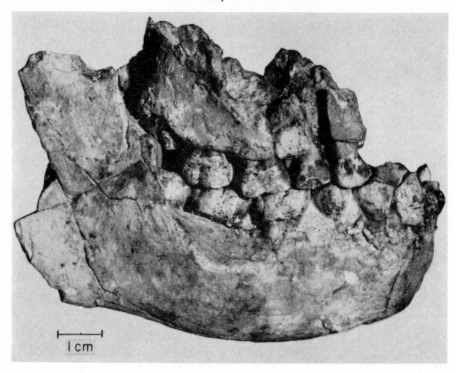

FIGURE 10. Part of the right maxilla (upper jawbone) and the mandible of the hominine (no. 13) from the lower part of Bed II, Olduvai Gorge. These jaws and teeth bear close comparison with those assigned to the Djetis Beds of Java (the Sangiran IV cranium and the Sangiran B mandible).

We may ask the question: Did *H. habilis* behave like an *Australopithecus* or like a *Homo*?

At each of the levels in Bed I where remains of *Homo habilis* have been found, primitive stone implements have been recovered. These artifacts are commonly made from pebbles or irregular fragments, and the cultural phase represented by the succession of stone industries constitutes the Oldowan Culture, formerly known as the Oldowan phase of the pre-Chelles-Acheul Culture. For long, the identity of the makers of the Oldowan Culture tools has been uncertain: some have maintained that the australopithecines were responsible, others have attributed the tools to early members of *Homo erectus* — but always on the basis of very indirect arguments. When in 1959 the cranium of the Olduvai australopithecine (*A. boisei*) was found on a living floor alongside Oldowan tools, at a time when no other adequate hominid remains were known to be associated with these tools, Leakey claimed that this australopithecine must have been the Oldowan toolmaker (*1*). This left a difficult problem: Why was the East African australopithecine associated with stone tools, whereas the Makapansgat australopithecine was associated with the bone, tooth, and horn tools described by Dart? Subsequently, however, remains of *H. habilis* were found on the same living floor as *A. boisei* and the tools. Furthermore, remains of *H. habilis* were found on the lower (earlier) living floors in Bed I, in each instance associated with Oldowan artifacts. While it is possible that both *A. boisei* and *H. habilis* made tools, it is probable that *H. habilis* was at least the more advanced toolmaker.

Furthermore, if we make a survey of all the evidence from South and East Africa, we see that *Australopithecus* alone has not yet been found with stone objects which are undoubtedly tools, except where advanced hominid remains were present as well (20, 25). Six out of 12 deposits have yielded australopithecine remains with no stone tools (27); four sites which have australopithecines and stone tools contain, in addition, indications of a more advanced hominid. The remaining two deposits contain only the more advanced hominid and stone tools. At no site where australopithecine remains are the only hominid remains present are there any stone implements; conversely, at every site which has yielded stone implements and associated hominid remains, these hominid remains include those of a more advanced hominid, whether or not australopithecine remains are present in addition. Furthermore, at every site which has yielded the more advanced hominid, stone tools are present.

It has tentatively been concluded from these associations that no unequivocal evidence exists that *Australopithecus* made Oldowan stone tools to a set and regular pattern and according to a developing cultural trend. On the other hand, it seems very probable that *H. habilis* was the maker of the Oldowan stone tools, while *H. erectus* made the later (Chelles-Acheul) implements.

Dart (28) has demonstrated that the australopithecines were capable of a wide range of cultural activities. It may, however, be argued that all of these activities fall into the categories which Napier (29) has classified as *ad hoc* tool-using, purposeful tool-using, tool-modifying for an immediate or even for a future purpose, and possibly even *ad hoc* tool-making. But it may be questioned whether these australopithecine activities constitute cultural tool-making — that is, whether they exhibit a set and regular complex of patterns which, moreover, show developmental trends with the passage of time.

If this interpretation is correct, ethological or cultural evidence could be added to the anatomical evidence which tends to ally *H. habilis* with the hominines rather than with the australopithecines.

One further probable manifestation of the culture of the early Olduvai hominids is a rough circle of loosely piled stones discovered on a living floor at DK I in the lower part of Bed I (3). It suggests a crude shelter or windbreak and is on the same level as that on which the earliest remains of *H. habilis* were found (MK I). *H. habilis* may have been responsible for this rude structure.

SIGNIFICANCE OF HOMO HABILIS

Both its structure and its place in time impart a unique significance to *Homo habilis,* while, culturally, it seems to provide us for the first time with a knowledge of the makers of the Oldowan Culture.

Structurally, *H. habilis* may be regarded as a most effective link between the Australopithecinae and the Homininae, between which, as has been mentioned, there is a larger gap than has hitherto been recognized. Its very intermediacy is underlined by the fact that some workers would regard the newly discovered form as the most advanced australopithecine and others as the most primitive hominine. Thus, even in the short time since the new fossils were discovered, various workers have believed that the habilines were simply another australopithecine (30), a new genus between *Australopithecus* and *Homo* (31), a new lowliest species of *Homo,* namely *H. habilis* (3), and even a new subspecies of *H. erectus,* namely *H. erectus habilis* (32). The position adopted by my colleagues and myself would seem to be a compromise between the extreme views on either side. Although argument on the exact taxonomic position may continue for some time, it seems that there is already fairly general agreement on this virtually uniquely linking position of *H. habilis.* Perhaps only *Meganthropus palaeojavanicus* of Sangiran, Java, lies in a similarly intermediate position between the Australopithecinae and the Homininae, albeit a little nearer to the australopithecines than is *H. habilis* (17).

Chronologically, the recognition of *H. habilis* means that a more hominized line of creatures was evolving alongside the somewhat less hominized australopithecines even in the Lower Pleistocene. Previously, the *H. erectus* remains of the Djetis Beds, agreed by most as belonging to the beginning of the mid-Pleistocene, represented the earliest recognized hominine. It was still possible then to claim that, if indeed the Homininae stemmed off from an australopithecine ancestral group, this lineage of *Homo* need not have arisen any earlier than the end of the Lower Pleistocene. It now seems clear that, if the habilines are in fact members of the Homininae, then hominines were already present in Africa, and perhaps in Asia, during at least the second half of the Lower Pleistocene. The departure of the hominine line from its presumed australopithecine ancestor must then have occurred as early as at least the Upper Pliocene or the first part of the Lower Pleistocene.

The early hominines must have been contemporaries of several diversified australopithecines — a megadont line (*A. boisei*), a macrodont line (*A. robustus*), and a mesodont line (*A. africanus*). In fact, at least in East Africa, and probably, too, in South Africa, *H. habilis* and *Australopithecus* spp. were sympatric and synchronic. More precisely,

Olduvai I provides us with early evidence of the sympatric coexistence of the largest-toothed australopithecine (*A. boisei*) and *H. habilis,* while Swartkrans gives us later evidence for the sympatric compresence of the large-toothed *A. robustus* and a more advanced hominine, *H. erectus* ("*Telanthropus*"). Doubtless, ecological differences permitted this situation to persist right through until the middle part of the mid-Pleistocene (Fig. 11).

BEARINGS ON HOMINID EVOLUTION

As a total morphological complex, *H. habilis* represents a more advanced grade of hominid organization than *Australopithecus.* Have the habilines arisen from the australopithecines? Since they are contemporary with *H. habilis,* the australopithecine populations represented by the actual fossils recovered to date are clearly too late — and possibly slightly too specialized — to have been on the actual human line, unless we are to postulate a polyphyletic origin of the Homininae at varying times from australopithecine stock. Morphologically, the gracile *A. africanus* is closest to *H. habilis* and seemingly least specialized. It would not be rash therefore to suggest that of the various australopithecines *A. africanus* has departed least from the common ancestor of *A. africanus* and *H. habilis.* On the other hand, the large-toothed, specialized *A. robustus* and *A. boisei* would seem to be far off the common *africanus-habilis* line. Two possible interpretations spring to mind:

(1) The Pliocene ancestral australopithecine was large-toothed and perhaps adapted to a vegetarian diet (33); *A. boisei* and *A. robustus* would then represent a conservative line which maintained these qualities right through into the Middle Pleistocene, while *A. africanus* developed different ecological requirements which, perhaps through a more carnivorous or, at least, omnivorous diet, led to a relaxation of selective pressures maintaining large teeth. The gracile *H. habilis* stemmed off from this smaller-toothed line of australopithecines and became selected for increasingly hominine features.

(2) The ancestral australopithecine was unspecialized, small-toothed, omnivorous. At some time in the Upper Pliocene, it diversified into macrodontic and megadontic lines (*A. robustus* and *A. boisei*), with specialized dentition, perhaps accompanying a specialized, essentially herbivorous diet. Another line remained little changed and unspecialized, eventually to dichotomize into a progressively more hominized line represented by *H. habilis* in Africa and perhaps *Meganthropus* in Asia and a more conservative residual line (*A. africanus*) which, because of ecological similarities to *H. habilis,* did not long outlast the emergence of this hominine.

Which of the two interpretations is correct, or whether other alternatives should be considered, only the direct evidence of Pliocene fossils will determine. Pending their discovery, I incline to favor the second view, on indirect lines of evidence to be presented elsewhere. That is,

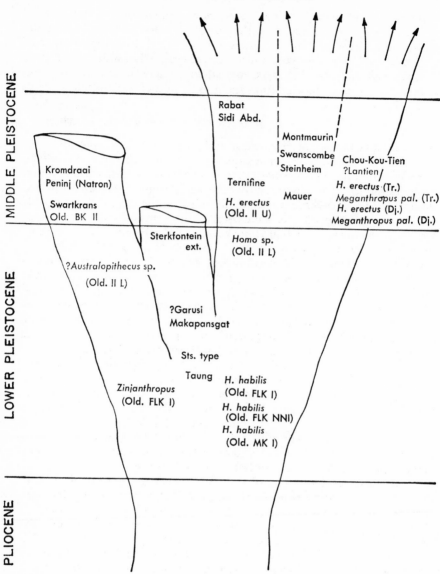

FIGURE 11. Schema of Lower and Middle Pleistocene hominids, showing the position in time and space of the most important specimens discovered to date. The left trunk of the tree represents the large-toothed australopithecine line; the middle trunk the small-toothed australopithecine line; and the right trunk the hominine line leading to modern man. *Sts.*, Sterkfontein; *Sidi Abd.*, Sidi Abderahman; *Old. II*, Olduvai Bed II; *U*, upper; *L.* lower; *Tr.*, Trinil Beds; *Dj.*, Djetis Beds.

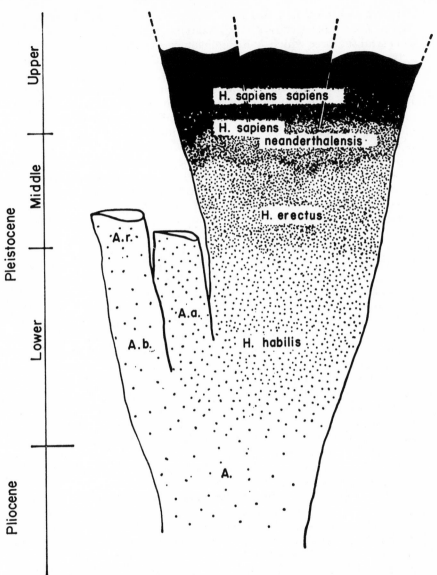

FIGURE 12. A provisional schema of hominid phylogeny from Upper Pliocene times to the Upper Pleistocene. Increasing intensity of shading represents increasing degrees of approach toward the structure and behavior of modern man. *A*, the hypothetical ancestral australopithecine; *A.b.*, *Australopithecus (Zinjanthropus) boisei*; *A.r.*, *Australopithecus robustus*; *A.a.*, *Australopithecus africanus*. The schema indicates the synchronic coexistence of several different hominids in the Lower and Middle Pleistocene, the australopithecines surviving into the Middle Pleistocene alongside more advanced hominids of the genus *Homo*. This figure should be considered in conjunction with Figure 11.

I tend to regard the large teeth and supporting structures of *A. robustus* and *A. boisei* as secondary specializations, rather than as primitive or ancestral features which J. T. Robinson seems to believe (33).

Irrespective of which interpretation we adopt, it seems reasonable to infer that late in the Pliocene, or thereabouts, some populations of ancestral *Australopithecus*-like hominids moved forward to a further grade of hominization, thus generating the Homininae. We may tentatively conclude that *H. habilis* is on this direct hominine line. Such is the message of his morphology and his culture, while his position in space and time is compatible with this conclusion (34). As a Lower Pleistocene hominine, he bids fair to provide us with a population, one or more sections of which were ancestral to the mid-Pleistocene hominines (Fig. 12). Nothing in the structure or dating of the relevant fossils rules out the possibility that some populations of *H. habilis* underwent further hominizing changes by phyletic evolution late in the Lower Pleistocene, to attain the *H. erectus* grade of hominization.

Such a reconstruction permits us to recognize a series of grades of hominization, within which we may classify the available fossils. Despite wide variation within each grade — only a fraction of which is as yet known for most grades — we may recognize: (i) an australopithecine grade, represented convincingly only in South and East Africa; (ii) a habiline grade from Africa, perhaps corresponding to a meganthropine grade in Asia; (iii) an earlier *H. erectus* grade, represented in Africa possibly by remains from middle Bed II, Olduvai, and by *"Telanthropus"* from Swartkrans, and in Asia by the Djetis Beds hominines from Sangiran, Java; (iv) a later *H. erectus* grade, represented in Africa by "Chellean Man" from upper Bed II, Olduvai and by *"Atlanthropus"* of Northwest Africa; in Asia by the Trinil Beds and Chou-Kou-Tien hominines; and in Europe possibly by the remains of Mauer; (v) an earlier *H. sapiens* grade (Neanderthal) widely distributed in the Old World; and (vi) a later *H. sapiens* grade, ultimately worldwide in distribution. This sequence shows remarkable parallels between Africa and Asia from grade 2 onwards (17).

We see in conclusion that *H. habilis* has bridged the last remaining major gap in the Pleistocene part of the story of human evolution.

Summary. Recent discoveries of early Pleistocene hominids in East Africa have revealed a new stage in human evolution. The remains of *Homo habilis*, discovered by L. S. B. Leakey and his family, bridge the hiatus between the most advanced australopithecines and the most primitive hominines. The new species was bigger-brained and smaller-toothed than *Australopithecus,* the fossil apeman from South and East Africa. It is very probable that *Homo habilis* was, as his name implies, a "handyman," maker of the earliest stone culture, the Oldowan.

These primitive hominines were already in existence in the Lower Pleistocene, living alongside a variety of more conservative hominids, the australopithecines. The closeness of morphology between *H. habilis* and *Australopithecus africanus* points strongly to a common ancestry in the Upper Pliocene or the very beginning of the Pleistocene. The large-toothed *A. robustus* and *A. boisei* were already diverging by specialization from the postulated unspecialized ancestral australopithecine. The first hominines must thus have come into being by the beginning of the Pleistocene. Later, some populations of *H. habilis* seemingly underwent further hominizing changes to generate a new species, *Homo erectus,* bigger men with larger and more effective brains, smaller and more modern human teeth, probably more complete adjustment to upright stance and bipedal gait, a more precise manual grip, and an appreciably advanced material culture.

Homo habilis thus fills in the last remaining major gap in the Pleistocene story of human evolution.

REFERENCES AND NOTES

* The author is professor and head of the Department of Anatomy at the University of the Witwatersrand, Johannesburg, Republic of South Africa.

1. L. S. B. Leakey, *Nature* **184,** 491 (1959); **189,** 649 (1961); _____ and M. D. Leakey, *ibid.* **202,** 5 (1964).
2. The skulls and teeth have been entrusted to me by Dr. Leakey for detailed study, while Drs. J. Napier, P. Davis, and M. Day of London are studying the other (postcranial) parts of the skeleton. Our detailed reports will appear in a new series of volumes on the Olduvai Gorge to be published by Cambridge University Press.
3. L. S. B. Leakey, P. V. Tobias, J. R. Napier, *Nature* **202,** 7 (1964).
4. R. Hay, *Science* **139,** 829 (1963).
5. L. S. B. Leakey, *Olduvai Gorge 1951–1961,* vol. 1, *A Preliminary Report on the Geology and Fauna* (Cambridge Univ. Press, Cambridge, 1965).
6. R. A. Dart, *Nature* **115,** 195 (1925).
7. There are some 54 additional teeth from Olduvai. Some of them belong to *H. habilis*; some may be australopithecine; while others are as yet of unknown affinities.
8. L. Kohl-Larsen, *Auf den Spuren des Vormenschen* (Strecker and Schröder, Stuttgart, 1943).
9. H. Weinert, *Z. Morphol. Anthropol.* **42,** 113 (1950); **43,** 73 (1951).
10. J. T. Robinson, *Am. J. Phys. Anthropol.* **11,** 1 (1953); **13,** 429 (1955).
11. L. S. B. Leakey, *Nature* **186,** 456 (1960).
12. P. V. Tobias, *ibid.* **197,** 743 (1963).
13. L. S. B. Leakey, *ibid.* **181,** 1099 (1958); J. T. Robinson, *ibid.* **185,** 407 (1960); G. H. R. von Koenigswald, *Koninkl. Ned. Akad. Wetenschap. Proc. Ser. B* **63,** 20 (1960); A. A. Dahlberg, *Nature* **188,** 962 (1960).
14. Y. Coppens, *Compt. Rend.* **252,** 3851 (1961); *Bull. Soc. Préhistorique Franc.* **58,** 756 (1961); in *Problèmes Actuels de Paléontologie (Évolution des Vertébrés)* (Centre National de Recherche Scientifique, Paris, 1962), p. 455.
15. M. Stekelis, L. Picard, N. Schulman, G. Haas, *Bull. Res. Council Israel* **9G,** 175 (1960).
16. F. Weidenreich, *Amer. Mus. Nat. Hist. Anthropol. Papers* **40,** 1 (1945).
17. P. V. Tobias and G. H. R. von Koenigswald, *Nature* **204,** 515 (1964).

18. G. H. R. von Koenigswald, *Koninkl. Ned. Akad. Wetenschap. Proc. Ser. B* **60**, 153 (1957).

19. E. L. Simons, *Science* **141**, 879 (1963).

20. P. V. Tobias, *Current Anthropol.*, in press.

21. F. Weidenreich, *Palaeontol. Sinica* n.s. **D10**, 1 (1943).

22. M. Boule and H. V. Vallois, *Fossil Men* (Thames and Hudson, London, 1957).

23. P. V. Tobias, "Festschrift on the 65th birthday of Juan Comas," in press.

24. H. J. Jerison, *Human Biol.* **35**, 263 (1963).

25. P. V. Tobias, in *Proc. 8th Intern. Congr. Anthropol. Ethnol. Sci., Moscow, August 1964*, in press.

26. P. V. Tobias, *Nature* **202**, 3 (1964).

27. Although cultural material and an australopithecine mandible are known from Peninj (Lake Natron), the implements are not associated with the mandible. I am indebted to Glynn Isaac for the information that excavation of the jaw site itself has yielded no cultural material. Scattered stone artifacts and two early Acheulian sites occur some distance from the mandible site. G. Isaac, *Quaternaria*, in press.

28. R. A. Dart, "The Osteodontokeratic Culture of *Australopithecus prometheus*," *Transvaal Museum Mem. 10* (1957).

29. J. R. Napier, in *Classification and Human Evolution*, S. L. Washburn, Ed. (Viking Fund, Chicago, 1963), p. 178.

30. W. E. Le Gros Clark, *Discovery* **25**, 49 (1964).

31. G. H. R. von Koenigswald, personal communication.

32. D. R. Hughes, *The Times*, London, 10 June 1964.

33. J. T. Robinson, in *Evolution und Hominisation*, G. Kurth, Ed. (G. Fischer, Stuttgart, 1962), p. 210; J. T. Robinson, *S. African Archaeol. Bull.* **19**, 3 (1964).

34. P. V. Tobias, in *Britannica Book of the Year, 1964* (Encyclopaedia Britannica, Chicago, in press).

35. As a second type of hominid (*Homo erectus* or *Telanthropus*) is known to be present in the Swartkrans deposit, the possibility cannot be excluded that some of the large numbers of isolated teeth from this deposit may *not* belong to the australopithecine.

36. I thank Dr. L. S. B. Leakey for entrusting the fossils to me for study; Prof. G. H. R. von Koenigswald and Dr. D. Hooijer for helpful cooperation; L. P. Morley, A. R. Hughes, Miss J. Soussi, and Mrs. R. W. Levine for technical assistance; the South African Council for Scientific and Industrial Research, the Boise Fund, the Wenner-Gren Foundation for Anthropological Research, Cambridge University, the University of the Witwatersrand, and the National Geographic Society for financial assistance.

THE ANALYSIS OF PRIMATE EVOLUTION
WITH PARTICULAR REFERENCE
TO THE ORIGIN OF MAN

S. L. WASHBURN[1]

Department of Anthropology, University of Chicago, Chicago, Illinois

There are three reasons why this is an appropriate time to discuss the origin of man. The first is the finding of abundant fossils of a new kind of missing link in South Africa. The man-like apes indicate an unanticipated stage in human evolution which radically alters all current theories of human origins. The second reason is that, through the work of numerous geneticists, zoologists, and paleontologists, a theoretical framework is now available which is far superior to any previous evolutionary theories. The third is the fact that evolutionary speculations can be experimentally checked to a far greater extent than has been realized in the past. It is the combination of new facts, new theories, and new hopes of proof which makes this an auspicious moment to reconsider the problems of human origins.

Why the matter needs reconsideration after all the mass of work done on it deserves a word of comment, which may be divided again under the headings of facts, theories, and proof. The facts bearing on human origins were largely collected in the nineteenth century, or according to principles developed at that time, and there has been no "New Comparative Anatomy" comparable to the "New Systematics" or any "Modern Synthesis" as in evolution. The result is that the vast quantity of materials of very unequal value (Zuckerman, 1933; Simpson, 1945) is difficult to use. Each author tends to use only a small part of the easily available information, and the basis for selection is by no means clear. If the papers by Schultz (1936) and Straus (1949) on human origins were examined, it would be hard to tell that the same animals were under discussion, for few facts are mentioned in both papers and their evaluation is totally different. The mere collection of more facts will not advance the understanding of human evolution. Before progress can be made, methods must be outlined for deciding which facts are important.

The evaluation of differences in fossil bones and living primates leads to the question of theory. Certainly the ideas of orthogenesis, irreversibility, and the supreme value of nonadaptive characters have thoroughly blocked the develop-

[1] Associate Professor of Anthropology, University of Chicago; Research Associate, Viking Fund.

Reprinted by permission of the author and Cold Spring Harbor Laboratory from the COLD SPRING HARBOR SYMPOSIA, **15**, 67–78 (1950).

ment of effective thinking about human evolution. They have been used to rule every known kind of primate out of the line of human evolution. Actually, scholars who specialized in human evolution (and it should be stressed that this includes many human anatomists and others besides physical anthropologists) are in an extremely poor position to develop evolutionary theory. Since they are interested in the origin and classification of a single group of animals, and in actual practice almost entirely with man, there are not enough examples to develop and prove theories. Those interested in human evolution must borrow their general theories and principles from others who have access to wider data and more manageable subjects. The task of the anthropologist is to fit knowledge of the primates into the framework of modern evolutionary theory, as described by numerous authors in "Genetics, Paleontology, and Evolution" (Jepsen, Simpson, Mayr, 1949) and as developed in "The Meaning of Evolution" (Simpson, 1949).

The importance of experiment arises from the nature of the anthropologist's task. If he would demonstrate that one theory is better than another he must have a method beyond personal opinion of deciding which facts are important. Facts and good theories are important, but people feel strongly on the subject of their own origin and there will be wide disagreement until a modern, experimental comparative anatomy can take its place among the tools of the student of evolution. At the moment, whether man is regarded as derived from an ape in the late Pliocene (Weinert, 1932) or an unknown, unspecialized, tarsioid of Eocene age (Jones, 1948) depends on personal evaluation of the same basic facts.

The origin of man has been studied by so many people, so many different ideas have been expressed, and the nomenclature is in such a complete state of confusion that it will clarify matters if I briefly outline my ideas first, then defend them in some detail and consider a series of problems of general zoological interest.

The earliest primates were distinguished from other primitive mammals by the use of the hands and feet for grasping. This is anatomically a complex adaptation, involving elongation of the digits, flattening of the terminal phalanges and thinning of the nails (Clark, 1936). This basic adaptation has been the foundation of the whole history of the primates, which has been in other ways remarkably diverse. There is no single trend with regard to way of locomotion (which included slow clingers and fast hoppers), or dentition (there are forms with huge incisors, aye aye; or none, Lepilemur; canines may be huge, mandrill; or small, many female Old World forms and hominids), or diet (many primates eat a mixed diet, but one group of lemurs, Indrisidae, and one group of monkeys, Colobidae, have specialized in leaf eating and have developed specialized viscera). It is this great diversity in secondary characters and ways of life which makes primate classification so difficult. Particularly in fossils the hands and feet are usually not preserved, and the main pattern is not reflected in the jaws and teeth. I believe that this accounts for the difficulty in placing many of the Eocene genera (Simpson, 1940).

The early primates took to the trees with the special senses of the primitive mammal. There were tactile hairs, movable ears, and a sense of smell which was predominant. The changes which produced the forms we call monkeys were either present in the advanced lemurs (or tarsiers, I doubt that this is a fundamental distinction) or developed by parallel evolution. For in both New and Old World monkeys active, arboreal forms developed, with reduced external ears and ear muscles, reduced sense of smell, and with stereoscopic, color vision. These arboreal quadrupeds replaced the lemurs, except where the latter remained protected (Madagascar) or by being strictly nocturnal (as the tarsiers, lorises and galagos). The brain greatly increased in size, and Elliot Smith (1924) was the first to appreciate the multitude of differences which came from converting a primitive smell-brain into a sight-brain. Changes at this stage are clearly reflected in the skull by the reduction in parts associated with the olfactory mechanism (reduction in the turbinal bones, interorbital region, and cribriform plate with correlated changes in the anterior fossa).

The origin of the primates was primarily a locomotor adaptation. The first radiation lasted approximately a third of the age of the mammals, perhaps twenty million years. The second was a reorganization of the special senses, making the monkeys successful in the Old World tropical forests by day. The third radiation of Old World primates depended again on a locomotor adaptation. In the apes, a series of modifications in the arms and trunk leads to locomotion of a sort not found in the quadrupedal monkeys. (Spider monkeys brachiate; this is another example of the extensive parallelism in the New and Old Worlds. But spider monkeys also move in typical quadrupedal fashion and have prehensile tails. The combination of brachiation and quadrupedal locomotion is not found in the Old World and shows how the ape type of locomotion may have arisen). Brachiation involves changes in the motion of the arms and the abandoning of the use of the back in the typical quadrupedal manner. The anatomical changes are in the wrist, elbow, shoulder, and thoracic region. None of these are duplicated in any of the monkeys, and brachiation is an elaborate behavioral and anatomical complex, every essential detail of which is shared by man and the living apes.

Some idea of the profound changes in anatomy which accompany brachiation, as practiced by the apes, is given by the changes in the muscles of the trunk and arm. The scalenes migrate upward; psoas major, rectus abdominis, and the origin of sacrospinalis migrate down; serratus anterior increases in size, as does the deltoid; pectoralis major migrates up, pectoralis minor changes its insertion to the coracoid process; origin and insertion of arm extensors are reduced and the flexors are increased. These are correlated with the changes in the joints previously mentioned. (Loth, 1931, is the best general source of information on the muscles of primates.)

The discovery of the pelves of the South African man-like apes, or small-brained men, has made it possible to outline the basic adaptation which is the foundation of the human radiation. These forms have brains which are in the range of the living apes, and their teeth show both human and ape characters, but the ilia are practically modern-human. Men were bipeds first, and later large-brained, small-faced bipeds. Just as the differences between monkey and ape are in the upper extremity and trunk, so those between ape and man are in the pelvis and foot. To mention but a few differences: in apes gluteus maximus is not maximus, gracilis is not gracile, biceps femoris has one head, and semitendinosus and membranosus are not as the names imply. The bone-muscle-functional complex of the leg distinguishes man from the apes as sharply as the comparable complex of the arms shows their similarity and distinguishes both from the monkeys.

The above outline differs from prevailing theories in several ways. The gibbons are regarded as typical apes and placed in the same family with the living apes and with numerous extinct forms. The South African forms are regarded as in the same family as man, part of the same radiation. However, the arrangement is in the main similar to many others (Hooton, 1946; Simpson, 1949; Zuckerman, 1933). Lemurs, monkeys, apes and men represent a series of radiations. Each is later in time and each is less variable than the one which preceded it.

Among the lemurs there are radically different locomotor, dietary, and dental patterns. At the other extreme man is represented by a single form, being far less variable (even if all fossil forms and the South African man-apes are added) than lorises, galagos, or indris-like lemurs.

Finally, anatomically speaking, man is highly specialized. He represents an extreme and odd form in his way of locomotion. In no other animal can the anatomy of pelvis and foot be matched. His trunk and thorax are very peculiar, their structure being shared only with the great apes. Obviously the brain is a recent and extreme adaptation. This modern, ground-living ape would amount to little without tools. The fact that we number more than a few thousand, ecologically unimportant bipeds living in the Old World tropics is due to the development of tools. And it is important to remember that tools are surely older than Java man. The appearance of all modern forms of men is long after tool using. The origin of the human radiation may be treated just as that of any other mammalian group, but the use of tools brings in a set of factors which progressively modify the evolutionary picture. It is particularly the task of the anthropologist to assess the way the development of culture affected physical evolution.

In defining the major groups of primates the effort has been made to use the most important characters, that is, to use the ones which made the evolutionary radiations possible. In general, characters may be divided into three categories: (1) Primary characters which are responsible for the radiations; (2) secondary characters which are a necessary consequence of the new selection, based on the acquisition of the primary ones; and (3) incidental characters which happen to be selected along with the primary ones. For example, if the group of apes which gave origin to man had a particular type of dentition, this would automatically become part of the original heritage of the hominids. Other features might be due to genetic drift in small groups of early men.

If modern man be examined, he is found to be a mixture of basic primate features, the primary characters of the first or lemuroid radiation. (The hands show a remarkable amount of the primitive grasping adaptation with long digits, nails, etc. It should be remembered that the most perfectly opposable and relatively largest thumbs among all the primates are found in the lorises, and not in man, as often stated. Human feet are a recent modification of the same pattern, fundamentally differing only in a single ligament and the length of the toes.) The next complex is that of the head, brain and special senses which is achieved, except for changes in proportions, in the monkey radiation. Then the arms and trunk become essentially modern. Perhaps then, many millions of years later, the bipedal complex was developed. Finally, the secondary features of the human radiation became general, the small face and the large brain.

Evolution proceeded at different rates in various parts of the body. This is not to suggest that at any time the animals were not functioning wholes adapted to a way of life, but it does mean that there may be a considerable degree of independence of a given part. The eye of monkey, ape, and man are remarkably similar despite major changes in other parts of the body. In spite of a variety of ways of life the same sort of visual mechanism was advantageous and was maintained by selection.

There are three implications of this scheme of evolution for the study of human origins: *First*, different characters are of very unequal taxonomic value at various stages in human evolution. If similarity in trunk and arm show the community of man and ape and if the difference lies primarily in pelvis and legs, a long list of characters in which both features of arm and leg are included may be misleading. Especially is it misleading to say that of so many characters man shares this percent with one form and that percent with another. Similarities in arms, legs, and skull have different meanings. The *second* implication is that there are real changes between ancestors and their descendants. To say that all apes have longer arms or canine teeth than man (Jones, 1948; Weidenreich, 1946) in no way bars them from human ancestry. The ancestors were parts of different radiations and were specialized accordingly. The search for the unspecialized common ancestor becomes either a denial of evolution or a hunt for an illusory, philosophical archetype. The *third* is that there will be many incidental differences at each level which are of no major importance. Even if every ape had one form of pterion and every human another, it would be of no importance. Actually the form varies in both groups and experimental alteration of suture patterns shows that this type of difference does not change the functional pattern of the cranial vault.

It is clear that adaptation to life on the ground is the basis of the human radiation. Many groups of Old World primates have come to the ground at different times and places, but no group of New World monkeys has taken up life on the ground. Two, perhaps three, different groups of baboons, patas monkeys, vervets and macaques have become ground-livers. On the other hand not a single group of the leaf-eating monkeys (Colobidae) have taken up life on the ground. The restriction here is clearly diet. The soft leaves and fruits of the tropical forests are not available in plains country, and monkeys adapted to this diet have not become ground-livers, although there seems no reason as far as the locomotor system is concerned why they could not. If the ground-living and tree-living Old World monkeys are contrasted, a series of differences appear which are of the greatest importance for the understanding of human evolution. The ground-living forms, which have far greater ranges and are divided into less distinct varieties than the tree-livers. For example, the vervets, which are only partially ground-livers, still are very similar from Uganda to the Cape. Whereas in the *nictitans* group of cercopiths there are several perfectly distinct varieties in Uganda alone. Or, to take an Asiatic example, macaques of the irus group (long-tail, long face, small size), are distributed throughout South East Asia, while the arboreal leaf-monkeys of the same area are divided into four major groups, three of which are subdivided into numerous species. As far as monkeys are concerned, the sort of difference which Dobzhansky (1950) has shown between the tropical and temperate forms exists in the tropics between the strictly arboreal forms and those well-adapted to the ground. The great number of forms are in the rain forests. The implication for classification is that the ones well-adapted to life on the ground will not divide up neatly into the sort of localized varieties which the tree-livers do. The attempt has been made repeatedly to divide the baboons into sharply defined groups. The chaos which has resulted is the result of expecting that plains forms, which have vast reaches of similar habitat open to them, will subdivide as the tree-restricted monkeys do.

The implication for human evolution is clear. Once man's ancestors were efficient plains-livers, they probably occupied large ranges with anatomical variation but without separation into distinct forms. In the case of early manlike forms, more difference should be demonstrated before taxonomic groups are set up than in the case of fossil anthropoids believed to have been tree-livers.

Turning from the general implications of efficient ground-living to the anatomy involved, I think that we have every reason to believe that this was fully achieved by the South African man-apes. The pelvis of these forms (known by three specimens, described by Broom, 1950a and b, and Dart, 1949b) is so human in form that some have argued that it must belong to an early hominid which became mixed in the man-ape deposits. Although the ilium is short and broad and of essentially human form (although differing in detail, especially in the shape of the iliac crest) the ischium is ape-like. The muscular attachment area of the ischium is separated from the glenoid cavity by a greater distance than is the case is modern man (Broom, 1950a). The differences are not great but are sufficient to preclude the possibility of the pelves belonging to other animals than the man-apes. The pelvis of a large baboon found in the same deposits is utterly unlike that of the man-apes, being typically baboon. According to all investigators (Broom, 1950a; Dart, 1949c; Camp, 1949; Barbour, 1949) there has been no great change in the climate of South Africa since these forms lived. They are associated with the bones of baboons and numerous antelope, the typical fauna of the African plains, and forest forms are lacking. The man-apes were bipedal, plains-living forms, derived from the forest-living apes. Morphologically they are ideal representatives of a stage in our evolution and chronologically they may be actual ancestors or the first cousins of the same (Clark, 1950). That is, these forms may be representative of populations which were directly ancestral to such humans as Java man.

The derivation of this type from an ape is best regarded as a case of rapid or quantum evolution (Simpson, 1944). It may soon turn out to be one of the best-documented cases. Since the South African materials are abundant and more are being found, and since there are an impressive number of well-preserved human fossils, the main features of the transition should soon be fully known.

Since this is the beginning of the human type of locomotion, the principal problem is to understand the locomotor changes. If an ape stands erect, it can walk, and the gibbon can get along fairly rapidly, but it cannot complete powerful extension of the leg. It should be stressed that it is not the extent of the motion which is different but the ability to finish with a real drive. When walking on a flat surface, the ape goes with a bent-knee gait (Hooton, 1946). In modern man the muscle which finishes swinging back the thigh is gluteus maximus. This is an exceedingly massive and powerful muscle, arising from the posterior part of the ilium and the sacrum. In modern man, if gluteus maximus is paralyzed, the trunk is said to jack-knife. That is, the extreme extension of the thigh necessary for normal human walking is not possible, but a flexed gait, comparable to that of the apes, is perfectly easy. The paralysis of this single muscle makes the human type of very-extended bipedal locomotion impossible. It shows that the form and function of this particular muscle is critical in the evolution of man's posture and gait.

In the apes gluteus maximus is a small muscle. In monkeys it is about one-half the size of gluteus medius! Since the ilium of the living apes is long, gluteus maximus lies primarily lateral to the greater trochanter and is an abductor of the thigh. (The relation to the hip joint, and so its function, varies with the position of the leg. A study based on action current is needed to tell when the muscle is really in action.) The primary effect of bending back the ilium is to bring gluteus maximus behind the hip joint, thus making it an extensor. Gluteus medius now lies lateral to the joint and becomes an abductor, taking over the old function of the maximus. Since selection is for function, it is clear that bending the ilium will change the selection on the gluteal muscles. It is my belief that this single change is the thing which initiates human evolution.

Before continuing to an examination of the circumstances under which such a change might occur, it should be pointed out that the statements above are susceptible to experimental verification. The function of these muscles in man and ape can be checked. This should be done. Further, I believe that it is impossible to reconstruct a gluteus maximus on the pelvis of a man-ape which is anything but an extensor. The importance of gluteus maximus in human locomotion, the effect of bending the ilium on the function of gluteus maximus, and the position of gluteus maximus in the man-apes can all be determined independently by as many people as want to take the trouble. In this sense there can be an experimental and ultimately quantitative study of the critical events in human evolution.

The pelvis has several different functions. It serves to connect the hind limb and the trunk, gives origin to many muscles, and serves as a bony birth canal. If the ilium becomes shorter, it must have a greater angle with the ischium in order to keep the same diameter of the canal. This is illustrated in the accompanying figure (Fig. 1). The figures for apes are from Weidenreich (1913). Many monkeys would be much the same, but in the leaf-monkey (*Presbytis rubicunda*) with a very short ilium the angulation of the ilium, relative to the ischium, is greater. Man and the man-apes are characterized by exceedingly short ilia, far shorter than apes of equivalent size. Without fossils it is impossible to tell whether shortening or bending came first, but a considerable shortening of the ilium (of the sort actually seen in other primates) would of necessity result in bending it, which would give the necessary pre-condition to the change in function of gluteus maximus. It should be noted that the difference between the langur and the "hypothetical" form is no greater than that between the hypothetical and the known human extremes. In the Bush race the sciatic notch is extremely wide (Orford, 1934; Washburn, 1949). Comparing an extreme human type to an extreme monkey type gives a totally different idea of the gap than comparing male European to living ape. It should be noted that continued bending, although an advantage from the locomotor point of view, is disadvantageous in females because it narrows the outlet of the birth canal. This accounts for the fact that the bending has been carried further in human males than in females. There is a notable sex difference in the sciatic notch which is directly related to locomotor and postural differences between men and women.

The argument runs as follows: among apes who were living at the edge of the forests and coming to the ground, were some who had shorter ilia. These ilia had to be more bent back for obstetrical reasons and in some this carried gluteus maximus far enough so that it became effective in finishing extension. This started a new selection which favored bigger gluteus muscles and ilia still further bent. The beginning is, of course, supposition, but the functional results can be experimentally checked and the initial shortening and bending is not much beyond the range of known forms.

Characters closely associated with the primary changes in the pelvis are those in the feet and in the muscles of the legs. The feet of the mountain gorilla have approached the human condition in many ways (Schultz, 1934). Changes from a foot of such a sort to the human would not involve any major evolutionary changes. After all, the joining of the first metatarsal to the second by a ligament may well account for a great many of the features which differentiate the feet of apes and men.

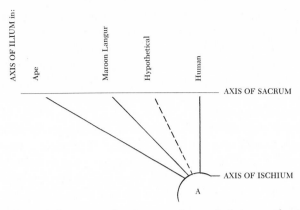

FIGURE 1. The effect of shortening the ilium on the angle between the ischium and the ilium. A = the acetabulum.

Changes in the muscles are extensive but follow a pattern already seen in the monkeys. When a man walks, he straightens the leg primarily with the muscles on the front of the thigh (Q. ex. femoris). This is the same action which an ape or monkey uses in climbing. In running, the apes and monkeys use primarily the muscles in the back of the thigh. If the mass (weight) of the muscles on the front of the thigh is compared to that of those on the back, (quadriceps to the hamstrings), it is found that the relation is 2/1 in man, 1.2/1 in mangabeys, .1/1 in arboreal cercopiths (nictitans), and 1/1.2 in mixed ground-livers (vervets), and 1/2 in baboons. The first and last figures are from Haxton (1947), the others from monkeys obtained in Uganda. Even by such a crude method it is clear that the proportions of the major muscle masses closely follow the habit of the animal. Climbing is pre-adaptive for human walking. Quadrupedal running tends to build a different pattern of muscles. Aside from mass, there are a number of differences in the leg muscles of man and ape, which can best be described as the attenuation of the muscles other than quadriceps, and the migration of the insertions closer to the knee. These changes are of degree only, and the functions are the same. There is no radical alteration of form and function as in the case of gluteus maximus. Once the major change in the pelvis had taken place, these other changes may well have followed rapidly.

It is difficult to determine to what extent these changes had already taken place in the man-apes. There are only fragments of limb bones. However, the ape-like character of the ischium suggests that the hamstrings may not yet have achieved modern human form. The lack of an iliac tuberosity suggests some differences, but many changes in the leg muscles are little, if at all, reflected in the skeleton. The differences between mangabeys and baboons for example, which are functionally important, make no discernible difference in the femur. However, in the man-ape, the distal end of the femur is very large. This is the critical point. If these forms were walking erect, the femur must have borne the weight and given origin and insertion to the enlarged muscles concerned with locomotion. I believe that the argument between Le

Gros Clark (1947) and Kern and Straus (1949) over the details of morphology of the femur is irrelevant. Any different group of animals may have somewhat different features of a particular bone. There is no reason why the femora of the man-apes should be identical with man, ape, or monkey. The morphology is of a general primate type and the size is in accord with the idea that these forms were bipeds. Granted a reasonable conformity of shape, the important thing functionally is size.

Considering the arms of the man-apes, the distal end of the humerus has been discovered, and Clark (1947) has claimed that it is of the human type and Straus (1948) that it is catarrhine. However, according to the plan suggested here, one would not expect any fundamental difference in the end of the humerus. The basic ape features, still preserved entirely in modern man, are the great size of the trochlea and conforming width of the proximal ulna and the rounded capitellum. The meaning of these features is that the stability of the elbow joint is determined by the fit between the trochlea and ulna, the radius being freed from stability and support is better adapted for rotation. Naturally, the precise detail of this pattern varies from group to group. These little variations are not of evolutionary significance. The major features and their importance can be easily determined. Cut the annular ligament (which holds the head of the radius in place) in a monkey, and the elbow joint loses its stability. Do the same in man, chimpanzee, or gibbon, and the hinge part of the joint functions nearly normally. The distal fragment of the humerus of the man-apes shows that they were typical members of the ape-human stock. The proximal humerus, clavicle, and scapula tell the same story, although detailed study will surely reveal some minor differences from other known forms.

Several authorities have claimed that forms such as the great apes could not be ancestral to man. The reasons given are that the ape's arms are too long and thumbs too small (with the thumb muscles reduced) and that changes in these proportions would break the law of irreversibility of evolution. First, it should be stressed that no one thinks that man is descended from one of the living apes (see Simpson, 1949, for discussion on this point). The question is: could man be descended from a form which had relatively longer arms and smaller thumbs than modern men? Precise differences from living forms are not the issue, but the relations of two kinds of organization. First for the facts: Schultz (1936) has shown that man's arms are, in fact, very long by general primate standards. There is far less difference in length between man and gorilla than between gorilla and orang. The same is true relative to the proportions of the hand. With regard to the thumb muscles, the long flexor is present in all gibbons, over half of chimpanzees, and lesser percentages of gorillas and orangs (Straus, 1949). Once our ancestors had become bipeds, the selection on the arms, hands and associated muscles would have been different from that of tree-living apes. Selection must be quite different for the living gorilla and orang. The issue is, then, could a trend toward long arms and small thumbs in apes be reversed in their descendants when selection pressures were radically changed? That such reversals can and do take place has been recently emphasized by Colbert (1949), Gregory (1949), and Simpson (1949). The idea that such reversals cannot take place seems to be based on the idea that the trends are due to orthogenesis, rather than to continued selection of the same sort over a long period. The fact that orthogenesis is not necessary to explain the facts of evolution seems well established and was dealt with at length by several authors in the volume "Genetics, Paleontology, and Evolution," also by Simpson's "Tempo and Mode in Evolution," and more recently by Jepsen (1949). In spite of all this one reads in "Races" published in 1950 (Coon, Garn and Birdsell) that, "Evolution, we are told, is irreversible." Wright (1934) has shown that the missing digits of the foot of the guinea pig may be brought back by mutation. These digits are normally not there at all. It seems that this is precisely the sort of situation in which the cooperation of geneticists, paleontologists and anthropologists is needed. Great knowledge of the proportions and variations of the primate arm and hand is rendered useless by outmoded concepts and by the failure to realize that reversals, far greater than changing the hand of the living chimpanzee into a human-proportioned hand, have actually been produced in the laboratory.

Turning to the skull, the teeth have been most extensively studied and the evidence has been carefully reviewed by Clark (1950). There is nothing in the dentition which would militate against the idea that these forms are direct ancestors of late Pliocene age. The molars of ape, man-ape, fossil man, and modern man form as nearly perfect a morphological record as one could hope to find (Gregory, 1949). There is no gap in the record at all, and, on the basis of molar teeth, one would have an exceedingly difficult time in deciding where apes left off and man began. This gradation is in marked contrast to the pelvis. It supports the idea that there was no sudden moment when selection on the dentition changed, rapidly producing a new type. These molar characters would then be regarded as incidental, useful in sorting, but not fundamental. It should be remembered that some arboreal monkeys have dentitions identical with plains-living ones. There seems to be no reason why the dentition should be different and, in fact, it is not.

The size of the molar teeth is of interest. As Broom (1946) has indicated, the best match for the teeth and jaws of the man-apes outside of Africa is the form named "*Meganthropus*" (Weidenreich, 1945). But the limb bones associated with the African forms are not large, the best match being with a small female Bushman, about the lower limit of size of living humans. This shows that large molars do not necessarily mean giant bodies. After all, a small monkey may have larger molars than a modern man. The correlation of body-size and tooth-size among primates is not high. Of course, if non-primates were considered too, the correlation would be far lower. Think if human standards were used to reconstruct body-size from a wart hog's molar! It is particularly dangerous to reconstruct body-size from the teeth of an unknown form.

The canine teeth offer points of interest. Von Koenigswald (1948) has shown that some at least are not as small as has been claimed. However, they are small compared to those of male apes. Of course, in female apes the canines may be exceedingly small, wearing like incisors and narrower than the first premolar (gorilla). In male monkeys the ground-living forms tend to have larger canines than the tree-livers. The extremes in canine size are all in male ground-livers (baboons, mandrills, some macaques) (Washburn and Howell, in preparation). The function of these teeth is in the organization and protection of the group. The males dominate in the social organization (Zuckerman, 1932), and no female has a chance in fighting against the great canine teeth of the males. The big males likewise act as sentries and guards. From the evidence of other primates one would expect a male plains-living ape to have at least as large canines as the forest-forms. The fact that they are much smaller in the man-ape suggests that the teeth were less important in protection and fighting than among the living apes. This supports Dart's (1949a) hypothesis that the man-apes were already using tools. However, this cannot be definitely proved at the present time. Differences in the size of the canine teeth should not be overemphasized because there is a complete series in size and form linking man and ape.

At least some of the problems of the dentition can be dealt with experimentally. It would be useful to know to what extent size and pattern of the teeth are independently inherited. The simpler pattern of the molars of some of the small modern domestic pigs suggests that reduction of cusps may be only one aspect of size reduction. Weidenreich (1941) indicated the same in small dogs. This could be checked experimentally. Also, it would be possible to prove the importance of the large canines in the social organization of the monkey. With groups such as those on an island off Puerto Rico, the social organization could be studied, the dominant male trapped and his canines removed. A quantitative, experimental approach is possible so that the significance of the changes shown in the evolutionary record could be documented by fact and raised beyond the level of individual opinion. Tree shrews would be ideal experimental animals for this type of problem. They are small, hardy, and can be raised in the laboratory. If anthropologists and geneticists plan to cooperate in the solution of problems of mutual interest, it will be necessary to develop some new laboratory animals, and tree shrews may well prove to be the most suitable. Some experimental analysis of cranial form has been attempted (Washburn, 1947).

The evolution of the brain has always been of particular interest in the primates. Since the brain of modern man is so big and since man likes to think of himself as a rational animal, there has been a tendency to define man in terms of brain size. (Keith, 1949, defined the border of man and apes as 750 cc.) The idea that mammals as a group have triumphed over the reptiles because of better brains received a set-back from the work of Edinger (1948). She showed that the brain tends to follow in evolution, that the earliest mammals did not have brains in advance of reptiles, and that at least several of the orders of mammals had established locomotor and dental adaptations prior to having their characteristic brain form. The hominids follow Edinger's pattern perfectly. The range of variation in cranial capacity is:

chimpanzee and gorilla	325– 650
man-apes	450– 650
Java man	750– 900
Pekin man	900–1,200
Neanderthal	1,100–1,550

The range for Java man is too small, because of the small number of specimens. The figure for the man-apes should perhaps be raised because of a later, partially-described find (Broom, 1949). So there is either a complete series or very close to one. There is no doubt that all human fossils described so far have human pelves and limb bones and the man-apes were remarkably human in these features. Therefore, it appears that the differences in the brain between apes and man, just as those in dentition, were attained after full human status had been achieved in the limbs and trunk (Clark, 1950).

If one considers the primates in general, the same pattern seems to hold. The lemurs have bigger brains than the tree shrews, the monkeys than the lemurs, the apes than the monkeys. With each major advance in primate evolution the brain doubled or even tripled its size. If the human brain is viewed from this point of view, the remarkable thing about man is that his ancestors went through three major different locomotor adaptations during the age of mammals and one major reorganization of the special senses. After each of these the brain at least doubled its size. Viewed in this way the remarkable size of the human brain is due to the number of times this organ had to adjust to new ways of life. This is added to the general tendency for mammalian brains to increase in size, and to the fact that at least the last doubling was after the use of tools, which may have greatly increased the selection for large brains.

The final adjustment in brain size seems to have been rapid. If capacities of 800–1000 were common in the early Pleistocene (and they may well have been less in the beginning), and 1200–1400 common in the third inter-glacial, the same rate of change would make the man-ape capacities expected in direct ancestors of the late Pliocene age. If the change in brain size follows the change in locomotion, it might be expected to continue rapidly until a new plateau is reached. If so, there is some justification in projecting the known rate back for at least a short period of time, and even a short prolongation of the known rate would reduce brain size to that of the apes and man-apes. Brains of this size may have been characteristic of apes for many millions of years. There is almost no direct evidence, but the skull found by Leakey (Clark, 1950) would be in accord with such an idea.

In summary, the critical primary adaptation initially responsible for the origin of man as a distinct group is in the pelvis. Efficient, bipedal locomotion of the human type involves primarily the pelvis and gluteus maximus, but a series of secondary changes in thigh, leg, and foot must have followed soon to complete the adaptive complex. This complex may have been further improved by continued selection, but, as far as can be determined from the skeleton, had reached modern form in the early Pleistocene. Changes in the teeth, brain size, and many other parts of the body took place at a much slower rate and continued on into late Pleistocene times. These changes are the result of the secondary selection patterns which followed after the establishment of the primary human pattern. Finally, there are many little differences between any two forms. These incidental features may be due to a variety of causes and should not be allowed to confuse the major patterns.

It is customary to present the results of phylogenetic speculations in the form of a classification. There has been so much overemphasis on classification and names, especially with regard to the primates, that common names have been used here as far as possible. At the moment they are better guides to the identity of living primates than the supposedly scientific ones. Without wishing to stress names or overemphasize their importance, the views expressed in this paper imply a reduction in the number of names of categories among the primates. If the term "family" is reserved for a group of animals representing a major adaptive radiation (such as the Indridae, Lorisidae, or Galagidae), then the gibbons belong in the same family as the great apes. Bipedal man might be put in a separate family. The reasons for granting bipedal man more taxonomic distinction from apes than the ground-living monkeys from the tree-living monkeys, is that there is a much greater series of anatomical changes in the case of man. Within the human family one genus, *Homo,* might easily include all the Pleistocene large-brained hominids (Java man, Pekin man, etc.). One other genus, *Australopithecus,* might contain the man-apes (*Australopithecus, Plesianthropus, Paranthropus,* and perhaps *Meganthropus* and even *Gigantopithecus*). Obviously, since little is known of the time when these forms lived, the extent of their range and how many local forms there may have been, the significance of this category is uncertain. If such forms were widely spread over the Old World in late Pliocene and early Pleistocene times probably there were quite distinct local groups. It seems convenient to place these small-brained men in a single genus, at least until there is more evidence to the contrary. The number of names is a function of the kind of interest of the investigator (Broom, 1950). If one is primarily interested in classification, in type specimens and priority, then the less there is known about fossil primates the more names there will be. If one is interested in the mechanics of evolution, in the understanding of process, a cumbersome and constantly changing classification is a great liability and the tendency will be to lump, to leave fragmentary bits unnamed, and to create new groups only when absolutely necessary.

In conclusion, it might be repeated that this is an appropriate time to reconsider the problems of the origin of man; for the traditional phylogenies have been upset by the discovery of new fossils; the old theories of orthogenesis, irreversibility and the supremacy of non-adaptive characters have been proved false; and because experimental procedures offer methods of raising some conclusions beyond the level of individual opinion. Looking to the future, fossils are being found at a rate undreamed of in the past. The cooperation of geneticists and paleontologists has produced a rich evolutionary theory which places the fundamental contribution of Darwin in modern form. Facts are increasing and new theories are challenging, but methods must be developed for proving and checking the importance of particular facts and the fit of any given theory. Such testing requires a knowledge of fossils, of living forms and the application of experimental procedures. All three types of evidence are necessary and a science of human origins can be built only upon this triple foundation.

Without fossils, ancestors can be reconstructed only by what has been called "mental triangulation." With all the vast effort which went into the comparative anatomy of the primates, no one reconstructed an animal with a human ilium and an ape's head. There were attempts in this direction and Weidenreich (1947) recognized that the evolution of the locomotor system preceded that of the head, but before the discovery of the man-apes, and before Edinger's investigations, it remained equally logical to maintain that the brain was the primary and initial factor in human evolution. The actual course of evolution can be determined only from fossils.

But, fossils, at best, constitute a very limited source of information. Adaptations in the digestive, circulatory, reproductive systems, and special senses affect the skeleton little or not at all. The significance of many changes in the skeleton cannot be determined, unless living forms of comparable structure are available for study. Unfortunately, much of the fossil record of primates is limited to teeth and jaws, and the extent to which these parts can be misleading is well-shown by the living lemurs. The skulls of lorises and galagos show not only detailed similarity but comparable trends, yet the whole post-cranial skeleton is different and the animals represent opposite extremes in locomotor adaptations. From the point of view of the comparative anatomist the primates have definite advantages, for there are living representatives of all the major primate radiations, and numerous parallel series offer opportunities for the analysis of the causes of anatomical similarity. Of course, the living forms are not ancestors and will not reveal the detailed anatomy of extinct types, but a far fuller understanding of a lemur can be gained by studying fossils and living forms than by the study of either one alone. Obviously, the chimpanzee is not studied to prove that it is *the* human ancestor but to understand the kind of organization which may have been characteristic of the ancestral forms.

After the study of fossils and living animals, when theories take definite form, then experiments should be planned. Particularly the importance of adaptive complexes and the precise nature of adaptation can be advanced far beyond the level of individual opinion. The fact that gluteus maximus functions differently in man and ape is not a matter of opinion but can be precisely determined. Again, the importance of gluteus in walking can be quantitatively investigated and placed beyond the realm of debate. The study of human origins requires an appreciation of the nature of evolutionary change in animals, an understanding of the specific problems of the primates, and a detailed comprehension of form and function of man and ape. Solution of the problems will require the cooperation of many scientists, and it is hoped that this conference may be the beginning of much close cooperation between anthropologists and others interested in the origin and differentiation of the human stock.

REFERENCES

BARBOUR, G. B., 1949, Yearbook of Physical Anthropology, 1948. Edited by G. W. Lasker and F. P. Thieme. The Viking Fund, Inc.

BROOM, R., 1949, Discoveries from South Africa. London Illust. News, September 10, p. 378.

1950a, The genera and species of the South African fossil ape-men. Amer. J. Phys. Anthrop., n.s., **8**: 1–13.

1950b, Finding the missing link. London: Watts & Co.

BROOM, R., and SCHEPERS, G. W. H., 1946, The South African fossil ape-men, the Australopithecinae. Transvaal Mus. Memoir no. 2, Pretoria.

CAMP, C. L., 1949, Yearbook of Physical Anthropology, 1948. Edited by G. W. Lasker and F. P. Thieme. Viking Fund, Inc.

CLARK, W. E. LE GROS, 1936, The problem of the claw in primates. Proc. Zool. Soc. Lond. pp. 1–24.

1947, Observations on the anatomy of the fossil Australopithecinae. J. Anat. **81**: 300–334.

1950, New palaeontological evidence bearing on the evolution of the Hominoidea. Quart. J. Geol. Soc. Lon. **105**: 225–264.

COLBERT, E. H., 1949, Some paleontological principles significant in human evolution. Studies in Phys. Anthrop. **1**: 103–147.

COON, C. S., GARN, S. M., and BIRDSELL, J. B., 1950, Races. Springfield: Charles C Thomas.

DART, R. A., 1949a, The predatory implemental technique of *Australopithecus*. Amer. J. Phys. Anthrop. n.s. **7**: 1–38.

1949b, The first pelvic bones of *Australopithecus prometheus*. Amer. J. Phys. Anthrop. n.s. **7**: 255–257.

1949c, Yearbook of Physical Anthropology, 1948. Edited by G. W. Lasker and F. P. Thieme. Viking Fund, Inc.

DOBZHANSKY, TH., 1950, Evolution in the tropics. Amer. Scientist **38**: 209–221.

EDINGER, T., 1948, Evolution of the horse brain. Geol. Soc. Amer. Mem. **25**.

GREGORY, W. K., 1949, The bearing of Australopithecinae upon the problem of Man's place in nature. Amer. J. Phys. Anthrop. n.s. **7**: 485–512.

HAXTON, H. A., 1947, Muscles of the pelvic limb. A study of the differences between bipeds and quadrupeds. Anat. Rec. **98**: 337–346.

HOOTON, E. A., 1946, Up from the ape. Revised edition. New York: Macmillan.

JEPSEN, G. L., 1949, Selection, "Orthogenesis" and the fossil record. Proc. Amer. Phil. Soc. **93**: 479–500.

JEPSEN, G. L., SIMPSON, G. G., and MAYR, E., 1949, Genetics, paleontology and evolution. Princeton: Princeton Univ. Press.

JONES, F. W., 1948, Hallmarks of mankind. Baltimore: Williams and Wilkins Co.

KEITH, A., 1949, A new theory of human evolution. New York: Philosophical Library.

KERN, H. M., and STRAUS, W. L., 1949, The femur of *Plesianthropus transvaalensis*. Amer. J. Phys. Anthrop. n.s. **7**: 53–77.

VON KOENIGSWALD, G. H. R., 1948, Remarks on the lower canine of *Plesianthropus transvaalensis* Broom. Robert Broom Commemorative Volume. Royal Society of South Africa, Cape Town.

LOTH, E., 1931, Anthropologie des parties molles. Paris: Masson & Cie.

ORFORD, M., 1934, The pelvis of the Bush race. S. Afr. J. Sci., **31**: 586–610.

SCHULTZ, A. H., 1934, Some distinguishing characters of the mountain gorilla. J. Mammal. **15**: 51–61.

1936, Characters common to higher primates and characters specific for man. Quart. Rev. Biol. **11**: 259–283, 429–455.

SIMPSON, G. G., 1940, Studies on the earliest primates. Bull. Amer. Mus. Nat. Hist. **77**: 185–212.

1944, Tempo and mode in evolution. New York: Columbia Univ. Press.

1945, The principles of classification and a classification of mammals. Bull. Amer. Mus. Nat. Hist. **85**.

1949, The meaning of evolution. New Haven: Yale Univ. Press.

SMITH, E. G., 1924, The evolution of man. Essays. Oxford Univ. Press.

STRAUS, W. L., 1948, The humerus of *Paranthropus robustus*. Amer. J. Phys. Anthrop. n.s. **6**: 285–311.

1949, The riddle of man's ancestry. Quart. Rev. Biol. **24**: 200–223.

WASHBURN, S. L., 1947, The relation of the temporal muscle to the form of the skull. Anat. Rec. **99**: 239–248.

1949, Sex differences in the pubic bone of Bantu and Bushman. Amer. J. Phys. Anthrop. n.s. **7**: 425–432.

WEIDENREICH, F., 1941, The brain and its role in the phylogenetic transformation of the human skull. Trans. Amer. Phil. Soc. n.s. **31**: 321–442.

1945, Giant early man from Java and South China. Vol. 40. Anthrop. Papers, Amer. Mus. Nat. Hist., pp. 5–134.

1946, Apes, giants, and men. Chicago: Univ. of Chicago.

1947, The trend of human evolution. Evolution **1**: 221–236.

WEINERT, H., 1932, Ursprung der Menschheit. Stuttgart.

WRIGHT, S., 1934, Polydactylous guinea pigs. J. Hered. **25**: 359–362.

ZUCKERMAN, S., 1932, The social life of monkeys and apes. London: Kegan Paul.

1933, Functional affinities of man, monkeys, and apes. New York: Harcourt, Brace and Company.

DISCUSSION

ANGEL: It seems clear that the bone mass genetically available to cover various sizes of brains must play a major part in both cranial index and details of cranial form. As in the examples you gave, a functional breakdown of head-form into antero-posterior and radial growth of the skull base and bone mass or brain size would, through the principle of relative growth, greatly reduce the number of genic factors apparently needed.

MACDOWELL: Dr. Washburn suggests that genetics can step in after experimental studies, such as those he has just reported on the dependence of certain bone configurations on muscles, have separated traits that are directly inherited from the secondary effects of such traits. It happens that genetics has already stepped in by contributing a mutation[1] among others that performs a similar experiment. In this case the configuration of a bone, the sternum, is found to be dependent upon the timing of growth of other bones, the ribs. This mutation occurred in a mouse, but it has led to an interpretation of the division of the sternum into segments, or sterne-

[1] MacDowell, E. C., J. S. Potter, T. Laanes, and E. N. Ward, 1942, *J. Hered.* **33**: 439–449.

brae, applicable to all mammals including man and the apes. Dr. Schultz showed drawings of several primate sterna varying from broad to narrow, with sternebrae varying in number and degree of separation. It now appears highly probable that all these variations, and countless others, are expressions of differences in the onto-genetic timing of rib elongation, and that, in regard to the pattern of this bone, the tissues of the different sterna are intrinsically alike. The anlage of the sternum appears as a pair of diverging bands, which the elongating ribs meet and push together. Differentiation towards cartilage and bone proceeds uniformly in the sternum, except at the points of contact with ribs. At these points, and in a zone radiating from them, differentiation is inhibited. This is the essential point revealed by the mutation. With normal rib growth the inhibited zones for a pair of ribs over-laps, so that differentiation first proceeds only intercostally, and, in the mouse, four slender sternebrae, with epiphyses, as in long bones, are formed. The recessive, monogenic mutation, called *screw-tail* from one of its various effects, temporarily retards the elongation of ribs[2] at a time when they would normally be uniting the halves of the sternum. Nevertheless, the halves do unite by cell migration from the inner margins, at the sacrifice of length and thickness. Thus the paired zones of inhibited differentiation do not meet, and at birth, instead of a series of four inter-costal bone centers, there is a single elongated bone center. Since the ends of the 6th and 7th ribs are attached side by side, a single zone of inhibition is formed but this is so large that it meets its opposite mate and so the xiphoid process starts with a separate bone center. Subsequently, instead of the inter-sternebral epiphyses lengthening the sternum, the zones of continued growth are lateral and a broad short, shield-shaped sternum is formed, with deep lateral indentations at the ends of the ribs resulting from the inhibition of differentiation. By the time rib-growth is resumed the new pattern of the sternum has been established. The adult ribs give no suggestion of abnormality or of their responsibility for the dramatic appearance of a sternum lacking sternebrae from the beginning.

In other mice, deviations in the position of attachment or growth of individual ribs or single pairs of ribs, which in some cases may fail to join the sternum, have given a wide range of sternal patterns, all in perfect accord with the interpretation that the rib-end induces an inhibition of differentiation of the sternum. The most bizarre of these patterns appeared in a strain in which rib growth was normal, but occasionally all the ribs on one side were attached slightly higher than those on the other, so that each rib end was opposite an intercostal space, and the zones of in-hibited differentiation were staggered and did not overlap. In these cases, at birth, the sternum had a single continuous bone-center, in the form of a wall of troy (meander pattern).

WASHBURN: I want to thank Dr. MacDowell for contributing this excellent exam-ple of the way genetics can aid our evolutionary thinking. If many apparently complex morphological changes can be the result of a single change in a process, in this case the slowing of growth of ribs, then it will be far easier to account for the sort of differences seen between various primates. As Dr. Angel points out, studies of relative growth will also help. At present there is a vast quantity of descriptive data, and what we need is more studies of the type recommended by Dr. Angel and so beautifully illustrated by Dr. MacDowell.

[2] Bryson, V., 1945, *Anat. Rec.* **91**: 119–141.

Ecology and the Protohominids[*]

By GEORGE A. BARTHOLOMEW, Jr. and JOSEPH B. BIRDSELL

ALTHOUGH the word ecology is used in both the biological and the social sciences, attempts to bring the biologist and students of human society together by analogical reasoning are beset with traps for the unwary. The biological world lies primarily within genetic and physiological limits while that of the social sciences lies within cultural limits. However, whatever else man is, he is first an animal and hence subject, although usually indirectly, to environmental and biological factors.

It is generally agreed that the ecological generalizations and points of view which have proved helpful in interpreting the natural history of most mammals can be applied virtually intact to all primates except man. It should, therefore, be possible to extrapolate upward from ecological data on other mammals and suggest the biological attributes of the protohominids and to extrapolate downward from ethnological data on hunting and collecting peoples and suggest the minimal cultural attributes of the protohominids.

We propose first to discuss in general terms some aspects of mammalian ecology which appear to be applicable to the protohominids; second, to apply these ideas to the available data on the australopithecines; and third, to discuss the application of a few ecological ideas to preagricultural humans. A history of the development of ecology and suggestions for its applications to anthropology which has recently been published by Bates (1953) provides basic historical orientation and perspective for such an effort.

Protohominids and tools. In retrospect, the vast sweep of evolution appears to lead inevitably to the appearance of man, but a rational interpretation of the evidence refutes this. During the Cenozoic there have been three separate mammalian evolutionary complexes, one in Australia, one in South America, and one in Eurasia, Africa, and North America. Of these complexes, only the last has produced organisms of the hominid level. Further, since the major orders of mammals were already distinct in the Eocene, each has had a separate genetic history for approximately 70,000,000 years, and only one, primates, has produced an organism at the hominid level of organization.

Since a number of mammalian orders have shown a strong independent evolutionary trend toward a large brain size, this trend is by no means peculiar to the order primates (Edinger 1948). This striking parallelism is presumably related to the fact that large brain size favors varied behavior and learning as supplements to genetically fixed responses. Why then did not the primates,

* This paper was originally accepted for publication in the *American Journal of Physical Anthropology*. In furtherance of the policy of procuring for the *American Anthropologist* articles of broad general interest, the article was resubmitted to this journal by W. W. Howells, Editor of AJPA, with the permission of the authors.

Reproduced by permission of the authors and the American Anthropological Association from the AMERICAN ANTHROPOLOGIST, 55, 481–498 (October 1953).

like the other mammals, reached an apparent evolutionary dead end in the Pliocene? The familiar and reasonable ideas concerning the importance of arboreal life in setting the stage for the appearance of man, i.e., dependence on vision, grasping hands, and the lack of restrictive skeletal adaptations, need not be labored here, but the importance of bipedalism can profitably be re-examined.

The primates comprise the only major order of mammals which is characteristically arboreal. There can be no doubt that this arboreal heritage has been of vital importance in human evolution, but the critical stage in the transition from ape to protohominid involves the assumption of a unique terrestrial mode of life. A number of cercopithecids have successfully invaded the terrestrial habitat, but these all show quadrupedal adaptations. This level of adaptation, while obviously effective if one may judge by the fossil record and by present abundance, appears to represent a stable, long-surviving, adaptive equilibrium.

The terrestrial adaptations of the hominid line represent a step into a new and previously unexploited mode of life in which the critical feature was bipedalism. Among mammals changes of this magnitude have occurred only rarely since the middle Cenozoic. Aside from the saltatorial rodents such as the jerboas and kangaroo rats, all placental terrestrial mammals other than man use both hind and front legs for locomotion. The extreme rarity of bipedalism among mammals suggests that it is inefficient except under very special circumstances (Hatt 1932; Bartholomew and Caswell 1951). Even modern man's unique vertical bipedal locomotion, when compared to that of quadrupedal mammals, is relatively ineffective, and this implies that a significant nonlocomotor advantage must have resulted from even the partial freeing of the forelimbs. This advantage was the use of the hands for efficient manipulation of adventitious tools such as rocks, sticks, or bones. Of course, the terrestrial or semi-terrestrial living primates have their hands free when they are not moving, but only man has his locomotion essentially unimpeded while carrying or using a tool. Man has been characterized as the "tool-using animal," but this implies a degree of uniqueness to man's use of tools which is unrealistic. Not only do other primates use tools—the use of sticks and rocks by chimpanzees and baboons is generally familiar—but such unlikely animals as the sea otter (Fisher 1939) and one of the Galapagos finches (Lack 1945) routinely use rocks or sticks to obtain food. Indeed, the natural history literature is replete with instances of the use of tools by animals, and there really is no clear-cut boundary between web-spinning, nest-building, and stick-wielding on the one hand, and tool use at the simplest human level on the other. However, in contrast to all other mammals, the larger arboreal primates are, in a sense, tool users in their locomotion. As they move through the maze of the tree tops, their use of branches anticipates the use of tools in that they routinely employ levers and angular momentum. The grasping hands on which the locomotion and feeding of primates depends, are of course obviously pre-adapted for tool use.

Rather than to say that man is unique in being the "tool-using" animal, it is more accurate to say that man is the only mammal which is continuously dependent on tools for survival. This dependence on the learned use of tools indicates a movement into a previously unexploited dimension of behavior, and this movement accompanied the advent of bipedalism. With the assumption of erect posture regular use of tools became obligatory; the ability occasionally to use tools must have preceded this in time.

Protohominids and body size. The conditions of terrestrial life for a bipedal tool-using mammal virtually demanded that the protohominids be big mammals, i.e., at least in the 50 to 100 pound range, for large size of itself offers important biological advantages (Carter 1951: 293). In the case of the protohominids two such advantages at once suggest themselves: First, large size would remove them from the category of potential prey for all carnivorous birds, reptiles, and all mammals except the big cats and the pack-hunting dogs; second, it would allow them to utilize without restrictive anatomical specialization and with simple instrumentation, virtually the entire range of food size utilized by all other terrestrial mammals.

Sociality. Social behavior is inextricably interwoven with ecology, and although it is not possible to review the subject in detail here, certain aspects of it are basic to the development of later ideas.

The transitional protohominids must have been social to the extent of forming relatively stable family groups. Even in the absence of direct evidence, such a statement can be made with complete confidence from knowledge of the other members of the suborder Anthropoidea. First, there is the absence of seasonal sexual periodism in man and the great apes. Thus sexual ties form a bond of sustained and continuing attraction which provides a biological basis for the long-surviving family unit. As has frequently been pointed out this is a central element in human sociality. Second, there is a long period of growth and maturation. The long childhood of man and the great apes is not a mere function of size—the blue whale, the largest mammal that has ever lived, grows to sexual maturity and to a length of 70 or more feet in two years (Mackintosh and Wheeler 1929)—but it is related to the unique dependence for survival on learning in the higher primates. The acquisition of competence for independent life demands several years of parental care in the chimpanzee and a decade or more in man. Hence, survival requires a mother-offspring relation which is sustained through many years and, like sexual attraction, is not just a seasonal interlude as in other social mammals. Since these factors shape the social behavior of both the great apes and man, they must have shaped the social life of the protohominids.

Other cohesive forces, by analogy with living primates, must have supplied integration to the social organization of the protohominids. Important among these must have been dominance-subordinance relationships. The concept of social dominance has proved to be a touchstone to the understanding of the social behavior of vertebrates. It is a key factor in the social behavior of mammals as diverse as deer (Darling 1937), seals (Bartholomew 1952), and primates (Yerkes 1939).

In every case in which it has been studied in mammals, dominance is established at least in part on the basis of aggressive behavior (Collias 1944), of which a large component is either directly or indirectly dependent on reproductive physiology. In mammals the male sex hormones stimulate aggressive behavior and contribute to greater body size, while the female sex hormones inhibit the former and do not contribute to the latter. Consequently, males tend to be dominant over females in most situations. In the higher primates, as in many other social mammals, sexual dimorphism in size reinforces the greater aggressiveness of the male and insures his superior social status in situations where force is involved. In most social mammals, gregariousness overcomes the disruptive effect of dominance-subordinance relations and maintains the social unit. In primates dominance is not an exclusively disruptive force, since the dominant animal may protect the subordinate animal which looks to it for protection as well as leadership (Noble 1939).

In nonprimate social mammals, the resolution of the forces produced by dominance and gregariousness typically produces a seasonal breeding unit which consists of a dominant male and a harem of females and which usually excludes the young of previous years.

The social unit in nonhuman primates is variable, and too few detailed field studies have been published to allow extrapolation from living anthropoids to the protohominids. In modern hunting and collecting groups of man the smallest unit is the biological family including immature offspring, and in many cultures the most important functional group is the extended family, or band. In the case of man, even at the simplest level, social dominance is not based exclusively on successful aggressive behavior. The distance between nonprimate mammals and man is too broad to be spanned by the bracketing technique previously used, but the semi-permanent biological family, including offspring, must have been a basic unit among the protohominids. Integration on any more extensive scale must have depended upon the degree of cultural attainment. It should be observed however, that fairly large groups have been reported for living nonhominid anthropoids (Carpenter 1942; Nissen 1951).

Territoriality. No aspect of the social behavior of wild vertebrates has attracted more attention than territoriality, a concept which includes the entire complex pattern of behavior associated with the defense of an area. The display of ownership of places and objects is very highly developed among human beings, but this behavior pattern is not peculiar to modern man. It is almost universally present in terrestrial vertebrates, either on a permanent or seasonal basis. The large literature on the subject with regard to birds has been reviewed by Nice (1941). Its status in mammals has been discussed by Burt (1943), and its relation to vertebrate populations has been examined by Errington (1946).

Territoriality springs from the necessity for finding and maintaining environmental conditions suitable for survival and reproduction. The techniques of territory maintenance, the precise factors immediately responsible for it, and the immediate significance of it vary from species to species.

The maintenance of territories either by individuals or by social groups has profound effects on distribution. Birds and mammals tend to be neither continuously distributed nor irregularly grouped, but to be spaced at more or less regular intervals through ecologically suitable habitat. This spacing is determined by conflicts between pairs of individuals or between interacting groups of animals. Thus, territorial boundaries are learned and vary in time and space. If anthropologists were willing, this might almost be considered proto-cultural behavior at a subhuman level; in any event, it emphasizes the continuity of human behavior with that of other vertebrates.

As a result of the centrifugal effects of aggressive behavior, territory maintenance forces animals to disperse into adjacent areas. It distributes the individual organisms or social units of a species throughout the entire accessible area of suitable habitat. Should the population increase, local population density does not continue to build up indefinitely. Instead territorial defense forces individuals out into marginal situations, and thus the resources of the optimal habitat are not exhausted. Most of the displaced individuals do not survive, but some may find unexploited areas of suitable habitat and thus extend the range of the species. The result is that a population tends to be maintained at or below the optimum density in the preferred habitat, and the excess individuals are forced to marginal areas to which they must adapt or die.

Thus territoriality is one of the primary factors which determine the density of population. It organizes a local population into a well-spaced array that allows adequate living conditions for all successful individuals. It limits the breeding population which can exist in suitable habitats and thus helps to prevent increase beyond the long-term carrying capacity of the range. This dispersive effect of territoriality can hardly help but be an important causal factor both in migration and in the spread of genes through a population. Hence, it must contribute importantly to rate of evolutionary change (Burt 1949).

The question of the importance of territoriality to the biology of proto-hominids at once presents itself. Carpenter (1934; 1940) has demonstrated that howler monkeys and gibbons maintain territory by group action. It is clear that territoriality exists in all complex human societies, and it is clearly established that group territoriality is also important at the simplest levels of human culture. It is, therefore, reasonable to assume that protohominids similarly possessed a well-developed territoriality, presumably on the basis of the family or extended family.

Population equilibrium. One of the most critical ecological factors which can be determined about an animal is the density of its population. The number of variables which contribute to the determination of population density is enormous; a complete analysis for even the best known of living wild mammals is difficult, perhaps impossible. Nevertheless, the framework within which such an analysis can be made is known, for the factors involved in population dynamics have been studied intensively in recent years. A useful discussion of populations from the point of view of the ecologist is given by Bodenheimer (1938), and Allee *et al.* (1949).

Since organisms are transient biochemical systems which require continuous expenditure of energy for their maintenance, the struggle for existence becomes, in one sense at least, a struggle for the free energy available for doing physiological work. This fact offers a point of view from which to approach the problem of estimating the population of protohominids, or any other mammal.

There exists a series of nutrient or trophic levels that expresses the energy relations which tie together the various organisms of the terrestrial environment. The primary trophic level is that of the green plants, for only they can use radiant energy to synthesize significant quantities of organic material. The trophic level of the herbivores includes all animals directly dependent on plants for food. The next higher trophic level, that of the meat-eaters which may be primary carnivores (eaters of herbivores), secondary carnivores (eaters of other carnivores), and so on. The final trophic level, the eaters of dead organic material, eventually returns materials to the inorganic state depleted of biologically available energy.

Materials which are used as building blocks and sources of energy by organisms cycle continuously through these trophic levels, and at each level there is an endless competition for them. There are a number of obvious corollaries which follow from these relationships. An important one is that nutrition plays a primary role in determining the major functional adaptations of animals. Life demands a continuous expenditure of energy, and this energy is available only through nutrition. These energy relations involve a sustained long-term pressure sufficiently constant to maintain and give direction to the major evolutionary trends apparent in the adaptive changes of the sort shown by hoofed mammals and the carnivorous mammals. As Simpson (1944: 31) and others have pointed out, these nutritive adaptations have for the most part led not only to greater efficiency but also to more and more specialization, with a consequent reduction in potentiality for new major nutritive adaptations. Thus adaptations toward increased efficiency in food getting, or toward avoidance of becoming food for other organisms, are largely restrictive from the standpoint of future evolutionary change.

The total weight of biological materials produced by one trophic level must necessarily be less than that of the level below it on which it depends, and greater than that of the level above, which it supports. Each nutritive level must in the long run live on the interest, not the capital, of the trophic level below it. From this there follows a maxim which allows of no exception. On a long-term basis the mean population of a species is in equilibrium with the trophic levels both above it and below it, as well as with the total limiting effects of the inorganic environment. This means that the birth rate must be great enough to balance the death rate from disease (a nutritive phenomenon from the standpoint of the disease-causing organism), predation, and accident. Consequently, birth rate is a factor subject to natural selection, and all natural populations represent approximate equilibria between biotic potentials and total resistance of the biological and physical environments. Short-lived mammals of high fecundity, such as rabbits and mice, are sometimes characterized by drastic short-term fluctuations in population size, the causes for which are still subject to active controversy (Cole 1951). However, in this paper we shall ignore the problem of population cycles, for drastic cyclic fluctuations have rarely been observed in large tropical mammals with low reproductive potentials.

It has been generally appreciated since the time of Darwin that animals, despite their capacity to increase in numbers, tend to maintain a population which fluctuates around some equilibrium figure. This idea is of such a basic nature that it forms a foundation for the concept of natural selection which now appears to be an omnipresent evolutionary force. The factors involved in the maintenance of these equilibria are complex and variable. Since, as pointed out above, an animal population cannot possibly permanently exceed its food resources, these fix an upper limit. The determination of the actual equilibrium figure is a subtle problem which must be solved independently for each population. A thoughtful analysis of the factors limiting population in a non-hominid primate under natural conditions is presented by Collias and Southwick (1952) in their study of howling monkeys. For a population to maintain itself above that lower critical level which means inevitable extinction (Darling 1938), many factors (which may vary independently) must be simultaneously satisfied. Such things as a suitable habitat which will include adequate food resources, water, and home sites, and climatic conditions that do not exceed the tolerance of the group must be present.

Since biological factors vary with time, values for population equilibria are not to be measured at a given point in time. They fluctuate about a balance which is determined, not by the mean condition, but by the extremes. Indeed, one of the most firmly established ecological generalizations is Liebig's law of the minimum, which states that a biological reaction at any level is controlled not by the factors which are present in excess, but by that essential factor which is present in minimal quantity. Since, as was previously pointed out, population density is the most critical single ecological datum, anthropologists studying the simpler cultures characterized by few storage techniques would do well to search for those critical limiting factors which do determine density. Such limiting factors are not necessarily either obvious or conspicuous at all points in time, and even when they occur their expression may be subtle or apparently indirect. A semi-arid area may have many fruitful years in succession, but a single drought year occurring once in a human generation may restrict the population to an otherwise inexplicably low density. For example, the Papago Indians of the lower Colorado River were forced in drought years to revert to a desert hunting and collecting economy for survival (Castetter and Bell 1942). Thus, their population density appears in part to have been strongly affected by the preagricultural carrying capacity of this area. In some cases the size of a population will be determined not by the availability of an abundance of food during ten months of the year but by a regular seasonal scarcity in the remaining two months.

The reproductive potential of animals is such that under favorable conditions, such as having available a previously unexploited habitat, the size of a population can increase at an essentially logarithmic rate. This capacity for rapid increase makes possible the recovery of populations following drastic population reduction. In a stable population, on the other hand, the reproductive potential is expressed only as a one-to-one replacement of adult individuals.

Anthropologists are properly impressed with the complexity of learned behavior in human groups, but may fail to appreciate its significance among other mammals. Even on the nonhuman level, population density may be controlled by behavioral factors, either genetic or learned. Territoriality and dominance relations, which are dependent on learned behavior, contribute to the determination of group relations and population density. Under certain circumstances behavioral factors may be more important than nutritive factors in determining population density. For example, recent work discussed by Calhoun (1952) has shown that the Norway rat under controlled experimental conditions, in which food is present in excess at all times, reaches a population equilibrium that is determined by strictly behavioral factors related to territoriality and competition for suitable homesites. Thus, experimental work confirms extensive field observations on a variety of vertebrates. Since learned behavior operates as an important factor determining density in all terrestrial mammals which have been studied, and in modern man, it must have been an important factor in determining the population density of the protohominids. The importance of learned behavior increases directly with its complexity, and in man at cultural levels above the hunting and collecting stage of economy it becomes increasingly difficult to identify the ecological factors affecting population size.

ECOLOGY AND THE AUSTRALOPITHECINES

The dating of the australopithecines has proved troublesome, and final decision is not now possible. Dart and Broom have suggested that these protohominids lived during a period extending from the Villafranchian into the middle Pleistocene. This time span overlaps the datings of early man in other parts of the world, and implies a collateral relationship with more evolved hominids. Another view has recently been given by de Chardin (1952), who places the australopithecines in Villafranchian time, and thus removes them from contemporaneity with known African hominids. Breuil (1948) seems to reflect a similar point of view. In the former case the australopithecines would have been competing in their closing phase with more advanced forms of man, and hence would have been decreasing in numbers and range. In the latter instance the australopithecines would apparently have been the sole occupants of the protohominid niche over wide areas in South Africa, with the resultant possibility of having an expanding population and range. For purposes of an ecological discussion it is necessary to assume one dating or the other; it is not important to decide whether or not the australopithecines were in fact ancestral to more advanced hominid types, but it is important to determine whether or not they were the sole occupants of the hominid niche in South Africa.

As de Chardin (1952) points out, the australopithecine-bearing breccias and the human industry-bearing deposits have never been found conformably associated in the same site. This assumes, as did de Chardin, that *Telanthropus* is but a variant of the australopithecine type. Therefore, for purposes of discussion we shall assume that the autralopithecines are Villafranchian in date and hence earlier than the markers of the pebble-cultures of South Africa. By analogy with the ecology of other animals it would be surprising if man and the australopithecines had remained contemporaries in the same area over very long periods of time, for closely-related forms with similar requirements rarely occupy the same area simultaneously.

Use of tools. Neither the archeological nor morphological evidence concerning australopithecines suggests an alternative to the assumption, which we made earlier, that protohominids were dependent on the use of tools for survival. It is generally agreed that the australopithecines were bipedal. Referring to our previous discussion, this strongly implies that the australopithecines routinely utilized adventitious or perhaps even slightly modified tools. Dart's evidence (1949) for the use of ungulate humeri as clubs offers empirical support for this theoretical position. Unmodified rocks used as tools can rarely be identified except by context. Familiar evidence from both archeology and ethnology shows that at the simplest level, rough tools commonly are discarded after initial use. Hence, a lack of recognizable stone tools in the breccias does not indicate that these were not used. Time alone precludes the survival of wooden implements such as clubs and digging sticks, although their use by australopithecines is certainly to be expected, for even the living great apes use sticks spontaneously.

The dentition of the partly carnivorous australopithecines (see section on food size) is uniformly characterized by reduced canines and incisors, and by nonsectorial premolars and molars (Le Gros Clark 1949). These dental characteristics are unique to them among all the large carnivorous mammals. The absence of teeth adapted for stabbing or shearing clearly implies the killing of game by weapons and butchering by simple tools. This observation would hold true even if the assignment of carnivorous habits to australopithecines were based only upon the abundant evidence that baboons were an important item in their diet. It is not dependent on the controversial question of their killing large hoofed mammals.

The dentition of australopithecines offers further evidence concerning their dependence on tools. As pointed out previously, intrasexual combat is characteristic of the males of virtually all strongly dimorphic mammals. Australopithecines are dimorphic, but they do not have the large piercing canines so characteristic of most of the larger living primates. This striking reduction of canines strongly implies that even in intrasexual (and intraspecific) combat, the australopithecines placed primary dependence on tools.

Scale of food size. It should be possible on theoretical grounds to fix the approximate upper and lower size limits of the food which could economically be handled by the australopithecines with nothing more elaborate than a crude stick for digging and a limb bone for a club. Their capabilities would allow the utilization of the following animal foods: virtually all terrestrial reptiles and the smaller aquatic ones; eggs and nesting birds; some fish; fresh-water mollusks and crustaceans; insects; all of the smaller mammals including some burrowing forms, and larger mammals up to and including baboons. It is difficult, perhaps impossible, to determine whether or not the remains of the large giraffids and bovids reported from the bone breccias (Dart 1948), represent kills by australopithecines or their scavenging from the kills of the larger cats. Since few meat eaters are loath to scavenge, and the implementation which would allow the australopithecines to kill such large animals is not apparent, we suggest that scavenging from the kills of the larger carnivores may have been systematically carried out.

Like most present-day hunting and collecting peoples, the australopithecines probably used plants as their major source of food. Without imputing to the australopithecines any cultural capabilities beyond the use of a simple stick for digging, at least the following types of vegetable food would be available to them: berries, fruits, nuts, buds and shoots, shallow-growing roots and tubers, and fruiting bodies of fungi. Some of the very small vegetable foods exploited by modern human groups were probably not extensively used. Effective utilization of grass seeds and other hard-shelled small seeds require specialized gathering implements and containers, and processing by grinding or cooking.

Such activities imply technologies which cannot be assigned *a priori* to the australopithecines, and for which there is no archeological indication until much later times. In this connection it may be noted that the evidence for the use of fire by *Australopithecus prometheus*, though impressive, is still regarded by some as controversial (Barbour 1949; Broom 1950). In summary, it seems reasonable to treat the australopithecines as generalized carnivorous animals for which the freeing of hands and the use of simple implements enormously broadened the scale of food size to include a surprisingly large proportion of the total food resources of the terrestrial environment.

Social Behavior. The biological bases for the family and social organization at the protohominid level which have already been discussed should apply to the australopithecines. Group organization beyond the family level is not indicated by the archeological context of the finds, because the rather large number of individuals recorded from Swartkrans and Sterkfontein might result from sampling of family-sized groups over many generations. However, there is at least one line of archeological evidence which suggests social organization beyond the simple family level. Since baboons travel in large aggregations and were a significant item of australopithecine diet, it would seem likely that the latter hunted in bands. A single australopithecine, even armed with a club, would not be a serious threat to a band of baboons (Dart 1949). Such group hunting does not necessarily imply a high level of communication, such as speech, or permanence of organization, for it is characteristic of a number of nonprimate carnivorous vertebrates—many canids, some fish-eating birds, and killer-whales. Broom (1950) has shown that the australopithecines were characterized by sexual dimorphism, a widespread trait in the primates, including man. In social mammals, sexual dimorphism is almost invariably a product of the sexual selection associated with competition between males for females. Characteristically this sexual selection produces males which are larger, and more aggressive than females, and which have specialized structures for offense and defense. Although these dimorphic characters are a product of competition between males, they usually result in the males assuming the role of group defender. We propose that the sexual dimorphism of the australopithecine males may have favored a secondarily-derived function related to aggressive behavior, namely the hunting of large prey, including perhaps other australopithecines (Dart 1949). Thus it may be that a sexual division of labor such as is present in all known hunting peoples was foreshadowed at this early level of hominid evolution.

The primates which first began to exploit a bipedal tool-using mode of life were establishing a level of adaptedness of enormous potentiality which had previously been inaccessible. They were entering a period of rapid change leading to a new kind of adaptedness. In the terminology of Simpson (1944) they were a group undergoing quantum evolution. It is to be expected that, like other similarly rapidly evolving groups, they would be represented in the fossil record not by a uniform long-persistent type, but by a variable group of related forms. The australopithecines, which probably occupy a stage near the end of a step in quantum evolution, fit this theoretical prescription nicely. The various australopithecine forms which have been named can be considered representatives of a highly polymorphic assemblage. Their polymorphism is consistent with the idea of a rapidly evolving and radiating group and thus favors the probability of the Villafranchian dating.

It is reasonable to assume that most of the recovered australopithecine fossils date from a period prior to the time they faced competition from more highly evolved hominid types. When, as they inevitably must have, the australopithecines came in contact with culturally advanced hominids, they must have been subject to rapid replacement in terms of geological time.

DISCUSSION

A paper such as this necessarily can be of only temporary utility. We feel that its principal contribution lies in raising questions, the answering of which may require orientation toward new points of view, the collection of new kinds of data, and perhaps the use of new techniques.

Students of animal ecology have developed a number of points of view which could be profitably applied to the study of preagricultural man. Two are particularly attractive. The first of these is that the basic problem of human behavior, like the behavior of other animals, is the obtaining of food, for the human body requires a continuous input of energy both for maintenance and for propagation. The second point of view involves the idea that population density normally is a complexly maintained equilibrium, dependent upon environmental as well as behavioral (and in the case of man, cultural) forces.

Anthropologists and archeologists to date have shown great ingenuity in utilizing the meager data for paleolithic and mesolithic man to establish tentative chronologies and outline cultural relationships. However, at the simplest level, the significance of material culture lies neither in the establishment of chronology nor as a measure of relationships, but as an indicator of efficiency in obtaining food. The lack of data concerning the food-getting effectiveness of the various items of material culture primarily results from preoccupation with typology rather than function. Even the best of typological labels tend to restrict functional interpretations and to ignore the role of varied behavior and human ingenuity in extending an implement's utility. Furthermore, functional interpretations can be determined only by studies of living peoples, and the ethnologist has not yet generally been stimulated to the realization of the basic importance of such data.

It is of interest that some food-getting devices which we presume to have been available to the australopithecines remain important today in the economy of hunting and gathering peoples. But there is little systematic quantitative information concerning the proportion of food obtained through the use of the hands alone, or that added by the use of the simple digging stick, club, or wooden spear. Nor at a more culturally sophisticated level is there quantitative data available to measure the increase in efficiency made possible by the invention of such devices as the spear-thrower and the bow and arrow. In making such analyses it would be useful to distinguish between the contributions of the relatively limited variety of primary tools and the more varied secondary tools. For example, the ecological significance of the fist-axes of the lower and middle Pleistocene varies enormously depending upon whether they are to be interpreted as primary tools used to make wooden implements such as clubs, digging sticks and spears, or whether they are regarded in the unlikely light of hand-held striking implements (see, for example, Tindale 1949).

As pointed out previously, all animal populations, including human populations, depend on radiant energy stored chemically by photosynthesis. Animals compete endlessly between themselves for the one per cent of incident solar energy which plants are able to capture. The competitive success of an individual animal can be determined from its metabolism and the success of a population can be expressed quantitatively as the product of population density times individual metabolism.

If one can obtain even approximate figures for (1) the production of organic material by plants, (2) population densities and, (3) metabolism, one can evaluate from one point of view the biological success of different organisms. One can compare lions and elephants, earthworms and mice, humans and all other organisms, or more pertinent to anthropologists, one can compare simple cultures existing in either similar or different environmental situations. Since human beings comprise a single species, inter-group comparisons can be made on the basis of weight per unit area. An instructive analysis of this sort for small North American mammals has been made by Mohr (1947).

To our knowledge this quantitative approach to human ecology has not been exploited by anthropologists; indeed, few attempts have been made by zoologists. Pearson (1948) has gathered figures which allow a comparison of Indians of northeastern United States with other animals common in the same area. Indians had less metabolic impact than deer, about the same impact as long-tailed shrews. Deevey (1951) presents calculations which show the amazing trophic impact of the present human population of the world. Both these efforts are frankly exploratory and depend on approximations, but they point up an approach which merits consideration by anthropologists. If one could obtain for given areas even crude figures for human population density and for the production of organic material by the flora, he could compare the nutritive efficiencies of rainforest and grassland cultures, or the efficiency of Great Basin Indians and Australian Aborigines even though the two peoples live in arid regions of a very different character. Similarly one could obtain quantitative estimates for the effects of rivers, lakes, sea shore, and particularly vegetation types (i.e., oak woodland) on the capacity of an area to support human populations at a simple cultural level.

As discussed earlier, natural populations tend to fluctuate about some equilibrium figure. This fact has long been recognized by biologists, but to date, despite the perspectives which it supplies, it has not significantly influenced the approach of most anthropologists. From a short-term point of view, populations are in only approximate equilibrium, but viewed from the time scale of the Pleistocene, slowly expanding populations of man can be considered as being essentially in equilibrium. It appears to us that the idea that the populations of early man were in approximate equilibrium with the environment can supply a point of view from which to interpret the dynamics of technologically simple human populations. It should greatly facilitate qualitative exploration of such considerations as spatial variation of population density; growth or decline in numbers; rates of movement as influenced by migration and gene flow; and, shifts of populations into new climatic situations which demand new modes of life and may involve biological as well as cultural changes in adaptedness. As such qualitative interpretations are refined it may be possible to develop models which depict these processes semiquantitatively and thus allow crude predictions.

Population density is a key to these dynamic processes, for either directly or indirectly it controls all of the others. As discussed in the sections on territoriality and population equilibrium, the density of early human populations, while immediately determined by a complex of variables in which behavior plays a central role, was ultimately controlled by the environment. Even in the most favorable environments the equilibrium density attained by natural populations is somewhat below the maximum which the environment can support. The factors restricting density are behavioral in an immediate sense and involve such things as aggressive behavior and territoriality. These behavioral factors must have brought dispersive forces to bear on Pleistocene man just as they do on other mammals. The existence of such dispersive forces suggests that the evolving australopithecines must have spread with great rapidity (i.e., almost instantaneously in terms of geological time) throughout the continental tropics and subtropics of the old world. Such an expansion would leave no suitable and accessible areas unoccupied. Consequently all subsequently evolved hominids in these regions must have expanded at the expense of already established populations. The replacement of the australopithecines by somewhat more advanced but related hominids may have followed the usual mammalian pattern of the gradual expansion of the more efficient form, and the slow reduction of the numbers of the less efficient. In many instances, however, population change must have resulted from gradual genetic penetration, and much of human evolution in the Pleistocene could easily have been powerfully affected by introgressive hybridization. In this regard it should be remembered that anatomical differences do not necessarily indicate genetic incompatability between groups, and that there is no evidence of reluctance to hybridize even between widely different human types. If rapid and dramatic group replacement did occur it must have been a rare event occurring in special circumstances.

Although mammals are less affected by climate in a direct physical sense than are most organisms, physiological differences among mammals adapted to different climatic conditions have been clearly demonstrated (Scholander, et al., 1950). Distributionally the primates are an order characteristic of the tropics or subtropics. Modern man himself appears to be unable to invade the higher latitudes without fairly elaborate cultural accoutrements. It may therefore be concluded that during the Pliocene, the evolving protohominids occupied only the tropics, subtropics and perhaps the fringes of the temperate zones. The only place in which human populations could have expanded into a vacuum was at the margins of the then habitable areas. Thus changing cultural, and possibly changing biological, adaptedness would have allowed hominid expansion from the tropics into the temperate regions and ultimately into the arctic regions of the Old World. Aside from the initial continental expansion of the Old World protohominids, man expanded into major vacuums in populating Australasia, the New World, and much later, Micronesia and Polynesia. Once entered, these areas must have become filled rapidly, so that subsequent immigrants were faced for the most part with the problem of replacing established populations. Migrations, although spectacular, were probably of less importance in the Pleistocene than the processes discussed previously, which proceed normally without local catastrophic environmental change.

The anthropologists' lack of concern with the idea of population equilibrium in the simpler and more static human cultures is explicable in historical terms. Anthropologists, reacting to the claim by some anthropogeographers that extreme environmental determinism was operative on man, soon demonstrated that details of culture were not controlled directly by the environment. This broad denial overlooked man's nutritive dependence upon the environment, and long inhibited quantitative investigation of the relationship between man's population density and environmental factors.

The present interpretation of the mechanism of evolution is based upon natural selection which demands that populations be in a state of approximate equilibrium at a given time. To unravel the evolution of Pleistocene man, inevitably hampered as one is with inadequate data, one must necessarily use the idea of a population in equilibrium with the carrying capacity of the environment.

Most ecologists agree that no data are more crucial than those bearing upon population size, structure and density. Anthropologists, even though generally unconcerned with population equilibria, in some instances have been aware of the concept (Krzywicki 1934; Steward 1938; and Evans-Pritchard 1940). But in general the importance of an ecological approach has not been appreciated. Some archeologists have hoped to reconstruct preagricultural population figures from studying the temporal and spatial distribution of sites, but the inescapable sampling errors in this approach render it unreliable. We suggest that an analysis of the energy relationships and the efficiency of the techniques for obtaining food offer a promising approach.

For several years it has been apparent that an ecological approach is imperative for all studies in population genetics, including those pertaining to man. It also offers a potentially useful point of view to the physical anthropologist, the ethnologist, and the archeologist, and it should provide an important integrative bridge between the various fields of anthropology.

SUMMARY

An attempt is made to apply ecological concepts which are widely used by vertebrate zoologists to protohominids in general and to australopithecines in particular.

Various aspects of the biology of protohominids are considered: tool use, bipedalism, body size, scale of food size, sociality, territoriality, population density and equilibria, dispersion, and nutrition.

Energy relations to the environment and population equilibria are discussed with regard to human preagricultural populations.

UNIVERSITY OF CALIFORNIA
LOS ANGELES, CALIFORNIA

BIBLIOGRAPHY

ALLEE, W. C., A. E. EMERSON, O. PARK, T. PARK, and K. P. SCHMIDT 1949 Principles of animal ecology. W. B. Saunders Co., Philadelphia.

BARBOUR, G. B. 1949 Ape or man? Ohio Journal of Science 49: 129–145.

BARTHOLOMEW, G. A., JR. 1952 Reproductive and social behavior of the northern elephant seal. University of California Publications in Zoology 47: 369–472.

BARTHOLOMEW, G. A., JR., and H. C. CASWELL, JR. 1951 Locomotion in kangaroo rats and its adaptive significance. Journal of Mammalogy 32: 155–169.

BATES, M. 1953 Human ecology. Anthropology Today: An Encyclopedic Inventory, ed. by A. Kroeber. University of Chicago Press, Chicago.

BODENHEIMER, F. S. 1938 Problems of animal ecology. Oxford Univ. Press, London.

BREUIL, ABBE HENRI 1948 Ancient raised beaches and prehistoric civilisations in South Africa. South African Journal of Science 44: 61–74.

BROOM, R. 1950 The genera and species of the South African ape-man. American Journal of Physical Anthropology n.s. 8: 1–13.

BURT, W. H. 1943 Territoriality and home range concepts as applied to mammals. Journal of Mammalogy 24: 346–352.

———, 1949 Territoriality. Journal of Mammalogy 30: 25–27.

CALHOUN, J. B. 1952 The social aspects of population dynamics. Journal of Mammalogy 33: 139–159.

CARPENTER, C. R. 1934 A field study of the behavior and social relations of howling monkeys. Comparative Psychology Monographs 10: 1–168.

———, 1940 A field study of the behavior and social relations of the gibbon. Comparative Psychology Monographs 16: 1–212.

———, 1942 Societies of monkeys and apes. Biological Symposia 8: 177–204.

CARTER, G. S. 1951 Animal evolution. Sedgwick and Jackson Ltd., London.

CASTETTER, E. F. and W. H. BELL 1942 Pima and Papago Indian agriculture. Inter-American Studies I. Univ. of New Mexico Press, Albuquerque.

COLE, LA MONT C. 1951 Population cycles and random oscillations. Journal of Wildlife Management 15: 233–252.

COLLIAS, N. E. 1944 Aggressive behavior among vertebrate animals. Physiological Zoology 17: 83–123.

COLLIAS, N. E., and C. SOUTHWICK 1952 A field study of population density and social organization in howling monkeys. Proceedings of the American Philosophical Society 96: 143–156.

DARLING, F. F. 1937 A herd of red deer. Oxford Univ Press, London.

———, 1938 Bird flocks and the breeding cycle. Cambridge Univ. Press.

DART, R. A. 1948 A (?) promethean *Australopithecus* from Makapansgat Valley. Nature 162: 375–376.

———, 1949 The predatory implemental technique of *Australopithecus*. American Journal of Physical Anthropology n.s. 7: 1–38.

DE CHARDIN, P. T. 1952 On the zoological position and evolutionary significance of australo-pithecines. Transactions of the New York Academy of Sciences Ser. II 14: 208–210.

DEEVEY, E. S., JR. 1951 Recent textbooks of human ecology. Ecology 32: 347–351.

EDINGER, TILLY 1948 Evolution of the horse brain. Geological Society of America Memoirs 25: 1–177.

ERRINGTON, P. A. 1946 Predation and vertebrate populations. Quarterly Review of Biology 21: 144–177 and 221–245.

EVANS-PRITCHARD, E. E. 1940 The Nuer: a description of the modes of livelihood and political institutions of a Nilotic people. Oxford Univ. Press, London.

FISHER, EDNA M. 1939 Habits of the southern sea otter. Journal of Mammalogy 20: 21–36.

HATT, R. T. 1932 The vertebral columns of ricochetal rodents. Bulletin of the American Museum of Natural History 63: 599–738.

KRZYWICKI, L. 1934 Primitive society and its vital statistics. Macmillan and Co., London.

LACK, D. 1945 The Galapagos finches (Geospizinae). A study in variation. Occasional Papers of the California Academy of Sciences 21: 1–151.

LE GROS CLARK, W. E. 1949 New palaeontological evidence bearing on the evolution of the Hominoidea. Quarterly Journal of the Geological Society of London 105: 225–264.

MACKINTOSH, N. A., and J. F. G. WHEELER 1929 Southern blue and fin whales. Discovery Reports 1: 257–540.

MOHR, C. O. 1947 Table of equivalent populations of North American small mammals. American Midland Naturalist 37: 223–249.

NICE, MARGARET M. 1941 The role of territory in bird life. American Midland Naturalist 26: 441–487.

NISSEN, H. W. 1951 Social behavior in primates. Chapt. 13 (pp. 423–457) *in* Comparative Psychology (3rd edit.), edited by C. P. Stone. Prentice-Hall, Inc., New York.

NOBLE, G. K. 1939 The experimental animal from the naturalist's point of view. American Naturalist 73: 113–126.

PEARSON, O. P. 1948 Metabolism and bioenergetics. Scientific Monthly 66: 131–134.

SCHOLANDER, P. F., R. HOCK, V. WALTERS, and L. IRVING 1950 Adaptation to cold in arctic and tropical mammals and birds in relation to body temperature, insulation, and basal metabolic rate. Biological Bulletin 99: 259–271.

SIMPSON, G. G. 1944 Tempo and mode in evolution. Columbia Univ. Press, New York.

STEWARD, J. H. 1938 Basin-plateau aboriginal sociopolitical groups. U. S. Government Printing Office, Washington, D. C.

TINDALE, N. B. 1949 Large biface implements from Mornington Island, Queensland and from South Western Australia. Records of the South Australian Museum 9: 157–166.

YERKES, R. M. 1939 Social dominance and sexual status in the chimpanzee. Quarterly Review of Biology 14: 115–136.

HOW MANY PEOPLE CAN THE WORLD SUPPORT?

If the population goes on increasing at about its present rate
for 900 years, there will be 20 million times as many
people as at present. That many can be fed and housed,
assuming reasonable progress in technology, but physical problems
of overheating will make further increase unlikely.

By Dr. J. H. Fremlin

Department of Physics, University of Birmingham

The world population is now about 3000 million and is increasing at a rate
corresponding to a doubling in 37 years. In view of the increasing importance
attached to the immediate effects of the rapid growth in human numbers,
it is of interest to examine ultimate technical limits to this growth. Tradition-
ally, these limits have usually been regarded as fixed by possible food supplies
although, in practice, at least in historical times, the actual limiting factor has
more often been disease.

Diseases are now nearly, and will soon be entirely, eliminated as effective
controllers of population growth but it is not at all clear that difficulties in
food production will take their place. It is true that there is a limit to the
improvement of agricultural output by application of existing scientific knowledge, but by the time this limit is reached other methods of food-production
will have been devised. In this article I shall explore the possibility that the
real limits are physical rather than biological.

I shall assume throughout an effective degree of world cooperation in the
application of food technology, etc. This is quite evidently essential if the
maximum world population is to be reached. There are of course many ways
of *not* reaching the maximum, but none of these will be discussed here.

In order to give a time scale, it is supposed that the rate of increase of
population remains constant at the present value—that is to say, doubling every
37 years. In fact the rate is itself accelerating, so that, in the absence of
limitations, this time scale will be too long.

STAGE 1: UP TO 400,000 MILLION
IN 260 YEARS' TIME.

Using existing crop plants and methods it may not be practicable to produce adequate food for more than four doublings of the world population,

Reprinted by permission of the author and the Editor from
New Scientist, **24**, 285–287 (1964).

though the complete elimination of all land wild-life, the agricultural use of roofs over cities and roads, the elimination of meat-eating and the efficient harvesting of sea food might allow two or three further doublings—say seven in all. That would give us, with the present doubling time of 37 years, 260 years to develop less conventional methods, and would allow the population of the world to increase to about 130 times its present size, or about 400,000 million.

STAGE 2: UP TO 3 MILLION MILLION IN 370 YEARS' TIME.

The area of ice-free sea is some three times that of land. Photosynthesis by single-celled marine organisms may be more efficient than that of the best land plants. If organisms could be found capable of the theoretical maximum efficiency (8 per cent of total solar radiation, according to A. A. Niciporovic) we should gain a factor of three in yield. We could then double our numbers a further three more times if all the wild-life in the sea, too, was removed and replaced by the most useful organisms growing under controlled conditions, with the optimum concentration of carbonates, nitrates and minerals. (Of course a reserve of specimens of potentially useful species could be preserved, perhaps in a dormant state.) Again, for maximum efficiency we must harvest and consume directly the primary photosynthesising organisms, rather than allow the loss of efficiency involved in the food-chains leading to such secondary organisms as zooplankton or fish.

By this stage, we should have had ten doublings, which at the present rate would take some 370 years, with a final world population of 3 million million. Since the world's surface (land and sea) is 500 million million square metres, each person would have a little over 160 square metres for his maintenance—about a thirtieth of an acre—which does not seem unreasonable by more than a factor of two, so long as no important human activity other than food pro-duction takes place on the surface.

No serious shortages of important elements need be envisaged so far, though extensive mining operations for phosphates might be needed, and we have not yet approached any real limit.

STAGE 3: UP TO 15 MILLION MILLION IN 450 YEARS' TIME.

At first sight, it seems that a very big leap forward could be taken if we use sources of power other than sunlight for photosynthesis. The solar power received at the earth's surface is only about 1 kilowatt per square metre at the equator at midday, and the average value over the day and night sides of the globe is a quarter of this. Over half of it is in the regions of the spectrum of no use for photosynthesis.

About one kilowatt-year per square metre could be produced by the com-plete fission of the uranium and thorium in about 3 cm depth of the Earth's crust or by fusion of the deuterium in about 3mm depth of seawater, so that adequate power should be available for some time. It is, however, difficult to see how the overall thermal efficiency from fuel to the light actually used for photosynthesis could be even as good as the ratio of useful to non-useful solar radiation (about 40 per cent).

It would, therefore, be better to use large satellite reflectors in orbit to give extra sunlight to the poles and to the night side of the Earth. A large number of mirrors could be maintained in quasi-stable orbits about 1½ million kilometres outside the Earth's orbit, any deviations being controlled by movable "sails" using the pressure of sunlight. To double our total radiation income would require a total area of about 100 million square kilometres of mirror which, in aluminum a tenth of a micron thick, would weigh about 30 million tons. With plenty of people to design and make the equipment it should not be difficult by the time it would be required, and it would bring the whole Earth to equatorial conditions, melting the polar ice and allowing one further doubling of population.

A second doubling of radiation income would give the whole Earth midday equatorial conditions round the clock, which would be exceedingly difficult to cope with without serious overheating. The overall efficiency of local power sources for photosynthesis is likely to be less than that of sunlight, so that no real gain in ultimate population size can be expected from their use, without an even more serious overheating of the entire globe.

If, however, the mirrors outside the Earth's orbit were made of selectively reflecting material, reflecting only the most useful part of the spectrum, and if a further satellite filter were used, inside the Earth's orbit, to deflect the useless 60 per cent of direct solar radiation, a further gain of a factor of 2½ should easily be possible without creating thermally impossible conditions, at the cost only of perhaps a 10–100 times increase of weight of mirror plus filter —not difficult for the larger population with an extra 50 years of technical development. We should then have attained a world population of 15 million million about 450 years from now.

STAGE 4: UP TO 1000 MILLION MILLION IN 680 YEARS' TIME.

A considerably larger gain is in principle obtainable if the essential bulk foods: fats, carbohydrates, amino acids and so on, could be directly synthesised. Biological methods might still be permitted for a few special trace compounds. The direct rate of energy production resulting from the conversion of our food into our waste products is only about 100 watts per person and, if high-temperature energy from nuclear fuel (or sunlight) could be efficiently used, waste products could in principle be changed back into food compounds with the absorption of little more energy. Cadavers could be homogenised and would not, at least for physical reasons, need to be chemically treated at all. The fresh mineral material which would have to be processed to allow for population growth would be much less than 1 per cent of the turnover, and its energy requirements can be neglected.

If we suppose that the overall efficiency could not be increased beyond 50 per cent, a further 100 watts per person would be dissipated as heat in the process of feeding him. We have some hundreds of years to work up the efficiency to this value, so at least this ought to be possible. Some further power would be needed for light, operation of circulation machinery, communications etc., but 50 watts per person should suffice.

As we have seen, the long-term average heat income of the Earth's surface is at present about 250 watts per square metre, and this could be doubled without raising the temperature above the normal equatorial value. (The initial rate of rise would be low till the polar ice had gone, which might take 100 years.) We thus have 500 watts per square metre which, at 250 watts per head, could support 1000 million million people altogether. The population density would be two per square metre, averaged over the entire land and sea surface of the Earth.

STAGE 4A: UP TO 12,000 MILLION MILLION IN 800 YEARS' TIME. DEAD END.

Above two people per square metre, severe refrigeration problems occur. If the oceans were used as a heat sink, their mean temperature would have to rise about 1°C per year to absorb 500 watts per square metre. This would be all right for the doubling time of 37 years, at the end of which we should have four people per square metre. Half another doubling time could be gained if efficient heat pumps (which, for reasons of thermal efficiency, would require primary energy sources of very high temperature) could be used to bring the ocean to the boil.

Two more doublings would be permitted if the oceans were converted into steam, though that would create an atmospheric pressure comparable with the mean ocean bottom pressure at present. Since the resulting steam blanket would also be effectively opaque to all radiation, no further heat sink could be organised and this procedure would therefore seem to lead to a dead end.

STAGE 5: UP TO 60,000 MILLION MILLION IN 890 YEARS' TIME.

A preferable scheme would be the opposite one of roofing in the ocean to stop evaporation (this would, in any case, probably have been done long before, for housing) and hermetically sealing the outer surface of the planet. All of the atmosphere not required for ventilation of the living spaces could then be pumped into compression tanks, for which no great strength would be needed if they were located on ocean bottoms. Heat pumps could then be used to transfer heat to the solid outer skin, from which, in the absence of air, it would be radiated directly into space. The energy radiated from a black body goes up as T^4, where T is the absolute temperature (°K), but for a *fixed rate* of heat extraction from the living space, at a fixed temperature (say, 30°C or 303°K), the heat-power *radiated* must for thermodynamic reasons be proportional to T even if the refrigeration equipment is perfectly efficient (see any good textbook on the principles of refrigeration). Hence the rate of heat extraction will go up no faster than T^4 where T is the outer surface temperature.

All the same, this gives more promising results than would the use of the ocean as a temporary heat sink. An outer skin temperature of 300°C would give a heat extraction of 3 kW per square metre and 1000°C would give an extraction ten times greater. If heat removal were the sole limitation, then we could manage about 120 persons per square metre for an outer skin temperature of 1000°C—which represents nearly six further doublings of population after the end of Stage 4, with a world population of 60,000 million million in 890 years' time. 1000°C may be a rather modest figure for the technology of AD 2854 and the population could, as far as heat is concerned, be able to double again for each rise of absolute skin temperature of $^3\sqrt{2}$ or 26 per cent. The difficulties in raising it much further while keeping all thermodynamic efficiencies high would, however, seem to be formidable. A rise to 2000°C would give us less than three further doublings.

We seem, therefore, to have found one possible absolute limit to human population, due to the heat problem, which at the present rate would be reached 800–1000 years from now, with a world population of 10^{16}–10^{18}.

I have not considered emigration to other planets because it seems to me unlikely that our technical capacity to do so will catch up with the population expansion. To keep world-population level we would have to be sending out 60 million people per annum *now*. It is so much cheaper to feed them here that this will not be done.

If, however, it were possible to export population on the scale required it would not make a great difference. Venus is much the same size as the Earth, so (assuming that it has all the raw materials needed) an extra 37 years would bring it to the same population density as the Earth. Mercury, Mars and the Moon together give half the same area, so that Venus and the Earth together would take them up to the same population density in a further 10 years. The moons of Jupiter and Saturn could give us another 2 years or so. It is not clear that normal human beings could live on Jupiter and Saturn themselves and impound their extensive atmospheres, and the outer planets would take a long time to reach; if all these extraordinary problems could be solved, nearly 200 years might be gained.

Other possible limitations.—Other possible limitations than heat will doubtless have occurred to readers, but these do not seem to be absolute. The most obvious is perhaps the housing problem, for 120 persons per square metre. We can safely assume, however, that in 900 years' time the construction of continuous 2000-storey buildings over land and sea alike should be quite easy. That would give 7½ square metres of floor space for each person in 1000 storeys (though wiring, piping, ducting and lifts would take up to half of that) and leave the other 1000 storeys for the food-producing and refrigerating machinery. It is clear that, even at much lower population densities, very little horizontal circulation of persons, heat or supplies could be tolerated and each

563

area of a few kilometres square, with a population about equal to the present world population, would have to be nearly self-sufficient. Food would all be piped in liquid form and, of course, clothes would be unnecessary.

Raw materials should not be a problem. The whole of the oceans and at least the top 10 kilometres of the Earth's crust would be available, giving a wide choice of building, plumbing and machine-building materials. Even with 8 tons of people per square metre (reckoning 15 people to the ton) all the necessary elements of life could be obtained; some from air and sea (C, H, O, N, Na, Cl, Ca, K and some trace elements) and some from the top 100 metres of solid crust (Fe, S, P, I and remaining trace elements). Only after a further hundredfold increase in population would it be needful to go below the top 10 km of crust for some elements (N, S, P, I). Such an increase would need an outer skin temperature of 5000°C (comparable with the surface of the Sun) to radiate away the body heat, which would seem to be well beyond the possible limits.

A question of obvious importance which is not easy to answer is whether people could in fact live the nearly sessile lives, with food and air piped in and wastes piped out, which would be essential. Occasional vertical and random horizontal low speed vehicular or moving-belt travel over a few hundred metres would be permissible, however, so that each individual could choose his friends out of some ten million people, giving adequate social variety, and of course communication by video-phone would be possible with anyone on the planet. One could expect some ten million Shakespeares and rather more Beatles to be alive at any one time, so that a good range of television entertainment should be available. Little heat-producing exercise could be tolerated. The extrapolation from the present life of a car-owning, flat-dwelling office-worker to such an existence might well be less than from that of the neolithic hunter to that of the aforesaid office-worker. Much more should be known about social conditioning in a few hundred years' time and, though it is difficult to be quite certain, one could expect most people to be able to live and reproduce in the conditions considered.

Many readers will doubtless feel that something unconsidered must turn up to prevent us from reaching the limiting conditions I have supposed. One point of this study is however to suggest that, apart from the ultimate problem of heat, we are now, or soon will be, able to cope with *anything* that might turn up. Anything which limits population growth in the future will, therefore, be something that we can avoid if we wish. It would be perfectly possible to choose not to eliminate some major killing disease or to neglect the world food problem and let famine do its work, but this would have to be a positive decision; it can no longer happen by mistake.

Consequently all methods of limitation of population growth will, from now on, be artificial in the sense that they are consciously planned for, whether or not the plan is carried out by individuals for themselves. We are, collectively, free to choose at what population density we want to call a halt, somewhere between the 0.000006 per square metre of the present and the 120 per square metre of the heat limit; if we do not choose, eventually we shall reach that limit.